PRENTICE HALL

Physical Science

Prentice Hall
Physical Science

DEAN HURD

Physical Science Instructor
Carlsbad High School
Carlsbad, California

MYRNA SILVER

Physical Science Instructor
Richardson Independent School District
Richardson, Texas

ANGELA BORNN BACHER

Chemistry Instructor
Methacton School District
Fairview Village, Pennsylvania

CHARLES WILLIAM McLAUGHLIN

Chemistry Instructor
Central High School
St. Joseph, Missouri

 **Prentice Hall**
Englewood Cliffs, New Jersey
Needham, Massachusetts

Prentice Hall Physical Science Program

Student Text and Annotated Teacher's Edition

Laboratory Manual with Annotated Teacher's Edition

Teacher's Resource Book

Test Bank with Software and DIAL-A-TEST™ Service

Physical Science Critical Thinking Skills Transparencies

Physical Science Courseware

Other programs in this series

Prentice Hall Life Science © 1991

Prentice Hall Earth Science © 1991

Prentice Hall Physical Science presents science as a process that involves research, experimentation, and the development of theories that can hold great explanatory and predictive power. This approach reflects the challenges and intellectual rewards available to students in the ever-changing discipline of science.

Photograph credits begin on p. 695

The photograph on the cover shows a magnetic disk levitating over a super-conducting material. (Gabe Palmer/The Stock Market)

Staff Credits

Editorial	Harry Bakalian, Pamela E. Hirschfeld, Maureen Grassi, Robert P. Letendre, Elisa Mui Eiger, Christine A. Portante
Art Direction	Arthur F. Soares, Susan Walrath, Laura Jane Bird
Production	Suse Cioffi, Betsy Torjussen, Lorraine Moffa, Lisa Meyerhoff, Cleasta Wilburn
Photo Research	Libby Forsyth
Marketing	Paul P. Scopa, Victoria Willows
Manufacturing	Loretta Moe, Denise Herkenrath
Consultant	Linda Grant

SECOND EDITION

© 1991, 1988 by Prentice-Hall, Inc., Englewood Cliffs, New Jersey 07632. All rights reserved. No part of this book may be reproduced in any form or by any means without permission in writing from the publisher. Printed in the United States of America.

ISBN 0-13-714171-8

10 9 8 7 6

Prentice Hall
A Division of Simon & Schuster
Englewood Cliffs, New Jersey 07632

Physical Science Reviewers:

Edward A. Dalton
President
National Energy Foundation
Salt Lake City, Utah

Jack Grube
Science Coordinator
Eastside Union High School
San Jose, California

John D. Hunt
Physics/Chemistry Instructor
Judson High School
Converse, Texas

Kenneth L. Krause
Physical Science Instructor
Harriet Tubman Middle School
Portland, Oregon

Ernest Kuehl
Physics Instructor
Lawrence High School
Cedarhurst, New York

David LaHart
Senior Instructor
Florida Solar Energy Center
Cape Canaveral, Florida

Joyce K. Walsh
Physical Science Instructor
Chesterfield School District
Chesterfield, Virginia

Reading Consultant

Patricia N. Schwab
Director of Undergraduate
Advisement and Lecturer
University of South Carolina
Columbia, South Carolina

Contents

UNIT ONE Diversity of Matter 2–85

CHAPTER 1 *Exploring Physical Science* 4–31

1-1 What Is Science? 6
1-2 Scientific Measurements 15
1-3 Tools of Measurement 21
1-4 Science Safety in the Laboratory 25

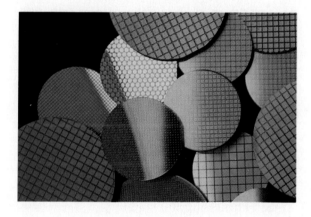

CHAPTER 2 *Properties of Matter* 32–59

2-1 General Properties of Matter 34
2-2 Phases of Matter 40
2-3 Phase Changes 47
2-4 Chemical Properties and Changes 53

CHAPTER 3 *Classification of Matter* 60–81

3-1 Classes of Matter 62
3-2 Mixtures 64
3-3 Elements 69
3-4 Compounds 72

SCIENCE GAZETTE
Paul MacCready and the Return of the Pterosaur 82
The Space Program: Is It Worth the Cost? 84

UNIT TWO Patterns in Matter 86–155

CHAPTER 4 *Structure of Matter* 88–109

4-1 Development of an Atomic Model 90
4-2 A Divisible Atom 93
4-3 Subatomic Particles 96
4-4 Forces Within the Atom 103

CHAPTER 5 *The Periodic Law* 110–129

5-1 Development of a Periodic Table 112
5-2 The Modern Periodic Table 115
5-3 Using the Periodic Table 120
5-4 Periodic Properties of the Elements 123

CHAPTER 6 *Families of Elements* 130–151

6-1 Properties of Metals and Nonmetals 132
6-2 Active Metals 135
6-3 Transition Metals 139
6-4 From Metals to Nonmetals 140
6-5 Halogens 143
6-6 Noble Gases 145
6-7 Rare-Earth Elements 147

SCIENCE GAZETTE
Stephen Hawking: Changing Our View of the Universe 152
The Fifth Force: Is It with Us? 154

UNIT THREE Interactions of Matter   156-283

CHAPTER 7 *Atoms and Bonding*   *158-179*

7-1	Chemical Bonding	160
7-2	Ionic Bonds	163
7-3	Covalent Bonds	167
7-4	Metallic Bonds	172
7-5	Predicting Types of Bonds	173

CHAPTER 8 *Chemical Reactions 180-203*

8-1	Nature of Chemical Reactions	182
8-2	Chemical Equations	185
8-3	Types of Chemical Reactions	189
8-4	Energy of Chemical Reactions	192
8-5	Rates of Chemical Reactions	196

CHAPTER 9 *Solution Chemistry*   *204-231*

9-1	Nature of Solutions	206
9-2	Making Solutions	210
9-3	Water—The Universal Solvent	215
9-4	Suspensions and Colloids	219
9-5	Acids	221
9-6	Bases	223
9-7	Acids and Bases in Solution: Salts	225

CHAPTER 10 *Carbon Chemistry*   *232-255*

10-1	Carbon and Its Compounds	234
10-2	Hydrocarbons	239
10-3	Substituted Hydrocarbons	244
10-4	Chemistry for Life	249

CHAPTER 11 *Nuclear Chemistry 256-279*

11-1	Radioactive Elements	258
11-2	Transmutation of Elements	262
11-3	Harnessing the Nucleus	268
11-4	Detecting and Measuring Radioactivity	272
11-5	Uses of Radioactivity	274

SCIENCE GAZETTE
Shirley Ann Jackson: Helping Others Through Science   *280*
Fusion Energy: Future Fuel or Folly?   *282*

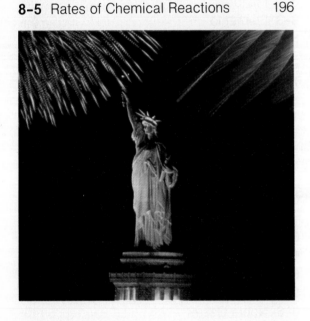

UNIT FOUR Motion, Forces, and Energy   284-391

CHAPTER 12 *Motion*   *286-303*

12-1	Frames of Reference	288
12-2	Speed and Velocity	290
12-3	Acceleration	295
12-4	Momentum	298

CHAPTER 13 *Forces*   *304-327*

13-1	Nature of Forces	306
13-2	Balanced and Unbalanced Forces	310
13-3	Force and Motion	313

13-4 Gravity   318
13-5 Weight and Mass   322

CHAPTER 14 *Forces in Fluids*   **328–345**

14-1 Fluid Pressure   330
14-2 Buoyancy   333
14-3 Hydraulics   336
14-4 Bernoulli's Principle   339

CHAPTER 15 *Work, Power, and Simple Machines*   **346–369**

15-1 Work   348
15-2 Power   350
15-3 Machines   353
15-4 Simple Machines   357
15-5 Compound Machines   365

CHAPTER 16 *Energy*   **370–387**

16-1 Nature of Energy   372
16-2 Kinetic and Potential Energy   375
16-3 Energy Conversion   377
16-4 Conservation of Energy   382

SCIENCE GAZETTE
Dick Rutan and Jeana Yeager: Making Aviation History *388*
Robots: Do They Signal Automation or Unemployment? *390*

UNIT FIVE Heat Energy   392–437

CHAPTER 17 *Heat*   **394–415**

17-1 Heat: A Form of Energy   396
17-2 Temperature and Heat   400
17-3 Measuring Heat   402
17-4 Heat and Phase Changes   404
17-5 Thermal Expansion   408
17-6 Heat and Internal Energy   410

CHAPTER 18 *Uses of Heat*   **416–433**

18-1 Heating Systems   418
18-2 Insulation   423
18-3 Cooling Systems   424
18-4 Heat Engines   425
18-5 Thermal Pollution   428

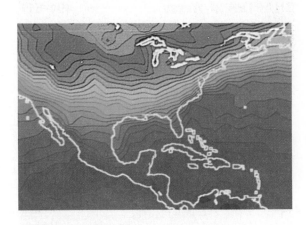

SCIENCE GAZETTE
Jenefir Isbister: She Does Dirty Work for Cleaner Coal *434*
Hothouse Earth: Will the Greenhouse Effect Occur? *436*

UNIT SIX Electricity and Magnetism 438–491

CHAPTER 19 *Electric Charges
and Currents* **440–465**

19-1	Electric Charge	442
19-2	Static Electricity	445
19-3	The Flow of Electricity	451
19-4	Electric Circuits	456
19-5	Electric Power	458

CHAPTER 20 *Magnetism* **466–487**

20-1	Properties of Magnets	468
20-2	The Earth As a Magnet	471
20-3	An Explanation of Magnetism	474
20-4	Electromagnetism	476
20-5	Electromagnetic Induction	479

SCIENCE GAZETTE
The Search for Superconductors *488*
Nuclear Power: Promise or Peril? *490*

UNIT SEVEN Waves: Sound and Light 492–583

CHAPTER 21 *Waves* **494–511**

21-1	Nature of Waves	496
21-2	Types of Waves	498
21-3	Characteristics of Waves	501
21-4	Speed of Waves	503
21-5	Interactions of Waves	504

CHAPTER 22 *Sound* **512–533**

22-1	Wave Model of Sound	514
22-2	Properties of Sound	517
22-3	Wave Interactions	523
22-4	Sounds You Hear	526
22-5	How You Hear	528

CHAPTER 23 *Light* **534–557**

23-1	Nature of Light	536
23-2	Electromagnetic Spectrum	539
23-3	Particle, Wave, or Both?	544
23-4	Reflection of Light	546
23-5	Refraction of Light	548
23-6	Color	550
23-7	How You See	552

CHAPTER 24 *Light and Its Uses* 558–579

24–1 Sources of Light 560
24–2 Reflection and Mirrors 562
24–3 Refraction and Lenses 566
24–4 Optical Instruments 570
24–5 Light and Technology 573

SCIENCE GAZETTE
John Caulfield's Wonderful World of Holography 580
Hypersonic Travel: Is Faster Better? 582

UNIT EIGHT Physical Science and Technology 584–665

CHAPTER 25 *Energy Resources* 586–607

25–1 Fossil Fuels 588
25–2 Solar Energy: Direct and Indirect 591
25–3 Nuclear Energy 596
25–4 Alternative Energy Sources 600

CHAPTER 26 *Energy and the Environment* 608–625

26–1 Pollution—What Is It? 610
26–2 Land Pollution 611
26–3 Air Pollution 613
26–4 Water Pollution 616
26–5 Pollution—What Can Be Done? 619

CHAPTER 27 *Chemical Technology* 626–639

27–1 Fuels from Petroleum 628
27–2 Petrochemical Products 630

CHAPTER 28 *Electronics and Computers* 640–661

28–1 Electronic Devices 642
28–2 Transmitting Sound 647
28–3 Transmitting Pictures 650
28–4 Computers 652

SCIENCE GAZETTE
Stan Ovshinsky: Pioneering a New Type of Glass 662
Nuclear Waste: What Can Be Done with Deadly Garbage? 664

Reference Section

For Further Reading 666

Appendix A The Metric System 668
Appendix B Science Safety Rules 669
Appendix C Mathematics Refresher 671
Appendix D Important Formulas 674
Appendix E The Chemical Elements 675

Glossary 676 **Index 687**

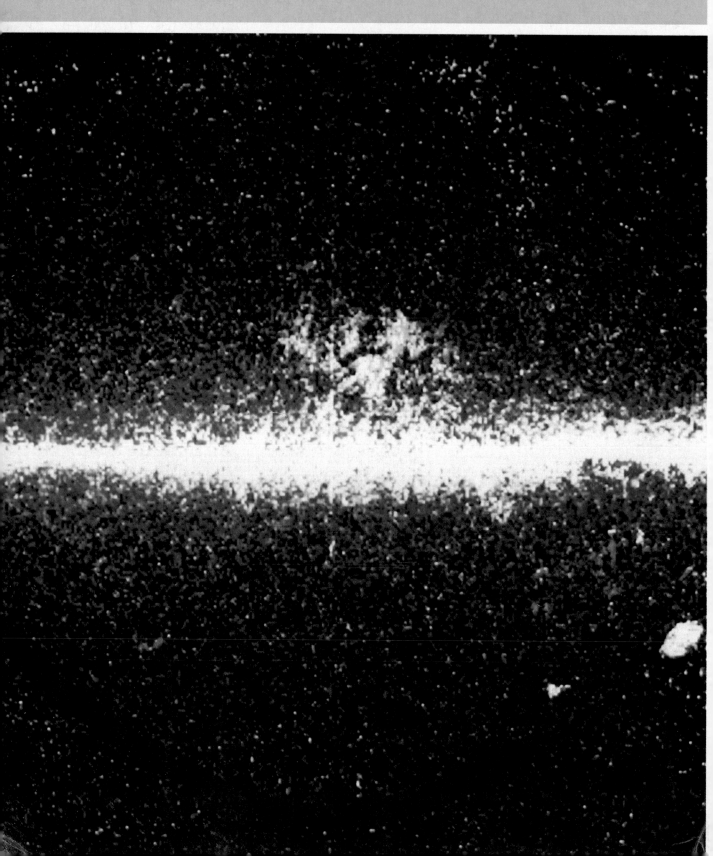

Diversity of Matter

In January 1983, the Infrared Astronomical Satellite (IRAS) was launched into space. Its job was to observe the universe through infrared sensors. Infrared is a form of light that is invisible to the human eye. Surveying the entire sky, IRAS discovered five new comets and a new asteroid. It examined galaxies hundreds of times brighter than the Milky Way. It even probed the gas and dust clouds between the stars. While scanning the star Vega, IRAS made an important discovery. A dusty ring surrounds this star. As yet, matter in the ring has not clumped together to form planets. But the existence of the ring is the first clear evidence that stars other than our sun may have planetary systems.

Spectacular photographs of a universe never before seen have been radioed back to the earth by IRAS. Scientists examining the data have confirmed an amazing scientific fact. All visible objects—be they huge galaxies of stars or tiny particles of matter floating in space—are made of the same matter that is found on the earth. Nowhere in the universe is there matter unlike that which exists "at home." For even the fiery stars are composed of the same basic materials as the air, the rocks, the seas, and you!

CHAPTERS

1 Exploring Physical Science

2 Properties of Matter

3 Classification of Matter

This image of the entire sky was assembled from data from the Infrared Astronomical Satellite (IRAS).

Exploring Physical Science

1

CHAPTER SECTIONS

1-1 What Is Science?

1-2 Scientific Measurements

1-3 Tools of Measurement

1-4 Science Safety in the Laboratory

CHAPTER OBJECTIVES

After completing this chapter, you will be able to

1-1 Describe the steps scientists use to investigate a question or problem.

1-1 Explain the difference between an experimental setup and a control setup.

1-2 Compare the different units of measurement in the metric system.

1-3 Identify the common laboratory tools used to measure length, volume, mass, and temperature.

1-4 List the important safety rules you must follow in the science laboratory.

What do a razor blade, a rocket engine, and swamp gas have in common? Today, researchers at Penn State University are hard at work to provide an answer. These scientists are trying to find a way to coat various objects with a thin film of synthetic diamond. Synthetic diamonds are made in the laboratory.

How do scientists go about making a synthetic diamond coating? They start with swamp gas, which is called methane. Methane is a chemical substance made of one carbon atom linked to four hydrogen atoms. The first step in the process is to "strip away" the hydrogen atoms from the carbon atom. When this happens, the carbon atoms from thousands of methane particles are left behind.

Diamonds are made of carbon atoms. By carefully controlling conditions in the laboratory, scientists can make the carbon atoms link together to form synthetic diamonds. As they link together they are deposited on the object to be coated. The synthetic diamonds are virtually 100 percent pure.

Diamonds are extremely hard and resistant to wear. By placing a diamond coating on a razor blade, the blade will last longer and stay sharper. Diamond coatings on rocket engines and cutting tools will increase their resistance to wear. In addition, diamond coatings can make lenses and windows almost scratchproof. The list of uses goes on and on.

As you read this book, you will be introduced to the realm of physical science. And you will learn about many other exciting discoveries that may change your world. Perhaps one day in a laboratory of the future, you will be working on a new scientific project!

Silicon chips coated with synthetic diamond will be sturdier, more efficient, and not overheat as quickly.

1–1 What Is Science?

You may not realize it, but you are a scientist. Does that statement surprise you? If it does, it is probably because you do not understand exactly what a scientist is. But if you have ever observed a rainbow or seen a fire burn, you were acting like a scientist. You also are a scientist when you watch waves breaking in the ocean and lightning bolts brightening the night sky. Or perhaps you have noticed drops of dew on the morning grass or a roller coaster dipping up and down the track. Whenever you observe the world around you, you are acting like a scientist. Does that give you a clue to the nature of science and scientists?

Scientists observe the world around them. But they do more than that. The word *science* comes from the Latin word *scire*, which means "to know." Science is more than just observing. And real scientists do more than just observe. They question what they see. They wonder what makes things the way they are. They attempt to find answers to their questions.

Figure 1–1 *It has long been a theory that a liquid does not retain its shape when removed from its container. However, scientists were forced to modify this theory after observing the photograph you see here. The photograph, taken with an exposure of a millionth of a second, shows that the water in the balloon retained its balloon shape for 12 to 13 milliseconds after the balloon had been burst by a dart.*

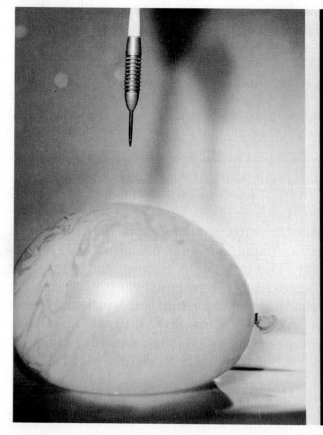

Theories and Laws

Scientists seek basic truths about nature. Such truths are often called facts. An example of a fact is that the sun is the source of heat and light on the earth. But scientists do more than seek facts. They use the facts to solve deeper mysteries of the universe. To do so, they must often tie together several facts in an orderly way. Using the facts they have learned, scientists propose explanations for the events they observe in their world. Then they perform experiments to test their explanations.

After a study of facts, observations, and experiments, scientists may develop a **theory.** A theory is the most logical explanation of events that occur in nature. Once a scientific theory has been proposed, it must be tested over and over again. If test results do not agree, the theory may be changed or even rejected. When a scientific theory has been tested many times and is generally accepted as true, scientists may call it a **law.** But even laws can be changed as a result of future observations and experiments. This points out the heart of science: Always allow questions to be asked and new scientific explanations to be considered.

Scientific Methods

Scientists investigate problems every day. Sometimes it takes many years to solve a problem and develop a theory. Sometimes a problem is quickly solved, especially when the tools needed to investigate the problem are available. And sometimes a problem goes unsolved.

When scientists try to solve a problem, they usually search for an answer in an orderly and systematic manner. To do so, scientists use the **scientific method.** The scientific method is a systematic approach to problem solving. **The basic steps in any scientific method are**

Stating the problem
Gathering information on the problem
Forming a hypothesis
Performing experiments to test the hypothesis
Recording and analyzing data
Stating a conclusion

see notes

Figure 1–2 *The cracks in these rocks were produced by a process called frost action. How can freezing water form such cracks?*

To see how the scientific method is used, consider the following problem. It is one you might have observed yourself. Let's see how a scientist would try to solve it.

Stating the Problem

Suppose you stay at a friend's house one cold winter night. In the morning, your friend's father decides to drive you to school. However, when he turns the key in the ignition, the car does not start. Your friend discovers that there is a pool of ice under the car's engine.

A quick check with a mechanic provides an explanation. The water in the engine's cooling system froze overnight. As the water froze, it expanded and caused the engine to crack in places. Some water leaked onto the ground where it, too, froze. "I forgot to put antifreeze in my car," states the father. You nod your head in agreement, without any real idea about what antifreeze does.

How is it that an engine with antifreeze and water in its cooling system will not freeze on a cold night, while an engine without antifreeze will? If you have ever wondered about this, you have taken the first step toward recognizing a scientific problem. This kind of problem is one a scientist might try to solve.

Before investigating any problem, a scientist must develop a clear statement defining the problem. In this example, a physical scientist might state the problem this way: In what way does antifreeze keep the water in a car's engine from freezing on cold nights?

Gathering Information on the Problem

Once the problem has been clearly stated, all available information related to the problem must be gathered. In this example, a scientist would discover that antifreeze is needed to prevent freezing only in areas where the temperature goes below the freezing point of water. The freezing point of water is the temperature at which liquid water becomes ice. A scientist would also discover that people who

Figure 1–3 *Motorists know that it is as important to put antifreeze in a car's engine during the winter (left) as it is during the summer (right). How does antifreeze protect a car's engine during both seasons?*

live in extremely cold areas must put more antifreeze in their cars than people who live in moderately cold areas. Finally, a scientist would note that water normally freezes at zero degrees Celsius, 0°C.

Forming a Hypothesis

After gathering all available information on the problem, a scientist would suggest a possible solution. A proposed solution to a scientific problem is called a **hypothesis** (high-PAHTH-uh-sihs). One hypothesis that might be considered is that antifreeze prevents water from freezing by lowering the temperature at which water freezes. A scientist might state the hypothesis as a question: Does antifreeze lower the freezing point of water?

Performing Experiments

A scientist does not stop once a hypothesis has been formed. Evidence that either supports or does not support the hypothesis must be found. So a scientist must test a hypothesis to see if it is correct. Such testing is usually done by performing one or more experiments.

A scientist performs experiments according to specific rules, so that the evidence uncovered will clearly support or not support the hypothesis. How might a scientist go about testing the hypothesis that antifreeze lowers the freezing point of water?

First a scientist would obtain two containers. Each container would be the same size and made of the same material. A measured amount of water would be placed in the first container. The same amount of water would be placed in the second container. A measured amount of antifreeze would then be added to the second container.

Next a thermometer would be placed in one container, just below the water line. The same kind of thermometer would be placed in the second container, just below the water–antifreeze mixture line. Then each container would be placed in a freezer or cooling device.

It may appear to you as if two experiments are being performed—one with water and one with a water–antifreeze mixture. Actually, both containers are part of the same experiment. But there is a difference between the two containers. One container holds antifreeze and the other does not. In this experiment, the antifreeze is the **variable.** A variable in any experiment is the one factor that is being tested. The part of the experiment that contains the variable is called the **experimental setup.**

In any experiment, a scientist attempts to test one variable and only one variable at a time. This is done to ensure that the results of the experiment are due to the variable and not some hidden factor. To make sure that the results of an experiment

Figure 1–4 *What is the variable in this experiment?*

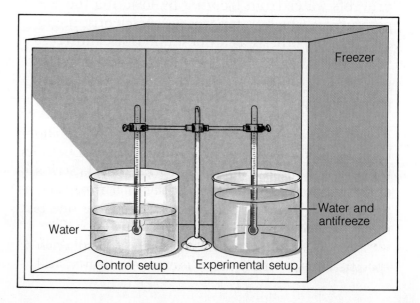

Freezer

Water

Water and antifreeze

Control setup   Experimental setup

HELP WANTED: SCIENCE TEACHER to teach junior high school science classes. Responsibilities include classroom, laboratory, and field activities. Teaching certification required. College degree in science preferred.

The bell rings and the last student enters the classroom to find a seat at a shiny, black lab table. The **science teacher** closes the door and eagerly looks out at the smiling faces of this year's science students.

A science teacher guides students in gathering information and learning new facts about the wonderful world of science. A science teacher helps students explore the weather, the stars, the nature of life, and the principles of physics. Frequently, these things cannot be seen, even with special equipment.

So the challenge to a science teacher is to present complex and abstract information in interesting, exciting, and clear ways. Satisfaction comes when students understand concepts they previously knew nothing about.

In addition to developing lesson plans for different topics, a science teacher must prepare lectures, demonstrations, laboratory projects, and field trips. A teacher must have a solid understanding of the material and be aware of the changes taking place in the world of scientific knowledge.

If you are interested in a career as a science teacher, contact the National Science Teachers Association, 1742 Connecticut Avenue NW, Washington, DC 20009.

are not caused by a hidden factor, a **control setup** is also run. A control setup is exactly like the experimental setup except the control setup does not contain the variable. By running a control setup, a scientist can be sure that the results of the experimental setup were due only to the variable. Which part of the antifreeze experiment is the control setup?

Recording and Analyzing Data

In any experiment, a scientist must observe the experiment and write down important information. Recorded observations and measurements are called **data.** In the antifreeze experiment, a scientist would observe the containers in both the experimental and the control setups at specific time intervals—perhaps every 10 minutes. The temperature in each container would be recorded every 10 minutes. And the temperature at which liquid froze in each container would be noted. To record the data, a scientist would set up data tables similar to the following:

WATER-ANTIFREEZE MIXTURE *(experimental setup)*

Time (min)	0	10	20	30	40	50	60	70	80	90	100	110	120
Temperature (°C)	20	19	17	14	11	8	4	0	−4	−8	−13	−17	*−20

*Asterisk means liquid has frozen.

WATER *(control setup)*

Time (min)	0	10	20	30	40	50	60	70	80	90	100	110	120
Temperature (°C)	20	19	17	14	11	8	4	*0	−4	−8	−13	−17	−20

Figure 1–5 *Scientists often record their observations in data tables. According to these data tables, what is the time interval for measurements?*

To visually compare the data, a scientist would next construct a graph from the data in each table. Since each data table contains two sets of measurements—time and temperature—the graph would have two axes. See Figure 1–6. The horizontal axis of the graph represents time. As you can see from this graph, the horizontal axis must be clearly labeled with the measurement and its units. Since time measurements were made at 10-minute intervals, the horizontal axis is marked in intervals of 10 minutes. The space between equal intervals must be equal. That is, the space between 10 minutes and 20 minutes must be the same as the space between 20 minutes and 30 minutes.

The vertical axis of the graph represents temperature. This axis too is clearly labeled with the measurement and its units. Since the experiment began at 20°C and ended at −20°C, the vertical axis would go from 20°C to −20°C.

After the axes for each graph were chosen and labeled, a scientist would graph the data from the experimental setup. Each pair of data points from the data table would be plotted. At 0 minutes, the temperature was 20°C. So a dot would be placed where 0 minutes and 20°C intersected on the graph—in the upper left corner. When each set of data points had been plotted on the graph, a scientist would draw a line connecting all the dots.

The same procedure would be followed for the data from the control setup. Soon a scientist would have a graph of the experimental setup side by side with a graph of the control setup. For these particular graphs, the final thing would be to indicate at what temperature the liquid in each container froze.

Stating a Conclusion

The results from a single experiment are not enough to reach a conclusion. A scientist must run an experiment over and over again before the data can be considered accurate.

Once the antifreeze experiment had been run many times, a scientist would examine the data and state a conclusion. Since the plain water froze at a temperature of 0°C and the water with antifreeze froze at a temperature of −20°C, a scientist would conclude that antifreeze lowers the temperature at which water freezes. The original hypothesis in this case would be correct.

Is the scientist finished? Actually, a good scientist would then ask *why* antifreeze lowers the freezing point of water. And that, of course, sounds very much like the beginning of a new problem. It often

Figure 1–6 *The information in data tables can be visually presented in graphs. What conclusions can you draw from this graph about the effect of antifreeze on the freezing point of water?*

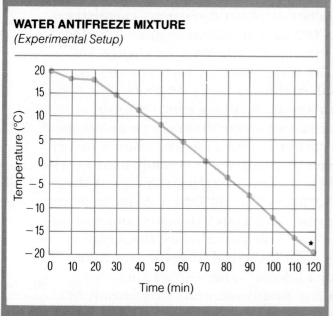

WATER ANTIFREEZE MIXTURE
(Experimental Setup)

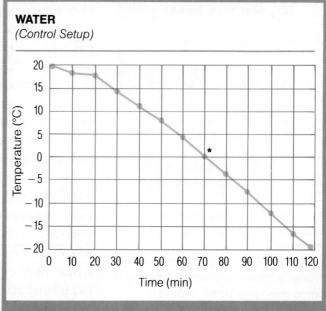

WATER
(Control Setup)

*Asterisk means liquid has frozen.

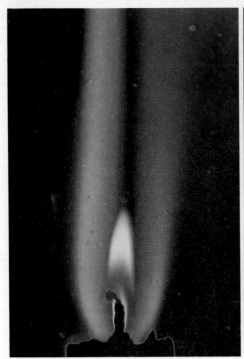
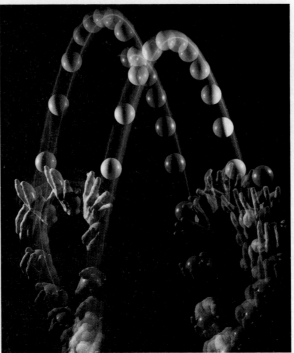

Figure 1–7 *Chemistry is the study of matter and the changes it undergoes (left). The laws of motion (right) are part of the science of physics.*

happens in science that the solution to one problem leads to yet another problem. The cycle of discovery in science goes on and on.

Branches of Physical Science

Science is divided into many branches, depending on the subject matter being studied. Physical science is the study of matter and energy. There are two main branches of physical science—**chemistry** and **physics.** Chemistry involves the study of what substances are made of and how they change and combine. Physics is the study of forms of energy and the laws of motion.

Just as with any branch of science, physical science has many special terms that may be unfamiliar to you. The chart in Figure 1–8 gives the meanings of some prefixes and suffixes commonly used in science vocabulary. If you learn the meanings of these prefixes and suffixes, you will find it easier to learn new science terms. And knowing the meaning of science terms will increase your understanding of physical science. For example, suppose you come upon the term *exothermic reaction.* You know from the chart that *exo-* means out and *-therm* means heat. So you probably can guess that in an exothermic reaction heat goes out, or heat is given off.

Sharpen Your Skills

Prefixes and Suffixes

Study the list of common science prefixes and suffixes in Figure 1–8.

1. Select three science words that have a prefix listed on the chart.

2. Select two science words that have a suffix listed on the chart.

3. Write a paragraph using the five words you have chosen.

4. Do you know any additional science prefixes and suffixes that you think should be added to the chart? Share your findings with your class.

14

SOME COMMON SCIENCE PREFIXES AND SUFFIXES

Prefix	Meaning	Prefix	Meaning	Suffix	Meaning
anti-	against	in-	inside	-ation	the act of
atmo-	vapor	inter-	between	-escent	becoming
chromo-	color	iso-	equal	-graphy	description of
con-	together	macro-	large	-logy	study of
di-	double	micro-	small	-meter	device for measuring
endo-	within	photo-	light	-scope	instrument for seeing
exo-	outside	sub-	under	-sphere	round
hetero-	different	syn-	together	-stasis	stationary condition
homo-	same	tele-	distant	-therm	heat
hydro-	water	trans-	across	-verge	turn

Figure 1–8 *A working knowledge of prefixes and suffixes used in science vocabulary will be of great help to you. According to this chart, what is the meaning of the term converge?*

SECTION REVIEW

1. Identify the steps in a scientific method.
2. Explain why any experiment must have only one variable.
3. People usually put antifreeze in a car engine during the summer when temperatures get very high. What effect do you think antifreeze has on water that makes it useful on very hot days?

1–2 Scientific Measurements

Section Objective

To identify the metric units used in scientific measurements

As you learned, experimenting is an important part of any scientific method. And most experiments involve measurements. Measurements made during experiments must be reliable and accurate as well as easily communicated to others. So a system of measurements based on standard units is used by scientists. With this system, scientists around the world can compare and analyze data.

The standard system used by all scientists is the **metric system.** The metric system is also referred to as the International System of Units, or SI. The metric system is a decimal system. That is, it is based on the number 10 and multiples of 10.

Scientists use metric units to measure length, volume, mass, density, and temperature. Some frequently used metric units and their abbreviations are listed in Figure 1–9.

Length

The basic unit of length in the metric system is the **meter (m).** A meter is equal to about 39.4 inches. Your height would be measured in meters. Most students your age are between 1½ and 2 meters tall.

To measure the length of an object smaller than a meter, the metric unit called the **centimeter (cm)** is used. The prefix *centi-* means one-hundredth. So there are 100 centimeters in a meter. The height of this book is about 26 centimeters.

Figure 1–9 *The metric system is easy to use because it is based on units of ten. How many centimeters are there in 10 meters?*

COMMONLY USED METRIC UNITS

Length	Mass
Length is the distance from one point to another.	Mass is the amount of matter in an object.
A meter is slightly longer than a yard.	
1 meter (m) = 100 centimeters (cm)	A gram has a mass equal to about one paper clip.
1 meter = 1000 millimeters (mm)	1 kilogram (kg) = 1000 grams (g)
1 meter = 1,000,000 micrometers (μm)	1 gram = 1000 milligrams (mg)
1 meter = 1,000,000,000 nanometers (nm)	1000 kilograms = 1 metric ton (t)
1 meter = 10,000,000,000 angstroms (Å)	
1000 meters = 1 kilometer (km)	

Volume	Temperature
Volume is the amount of space an object takes up.	Temperature is the measure of hotness or coldness in degrees Celsius (°C).
A liter is slightly larger than a quart.	0°C = freezing point of water
1 liter (L) = 1000 milliliters (mL) or 1000 cubic centimeters (cm^3)	100°C = boiling point of water

Figure 1–10 *This spectacular photograph of the rings of Saturn was taken by the* Voyager *satellite as it passed by the distant planet. Which metric unit is best for measuring the distance to Saturn?*

To measure even smaller objects, the metric unit called the **millimeter (mm)** is used. The prefix *milli-* means one-thousandth. As you might expect, there are 1000 millimeters in a meter. How many millimeters are there in a centimeter?

Sometimes scientists want to measure long distances, such as the length of the Nile River in Africa. Such lengths can be measured in meters, centimeters, or even millimeters. But when measuring long distances with small units, the numbers become very large and difficult to work with. For example, the length of the Nile River is about 6,649,000,000 millimeters. To avoid such large numbers, the metric unit called the **kilometer (km)** is used. The prefix *kilo-* means one thousand. So there are 1000 meters in a kilometer. The length of the Nile River is about 6649 kilometers. How many meters is this? How many centimeters are there in one kilometer? How many millimeters?

Volume

Volume is the amount of space an object takes up. The basic unit of volume in the metric system is the **liter (L).** A liter is slightly more than a quart. To measure volumes smaller than a liter, scientists use the **milliliter (mL).** There are 1000 milliliters in a liter. An ordinary drinking glass holds about 200 milliliters of liquid.

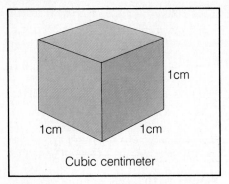

Figure 1–11 *A cubic centimeter (cm³, or cc) is the volume of a cube that measures 1 cm by 1 cm by 1 cm. How many milliliters are in a cubic centimeter?*

Liters and milliliters are used to measure the volume of liquids. The metric unit used to measure the volume of solids is called the **cubic centimeter (cm³ or cc).** A cubic centimeter is equal to a milliliter. Cubic centimeters often are used in measuring the volume of liquids as well as solids. How many cubic centimeters are there in a liter?

Mass

The basic unit of mass in the metric system is the **kilogram (kg).** Mass is a measure of the amount of matter in an object. For example, there is more matter in a dumptruck than in a compact car. So a dumptruck has more mass than a compact car. A kilogram is about 2.2 pounds. What is your mass in kilograms?

The kilogram is used to measure the mass of large objects. To measure the mass of small objects, such as a nickel, the **gram (g)** is used. If you remember what the term *kilo-* means, then you know that a kilogram contains 1000 grams. A nickel has a mass of about 5 grams.

The mass of even smaller objects is measured in **milligrams (mg).** A milligram is one-thousandth of a gram. So there are 1000 milligrams in a gram. How many milligrams are there in a kilogram?

Density

Sometimes it is useful to know the amount of mass in a given volume of an object. This quantity is known as **density.** Density is defined as the mass per unit volume of a substance. The following formula shows the relationship between density, mass, and volume:

$$\text{density} = \frac{\text{mass}}{\text{volume}}$$

Suppose a substance has a mass of 10 grams and a volume of 10 milliliters. If you divide the mass of 10 grams by the volume of 10 milliliters, you obtain the density of the substance:

$$\frac{10 \text{ g}}{10 \text{ mL}} = \frac{1 \text{ g}}{\text{mL}}$$

Figure 1–12 *The hippopotamus is one of the largest land animals on the earth. Harvest field mice are the smallest mice on the earth. Which metric unit would be best for measuring the mass of a hippopotamus? Of field mice?*

As it turns out, this substance is water. The density of water is 1 g/mL. Objects with a density less than that of water will float on water. Objects with a density greater than that of water will sink in water. Does wood have a density less than or greater than 1 g/mL?

Temperature

In the metric system, temperature is measured on the **Celsius** (SEHL-see-uhs) scale. On the Celsius temperature scale, water freezes at 0°C and boils at 100°C. There are exactly 100 degrees between the freezing point and boiling point of water. Each Celsius degree represents 1/100 of this temperature range. Normal body temperature in humans is 37°C. Comfortable room temperature is about 21°C.

Dimensional Analysis

Now that you know the basic units of the metric system, it is important that you understand how to go from one unit to another. The skill of converting one unit to another is called **dimensional analysis.** Dimensional analysis involves determining in what units a problem is given, in what units the answer should be, and the factor to be used to make the conversion from one unit to another.

To perform dimensional analysis, you must use a **conversion factor.** A conversion factor is a fraction

Figure 1–13 *Notice the steam rising out of the sulfur springs on the island of Saint Lucia. What instrument would be used to measure the temperature of the sulfur springs?*

Metric Conversions

Use conversion factors to make the following metric conversions. *Do not write in this book.*

10 m = _____ km

2 km = _____ cm

250 mL = _____ L

2000 g = _____ kg

10 kg = _____ mg

1500 cc = _____ L

that always equals 1. For example, 1 kilometer equals 1000 meters. So the fraction 1 kilometer/ 1000 meters equals 1. So does the fraction 1000 meters/1 kilometer. The top number in a fraction is called the numerator. The bottom number in a fraction is called the denominator. In a conversion fraction the numerator always equals the denominator so that the fraction always equals 1.

Let's see how dimensional analysis works. Suppose you are told to convert 2500 grams to kilograms. This means that grams are your given unit and you must express your answer in kilograms. The conversion factor you choose must contain a relationship between grams and kilograms that has a value of 1. You have two possible choices:

$$\frac{1000 \text{ grams}}{1 \text{ kilogram}} = 1 \quad \text{or} \quad \frac{1 \text{ kilogram}}{1000 \text{ grams}} = 1$$

To convert one metric unit to another, you must multiply the given value times the conversion factor. Remember that multiplying a number by 1 does not change the value of the number. So multiplying by a conversion factor does not change the value, just the units.

Now, which conversion factor should you use to change 2500 grams into kilograms? Since you are going to multiply by the conversion factor, you want the unit to be converted to cancel out during the multiplication. This is just what will happen if the denominator of the conversion factor has the same units as the value you wish to convert. Since you are converting grams into kilograms, the denominator of the conversion factor must be in grams and the numerator in kilograms. The first step in dimensional analysis, then, is to write out the value given, the correct conversion factor, and a multiplication symbol between them:

$$2500 \text{ grams} \times \frac{1 \text{ kilogram}}{1000 \text{ grams}}$$

The next step is to cancel out the same units:

$$2500 \text{ \cancel{grams}} \times \frac{1 \text{ kilogram}}{1000 \text{ \cancel{grams}}}$$

The last step is to multiply:

$$2500 \times \frac{1 \text{ kilogram}}{1000} = \frac{2500 \text{ kilograms}}{1000}$$

$$\frac{2500 \text{ kilograms}}{1000} = 2.5 \text{ kilograms}$$

SECTION REVIEW

1. What are the basic units of length, volume, mass, and temperature in the metric system?
2. What metric unit of length would be appropriate for expressing the distance from the earth to the sun? Why?
3. To measure the size of atoms, scientists use the unit called the Angstrom. An Angstrom is one ten-billionth of a meter. How many Angstroms are in a meter?
4. Without placing an object in water, how can you determine if it will float?

1–3 Tools of Measurement

Section Objective

To describe how common laboratory tools are used to make scientific measurements

Physical scientists use a wide variety of tools in order to study the world around them. Some of these tools are rather complex; others are relatively simple. As you read this book, you will be introduced to many of these tools. You will have an opportunity to use some of these laboratory tools when you perform physical science experiments. **The basic laboratory tools that you will learn to use are the metric ruler, triple-beam balance, graduated cylinder, and Celsius thermometer.**

Measuring Length

A metric ruler is used to measure the length of objects. A metric ruler is divided into centimeters. Common metric rulers are 15 or 25 centimeters in length. Each centimeter is further divided into 10 millimeters. Figure 1–14 on page 22 shows a metric ruler and the centimeter and millimeter divisions. Keep in mind that this ruler is not drawn to scale. You cannot use it to make calculations.

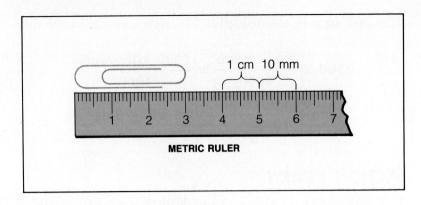

Figure 1–14 *A metric ruler is used to measure the length of small objects. What is the length of this paper clip?*

METRIC RULER

To measure an object whose length is longer than a metric ruler, you would use a meterstick. A meterstick is one meter long and contains 100 centimeters. How many millimeters are in a meterstick?

Measuring Mass

Recall that the kilogram is the basic unit of mass in the metric system. A kilogram contains 1000 grams. Most of the measurements you will make in physical science will be in grams. One of the most common tools used to measure mass in grams is the triple-beam balance shown in Figure 1–15.

As you might expect, a triple-beam balance has three beams. Each beam is marked, or calibrated, in grams. The front beam is the 10-gram beam. Markings divide the beam into 10 segments of 1 gram each. On some triple-beam balances, each 1-gram segment on the front beam is further divided into units of one-tenth gram. The middle beam, often called the 500-gram beam, is divided into 5 segments of 100 grams each. The back beam, or 100-gram beam, is divided into 10 segments of 10 grams each. What is the largest mass you can measure with a triple-beam balance?

To measure the mass of a solid, such as a small rock, follow these steps. First, place the rock on the flat pan of the balance. Then slide the rider on the middle beam notch by notch until the pointer drops below zero. Move the rider back one notch. Next, slide the rider on the back beam notch by notch until the pointer drops below zero. Move this rider back one notch. Finally, move the rider on the front beam notch by notch until the pointer points exactly to the zero mark. The mass of the object is equal to the *sum* of the readings on the three beams.

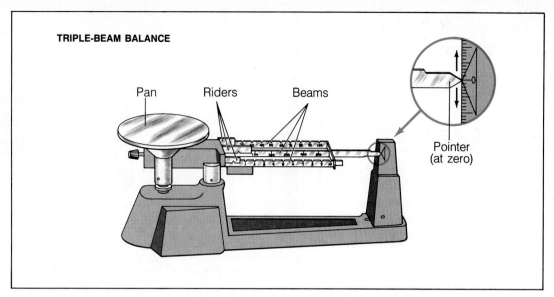

TRIPLE-BEAM BALANCE

Pan   Riders   Beams

Pointer
(at zero)

If you want to find the mass of a powder or of crystals, you will have to place the sample on a sheet of filter paper on top of the pan. You must never place such a sample directly on the balance pan. The mass of the filter paper must first be determined. Once this is done, you can pour the sample onto the filter paper and find the mass of the filter paper and sample combined. Subtract the mass of the filter paper from the mass of filter paper and sample to determine the mass of the sample.

A similar method can be used to find the mass of a liquid. In this case, place an empty beaker or flask on the pan and find its mass. Then pour the liquid into the beaker. Find the combined mass of the beaker and liquid. Subtract the mass of the beaker from the mass of the beaker and liquid to determine the mass of the liquid.

Measuring Volume

You learned that the basic unit of volume in the metric system is the liter. Most of the measurements you will make in physical science, however, will be in milliliters or cubic centimeters. Remember there are 1000 milliliters or cubic centimeters in a liter.

To find the volume of a liquid, you will use a graduated cylinder. See Figure 1–17. A graduated cylinder is usually calibrated in milliliters. Each line on the graduated cylinder is one milliliter. To measure the volume of a liquid, pour the liquid into the graduated cylinder. You will notice that the surface of the liquid is curved. To determine the volume of

Figure 1–15 *A triple-beam balance is one of the instruments used to measure mass in grams. Can mass in kilograms be measured by using a triple-beam balance? Explain your answer.*

Figure 1–16 *A triple-beam balance is used to determine the mass of an object. What is the mass of the solid?*

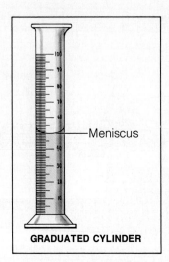

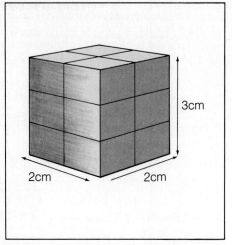

Figure 1–17 *A graduated cylinder is used to measure volume (left). To get an accurate measurement, where should you read the markings on the graduated cylinder? What is the volume of this rectangular block in cubic centimeters (cm³) (right)?*

the liquid, read the milliliter marking at the *bottom* of the curve. This curve is called the **meniscus** (mih-NIHS-kuhs). Keep in mind that although a graduated cylinder is marked off in milliliters, each milliliter is equal to one cubic centimeter.

To find the volume of a solid that is rectangular in shape, you will use a metric ruler. A rectangular solid is often called a regular solid. The volume of a regular solid is determined by multiplying the length of the solid times the width of the solid times the height of the solid. The formula you can use to find the volume of a regular solid is

volume = height times length times width

or

$$v = h \times l \times w$$

Figure 1–17 shows a rectangular solid with a length of 2 centimeters, a width of 2 centimeters, and a height of 3 centimeters. If you multiply 2 cm times 2 cm times 3 cm, you obtain the volume, which is 12 cm³, or 12 cc. What is the volume of a regular solid 3 cm by 4 cm by 5 cm?

Suppose you wish to determine the volume of a solid that is not rectangular in shape, or an irregular solid. You cannot measure its height, width, or length with a metric ruler. So to determine the volume of an irregular solid, you will use a graduated cylinder again. First fill the cylinder about half full with water. Record the volume of the water. Then carefully place the solid into the liquid. Record the volume of the liquid and solid combined. Then subtract the volume of the liquid from the combined volume of the liquid and solid. The answer will be the volume of the irregular solid. Will the volume be in milliliters or in cubic centimeters?

Measuring Temperature

To measure temperature, you will use a Celsius thermometer. The two fixed points on a Celsius thermometer are the freezing point of water, 0°C, and the boiling point of water, 100°C. Some Celsius thermometers go as low as −25°C so that temperatures below the freezing point of water can be measured. Each calibration on a Celsius thermometer is equal to one degree Celsius.

Within the glass tube of a Celsius thermometer is a colored liquid. Alcohol or mercury are the two liquids most commonly used. In order to measure the temperature of a substance, place the thermometer in the substance. The liquid in the thermometer will begin to change. Wait until the liquid stops changing. Then read the number next to the mark on the thermometer that lines up with the top of the liquid. This number is the temperature of the substance.

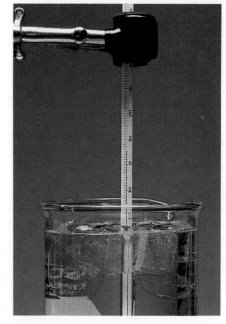

Figure 1–18 *A Celsius thermometer is used to measure temperature. What is the temperature of the ice-water mixture in the beaker?*

SECTION REVIEW

1. Each side of a regular solid is 5 centimeters long. What is the volume of the solid?
2. What instrument would you use to measure length? Mass? Volume? Temperature?
3. If you want to find the density of an irregular object, what tools will you need? How will you go about making this measurement?

1–4 Science Safety in the Laboratory

Section Objective

To apply safety rules in the laboratory

The science laboratory is a place of adventure and discovery. Some of the most exciting events in the history of science have taken place in laboratories. The discovery of X-rays is one example. Another example is the discovery of oxygen. The relationship between electricity and magnetism was also discovered by scientists working in a laboratory. The list goes on and on.

To better understand the facts and concepts you will read about in physical science, you may work in the laboratory this year. If you follow instructions and are as careful as a scientist would be, the laboratory will turn out to be an exciting experience.

When working in the laboratory, scientists know that it is very important to follow safety procedures. All of the work you will do in the laboratory this year will include experiments that have been done over and over again. When done properly, the experiments are interesting and safe. However, if they are done improperly, accidents can occur. How can you avoid such problems?

First and foremost, always follow your teacher's directions or the directions in your textbook exactly as stated. Never try anything on your own without asking your teacher first. And when you are not sure what you should do, always ask first. As you read the laboratory investigations in the textbook, you will see safety alert symbols next to certain procedures that require special safety care. Look at Figure 1–20 to learn the meanings of the safety symbols and the important safety precautions you should take.

In addition to the safety procedures listed in Figure 1–20, there is a more detailed list of safety procedures in Appendix B on page 669 of this textbook. Before you enter the laboratory for the first time, make sure that you have read each rule carefully. Then read them over again. Make sure that you understand each rule. If you do not

Figure 1–19 *It is important to always point a test tube that is being heated away from yourself and your classmates (left). What two safety precautions is this student taking before picking up a hot beaker (right)?*

Glassware Safety

1. Whenever you see this symbol, you will know that you are working with glassware that can easily be broken. Take particular care to handle such glassware safely. And never use broken glassware.
2. Never heat glassware that is not thoroughly dry. Never pick up any glassware unless you are sure it is not hot. If it is hot, use heat-resistant gloves.
3. Always clean glassware thoroughly before putting it away.

Fire Safety

1. Whenever you see this symbol, you will know that you are working with fire. Never use any source of fire without wearing safety goggles.
2. Never heat anything—particularly chemicals—unless instructed to do so.
3. Never heat anything in a closed container.
4. Never reach across a flame.
5. Always use a clamp, tongs, or heat-resistant gloves to handle hot objects.
6. Always maintain a clean work area, particularly when using a flame.

Heat Safety

Whenever you see this symbol, you will know that you should put on heat-resistant gloves to avoid burning your hands.

Chemical Safety

1. Whenever you see this symbol, you will know that you are working with chemicals that could be hazardous.
2. Never smell any chemical directly from its container. Always use your hand to waft some of the odors from the top of the container toward your nose—and only when instructed to do so.
3. Never mix chemicals unless instructed to do so.

4. Never touch or taste any chemical unless instructed to do so.
5. Keep all lids closed when chemicals are not in use. Dispose of all chemicals as instructed by your teacher.
6. Immediately rinse with water any chemicals, particularly acids, off your skin and clothes. Then notify your teacher.

Eye and Face Safety

1. Whenever you see this symbol, you will know that you are performing an experiment in which you must take precautions to protect your eyes and face by wearing safety goggles.
2. Always point away from you and others a test tube or bottle that is being heated. Chemicals can splash or boil out of the heated test tube.
3. Always wear safety goggles when you see this symbol.

Sharp Instrument Safety

1. Whenever you see this symbol, you will know that you are working with a sharp instrument.
2. Always use single-edged razors; double-edged razors are too dangerous.
3. Handle any sharp instrument with extreme care. Never cut any material toward you; always cut away from you.
4. Notify your teacher immediately if you are cut in the lab.

Electrical Safety

1. Whenever you see this symbol, you will know that you are using electricity in the laboratory.
2. Never use long extension cords to plug in an electrical device. Do not plug too many different appliances into one socket or you may overload the socket and cause a fire.
3. Never touch an electrical appliance or outlet with wet hands.

Figure 1–20 *This chart shows the safety precaution symbols you will often find next to the procedure in the laboratory investigations in this book. Which symbol would you expect to see when the investigation calls for using a Bunsen burner?*

understand a rule, ask your teacher to explain it. You may even want to suggest further rules that apply to your particular classroom.

SECTION REVIEW

1. What is the most important general rule to follow when working in the laboratory?
2. Why is it important to point a test tube away from yourself and others when it is being heated?
3. Where is the nearest fire extinguisher located in your laboratory or classroom?

Uncertainty of Measurements

Purpose

How accurately can matter be measured?

Materials *(per station)*

Station 1: meterstick
Station 2: metric ruler
          regular object
Station 3: graduated cylinder
          beaker with colored liquid
Station 4: triple-beam balance
          small pebble
Station 5: graduated cylinder
          beaker of water
          irregular object
Station 6: Celsius thermometer
          beaker with ice and water
          paper towel

Procedure

1. Station 1: Use the meterstick to measure the length and width of the desk or lab table. If the table is irregular, measure the shortest width and the longest length. Express your measurements in centimeters.
2. Station 2: Use the metric ruler to find the volume of the regular object. Express the volume in cubic centimeters.
3. Station 3: Use the graduated cylinder to find the volume of the colored liquid in the beaker. Then pour the liquid back into the beaker. Express your measurement in milliliters.
4. Station 4: Place the pebble on the pan of the triple-beam balance. Move the riders until the pointer is at zero. Record the mass of the pebble in grams. Remove the pebble and return all riders back to zero.
5. Station 5: Fill the graduated cylinder half full with water. Find the volume of the irregular object. Express the volume of the object in cubic centimeters. Carefully

remove the object from the graduated cylinder. Pour the water back into the beaker.

6. Station 6: Use the Celsius thermometer to find the temperature of the ice water. Record the temperature in degrees Celsius. Remove the thermometer and carefully dry it with a paper towel.

Observation

Your teacher will construct a large class data table for each of the work stations. Record the data from each group on the class data table.

Conclusions

1. Do all the class measurements have the exact same value for each station?
2. Which station had measurements that were most nearly alike? Explain why these measurements were so similar.
3. Which station had measurements that were most varied? Explain why these measurements were so varied.

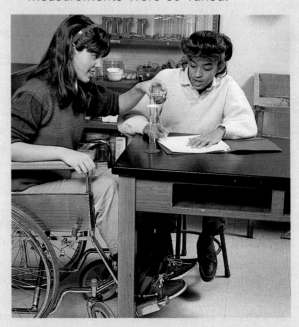

CHAPTER REVIEW

1–1 What Is Science?

❑ A theory is the most logical explanation of events that occur in nature.

❑ When a scientific theory has been tested many times and is accepted as true, scientists may call it a law.

❑ The scientific method is a systematic approach to problem solving.

❑ A variable is the one factor that is being tested in an experiment.

❑ The two main branches of physical science are chemistry and physics.

1–2 Scientific Measurements

❑ The standard system of measurement used by all scientists is the metric system.

❑ The basic unit of length in the metric system is the meter. One meter is equal to 100 centimeters or 1000 millimeters.

❑ A kilometer is equal to 1000 meters.

❑ The basic unit of volume in the metric system is the liter. A liter contains 1000 milliliters or 1000 cubic centimeters.

❑ The kilogram is the basic unit of mass in the metric system.

❑ A kilogram is equal to 1000 grams.

❑ Density is defined as the mass per unit volume of an object.

❑ The basic unit of temperature in the metric system is the degree Celsius.

❑ Dimensional analysis is a method of converting from one unit to another in the metric system by multiplying the given unit by a conversion factor.

1–3 Tools of Measurement

❑ The metric ruler is used to measure length. A metric ruler is divided into centimeters and millimeters.

❑ The triple-beam balance is used to measure mass.

❑ A graduated cylinder is used to find the volume of a liquid or the volume of an irregular solid.

❑ The volume of a regular solid can be determined by multiplying its height by its width by its length.

❑ A Celsius thermometer is used to measure temperature.

1–4 Science Safety in the Laboratory

❑ When working in the laboratory, it is important to take all necessary safety precautions. These include using safety equipment and following all instructions carefully.

❑ If all safety rules are followed, the laboratory can be a safe and exciting place.

VOCABULARY

Define each term in a complete sentence.

Celsius	density	law	physics
centimeter	dimensional analysis	liter	scientific method
chemistry		meniscus	
control setup	experimental setup	meter	theory
conversion factor	gram	metric system	variable
cubic centimeter	hypothesis	milligram	
data	kilogram	milliliter	
	kilometer	millimeter	

CONTENT REVIEW: MULTIPLE CHOICE

On a separate sheet of paper, write the letter of the answer that best completes each statement.

1. An orderly, systematic approach to problem solving is called a (an)
   a. experiment.   b. conclusion.
   c. scientific method.   d. dimensional analysis.
2. A proposed solution to a scientific problem is called a
   a. conclusion.   b. theory.   c. data.   d. hypothesis.
3. In any experiment, the one factor being tested is the
   a. data.   b. control.   c. hypothesis.   d. variable.
4. The basic unit of length in the metric system is the
   a. kilometer.   b. centimeter.   c. meter.   d. liter.
5. A cubic centimeter is equal in volume to a
   a. liter.   b. milliliter.   c. gram.   d. milligram.
6. The basic unit of mass in the metric system is the
   a. kilogram.   b. liter.   c. milligram.   d. gram.
7. The amount of matter in an object is called its
   a. volume.   b. density.   c. mass.   d. dimension.
8. To measure the mass of a solid, you should use a
   a. graduated cylinder.   b. triple-beam balance.
   c. meterstick.   d. Celsius thermometer.
9. A graduated cylinder is calibrated in
   a. milliliters.   b. liters.   c. grams.   d. degrees Celsius.
10. When working with a flame, always wear
   a. heat-resistant gloves.   b. safety goggles.
   c. a short-sleeved shirt.   d. a laboratory apron.

CONTENT REVIEW: COMPLETION

On a separate sheet of paper, write the word or words that best complete each statement.

1. When a theory is accepted as true, scientists may call it a _____.
2. A hypothesis is a _____ to a problem.
3. In any experiment, the part of the experiment that contains the variable is called the _____.
4. The branch of physical science that deals with the laws of motion is called _____.
5. The _____ is the standard system of measurement used by scientists.
6. To measure the distance across the United States, you would likely use the unit of measurement called the _____.
7. A liter contains 1000 _____, or 1000 _____.
8. On the Celsius temperature scale, water _____ at 100°C and _____ at 0°C.
9. A conversion factor is a _____ that always equals one.
10. The bottom of the curve formed by a liquid in a graduated cylinder is called the _____.

CONTENT REVIEW: TRUE OR FALSE

Determine whether each statement is true or false. Then on a separate sheet of paper, write "true" if it is true. If it is false, change the underlined word or words to make the statement true.

1. An experiment should have <u>two variables</u>.
2. The <u>experimental setup</u> contains the variable.
3. Recorded observations are called <u>data</u>.
4. The prefix *kilo-* means <u>one hundred</u>.
5. A liter contains <u>100 milliliters</u>.
6. Mass is measured in <u>liters</u>.
7. Density is <u>volume</u> per unit <u>mass</u>.
8. A conversion fraction must equal <u>one</u>.
9. The <u>front beam</u> of a triple-beam balance is often called the 500-gram beam.
10. To find the volume of a regular solid, you <u>multiply</u> height times width times length.

CONCEPT REVIEW: SKILL BUILDING

Use the skills you have developed in this chapter to complete each activity.

1. **Applying concepts** What tool or tools would you use to make the following measurements? What units would you use to express your answers?

   volume of a glass of water
   length of a sheet of paper
   mass of a liter of milk
   length of a football field
   volume of an irregular object
   mass of a hockey puck
   ocean temperature

2. **Making calculations** Use dimensional analysis to convert each of the following:

   a. A blue whale is about 33 meters in length. How many centimeters is this?
   b. The Statue of Liberty is about 45 meters tall. How tall is the statue in millimeters?
   c. Mount Everest is about 8.8 kilometers high. How high is it in meters?
   d. A Ping-Pong ball has a mass of about 2.5 grams. What is its mass in milligrams?
   e. An elephant is about 6300 kilograms in mass. What is its mass in grams?

3. **Making measurements** Fill a cooking pan half full with water. Place the pan on the burner of your stove at home. Turn the dial to the lowest setting. **CAUTION:** *Be very careful when working with an open flame or electric burner.* Hold a Celsius thermometer in the water, making sure you do not let the thermometer touch the sides or bottom of the pan. Have a classmate or parent record the temperature of the water at one-minute intervals until the water begins to boil. Make a graph of your data with temperature versus time axes. At what point did the temperature of the water begin to rise? How long did it take before the water began to boil? Did the heated water rise in temperature by the same amount each minute?

4. **Designing an experiment** Antifreeze is put into a car's cooling system during hot summer months. Design an experiment to test whether antifreeze has any effect on the boiling point of water. Make sure you include an experimental and control setup. If you were to graph your data, how would you label the two axes of the graph?

CONCEPT REVIEW: ESSAY

Discuss each of the following in a brief paragraph.

1. Describe the steps in a scientific method.
2. Explain why the results of an experiment are not valid if there are two variables.
3. Describe the need for a standard system of measurement.
4. Explain how you are a scientist.

Properties of Matter 2

CHAPTER SECTIONS

2–1 General Properties of Matter

2–2 Phases of Matter

2–3 Phase Changes

2–4 Chemical Properties and Changes

CHAPTER OBJECTIVES

After completing this chapter, you will be able to

2–1 Describe the general properties of matter.

2–1 Relate mass and inertia.

2–1 Distinguish between mass and weight.

2–1 Define and calculate density.

2–2 Classify matter based on phase.

2–2 Describe the arrangement and movement of particles in solids, liquids, and gases.

2–2 State the Gas Laws.

2–3 Identify phase changes in matter.

2–3 Interpret a phase-change diagram.

2–4 Differentiate between chemical and physical properties and changes.

2–4 Distinguish between chemical properties and chemical changes.

The day had dawned sunny and bright, although a bit chilly. But throughout the day, the temperature had steadily dropped. And now it was so cold that few of those working in the orange grove could remember a day like it. The workers talked about the unusual Florida weather, but what was really on their minds were the hundreds of orange trees whose branches were heavy with fruit not yet ripe enough for picking. Such low temperatures could wipe out the entire crop. The juice in the orange would freeze, ruining the fruit as well as the farmer's profits.

The workers knew something had to be done, and done quickly, to save the orange crop. So they lighted small fires in smokepots scattered throughout the fields. But they soon realized that the heat produced this way would never be enough to save the fruit. Suddenly, some workers raced out into the grove hauling long water hoses. Fighting time and temperature, the workers sprayed the trees with water. The water would freeze and turn into ice as the temperature continued to drop. The ice would keep the oranges warm!

With sunrise the next day, the temperature began to climb. The glistening ice that had coated the fruit trees melted away. The fruit was undamaged—cold but not frozen. The orange crop had been saved!

Does it seem strange to you that oranges can be kept warm with ice? Freezing water can sometimes do a better job of keeping things warm than fire can. As the liquid water sprayed onto the trees froze, it released heat energy. Some of this heat energy was released into the oranges, preventing them from freezing. In this chapter, you will learn more about the substances and processes in nature.

To keep oranges from being destroyed by the cold, the oranges are actually covered with water that quickly freezes. Is this science or magic? The answer lies within the pages of this chapter.

2–1 General Properties of Matter

Suppose you received a gift and wanted to tell your friend about it. Only you wanted to describe the gift without actually naming the object. What are some of the characteristics you would use?

You might start with the size and shape of the object. Next, you might describe how the object feels to your touch. Is it soft, hard, spongy, or fluffy? Is it smooth or rough? Is it solid or hollow? If it is hollow, does it contain other objects? Would the object float, sink, or perhaps even swim in water? Does it have an identifying color or odor?

The words you use to describe the object are its characteristics. All objects have certain characteristics that help you identify them. And although most of the objects around you have different characteristics, they share one important quality. They are all forms of **matter.** Matter is what the world is made of. All objects consist of matter.

Your senses of smell, sight, taste, and touch help you become familiar with the variety of matter that surrounds you. Some kinds of matter are easily recognized. Plants, animals, rocks, soil, water, glass, salt, and silver are examples of matter that are easily observed. Less easily observed, but still matter, are oxygen, carbon dioxide, nitrogen, ammonia, and air.

Figure 2–1 *What characteristics would you use to describe the various forms of matter seen in this photograph of the John Muir Trail in the High Sierra Mountains of California?*

Are these different kinds of matter similar in some ways? Is glass anything like ammonia? Do silver and oxygen have anything in common?

In order to answer these questions, you must know something about the **properties,** or characteristics, of matter. Properties describe an object. Color, odor, shape, texture, and hardness are properties of matter. They are very specific properties of matter, however. Specific properties make it easy to tell one kind of matter from another.

Some properties of matter are more general. Instead of describing the differences among forms of matter, general properties describe how all matter is the same. **General properties of matter include mass, weight, volume, and density.**

Mass

The most important general property of matter is that it has **mass.** Mass is the amount of matter in an object. The mass of an object is constant. It does not change unless some matter is either added to the object or removed from the object. This means that the mass of an object does not change when you move the object from one location to another. For example, you have the same mass whether you are on top of a mountain, at the bottom of a deep mine, or on the moon!

Scientists define mass in another way. Mass is a measure of the **inertia** (ihn-ER-shuh) of an object. Inertia is the resistance of an object to changes in its motion. Objects that have mass resist changes in their motion. Thus, objects that have mass have inertia. For example, if an object is at rest, a force must be used to make it move. If an object is moving, a force must be used to slow it down or stop it.

The more mass an object has, the greater is its inertia. The force that must be exerted to overcome that inertia is also greater. Which would be harder to pull up a hill, an empty wagon or a wagon occupied by two of your friends? Which would be harder to stop at the bottom of a hill?

Mass is measured in units called grams (g) and kilograms (kg). One kilogram is equal to 1000 grams. The mass of small objects usually is expressed in grams. A nickel, for example, has a mass

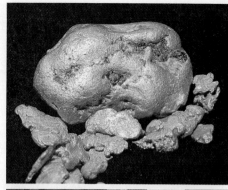

Figure 2–2 *Because their specific properties are similar, gold nuggets (top) are often confused with pyrite, or "fool's gold" (bottom), by gold prospectors. What specific properties do both minerals have in common? What general property of matter can be used to distinguish the two minerals?*

Figure 2–3 *It may seem like magic, but it is just a demonstration of inertia. As the table is moved quickly, the dinner setting is suspended in air for an instant. What do you think probably happened seconds after this photograph was taken?*

of about 5 grams. The mass of this book is about 1700 grams, or 1.7 kilograms. The estimated mass of the sun in kilograms is 2 followed by 30 zeros!

Mass is measured on an instrument called a balance. The mass of an object is determined by comparing its mass on the balance to the known masses of standard objects.

Weight

Another general property of matter is **weight.** An object has weight because it has mass. Weight is the response of mass to the pull of **gravity.**

The force of attraction between objects is called gravity. You probably have noticed that a ball thrown up in the air soon falls to the ground. And you know that an apple that drops off a tree falls down, not up. The ball and the apple fall to the earth because of gravity, the earth's force of attraction for all objects.

All objects exert a gravitational attraction on other objects. Gravity is not a property of the earth alone. Your two hands attract each other, and you are attracted to books, chairs, and trees. But you are not pulled toward these objects as you are toward the earth because the attractions in these cases are too weak for you to notice them. What do you think makes these attractions weak but the attraction of the earth great?

The earth's gravity is great because the earth has a large mass. The greater the mass of an object, the greater its gravitational force. How do you think the gravity of Jupiter compares with the gravity of the earth? How does the moon's gravity compare with the gravity of the earth or Jupiter?

The pull of gravity on an object determines the object's weight. On the earth, your weight is a direct measure of the planet's force pulling you toward the center. But the pull of gravity between objects weakens as the distance between the centers of the objects increases. At a high altitude—for example at the top of a mountain—an object weighs less than it does on the surface of the earth. This is because the object is farther from the center of the earth. How would an object's weight at the bottom of a deep mine compare with its weight on the earth's surface?

When an object is sent into space far from the earth, the object is said to be weightless. However, the object does not become massless. Mass does not change when location changes. No matter what happens to the force of gravity, mass remains constant. Only weight changes.

The metric unit of weight is the newton (N). The newton is used because it is a unit of force, and weight is the amount of force the earth's gravity exerts on an object. An object with a mass of 1 kilogram is pulled toward the earth with a force of 9.8 newtons. So the weight of the object is 9.8 N. An

Figure 2–4 *Astronauts Jerry Ross and Sherwood Spring appear to be "weightless" as they practice construction of a space station. Why are the astronauts said to be "weightless"? What has happened to their mass during the space walk?*

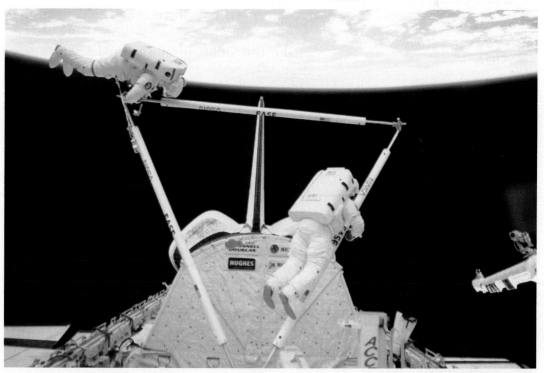

1. Fill a measuring cup with water and note the volume of the water.

2. Place a small, solid object in the measuring cup. You might choose a rock, a block of wood, or a bar of soap. If the object floats, use a stiff piece of wire to push it under the water's surface. Note the volume of the water with the object in it.

3. Subtract the original volume from the new volume. This difference in volume is the volume of the object.

object with a mass of 50 kilograms is pulled toward the earth with a force of 50 × 9.8, or 490 newtons. The object's weight is 490 N. What is your weight on the earth?

Volume

Another important general property of matter describes the amount of space it occupies. The amount of space an object takes up is called its **volume.**

Volume is measured in liters (L), milliliters (mL), and cubic centimeters (cm³). One liter is equal to 1000 milliliters or 1000 cubic centimeters. How many milliliters are there in 3.5 liters?

You now know two important general properties of matter. Matter has mass and occupies space. Using these two properties, you can now define matter in a more scientific way: Matter is anything that has mass and volume.

Density

The properties of mass and volume can be used to describe another important general property of matter called **density.** Density is the mass per unit volume of an object. Density is an important property because it allows you to compare different types of matter.

Suppose you were asked to determine whether wood or lead is heavier. You probably could not make this determination unless you knew the sizes

Figure 2–5 *The objects and liquids in this container have different densities. So some float while others sink. Suppose you did not know the density of each substance. How could you use this photograph to determine the relative densities of the objects and liquids?*

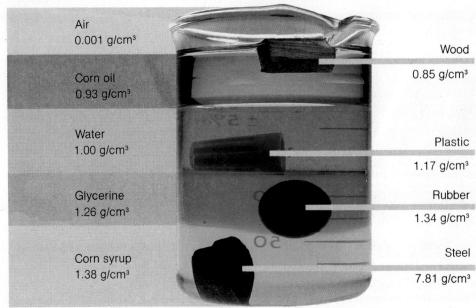

Air
0.001 g/cm³

Corn oil
0.93 g/cm³

Water
1.00 g/cm³

Glycerine
1.26 g/cm³

Corn syrup
1.38 g/cm³

Wood
0.85 g/cm³

Plastic
1.17 g/cm³

Rubber
1.34 g/cm³

Steel
7.81 g/cm³

of the pieces of wood and lead you were comparing. And even then, would it be correct to compare a small chip of lead with a baseball bat of wood?

In order to compare the masses of objects, equal volumes must be used. If you compared pieces of wood and lead that were the same size, you would find that the piece of lead has a greater mass than the piece of wood. A cubic centimeter of lead is more massive than a cubic centimeter of wood. Another way to state this is that lead has a higher density than wood. The density of a specific kind of matter is a property that helps to identify it and distinguish it from all other kinds of matter.

Since density is mass per unit volume, the following formula can be used to find the density of an object.

$$\textbf{density} = \frac{\textbf{mass}}{\textbf{volume}}$$

Mass usually is expressed in grams, and volume is expressed in milliliters or cubic centimeters. So density is expressed in grams per milliliter (g/mL) or grams per cubic centimeter (g/cm^3).

Sample Problem	If 96.5 grams of gold has a volume of 5 cubic centimeters, what is the density of gold?

Solution

Step 1	Write the formula	$\textbf{density} = \dfrac{\textbf{mass}}{\textbf{volume}}$
Step 2	Substitute given numbers and units	$\textbf{density} = \dfrac{\textbf{96.5 grams}}{\textbf{5 cubic centimeters}}$
Step 3	Solve for unknown variable	$\textbf{density} = \dfrac{\textbf{19.3 grams}}{\textbf{cubic centimeters}}$

Practice Problems

1. If 96.5 g of aluminum has a volume of 35 cm^3, what is the density of aluminum? How does its density compare with the density of gold?

2. If the density of a diamond is 3.5 g/cm^3, what would be the mass of a diamond whose volume is 0.5 cm^3?

DENSITIES OF SOME COMMON SUBSTANCES	
Substance	**Density** *(g/cm³)*
Air	0.0013
Gasoline	0.7
Wood (oak)	0.85
Water (ice)	0.92
Water (liquid)	1.0
Aluminum	2.7
Steel	7.8
Silver	10.5
Lead	11.3
Mercury	13.5
Gold	19.3

Figure 2–6 *This chart shows the density of some common substances. Which substances will float on liquid water? Why? What will happen when a piece of lead is put in mercury? When a piece of gold is put in mercury?*

The density of water is 1 g/mL. An object will float in water if its density is less than the density of water. Wood floats in water because its density is about 0.8 g/cm^3. What happens to a piece of lead when it is put in water? See Figure 2–6.

Because you know that ice floats, you should now know that it is less dense than liquid water. Actually, the density of ice is about 89 percent that of cold water. This means that only about 11 percent of a block of ice stays above the surface of the water. The rest is below the water. How does this fact explain why icebergs are so dangerous?

Scientists often compare the density of an object to the density of water, which is 1 g/mL. The comparison, or ratio, of the mass of a substance to the mass of an equal volume of water is called **specific gravity.** The specific gravity of water is 1. The specific gravity of gold is 19.3. What is the specific gravity of mercury? Of lead?

Specific gravity has no units. It is simply a number. This is because the units cancel out when the densities of the two substances are compared.

SECTION REVIEW

1. How can matter be described using two general properties?
2. What two properties of matter are related to its mass?
3. What is density? How is it calculated?
4. Each year some college students have a contest to build and race concrete boats. What advice would you give the students to make sure their boats float?

Section Objective

To classify matter according to its phases

2–2 Phases of Matter

The general properties of matter such as mass, weight, volume, and density are examples of **physical properties.** Color, shape, hardness, and texture are also physical properties. Physical properties are those that can be observed without changing the identity of the substance. Wood is still wood whether it is in the form of a baseball bat or wood chips.

Figure 2–7 *As the air in these colorful balloons is heated, the balloons begin to rise (right). Is the hot air in the balloons more or less dense than the surrounding atmosphere? This iceberg floats in the water near Baffin Bay, Greenland (left). Is all of the iceberg floating on top of the water?*

Ice, liquid water, and water vapor may seem very different to you. Certainly, they have different appearances and uses. But actually they are all made of exactly the same substance in different states. These states are called **phases.** Phase is an important physical property of matter. Scientists use the phases of matter to classify the various kinds of matter in the world. **Matter can exist in four phases—solid, liquid, gas, and plasma.**

Solids

A pencil, a cube of sugar, a metal coin, and an ice cream cone are examples of **solids.** Because they are solids they share two important characteristics. Solids have a definite shape and a definite volume. The tiny particles that make up a solid are packed very close together, so the solid keeps its shape. The particles cannot move far out of their places, nor can they flow over or around each other. The basic movement of particles in a solid is vibration.

In many solids, the particles are arranged in a regular, repeating pattern called a **crystal** (KRIHS-tuhl). Solids made up of crystals are **crystalline solids.** Common table salt is a good example of a crystalline solid. Figure 2–8 on page 42 shows some other examples of crystalline solids.

Sharpen Your Skills

Determining Particle Space

1. Fill one 250-mL beaker with marbles, another with sand, and a third with water.

2. Describe the appearance of the beaker filled with marbles. Do the marbles occupy all the space in the beaker?

3. Carefully pour some sand from its beaker into the beaker of marbles. How much sand fits? Is all the space in the beaker now occupied by sand and marbles?

4. Carefully add some water from its beaker to the beaker of marbles and sand. How much water can you add?

Is there space between the particles of a solid or a liquid?

Figure 2–8 *The regular, repeating arrangement of particles in a solid forms a crystal. Crystals have definite patterns, several of which you can see in these samples of quartz (left), wavellite (center), and chrysocolla (right). How would you describe each crystal?*

In some solids, the particles are not arranged in a rigid way. These solids do not keep a definite shape because they are not made of crystals. Unlike most solids, the particles in these solids can slowly flow around one another. Solids that lose their shape under certain conditions are called **amorphous** (uh-MOR-fuhs) **solids.** If you have ever worked with sealing wax or silicone rubber, you are familiar with an amorphous solid.

Some scientists think of amorphous solids as slow-moving liquids. Tar, candle wax, and glass are examples. If you can look at windowpanes in very old houses, you might notice that the panes are thicker at the bottom than at the top. The glass has flowed slowly downward, just like a liquid! Glass is sometimes described as a supercooled liquid. It is formed when a material in the liquid phase is cooled to a rigid condition but no crystals form.

Liquids

The particles in a **liquid** are close together but are free to move. So a liquid has no definite shape. A liquid takes the shape of its container. A liquid in a square container is square. That same liquid in a round container is round.

Although liquids do not have a definite shape, they do have a definite volume. One liter of water in a round container or a square container is still one liter of water. If that one liter of water is poured into a two-liter bottle, it will not fill the bottle. The water does not spread out to fill the entire volume of the bottle. What would happen if you tried to pour one liter of water into a half-liter bottle?

Figure 2–9 *Sealing wax is an amorphous solid. The particles making up the wax are not arranged in a rigid pattern, so they can flow around one another. Does an amorphous solid keep its shape?*

Even though the particles in a liquid are close together, they can flow easily around one another. Some liquids flow more easily than others, however. The resistance of a liquid to flow is called **viscosity** (vihs-ĸos-ih-tee). Honey has a high viscosity compared to water. If you have ever poured honey, you know it flows less easily than water. Motor oils also have a high viscosity.

Gases

A **gas** does not have a definite shape or a definite volume. A gas fills all the available space in a container, regardless of the size or the shape of the

Figure 2–10 *This figure shows how the particles of matter are arranged in a solid, a liquid, and a gas. In a solid, such as table salt (left), the particles are packed close together and cannot move far out of place. In a liquid, such as molten iron (center), the particles are close together but are free to move about or flow. In a gas, such as iodine vapor (right), the particles are free to spread out and occupy a large volume.*

Sharpen Your Skills

Observing Viscosity

1. Obtain samples of the following liquids: catsup, corn syrup, milk, honey, maple syrup.

2. Cover a piece of cardboard with aluminum foil.

3. Place the cardboard on a plate or baking pan at about a 50–55-degree angle with the bottom of the plate or pan.

4. With four classmates helping you, pour a measured sample of each liquid from the top of the cardboard at a given signal from another classmate.

5. Determine the order in which the liquids reach the bottom of the cardboard.

Which liquid is the most viscous? The least viscous?

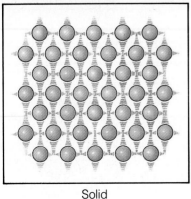

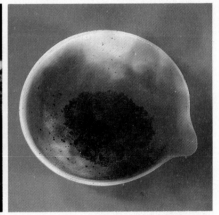

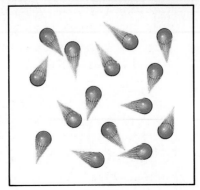

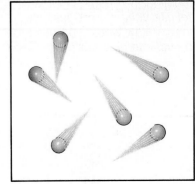

Solid

Liquid

Gas

1. Inflate a balloon, making sure it is not so large that it will break easily. Tie the end of the balloon so that air cannot escape.

2. Measure and record the diameter of the balloon.

3. Put the balloon in an oven set at a low temperature—not more than 150°F (65°C). Leave the balloon in the oven for about 15 minutes.

4. Remove the balloon and quickly measure its diameter. Record this measurement.

5. Now place the balloon in a freezer or refrigerator for 15 minutes.

6. Remove the balloon and measure and record its diameter. What happens to the size of the balloon at the higher temperature? At the lower temperature? Do your results agree with Charles's Law?

container. When air is pumped into a bicycle tire or a balloon, a large amount of gas is being squeezed into a small volume. Fortunately, the particles in a gas can be pushed close together.

The particles of a gas can also spread out to fill a large volume. The smell of apple pie baking in the oven comes to you because gases in the pie spread out to every part of the room. In fact, if allowed to, gases will expand without limit. If not for the pull of gravity, the gases making up the earth's atmosphere would soon expand into deep space! Why do you think a tiny planet like Mercury has little or no atmosphere?

This behavior of gases can be explained in terms of the arrangement and movement of the particles making up the gases. The particles in a gas are spread very far apart. There is a lot of empty space between the particles. The particles also move about freely and rapidly at speeds of about 500 meters per second. Whizzing around like this, the particles are constantly hitting one another. In fact, each particle undergoes about 10 billion collisions per second! Added to that are the collisions the particles make with the walls of the container. The effect of all these collisions is an outward pressure, or push, exerted by the gas. The pressure is what makes the gas expand to fill its container. What do you think happens to a container when the pressure becomes too great?

Figure 2–11 *A liquid has a definite volume but not a definite shape. It takes the shape of its container. A gas has neither a definite volume nor a definite shape. How would you describe the volume of a gas?*

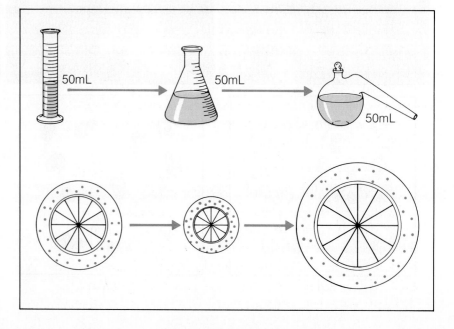

HELP WANTED: ARCHITECT to design high-rise housing complex planned for downtown area. College degree or extensive experience as well as state license required.

Pretend for a minute that you are about to move into a brand-new building. At first you might ask what building materials were used. Was it constructed with stone, brick, wood, or steel? Is it an attractive building?

As your moving day approaches, you may ask more complex questions about the building: "Will the living room floor be able to support a piano and a giant fishtank? Will I hear the neighbor's stereo in my room? How is the building heated and cooled?"

The person who can answer these questions is the **architect** who designed the building and selected the materials from which it was constructed.

The properties of materials are important to architects. In order to design a building that is safe, functional, and attractive, an architect must know about the strength, durability, size, and weight of building materials. An architect also must know how many people will occupy the building and what type of furniture and machines the people will bring with them. Architects constantly use their knowledge of materials in designing buildings to meet peoples' needs.

For more information about a career in architecture, write to the American Institute of Architects Information Center, 1735 New York Avenue NW, Washington, DC 20006.

BOYLE'S LAW If the volume of a gas is greatly reduced, the number of particle collisions within the gas will increase. So the pressure of the gas will increase. This relationship between volume and pressure is called **Boyle's Law.** According to Boyle's Law, the volume of a fixed amount of gas varies inversely with the pressure of the gas. An inverse proportion, or variation, means that as one factor increases, the other factor decreases. If the pressure increases, the volume decreases. If the pressure decreases, the volume increases. How can you relate Boyle's Law to what you feel when you squeeze part of an inflated balloon?

CHARLES'S LAW If the temperature of a gas is changed but the pressure is kept constant, then the volume of the gas must also change in order to keep the number of particle collisions the same. This relationship between temperature and volume is called **Charles's Law.** According to Charles's Law, the volume of a fixed amount of gas varies directly with the temperature of the gas. A direct

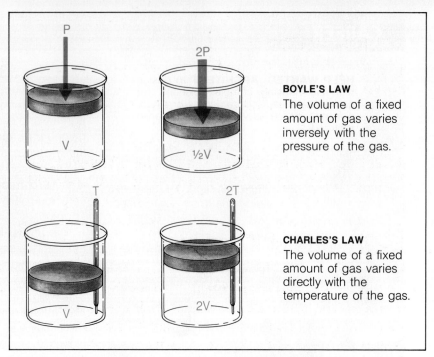

Figure 2–12 *You can see in this illustration that if the pressure of a fixed amount of gas increases, the volume of the gas decreases (top). This inverse proportion between pressure and volume is called Boyle's Law. According to Charles's Law, if the temperature of a fixed amount of gas increases, the volume of the gas increases (bottom). The relationship between temperature and volume is a direct proportion. According to Boyle's Law, what happens to the volume of a gas if the pressure doubles? According to Charles's Law, what happens to the volume of a gas if the temperature doubles?*

BOYLE'S LAW
The volume of a fixed amount of gas varies inversely with the pressure of the gas.

CHARLES'S LAW
The volume of a fixed amount of gas varies directly with the temperature of the gas.

proportion, or variation, means that as one factor increases, the other factor also increases. If the temperature of a gas increases, the volume increases. What do you think happens as the temperature of a gas decreases? Test your hypothesis by putting an inflated balloon in your freezer.

Boyle's Law and Charles's Law together are called the Gas Laws. The Gas Laws describe the behavior of gases with changes in pressure, temperature, and volume.

Plasma

The fourth phase of matter is called **plasma.** Plasma is quite rare on the earth. But the plasma phase is actually one of the most common phases in which matter is found in the universe. Stars have matter in the plasma phase.

Matter in the plasma phase is very high in energy and therefore dangerous to living things. Plasma can be made on the earth only by using equipment that produces very high energy. But the plasma cannot be contained by the walls of ordinary matter, which it would immediately destroy. Instead, magnetic fields produced by powerful magnets keep the high-energy plasma from escaping. One day, producing plasmas on the earth may meet most of our energy needs.

Figure 2–13 *This photograph of the sun shows the largest solar flare (upper left) ever recorded. In what phase does matter on the sun exist?*

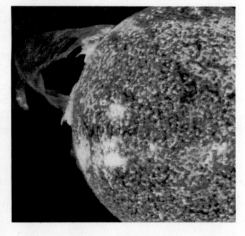

1. What are the four phases of matter?
2. What are physical properties?
3. How does a crystalline solid differ from an amorphous solid?
4. What is Boyle's Law? Charles's Law?
5. How would the volume of a gas be affected if the temperature and the pressure were both doubled?

2-3 Phase Changes

Ice, liquid water, and steam are all the same substance. What, then, causes the particles of a substance to be in one particular phase rather than another? The answer has to do with energy—heat energy that can cause the particles to move faster and farther apart.

A liquid tends to have more energy than that same substance in the solid phase. A gas has more energy than the solid and liquid phases of that same substance. So steam has more energy than both liquid water and ice. The greater heat content of steam is what makes a burn caused by steam more serious than a burn caused by hot water.

Because energy content is responsible for the different phases of matter, substances can be made to change phase by adding or taking away energy. The easiest way to do this is to heat or cool the substance, allowing heat energy to flow into or out of it. You are probably familiar with this idea, since you may have put liquid water in the freezer to make ice or heated liquid water on the stove and made steam. **The phase changes in matter are melting, freezing, vaporization, condensation, and sublimation.**

Changes in phase are examples of **physical changes.** A physical change is a change in which physical properties of a substance are altered but the substance remains the same kind of matter. When a tree trunk is sawed into wood chips or a sheet of paper is shredded, a physical change is taking place. In these cases, the size and shape of the substance are being changed but the identity of the substance remains the same.

Figure 2-14 *When heat is applied, ice changes to liquid water and then to water vapor. What are these two processes called?*

Figure 2–15 *At Aspen, Colorado, a snow-making machine turns liquid water into snow (left). In a bakery, a loaf of bread is cut into slices by a bread slicer (right). What type of changes are these?*

Figure 2–16 *The force of freezing water can cause a violent explosion. A cast-iron container about 0.6 centimeter in width is filled with water and placed in a beaker of dry ice and alcohol (top). As the water freezes and expands, a huge amount of energy is exerted against the walls of the container, causing an explosion (bottom).*

Another example of a physical change occurs when a cube of sugar is dissolved in a glass of warm water. The sugar disappears from sight and the liquid remains clear. You might be tempted to think that somehow the sugar has changed its identity—that it is no longer sugar. But if you taste the liquid, you will know that the sugar is still there. The liquid has a sweet taste. Although the sugar has lost its white color and its original shape, it is still the same kind of matter.

Solid–Liquid Phase Changes

What happens to your ice cream pop on a hot day if you do not eat it fast enough? Right—it begins to melt. **Melting** is the change of a solid to a liquid. Melting occurs when a substance absorbs heat energy. The rigid crystal structure of the particles breaks down, and the particles are free to flow around one another.

The temperature at which a solid changes to a liquid is called the **melting point.** Most substances have a characteristic melting point. It is a physical property that helps identify the substance. The melting point of ice is 0°C. The melting point of table salt is 801°C, while that of a diamond is 3700°C.

The opposite phase change, that of a liquid to a solid, is called **freezing.** Freezing occurs when a substance loses heat energy. The temperature at which a liquid changes to a solid is called the **freezing point.** The freezing point of a substance is equal to its melting point. What is the freezing point of water?

When a substance undergoes a phase change, its volume changes but its mass remains the same. As a result, the density of the substance changes. Generally, when a solid melts, its volume increases so its density decreases. The liquid phase is less dense than the solid phase. Water, however, is an exception to this general rule. Between 0° and 4°C, the density of water increases as ice melts to water. Ice is less dense than water. What everyday experiences tell you that this is true?

Liquid–Gas Phase Changes

The change of a substance from a liquid to a gas is called **vaporization** (vay-puhr-ih-ZAY-shuhn). During this process, particles in a liquid absorb enough heat energy to escape from the liquid phase. Vaporization at the surface of a liquid is called **evaporation** (ih-vap-uh-RAY-shuhn).

Evaporation is sometimes thought of as a cooling process. You can better understand this if you think of perspiration on the surface of your skin. As the perspiration evaporates, it absorbs and carries away heat energy from your body. In this way, your body is cooled. Why is it important to perspire on a very hot day?

If enough energy is supplied to a liquid, particles inside the liquid as well as those on the surface change to gas. These particles travel to the surface of the liquid because they are less dense than the liquid. The particles then travel into the air. This process is called **boiling.** The temperature at which a liquid boils is called the **boiling point.** The boiling point of water at the earth's surface under normal conditions is 100°C. The boiling point of table salt is 1413°C and that of a diamond is 4200°C!

The boiling point of a liquid is related to the pressure of the air above it. The gas particles that escape from the surface of the liquid must have enough "push" to equal the "push" of the air pressing down. So the lower the air pressure, the more easily the bubbles of gas can form within the liquid and then escape. Lowering the air pressure lowers the boiling point.

Figure 2–17 *During both evaporation (top) and boiling (bottom), particles of a liquid absorb heat energy and change from the liquid phase to the gas phase. Based on this illustration, what is the difference between evaporation and boiling?*

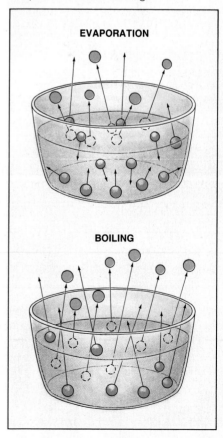

EVAPORATION

BOILING

Figure 2–18 *In the cool morning air, water vapor may condense and form dew on grass. What happens to the dew by mid-afternoon?*

Figure 2–19 *Certain substances such as dry ice (top) and iodine (bottom) go from the solid phase directly to the gas phase. What is this process called?*

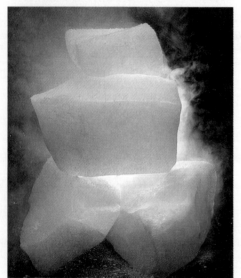

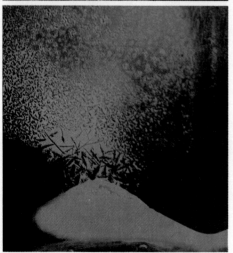

At high altitudes, air pressure is much lower, so the boiling point is reduced. Water will boil at a temperature lower than 100°C at high altitudes. If you could go 15 kilometers or more above the earth's surface, the pressure of the air would be so low that you could boil water at ordinary room temperature! However, this boiling water would be cool. Certainly, you would not be able to cook anything in this water, at least not for the usual amount of time. It is the heat in boiling water that cooks food, not simply the boiling process.

The opposite phase change—that of a gas to a liquid—is called **condensation** (kahn-dehn-SAY-shuhn). During condensation, a substance in the gas phase loses heat energy and changes into a liquid. Have you ever noticed that cold objects, such as glasses of iced drinks, tend to become wet on the outside? Where does this "extra" water come from? Water vapor in the surrounding air loses heat energy when it comes in contact with the cold glass. The water vapor condenses and becomes liquid drops on the glass.

Solid–Gas Phase Changes

Certain substances go from the solid phase directly to the gas phase without passing through the liquid phase. Such substances are said to sublime, and the phase change is called **sublimation** (suhb-lih-MAY-shuhn). During sublimation, the surface particles of a solid escape directly into the gas phase.

If you live in an area where winters are very cold and there is a lot of snow, you may have observed sublimation. Even when the temperature stays below the melting point of the water that makes up the snow, the fallen snow slowly disappears. But it does not leave behind puddles of water. The snow undergoes sublimation.

Dry ice is a substance used to keep other substances, such as ice cream, very cold. Dry ice is solid carbon dioxide. At ordinary pressures, it cannot exist in the liquid phase. As it absorbs heat energy, it sublimes, or changes directly to a gas. By absorbing and carrying off heat energy as it changes from a solid to a gas, dry ice keeps substances that are near it cold and dry. What would happen to an ice cream cake if it were packed in regular ice rather than dry ice?

Heat, Temperature, and Phase Changes

As you now know, heat plays an important role in phase changes. Heat is energy that causes the particles of matter to move faster and farther apart. As the particles move faster, they leave one phase and pass into another.

The addition of heat to a substance is usually accompanied by a rise in temperature. But if you kept a record of the temperature and the heat energy involved in changing ice to steam, you would notice several interesting things. These observations can best be explained by constructing a phase-change diagram, such as the one in Figure 2–20.

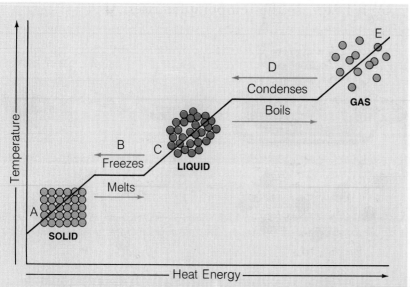

Figure 2–20 *This phase-change diagram shows what happens as a cube of ice absorbs heat energy. At which points on the diagram does the addition of heat energy cause an increase in temperature? At which points is there no temperature change with the addition of heat energy? What are these points called?*

51

The vertical, or Y, axis represents the temperature. The horizontal, or X, axis represents heat energy. The lettered line segments represent different stages in the change of ice from the solid phase to the gas phase.

In segment A, the ice cube receives heat from an outside source and the particles of the solid begin to vibrate faster. This faster vibration is indicated by a rise in temperature. Segment B shows that there is no change in temperature. But there is an increase in heat energy. Even though the ice cube is still absorbing heat, there is no accompanying rise in temperature. This is the phase change called melting. The energy the ice particles gain is used to break down the rigid solid structure of ice. The temperature does not rise during the phase change.

In segment C, the temperature once again begins to rise as heat is added. As the particles of the liquid gain energy, they continue to move faster, but not fast enough to change phase.

At the beginning of segment D, the temperature again levels off to a constant value. This value is the boiling point of water. Segment D represents the phase change called boiling. Once again, added heat energy is used to bring about a phase change. During this phase change, the forces holding the particles of the liquid together are overcome by the added heat energy and the liquid changes to a gas. Segment E represents the continued heating of the gas phase with an accompanying rise in temperature. When the gas absorbs heat, its particles move even faster, so the temperature rises.

Figure 2–21 *The addition of heat energy to ice at 0°C causes the phase change called melting. Water at 100°C undergoes the phase change called boiling when heat energy is added. What happens to the temperature during each phase change? To the movement of molecules?*

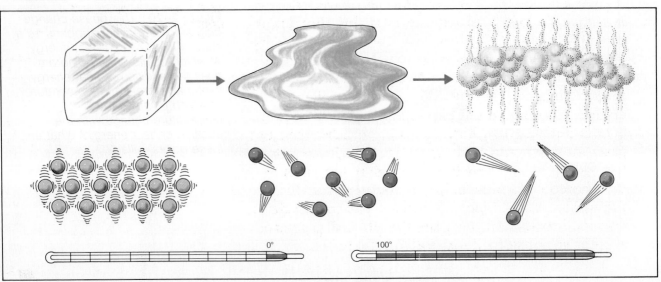

This diagram clearly shows that phase changes are accompanied by increases in heat energy but not by increases in temperature. The heat energy that is absorbed is used to overcome forces that hold the particles of the substance together. Once the forces have been overcome and the substance has changed phase, added energy causes a rise in temperature.

It is important for you to remember that the gas phase consists of exactly the same particles of matter as the liquid phase and the solid phase. Phase changes produce changes in the physical properties of matter only. Regardless of its phase, it is still the same kind of matter.

SECTION REVIEW

1. What three phase changes involve the absorption of heat? What two phase changes involve the release of heat?
2. How are evaporation and boiling different?
3. What is sublimation?
4. Why does the temperature remain constant during a phase change even though the substance is absorbing heat energy?
5. In Boston, Massachusetts, it takes three minutes to soft-boil an egg. In Denver, Colorado, it takes longer. Explain why.

2–4 Chemical Properties and Changes

Section Objective

To distinguish between a chemical property and a chemical change

The properties of matter that you have learned about can be observed without changing the identity of the substance. They are physical properties. Very often the physical properties alone will enable you to tell the substances apart. You can rely on color, shape, hardness, density, odor, and the ability to dissolve in water to tell one substance from another.

But suppose you have to distinguish between two gases—oxygen and hydrogen. Both gases are colorless, odorless, and tasteless. Since they are gases, they have no definite shape or volume. And although each has a specific density, you cannot determine it easily. In this case, the physical properties are not very helpful in identifying the gases.

Figure 2–22 *Timber fires cause millions of dollars in damage each year. During the combustion of wood, what substance in the atmosphere combines with the wood? Is this a physical or a chemical change?*

Sharpen Your Skills

Physical and Chemical Changes

1. In a dry beaker, mix a teaspoon of citric acid crystals with a tablespoon of baking soda. Observe what happens.
2. Fill another beaker halfway with water. Pour the citric acid-baking soda mixture into the water. Observe what takes place.

What type of change took place in the first step of the procedure? In the second step? Did the water have an important role in the procedure? If so, what do you think was its purpose? Why are some substances marked "Store in a dry place only"?

Fortunately, determining the physical properties is not the only way to identify a substance. Both oxygen and hydrogen can combine with other substances and take on new identities. The way in which they do this can be useful in determining the gas. The properties that describe how a substance changes into other new substances are called **chemical properties.**

Flammability (flam-uh-BIHL-ih-tee) is a chemical property. Hydrogen has the chemical property of flammability. Flammability is the ability to burn. If you were to place a glowing wooden stick into a test tube of hydrogen, you would hear a loud pop. The pop results when hydrogen combines with oxygen in the air, or burns. A new kind of matter forms as the hydrogen burns. This substance is water—a combination of hydrogen and oxygen.

The ability to support burning is another chemical property. Oxygen has the chemical property of supporting burning. But oxygen is not a flammable gas. It does not burn. So you can distinguish oxygen from hydrogen through the chemical properties of flammability and supporting burning. A glowing wooden stick placed in a test tube of oxygen will continue to burn until the oxygen is used up. In the process, oxygen combines with other substances to form new and different substances.

The changes that substances undergo when they change into new and different substances are called **chemical changes.** Chemical changes are closely related to chemical properties, but they are not the same. **A chemical property describes a substance's ability to change into a different substance; a chemical change is the process by which the substance changes.** For example, the ability of a substance to burn is a chemical property. The process of burning is a chemical change.

As you can see, physical properties are different from chemical properties because physical properties can be observed without changing the identity of the substance. Chemical properties involve a change in the identity of the substance. Physical changes do not produce a new substance. Chemical changes produce one or more new substances.

Chemical changes are taking place around you and even inside you all the time. Respiration and

Figure 2–23 *As the leaves change color each autumn in Vermont, this old piece of farm equipment rusts a little more (left). Fireworks dot the Houston skyline during a Fourth of July celebration (right). What three chemical changes can you identify in the photographs?*

digestion are chemical changes you could not live without. Photosynthesis, or the food-making process in green plants, is a chemical change. Rusting and the changing colors of leaves in the fall are chemical changes. Can you name some other examples?

Chemical changes are often called **chemical reactions.** Chemical reactions involve chemically combining different substances. The chemical reaction produces new substances with new and different physical and chemical properties. However, matter is never destroyed in a chemical reaction. The particles of one substance are rearranged to form a new substance, but the same number of particles exists before and after the reaction.

SECTION REVIEW

1. How is a chemical property different from a chemical change?
2. Give an example of a chemical property and a chemical change.
3. What is the difference between a physical property and a chemical property? Between a physical change and a chemical change?
4. What is a chemical reaction?
5. Identify the following processes as either physical changes or chemical changes: boiling water, digesting food, burning coal, melting butter, tarnishing silver, baking brownies, dissolving sugar, exploding TNT.

Observing a Candle

Problem

How can physical and chemical properties be distinguished?

> **Materials** (*per student*)
>
> small candle
> glass plate or aluminum foil holder
> matches

Procedure

1. On your laboratory worksheet, prepare a data table similar to the one shown here.
2. Observe the unlighted candle for about 10 minutes. List as many physical and chemical properties as you can.
3. Carefully light the candle and continue to make your observations. Record the observations in the correct columns in your data table.

	Physical properties	Chemical properties
Unlighted candle		
Lighted candle		

Observations

1. What general properties of the candle did you observe as physical properties?
2. What senses did you use when making these observations?
3. After lighting the candle, what physical changes did you observe?
4. What did you have to do to observe a chemical property of the candle?
5. What evidence of a chemical change did you observe?

Conclusions

1. Which type of property—physical or chemical—is easier to determine? Why?
2. What do you think is the basic difference between a physical property and a chemical property?
3. Can a physical property be observed without changing the substance? A chemical property?
4. What name is given to a process such as burning a candle? What is the result of such a process?

CHAPTER REVIEW

SUMMARY

2-1 General Properties of Matter

❑ Mass is the amount of matter in an object.

❑ Inertia is the resistance of an object to changes in its motion. Mass is a measure of the inertia of an object.

❑ Weight is the response of mass to the pull of gravity. Gravity is the force of attraction between objects.

❑ Volume is the amount of space an object takes up.

❑ Density is the mass per unit volume of an object. Density equals mass divided by volume.

❑ The ratio of the mass of a substance to the mass of an equal volume of water is called specific gravity.

2-2 Phases of Matter

❑ A physical property can be observed without changing the identity of the substance.

❑ A solid has a definite shape and volume.

❑ A liquid has a definite volume but no definite shape. A liquid takes the shape of its container.

❑ A gas does not have a definite shape or a definite volume.

❑ Boyle's Law states that the volume of a fixed amount of gas varies inversely with the pressure of the gas. Charles's Law states that the volume of a fixed amount of gas varies directly with the temperature of the gas.

2-3 Phase Changes

❑ A physical change is a change in which physical properties of a substance are altered but the substance remains the same kind of matter. Phase changes are physical changes.

❑ Temperature does not rise during a phase change.

2-4 Chemical Properties and Changes

❑ Chemical properties describe how a substance changes into other new substances.

❑ A chemical change produces a new and different substance.

❑ A chemical reaction produces a new substance with new and different physical and chemical properties.

❑ Matter is never destroyed in a chemical reaction—the same number of particles still exist.

VOCABULARY

Define each term in a complete sentence.

amorphous solid	condensation	inertia	plasma
boiling	crystal	liquid	property
boiling point	crystalline solid	mass	solid
Boyle's Law	density	matter	specific gravity
Charles's Law	evaporation	melting	sublimation
chemical change	flammability	melting point	vaporization
chemical property	freezing	phase	viscosity
chemical reaction	freezing point	physical change	volume
	gas	physical property	weight
	gravity		

CONTENT REVIEW: MULTIPLE CHOICE

On a separate sheet of paper, write the letter of the answer that best completes each statement.

1. Which of the following is not a general property of matter?
   a. mass   b. volume   c. density   d. flammability
2. The density of an object is equal to
   a. mass/inertia.   b. mass × volume.   c. mass/volume.   d. mass × weight.
3. Matter that has a definite shape and a definite volume is
   a. solid.   b. plasma.   c. liquid.   d. gas.
4. The phase of matter in which the particles move the fastest and are farthest apart is the
   a. solid.   b. plastic.   c. liquid.   d. gas.
5. The phase change from gas to liquid is called
   a. evaporation.   b. condensation.   c. melting.   d. boiling.
6. Which of the following substances does not undergo sublimation?
   a. snow   b. iodine   c. wood   d. dry ice
7. During a phase change,
   a. heat is absorbed and the temperature rises.
   b. heat is absorbed but there is no rise in temperature.
   c. heat is given off and the temperature goes down.
   d. heat is given off and the temperature rises.
8. Which of the following is not a chemical change?
   a. burning coal   b. digesting food   c. tearing paper   d. respiration
9. Which of the following is a chemical property?
   a. inertia   b. density   c. color   d. flammability
10. Four liquids have the following densities: A = 1.0 g/mL, B = 0.8 g/mL, C = 0.6 g/mL, D = 1.2 g/mL. In what order would the liquids form layers from top to bottom if they were carefully placed in a container?
    a. C, B, A, D   b. D, A, B, C   c. A, B, C, D   d. D, C, B, A

CONTENT REVIEW: COMPLETION

On a separate sheet of paper, write the word or words that best complete each statement.

1. The amount of matter in an object is called _____.
2. Resistance to changes in motion is called _____.
3. Mass divided by volume is called _____.
4. Matter in the _____ phase has a definite volume but no definite shape.
5. A (An) _____ solid has a regular, repeating internal structure.
6. The resistance of a liquid to flow is called _____.
7. According to Boyle's Law, if the volume of a fixed amount of gas is halved, the pressure is _____.
8. A change in matter from the liquid phase to the gas phase at the surface of the liquid is called _____.
9. Certain substances can change from a solid directly to a gas in a phase change called _____.
10. A change that produces a new substance is called a (an) _____ change.

CONTENT REVIEW: TRUE OR FALSE

Determine whether each statement is true or false. Then on a separate sheet of paper, write "true" if it is true. If it is false, change the underlined word or words to make the statement true.

1. Some general physical properties, or characteristics, of matter include mass, weight, plasma, and density.
2. The weight of an object is determined by the pull of inertia.
3. An object with a small mass and a large volume would have a low density.
4. Crystalline solids lose their shape under certain conditions.
5. According to Charles's Law, the volume of a fixed amount of gas varies directly with the temperature of the gas.
6. The solid phase is one of the most common phases of matter in the universe.
7. When evaporation occurs, the volume of matter generally increases.
8. As the pressure of the air above a liquid decreases, the boiling point of the liquid increases.
9. During a phase change, the temperature of a substance increases.
10. A chemical change produces a new substance with new and different physical and chemical properties.

CONCEPT REVIEW: SKILL BUILDING

Use the skills you have developed in the chapter to complete each activity.

1. **Making comparisons** You are given two samples of pure copper, one with a mass of 20 grams and the other with a mass of 100 grams. Compare the two samples in terms of (a) volume, (b) weight, (c) melting point, (d) density, and (e) boiling point.
2. **Applying concepts** Explain the following statements:
   a. Selling cereal by mass rather than by volume is fairer to the consumer.
   b. "I have to lose weight" is not an accurate statement for a person to make if his or her clothes fit too tightly.
   c. You feel cooler on a hot day when you turn on a fan even though the air being blown around is hot.
   d. Frozen peas have to be cooked for a longer time in high-altitude locations.
3. **Applying formulas** Using the formula for density, show why specific gravity is a number with no units.
4. **Making diagrams and designing experiments** A student makes the statement: "Cold water boils faster than hot water."
   a. Use a phase-change diagram to prove or disprove the statement.
   b. Describe an experiment that would prove or disprove the statement.

CONCEPT REVIEW: ESSAY

Discuss each of the following in a brief paragraph.

1. If the density of a certain plastic used to make a bracelet is 0.78 g/cm^3, what mass would a bracelet of 4 cm^3 have? Would this bracelet sink or float in water?
2. Explain how wet clothes hung on a clothesline on a very cold day dry.
3. Compare the solid, liquid, and gas phases of matter in terms of shape, volume, and arrangement and movement of particles.
4. Explain why fish are able to survive in lakes during very cold winter months when the lakes freeze.

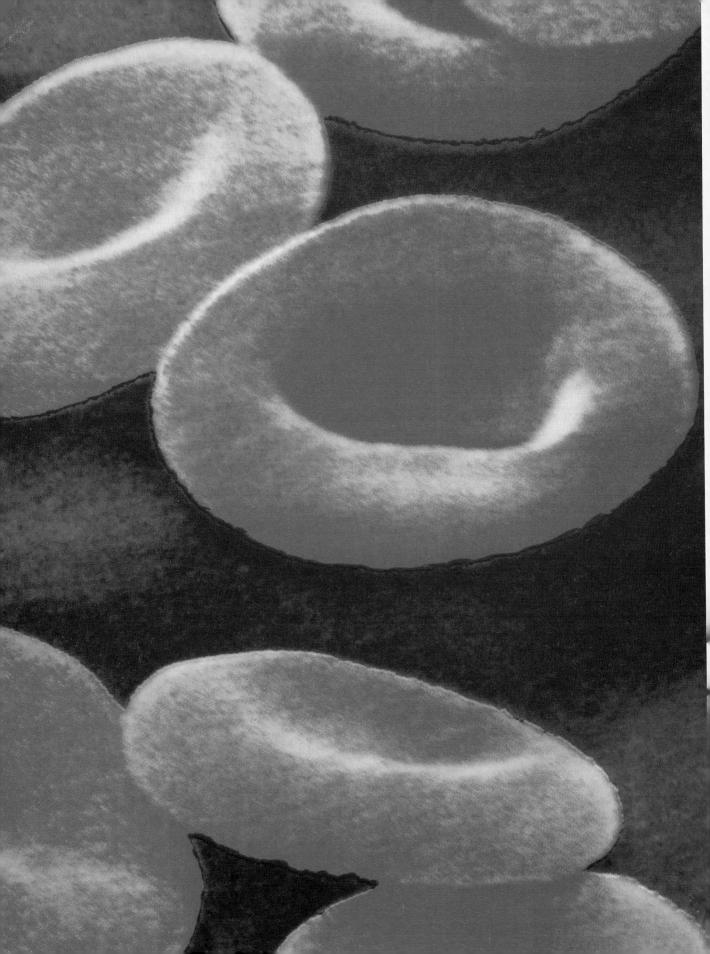

Classification of Matter

3

CHAPTER SECTIONS

3–1 Classes of Matter

3–2 Mixtures

3–3 Elements

3–4 Compounds

CHAPTER OBJECTIVES

After completing this chapter, you will be able to

3–1 Explain the importance of a system of classification.

3–1 Classify matter according to its makeup.

3–2 Describe the properties of mixtures.

3–2 Distinguish between homogeneous and heterogeneous mixtures.

3–2 Compare the properties of solutions with other mixtures.

3–3 Explain why elements are pure substances.

3–4 Explain why compounds are pure substances.

3–4 Discuss how chemical symbols, formulas, and balanced equations are used to describe a chemical reaction.

Have you ever thought about how important chemistry is to the healthy functioning of your body? The solids, liquids, and gases that make up your body are chemical substances—some simple and some complex. The basic processes that keep you alive—digestion, circulation, and respiration, for example—are chemical reactions. And the materials you add to your body, such as foods and medicines, are chemical substances you could not live without.

One of the most important chemical substances in the body is blood. This life stream of the human body is a unique chemical combination of liquid and solid parts. The fluid portion of blood, called plasma, accounts for about 56 percent of whole blood. Various chemical substances dissolved in water make up plasma. Suspended in the plasma are the solid parts of blood: red blood cells, white blood cells, and platelets. This amazing combination of solid and fluid substances is involved in the complex chemical reactions that keep you alive.

All the substances that make up your body—in fact, all the substances that make up the universe— can be classified into four basic categories. In this chapter, you will learn about these four categories. And you also will learn how the system of classification makes it easier for scientists, and for you, to understand the nature of matter.

These red blood cells, along with white blood cells and platelets, make up the solid part of the blood.

3–1 Classes of Matter

Have you ever had a button, leaf, or marble collection? If so, you probably know how important it is to group, or classify, the objects in the collection. To do this, you might use characteristics such as color, size, shape, or texture. Or maybe you would classify the objects according to their uses. In any event, you would be using a classification system based on a particular property to group the objects.

Classification systems are used all the time to organize objects. Books in a library or bookstore are arranged in an organized manner. So too are clothes in a department store and food in a supermarket. Next time you are in a record store, notice how the records and tapes are organized.

In order to make the study of matter easier to understand, scientists have developed different ways to classify matter. In Chapter 2, you learned that matter exists in four phases—solid, liquid, gas, and plasma. Phases are one way to classify matter.

But classifying matter according to phases is not specific enough and can lead to confusion. One kind of substance can exist in more than one phase. Water is a good example. Water can be a solid in the form of ice, a liquid, or a gas in the form of water vapor. How would you classify water?

Figure 3–1 *Classification is as important to storekeepers as it is to scientists. How has the produce in this outdoor market been classified (left)? In what ways has the classification of yarn (right) made it easier for customers to select the yarn they need?*

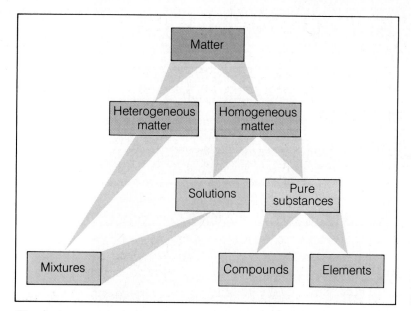

Figure 3–2 *This chart shows one way matter can be classified. In this particular classification system, what are the two main groups into which matter can be classified?*

Figure 3–3 *The water droplets on this stalk of grass and the droplets of mercury are both in the liquid phase. Do you think classifying objects by phase is helpful to scientists?*

Classifying matter according to phases often puts very different substances in the same group. Table salt, gold, steel, and sand are all solids. Should they be grouped together? What about water and gasoline, which are both clear liquids? How are these two liquids different?

In order to make the study of matter easier, scientists have used a classification system based on the makeup of matter. **According to makeup, matter exists as elements, compounds, mixtures, or solutions.**

As you read further, you will learn that some of these forms of matter have identical properties throughout, and some do not. Matter that has identical properties throughout is called **homogeneous** (hoh-muh-JEEN-ee-uhs) **matter.** All parts of homogeneous matter are alike. The properties of any one part of the matter are identical to the properties of all the other parts. Sugar, salt, water, and whipped cream are examples of homogeneous matter. What homogeneous materials can you think of?

Matter that has parts with different properties is called **heterogeneous** (heht-uhr-uh-JEEN-ee-uhs) **matter.** All parts of heterogeneous matter are not alike. The properties of any one part of the matter are different from the properties of all the other parts.

Figure 3–4 *These gold nuggets from the San Francisco Mint are made of pure gold (left). The granite boulder from Mount Stuart in Washington is made of several different minerals (right). How would you classify each object?*

The rock granite is heterogeneous because granite is composed of several different minerals, each having characteristic properties. Soil is heterogeneous matter, as is a super cheeseburger and cereal with raisins! Can you name some heterogeneous materials?

SECTION REVIEW

1. According to makeup, what are the four classes of matter?
2. What is homogeneous matter? Heterogeneous matter?
3. Classify the following materials as either homogeneous or heterogeneous: sausage pizza; chocolate chip cookies; air inside a balloon; glass of water.
4. Why is it more useful to classify matter according to makeup rather than according to phase?
5. Most milk sold in stores is homogenized. What do you think this means?

Section Objective

To describe the properties and types of mixtures

3–2 Mixtures

Look at the piece of granite in Figure 3–4. Granite is heterogeneous matter. It is made of different minerals mixed together. You can see some of these minerals—quartz, mica, and feldspar— when you look at the granite. Sand is also heterogeneous matter. When you pick up a handful of sand, you see dark and light grains mixed together. Granite, sand, concrete, and salad dressing are examples of matter that consist of several substances mixed together.

Matter that consists of two or more substances mixed together but not chemically combined is called a mixture. A **mixture** is a combination of substances. Each of the substances making up a mixture is a homogeneous substance. For example, granite is a mixture of minerals. It does not have the same properties throughout. But the minerals that make up granite are homogeneous substances. Every piece of quartz has the same properties as every other piece of quartz. This is true of mica and feldspar also.

Properties of Mixtures

The substances in a mixture are not chemically combined. The substances keep their separate identities and most of their own properties. When sugar and water are mixed, the water is still a colorless liquid. The sugar still keeps its property of sweetness

Figure 3–5 *Although it may look completely black, the sand on Kaimu beach in Hawaii contains some particles of white sand. What other mixtures can you identify in this photograph?*

even though it is dissolved in the water. Your sense of taste tells you this is so.

Substances in a mixture may change in physical appearance when they dissolve. Some physical properties of the mixture such as melting point and boiling point also may change. But the substances do not change in chemical composition. In the sugar-water mixture, the same particles of water and sugar are present after the mixing as before it. No new chemical substances have been formed.

The substances in a mixture can be present in any amount. A salt-and-pepper mixture can be one-third salt and two-thirds pepper, or one-half salt and one-half pepper. You can mix in lots of sugar or only a little in your iced tea. But in both cases, the mixture is still iced tea.

Because the substances in a mixture retain their original properties, they can be separated out by simple physical means. Look at Figure 3–6. A mixture has been made by combining powdered iron with powdered sulfur. Iron is black and sulfur is yellow. The mixture has a grayish color, although iron and sulfur particles are clearly visible. Because iron is attracted to a magnet and sulfur is not, iron can be separated from the mixture by holding a strong magnet near the mixture.

All the methods used to separate substances in a mixture are based on the physical properties of the substances making up the mixture. No chemical reactions are involved. What physical property of iron made it possible to separate it from sulfur in the iron-sulfur mixture? What are some other physical properties that might be used to separate mixtures?

Types of Mixtures

Both concrete and stainless steel are mixtures. Concrete consists of pieces of rock, sand, and cement. Stainless steel is a mixture of chromium and iron. From your experience, you may know that stainless steel seems "better mixed" than concrete. You cannot see individual particles of chromium and iron in the steel, but particles of rock, sand, and cement are visible in concrete. Mixtures are classified according to how "well mixed" they are.

Figure 3–6 *By combining powdered iron (top) with powdered sulfur (center), an iron-sulfur mixture is formed. What physical property of iron is being used to separate the mixture (bottom)?*

HETEROGENEOUS MIXTURE A mixture that does not appear to be the same throughout is said to be heterogeneous. A **heterogeneous mixture** is the "least mixed" of mixtures. The particles are large enough to be seen and to separate from the mixture. Concrete is a heterogeneous mixture.

Not all heterogeneous mixtures contain solid particles. Shake up some pebbles or sand in water to make a solid-liquid mixture. This mixture is easily separated just by letting it stand. Oil and vinegar make up a liquid-liquid heterogeneous mixture. When the mixture is well shaken, large drops of oil spread throughout the vinegar. This mixture, too, will separate when allowed to stand.

HOMOGENEOUS MIXTURE A mixture that appears to be the same throughout is said to be homogeneous. A **homogeneous mixture** is "well mixed." The particles of the mixture are very small, not easily recognized, and do not settle when the mixture is allowed to stand. Stainless steel is a homogeneous mixture.

Figure 3–7 *This gold miner in Finland is separating heavy pieces of gold from rock, sand, and dirt by shaking the mixture in a pan of water (left). The gold will settle to the bottom of the pan. Salt water is a mixture of various salts and water. When the water evaporates, deposits of salt, such as these in Mono Lake, California, are left behind (right).*

Solutions: Special Homogeneous Mixtures

A **solution** (suh-LOO-shuhn) is a type of homogeneous mixture formed when one substance dissolves in another. You might say that a solution is the "best mixed" of all mixtures. You are probably

Figure 3–8 *This "superburger" is a delicious example of a mixture, consisting of one layer of food upon another. Toothpaste is also a mixture. It is a type of mixture known as a solution. In a solution, all of the substances are evenly spread out. What type of mixture does each substance represent?*

Sharpen Your Skills

Is It a Solution?

1. Obtain samples of the following substances: sugar, flour, powdered drink, cornstarch, instant coffee, talcum powder, soap powder, gelatin.

2. Keeping the materials separate, crush each material into pieces of equal size.

3. Determine how much of each substance you can dissolve in samples of a given amount of water.

Using your knowledge of the properties of solutions, determine which substances formed true solutions. Also determine which substances dissolved fastest and to the greatest extent. Report your findings in a data table.

familiar with many different solutions. Ocean water is one example. In this solution, different salts are dissolved in water. Another example of a solution is antifreeze. Some solutions you can drink. Lemonade and tea are good examples. One very important solution keeps you alive! Air is a solution of oxygen and other gases dissolved in nitrogen.

All solutions have two important properties. One property is that the particles in a solution are not large enough to be seen. For this reason, most solutions cannot easily be separated by simple physical means.

Another property of solutions is that the particles are evenly spread out. All parts of a solution are identical. And, as in any mixture, the substances making up a solution retain most of their original properties.

Not all solutions are liquid. Solutions can be in any of the three phases—solid, liquid, or gas. Metal solutions called **alloys** are examples of solids dissolved in solids. Gold jewelry is actually a solid solution of gold and copper. Brass is an alloy of copper and zinc. Sterling silver contains small amounts of copper in solution with silver. Stainless steel is an alloy of chromium and iron. You may find it interesting to learn about the makeup of other alloys, such as pewter, bronze, and solder. How do you think alloys are made? In Chapter 9, you will learn more about the nature of solutions.

SECTION REVIEW

1. What is a mixture? What are three properties of a mixture?
2. How is a heterogeneous mixture different from a homogeneous mixture?
3. What is a solution? What are two properties of a solution?
4. Describe how you would separate salt from water in a saltwater mixture. What physical properties of the substances are you using to separate the mixture?

Figure 3–9 *The molten stainless steel being poured from the vat is a solution of iron and chromium, known as an alloy. What type of mixture is stainless steel?*

3–3 Elements

Section Objective

To relate elements to pure substances

In the previous sections you learned that according to its makeup, matter is classified as homogeneous or heterogeneous. And you also learned about one type of heterogeneous matter—mixtures. Now you will find out about the two types of homogeneous matter.

Homogeneous matter is also known as a **pure substance.** A pure substance is made of only one kind of material and has definite properties. A pure substance is the same throughout. All the particles in a pure substance are exactly the same. Iron, aluminum, water, sugar, and table salt are examples of pure substances. So is the oxygen you breathe. A sample taken from any of these substances is identical to any other sample taken from that substance. For instance, a drop of pure water is the same— whether it comes from Arizona, Australia, or Antarctica.

Elements are the simplest pure substance. An **element** cannot be changed into simpler substances by heating or by any chemical process. The particles making up an element are in their simplest form. Suppose you melt a piece of iron by adding heat energy to it. You may think that you have changed

Figure 3–10 *Elements are the simplest type of pure substance. These yellow crystals from Arigento, Sicily, are made of the element sulfur (left). The computer chips are made from the element silicon (right). What other objects can you think of that are made of only one kind of element?*

Figure 3–11 *In this photograph, you can see solid iodine crystals at the top of the beaker changing directly to iodine vapor. The gaseous iodine is formed by dropping the solid iodine crystals into a heated glass beaker. During this phase change has any new or simpler substance been formed?*

the iron into a simpler substance. But the liquid you now have still contains only iron particles. True, the iron has changed phase—from solid to liquid. But it is still iron. No new or simpler substance has been formed.

Elements and Atoms

The smallest particle of an element that has the properties of that element is called an **atom.** An atom is the basic building block of matter. All elements are made of atoms. Atoms of the same element are alike. Atoms of different elements are different.

Scientists now know that an atom is made of even smaller particles. These particles, however, do not have the properties of the elements they make up. You will learn more about the structure of an atom in Chapter 4.

Chemical Symbols

Elements are represented by **chemical symbols.** Chemical symbols are a shorthand way of representing the elements. Each symbol consists of one or two letters, usually taken from the element's name. The symbol for the element oxygen is O. The symbol for hydrogen is H; for carbon, C. The symbol for aluminum is Al; and for chlorine, Cl. You should note that when two letters are used in a symbol, the first letter is always capitalized but the second letter is never capitalized. Two letters are needed for an element's symbol when the first letter of that element's name has already been used as the symbol for another element. For example, the symbol for carbon is C, for calcium it is Ca, and for copper it is Cu.

Scientists often use the Latin name of an element to create its symbol. The symbol for gold is Au. The Latin name for gold is *aurum*. The symbol for silver is Ag, from the Latin word *argentum*. The Latin word for iron is *ferrum*. So the symbol for this element is Fe. Mercury's symbol is Hg, from the Latin

CAREER

Assayer

HELP WANTED: CHEMICAL ASSAYER to determine the gold and silver content of rock samples. College degree in chemistry required. Accuracy and attention to detail essential.

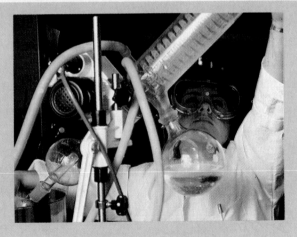

For several weeks the prospectors work under the blazing sun, examining the landscape, collecting rock samples, and drilling into sun-baked hillsides. They hope to discover sites containing valuable traces of gold, silver, or other minerals.

The amounts of valuable metals in the prospectors' samples are usually so small that they can be measured only with special equipment. So after rock samples are collected from possible mining sites, they are sent to a laboratory to be tested by an **assayer** (a-SAY-er). The assayer determines the exact mineral content of the sample. The specific properties of elements allow the assayer to separate valuable metals from other elements in the sample.

Many assayers work for mining companies. Others work for the government. Some assayers specialize in testing and analyzing precious metals, such as gold and silver. They may work under the direction of the U.S. Mint.

People who want to become assayers should major in chemistry in college. They should be able to concentrate on detail and work independently. To learn more about this career, write to the American Society for Metals, Chapter and Membership Development, Metals Park, OH 44073.

COMMON ELEMENTS

Name	Symbol	Name	Symbol	Name	Symbol
Aluminum	Al	Hydrogen	H	Oxygen	O
Bromine	Br	Iodine	I	Phosphorus	P
Calcium	Ca	Iron	Fe	Potassium	K
Carbon	C	Lead	Pb	Silicon	Si
Chlorine	Cl	Lithium	Li	Silver	Ag
Chromium	Cr	Magnesium	Mg	Sodium	Na
Copper	Cu	Mercury	Hg	Sulfur	S
Fluorine	F	Neon	Ne	Tin	Sn
Gold	Au	Nickel	Ni	Uranium	U
Helium	He	Nitrogen	N	Zinc	Zn

Figure 3–12 *This table shows the chemical symbols for some of the most common elements. Why is Fe the symbol for iron?*

name *hydrargyrum*. The table in Figure 3–12 lists some common elements and their symbols.

SECTION REVIEW

1. What is a pure substance? Why are elements pure substances?
2. What is an atom? How do atoms of the same elements compare? Of different elements?
3. Write the chemical symbols for aluminum, calcium, iron, sulfur, sodium, and helium.

Section Objective

To relate compounds to pure substances

3–4 Compounds

The simplest type of pure substance is an element. But not all pure substances are elements. Water and table salt, for example, are pure substances. They are made of only one kind of material having definite properties. But water and table salt are not elements. They can be broken down into

Figure 3–13 *The element sodium is often stored in kerosene because it reacts explosively with water (top). The element chlorine is a poisonous gas (center). The compound formed from sodium and chlorine, called sodium chloride, is a substance necessary for good health (bottom). What is the common name for sodium chloride?*

simpler substances. Water breaks down into the elements hydrogen and oxygen. Salt breaks down into the elements sodium and chlorine. Thus water and salt, like many other pure substances, are made of more than one element.

Pure substances that are made of more than one element are called compounds. A **compound** is two or more elements chemically combined. Sugar is a compound made of the elements carbon, hydrogen, and oxygen. Carbon dioxide, ammonia, baking soda, and TNT are also compounds. Can you name some other familiar compounds?

Unlike elements, compounds can be broken down into simpler substances. Heating is one way of separating some compounds into their elements. The compound copper sulfide can be separated into the elements copper and sulfur in this way.

Electric energy is often used to break down compounds that do not separate upon heating. By passing an electric current through water, the elements hydrogen and oxygen are obtained. What elements would you get by passing an electric current through melted salt?

In general, the properties of a compound are very different from the properties of the elements in it. Salt is a white crystalline solid used to flavor food and needed for good health. But what is salt made of? One element in salt is sodium, a silvery metal that reacts explosively with water. The other element is chlorine, a poisonous greenish gas. Neither element in its pure form can be used by your body. Yet they combine to form salt, or sodium chloride, a substance you cannot and probably would not want to live without.

Compounds and Molecules

Most compounds are made of **molecules** (MAHL-uh-kyoolz). A molecule is made of two or more atoms chemically bonded together. A molecule is the

PURE SUBSTANCES - one kind of molecule		MIXTURES - more than one kind of molecule	
Element - one kind of atom		Heterogeneous - do not appear the same throughout	
Compound - more than one kind of atom		Homogeneous - appear the same throughout	

Figure 3–14 *Matter can be classified as either a pure substance or a mixture. Into which group does water fit? Where would you place ocean water?*

smallest particle of a compound that has all the properties of that compound.

Water is a compound. A molecule of water is made up of 2 atoms of hydrogen chemically bonded to 1 atom of oxygen. One molecule of water has all the properties of a glass of water, a bucket of water, or a pool of water. If a molecule of water were broken down into atoms of its elements, would the atoms have the same properties as the molecule?

Just as all atoms of a certain element are alike, all molecules of a compound are alike. Each molecule of ammonia, for example, is like every other. Because it is made of only one kind of molecule, a compound is the same throughout. So compounds, like elements, are pure substances.

Sharpen Your Skills

Classifying Common Objects

1. Obtain samples of the following materials for observation: sugar, salt water, copper wire, taco shell, pencil eraser.
2. Use simple physical tests to determine which substances are mixtures, solutions, elements, or compounds.
3. Present your observations in a chart.

Figure 3–15 *As you can see from this diagram, molecules are made of two or more atoms chemically bonded together. Here you see a water molecule and an ammonia molecule. What are the chemical formulas for these two compounds?*

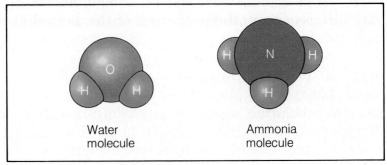

Water molecule

Ammonia molecule

Chemical Formulas

Combinations of chemical symbols are called **chemical formulas.** Most chemical formulas represent compounds. For example, ammonia is a compound made of the elements nitrogen and hydrogen, N and H. A molecule of ammonia contains

1 atom of nitrogen and 3 atoms of hydrogen. The formula for ammonia is NH_3. The formula for rubbing alcohol is C_3H_7OH. What elements make up this compound? How about silver nitrate, $AgNO_3$?

Sometimes a formula represents a molecule of an element, not a compound. For example, the symbol for the element oxygen is O. But oxygen occurs naturally as a molecule containing 2 atoms of oxygen bonded together. So the formula for a molecule of oxygen is O_2. Some other gases that exist only in pairs of atoms are hydrogen, H_2, nitrogen, N_2, fluorine, F_2, and chlorine, Cl_2. Remember that the symbols for the elements just listed are the letters only. The formulas are the letters with the small number 2 at the lower right.

When writing a chemical formula, you use the symbol of each element in the compound. You also use small numbers called **subscripts.** Subscripts are placed to the lower right of the symbols. A subscript gives the number of atoms of the element in the compound. When there is only 1 atom of an element, the subscript 1 is not written. It is understood to be 1.

Carbon dioxide is a compound of the elements carbon and oxygen. Its formula is CO_2. By looking at the formula, you can tell that every molecule is

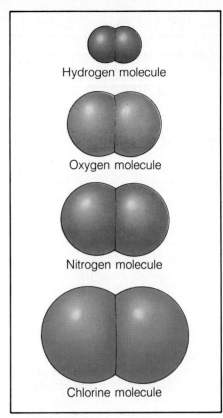

Hydrogen molecule

Oxygen molecule

Nitrogen molecule

Chlorine molecule

Figure 3–16 *Some elements are found in nature as molecules consisting of two atoms of that element. Hydrogen, oxygen, nitrogen, and chlorine are examples of such elements. What is the chemical formula for a molecule of each of these elements?*

Figure 3–17 *This table shows the common properties of elements, compounds, and mixtures. Which of the three substances does not have the same properties throughout?*

PROPERTIES OF ELEMENTS, COMPOUNDS, AND MIXTURES

Elements	Compounds	Mixtures
Made up of only one kind of atom	Made up of more than one kind of atom	Made up of more than one kind of molecule
Cannot be broken down by chemical means	Can be broken down by chemical means	Can be separated by physical means
Has same properties as atoms making it up	Has different properties from elements making it up	Has same properties as substances making it up
Has same properties throughout	Has same properties throughout	Has different properties throughout

Figure 3–18 *This illustration shows the chemical reaction that occurs when carbon and oxygen combine to form carbon dioxide. What is the chemical formula for carbon dioxide?*

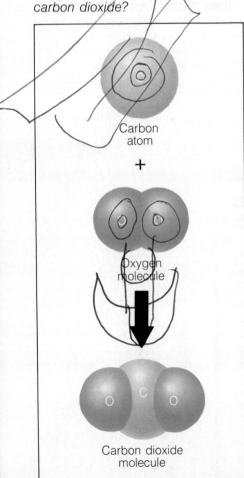

Carbon atom

+

Oxygen molecule

Carbon dioxide molecule

made up of 1 atom of carbon, C, and 2 atoms of oxygen, O. Sulfuric acid has the formula H_2SO_4. How many hydrogen atoms, sulfur atoms, and oxygen atoms are there in a molecule of sulfuric acid?

Chemical Equations

In Chapter 2 you learned that during chemical reactions, substances are changed into new and different substances through a rearrangement of their atoms. By using chemical symbols and formulas, you can describe chemical reactions.

The description of a chemical reaction using symbols and formulas is called a **chemical equation.** An equation is another example of chemical shorthand. Instead of using words to describe a chemical reaction, you can use a chemical equation.

Here is an example. When charcoal burns in a barbecue grill, carbon atoms combine with oxygen molecules in the air to form carbon dioxide:

Carbon atoms plus oxygen molecules produce carbon dioxide.

By using symbols and formulas, the reaction can be written in a simpler way:

$$C + O_2 \longrightarrow CO_2$$

The symbol C represents an atom of carbon. The formula O_2 represents a molecule of oxygen. And the formula CO_2 represents a molecule of carbon dioxide. The arrow is read "yields," which is another way of saying "produces."

The chemical equation for the formation of water from the elements hydrogen and oxygen is

$$H_2 + O_2 \longrightarrow H_2O$$

Look closely at this equation. It tells you what elements are combining and what product is formed. But something is wrong. Do you know what it is?

Look at the number of oxygen atoms on each side of the equation. Are they the same? On the left side of the equation there are 2 oxygen atoms. On the right side there is only 1 oxygen atom. Could 1 oxygen atom have disappeared? Scientists know that atoms are never created or destroyed in a chemical reaction. Atoms can only be rearranged. So there must be the same number of atoms of each element

Figure 3–19 *During chemical reactions, substances are changed into new and different substances. The polyethylene film you see being blown into a spherical shape is the product of a complex chemical reaction (right). A more common chemical reaction occurs during cooking as eggs, butter, and other ingredients are chemically combined to make crepes (left).*

on each side of an equation. The equation must be balanced. The balanced equation for the formation of water is

$H_2O + H_2O$

$$2H_2 + O_2 \longrightarrow 2H_2O$$

Now count the atoms of each element on each side of the equation. You will find they are the same: 4 atoms of hydrogen on the left and on the right, and 2 atoms of oxygen on the left and on the right. The equation is correctly balanced.

An equation can be balanced by placing the appropriate number in front of the chemical formula. This number is called a **coefficient** (koh-uh-FIH-shuhnt). The equation now tells you that 2 molecules of hydrogen combine with 1 molecule of oxygen to produce 2 molecules of water. A balanced chemical equation is evidence of a chemical reaction.

SECTION REVIEW

1. What is a compound?
2. How is a compound different from an element?
3. What is a molecule? How is a molecule of an element or compound represented?
4. What two things does a formula indicate about a compound?
5. Why must a chemical equation be balanced?
6. What three things does a chemical equation indicate about a chemical reaction?

Figure 3–20 *During the formation of water, two hydrogen molecules combine with an oxygen molecule to form two water molecules. What is the chemical equation for this reaction?*

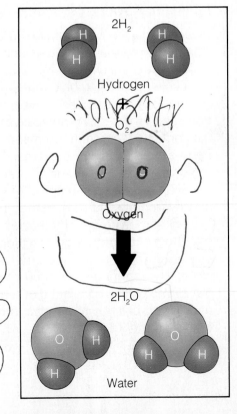

Making Models of Chemical Reactions

Problem

How do atoms and molecules of elements and compounds combine in chemical reactions?

Materials *(per group)*

toothpicks
red, yellow, green, blue, purple (red-blue), orange (yellow-red) food coloring
25 large marshmallows

Procedure

A. *Making Marshmallow Atoms*

1. Prepare marshmallow atoms by applying food coloring as follows:

   N (nitrogen)—red (2)
   H (hydrogen)—blue (6)
   Cu (copper)—green (4)
   O (oxygen)—yellow (6)
   K (potassium)—orange (2)
   Cl (chlorine)—purple (2)

2. Let the marshmallows dry for two hours.

B. *Assembling the Marshmallow Molecules*

1. Using two red marshmallows and a toothpick, make a molecule of N_2. Then make a molecule of H_2 using blue marshmallows.

2. Ammonia, NH_3, is used in cleaning solutions and fertilizers. A molecule of ammonia contains 1 nitrogen atom and 3 hydrogen atoms. Using the marshmallow molecules that you made in step 1, produce an ammonia molecule of nitrogen and hydrogen. You may use as many nitrogen and hydrogen molecules as you need to make ammonia molecules as long as you do not have any atoms left over. Note: Hydrogen and nitrogen must start out as molecules consisting of two atoms each. Now balance the equation that produces ammonia.

   ___ N_2 + ___ $H_2 \longrightarrow$ ___ NH_3

3. Using two green marshmallows for copper and one yellow marshmallow for oxygen, prepare copper oxide, Cu_2O. Using a white marshmallow for carbon, manipulate the molecules to represent and balance this equation, which produces metallic copper.

   ___ Cu_2O + ___ C → ___ Cu + ___ CO_2

4. Using orange for potassium, purple for chlorine, and white for oxygen, assemble potassium chlorate, $KClO_3$.

5. The decomposition of $KClO_3$ is a way to produce O_2. Take apart your $KClO_3$ to make KCl and O_2. You may need more than one molecule of $KClO_3$ to do this.

Observations

1. How many molecules of N_2 and H_2 are needed to produce two molecules of NH_3?
2. How many molecules of copper are produced from two molecules of Cu_2O?
3. How many molecules of O_2 are produced from two molecules of $KClO_3$?

Conclusions

1. Which substances that you made are elements? Which are compounds?
2. What is the difference between an atom of nitrogen and a molecule of nitrogen?
3. If you had to make five molecules of ammonia, NH_3, how many red marshmallows would you need? How many blue marshmallows?
4. What three important facts about a chemical reaction does a chemical equation provide?
5. What happens to atoms in a chemical reaction?

CHAPTER REVIEW

SUMMARY

3–1 Classes of Matter

❑ Matter is classified according to makeup as elements, compounds, mixtures, or solutions.

❑ Homogeneous matter has identical properties throughout. Heterogeneous matter has different properties throughout.

3–2 Mixtures

❑ A mixture is composed of two or more substances mixed together but not chemically combined.

❑ The substances that make up a mixture keep their separate identities and most of their own properties.

❑ The substances in a mixture can be present in any amount.

❑ The substances in a mixture can be separated by simple physical means.

❑ A mixture that does not appear to be the same throughout is a heterogeneous mixture. It is the "least mixed" of mixtures.

❑ A mixture that appears to be the same throughout is a homogeneous mixture. It is a "well mixed" mixture.

❑ A solution is a type of homogeneous mixture formed when one substance dissolves in another. It is the "best mixed" of mixtures.

❑ The particles in a solution are not large enough to be seen. So most solutions cannot easily be separated.

❑ Alloys are metal solutions in which solids are dissolved in solids.

3–3 Elements

❑ A pure substance is homogeneous matter. It is made of only one kind of material and has definite properties.

❑ Elements are the simplest type of pure substances. They cannot be broken down into simpler substances without losing their identity.

❑ Elements are made of atoms, which are the building blocks of matter.

❑ Elements are represented by chemical symbols.

3–4 Compounds

❑ Compounds are two or more elements chemically combined.

❑ Compounds can be broken down into simpler substances.

❑ Most compounds are made of molecules. A molecule is made of two or more atoms chemically bonded together.

❑ A molecule is the smallest particle of a compound that has all the properties of that compound.

❑ A chemical formula, which is a combination of chemical symbols, usually represents a molecule of a compound. For certain elements, the chemical formula represents a molecule of the element.

❑ A subscript gives the number of atoms of the element in the compound.

❑ A chemical equation describes a chemical reaction.

VOCABULARY

Define each term in a complete sentence.

✓alloy	✓coefficient	✓heterogeneous mixture	✓mixture
✓atom	✓compound	✓homogeneous matter	✓molecule
✓chemical equation	✓element	✓homogeneous mixture	✓pure substance
✓chemical formula	✓heterogeneous matter		✓subscript
✓chemical symbol			

CONTENT REVIEW: MULTIPLE CHOICE

On a separate sheet of paper, write the letter of the answer that best completes each statement.

1. According to makeup, matter exists as
   a. elements, solids, metals, liquids.
   b. elements, compounds, mixtures, solutions.
   c. solids, liquids, gases, plasma.
   d. solids, compounds, mixtures, liquids.

2. Which of the following is *not* homogeneous matter?
   a. water   b. carbon dioxide   c. granite   d. uranium

3. Matter that consists of two or more substances mixed together but not chemically combined is called a (an)
   a. element.   b. compound.   c. pure substance.   d. mixture.

4. An example of a heterogeneous mixture is
   a. salt water.   b. salad dressing.   c. stainless steel.   d. salt.

5. The simplest type of pure substance is a (an)
   a. compound.   b. alloy.   c. solution.   d. element.

6. The basic building block of matter is the
   a. molecule.   b. atom.   c. element.   d. compound.

7. The chemical symbol for helium is
   a. HE.   b. H.   c. He.   d. h.

8. Pure substances made of more than one element are called
   a. compounds.   b. mixtures.   c. alloys.   d. solutions.

9. The chemical formula for a molecule of nitrogen is
   a. N.   b. N_2.   c. N_3.   d. Ni.

10. The balanced equation for the formation of water from the elements hydrogen and oxygen is
    a. $H_2 + O_2 \longrightarrow H_2O$.   b. $2H_2 + 2O_2 \longrightarrow 2H_2O$.
    c. $2H_2 + O_2 \longrightarrow 2H_2O$.   d. $H_2 + 2O_2 \longrightarrow 2H_2O$.

CONTENT REVIEW: COMPLETION

On a separate sheet of paper, write the word or words that best complete each statement.

1. Matter that has identical properties throughout is called _____.

2. Soil is an example of _____ matter.

3. Two or more substances mixed together but not chemically combined are called a (an) _____.

4. Substances making up a mixture can be separated according to _____.

5. When one substance dissolves in another, a (an) _____ is formed.

6. Bronze and pewter are solid solutions called _____.

7. A pure substance that contains only one kind of atom is a (an) _____.

8. The name of an element is represented by a (an) _____.

9. A pure substance that contains more than one element is a (an) _____.

10. The smallest particle of a substance that has all the properties of the substance is called a (an) _____.

CONTENT REVIEW: TRUE OR FALSE

Determine whether each statement is true or false. Then on a separate sheet of paper, write "true" if it is true. If it is false, change the underlined word or words to make the statement true.

1. Concrete is an example of <u>homogeneous</u> matter.
2. Substances in a <u>mixture</u> keep their separate identities and most of their own properties.
3. Mixtures can be separated by simple <u>chemical</u> means.
4. The "least mixed" of mixtures is a <u>homogeneous</u> mixture.
5. The "best mixed" of mixtures is a <u>solution</u>.

6. The basic building block of matter is the <u>molecule</u>.
7. The <u>chemical formula</u> for gold is Au.
8. The elements that make up table salt are <u>sodium and chlorine</u>.
9. When elements combine to form compounds, their properties <u>do not</u> change.
10. To balance a chemical equation, numbers called <u>subscripts</u> are placed in front of the appropriate chemical formulas.

CONCEPT REVIEW: SKILL BUILDING

Use the skills you have developed in the chapter to complete each activity.

1. **Classifying data** Develop a classification system for the months of the year. State the property or properties according to which you will classify the months. Do *not* use the four seasons. Try to make your system as useful and as specific as possible.
2. **Applying concepts** Explain why heterogeneous mixtures can be separated by filtering but solutions cannot.
3. **Relating facts** You learned that mixtures have three important properties. Using the example of breakfast cereal with milk and blueberries, illustrate each property.

4. **Designing an experiment** Describe an experiment to demonstrate that
   a. water is a compound, not an element.
   b. salt water is a solution, not a pure substance.
5. **Making calculations** Balance the following equations:
   a. $Mg + O_2 \longrightarrow MgO$
   b. $NaCl \longrightarrow Na + Cl_2$
   c. $CH_4 + O_2 \longrightarrow CO_2 + H_2O$
   d. $H_2 + O_2 \longrightarrow H_2O$

CONCEPT REVIEW: ESSAY

Discuss each of the following in a brief paragraph.

1. Explain why a solution is classified as a mixture instead of as a compound.

2. Describe a method of separating the following mixtures:
   a. sugar and water
   b. powdered iron and powdered aluminum
   c. wood and gold
   d. nickels and dimes

3. Explain why the system of chemical symbols and formulas is important to making the language of chemistry a universal language.

4. Write the symbols for the following elements and describe one use of each: (a) zinc, (b) potassium, (c) sodium, (d) magnesium, (e) oxygen, (f) chlorine, (g) silver, (h) gold, (i) carbon.

Adventures in Science

Paul MacCready and the Return of the Pterosaur

Long before modern birds flew, a fearsome pterosaur with wings large enough to cover a small house soared over the earth. Sixty-five million years later, on May 17, 1986, a model of the ancient animal once again took to the sky, struggling to stay aloft. But it failed and crashed to the ground in front of hundreds of spectators.

"Now we know why pterosaurs are extinct," said the model's designer, Paul MacCready, of the flying creature he had built. MacCready accepts such mishaps as opportunities to gain insight into the dynamics of flight. Such information will help him continue to design unusual flying machines.

MacCready's model pterosaur took two years to build. The project was inspired by the discovery in 1972 of the fossilized wing bones of a pterosaur. The bone fragments were found scattered in a gully in western Texas.

SUPER "BAT"

Using these bones and other fossils, scientists put together a blueprint for the flying dinosaur, whom they affectionately named QN. QN stands for the pterosaur's scientific name, *Quetzalcoatlus northropi*.

The pterosaur's mass was about 63 kilograms, and its wings measured about 11 meters from tip to tip. With a large head, slender beak, long neck, and no tail, the pterosaur was not well adapted for flight. But most scientists agree that it did fly the ancient skies. How could it do so? Paul MacCready and his team were determined to find out.

Scientists believe that the pterosaur's wings were membranous and bare—more like the wings of a bat than a bird. This means that airflow over the wings would have been smooth and efficient. The pterosaur's wings would have behaved much the same as an airplane's wings. Learning that this animal lacked a tail, MacCready theorized that QN must have been able to flap, twist, and bend its wings in order to stabilize itself while flying. MacCready also reasoned that QN must have been a very powerful flapper in order to lift its body off the ground. Once in the air, though, QN would have been able to glide on outstretched wings. Did these ideas make sense?

To find out, MacCready began the task of building a model of the pterosaur that would prove the reptile did fly. MacCready used lightweight carbon tubes for the pterosaur's hollow bones. He used tough plastic material to cover the artificial skeleton, carefully molding and shaping it over the model's wing bones. Other "scientific" material used by MacCready included rubber bands, toothpicks, and popsicle sticks. The finished product closely resembled scientists' model of a living pterosaur. With its flexible wings fully extended, the model spans 5.5 meters, or one-half the size of the original pterosaur.

BIONIC "BIRD"

Building the model was one thing, but getting it to fly was another. MacCready's model pterosaur needed a "brain." After all, the flying model had to orient itself to wind currents and respond to changing air pressure. Somehow the pterosaur had to "know" when and how to tilt and flap its wings. To direct its flight functions, MacCready tucked a tiny computer into the model's body. The computer controlled QN's 13 electric motors. MacCready also provided his bionic animal with a battery to run the motors.

In a private test conducted months before its first public flight, QN flew successfully over the Mojave Desert in California. But the May crash will send MacCready back to the drawing board to improve his model. MacCready fully believes that his model—or one like it— will one day prove that pterosaurs did fly. "Nature does nothing that is stupid," he has said. "The purpose of those huge wings is to fly." If that is indeed true, Paul MacCready will be the one to finally prove it. As for the battered QN, it is retired now and will roost permanently in the Smithsonian Institution's Air and Space Museum in Washington, DC.

Paul MacCready and his model pterosaur, QN.

Issues in Science

THE SPACE PROGRAM:

One of the great challenges that sparks scientific exploration is making the unknown known. People have always been fascinated by the unknown. The planets and their moons and the stars beyond hold mysteries, many of which if solved would unravel secrets of our own planet. Space scientists argue that such basic information could be important to our survival on Earth.

Perhaps, some people say, but we have problems on Earth that need solving too—problems such as poverty and hunger. Space exploration is simply too expensive, they say. The money could be better spent on Earth.

People in favor of the space program claim that it is not especially costly. In 1982, less than 1 percent of the U.S. federal budget was spent on space exploration. The two *Voyager* missions to Saturn cost each American about $2.00.

Another thing to remember, say those in favor of space exploration, is that money spent on space exploration is not money spent in space. The space program creates jobs on the earth. People build the spacecraft. Others monitor the spacecraft, give instructions, and collect the data sent back. If the space program were discontinued, thousands of people would be out of a job.

Of course, the space program costs money. But those in favor of continuing and expanding space technology point out an additional benefit—"spinoffs." Spinoffs are products that were invented and first used in the space program but that have turned out to have practical uses on Earth.

You may not be aware of some of the space program spinoffs, such as the shiny metallic blankets marathon runners wrap themselves in after a race. These blankets keep the runner's body from losing heat. Made of thin fabric covered with a layer of aluminum particles, these blankets were developed from space technology. The National Air and Space Administration, or NASA, used similar metallic material to bounce radio signals off the

IS IT WORTH THE COST?

Echo I communications satellite back in 1960. Other uses for this material include packaging for frozen foods, window shades, and candy wrappers.

Fireproof fabrics developed for spacesuits are now used to make fireproof clothing and blankets. Other materials developed to stop spacecrafts from vibrating are now being used to soundproof buildings.

People who believe the space program worthwhile point to other important benefits, such as the many orbiting communications satellites that allow people to telephone all over the world. These satellites also make possible live TV transmission from one place on the earth to any other place. Satellites that orbit the earth also keep us informed of changing weather conditions. The list of practical uses of space technology is very long.

Still, many people worry about the cost of the space program. They ask, "Are we spending too much money on space? Could the money be better spent on Earth?"

Space scientists say that the cost of future space missions could be reduced. They recommend a program of 14 space missions, to be launched between 1988 and 2000. This would lower the cost of each mission. Furthermore, scientists argue, the same kind of spacecraft could be used on all the missions. This would be less expensive than building a different spacecraft for each mission.

Could space exploration lead to practical benefits on Earth? Scientists point to the many valuable spinoffs from space technology that are now used on Earth. They also say that there are many valuable natural resources in space, especially metals of all kinds. In the future, these metals may be brought back and used on Earth.

Spinoffs, space resources, and the answers to puzzling questions are all valuable "products" of space exploration. But, are they worth the money? Should the money now used in exploring space be spent instead to solve problems on Earth? What do you think?

The fireproof suit this firefighter is donning will help protect him. It is made from fabric developed for the space program. Fireproof fabric is but one of the many spinoffs from space exploration.

UNIT TWO

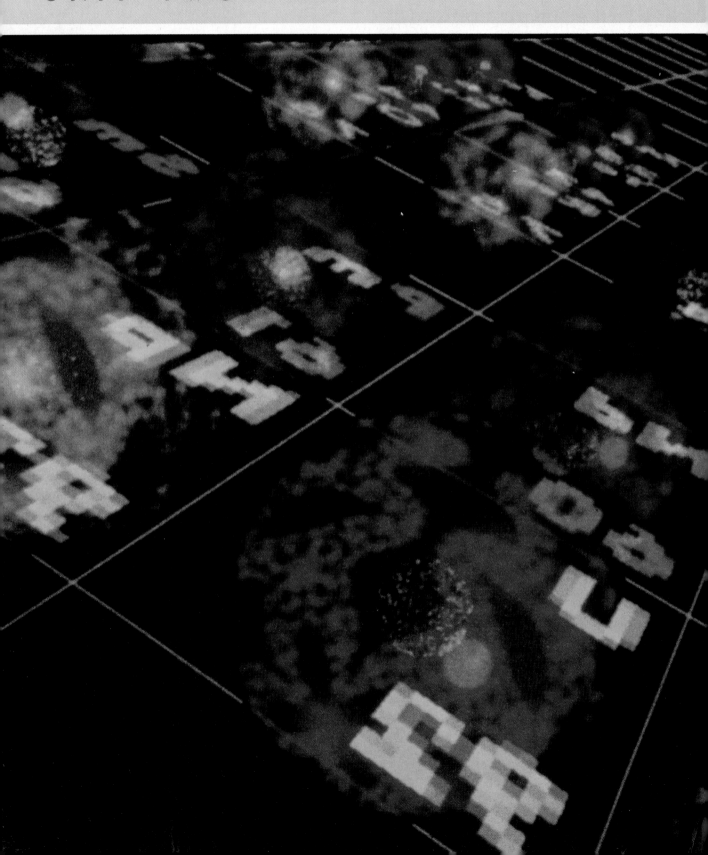

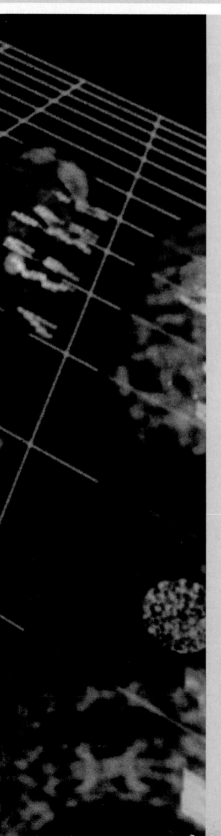

Patterns in Matter

Dmitri Mendeleev's periodic table of the elements was proposed in 1869. The discovery of the element scandium in 1879 was just one dramatic verification of the pattern of elements predicted by Mendeleev. Others followed. More than one hundred years later, the question facing chemists and physicists was this: could the pattern be extended to create an element new to the earth? For six years, physicists at Germany's Institute for Heavy Ion Research devoted their time and efforts to finding an answer. At 4:10 P.M. on August 29, 1982, their work finally paid off. They had it—a new element! Using a particle accelerator, the team of physicists had bombarded the nucleus of an atom of the element bismuth with a nucleus of an atom of the element iron. Their hope was to get the two nuclei to combine. After ten days of experimenting, a single atom was produced. A new element, element 109, was born.

Element 109 existed for just one five-thousandth of a second. But its short life gave scientists a greater understanding of matter. As you read the chapters in this unit, you will have an opportunity to explore the nature and patterns of matter that made the short life of element 109 possible.

CHAPTERS

4 Structure of Matter

5 The Periodic Law

6 Families of Elements

This computer-generated graphic represents atoms of some elements in the periodic table.

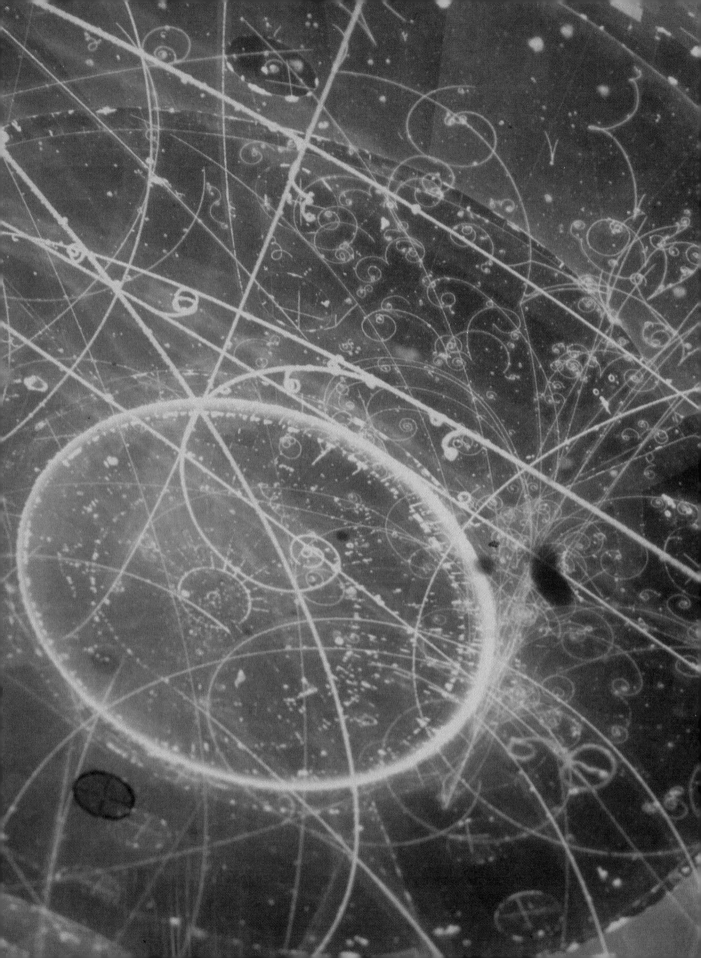

Structure of Matter 4

CHAPTER SECTIONS

4–1 Development of an Atomic Model

4–2 A Divisible Atom

4–3 Subatomic Particles

4–4 Forces Within the Atom

CHAPTER OBJECTIVES

After completing this chapter, you will be able to

4–1 Describe the important steps in the development of an atomic model.

4–2 Describe various models of the atom.

4–3 Classify three subatomic particles according to their location, charge, and mass.

4–3 Define the terms atomic number, isotope, mass number, and atomic mass.

4–4 Describe the four forces in nature and their relationship to atomic structure.

In James Bond movies, the science laboratory—hidden deep beneath the earth's surface—is large, comfortable, and well decorated. Thick carpeting covers the floor and lush green plants grace the corners of the room. Scientists garbed in starched white coats move about the laboratory effortlessly, gathering data from a variety of machines that buzz, blink, crackle, and hum. Before long the dramatic discovery is made. The solution to another important scientific problem is achieved!

But the world of movie thrillers is not the real world for scientists such as Ettore Fiorini, Larry Sulak, and Masatoshi Koshiba. These physicists work in tiny uncomfortable rooms with bare concrete walls and stale, hot air. Or they work in sealed plastic bubbles inside of which are six-story swimming pools containing the purest water possible. And, more importantly, they work for many years gathering data from their experiments. If they are lucky, the data may yield an answer. More often than not, the data are inconclusive and the search continues.

The question Fiorini, Sulak, and Koshiba are trying to answer has puzzled scientists for more than half a century. It has to do with whether tiny particles that make up matter disintegrate. If the physicists can determine that these particles do decay, or break down, they will be on their way to testing one of the newest and most meaningful theories of matter and energy—a theory that predicts the fate of the universe! In this chapter, you will learn about this particle and the role it plays in the structure of all forms of matter.

Using particle tracks such as these of a neutrino in a bubble chamber, scientists are attempting to test some of the most basic theories of matter and energy and to predict the fate of the universe.

4–1 Development of an Atomic Model

To relate indirect evidence to the development of an atomic model

All materials are made of **matter.** Matter is anything that has mass and volume. But what is matter made of?

For thousands of years, philosophers and scientists have tried to answer this question using a variety of experiments and observations. Because the basic building blocks of matter cannot actually be seen, researchers have relied on observations of how matter behaves. Such observations are called indirect evidence. Indirect evidence about an object is evidence you get without actually seeing or touching the object. As you gather indirect evidence, you can develop a mental picture, or model. A model uses familiar ideas to explain unfamiliar facts observed in nature. A model can be changed as new information is collected. As you read further, you will learn how a model of matter was developed and changed over many years. **From the early Greek concept of the atom to the modern atomic theory, scientists have built on and modified existing models of the atom.**

The Greek Model

The search for a description of matter began with the Greek philosopher Democritus (dih-MAHK-rih-tuhs) more than 2400 years ago. He and many other philosophers had puzzled over this question: Could matter be divided into smaller and smaller

Figure 4–1 *Scientists often rely on indirect evidence to develop a model of something that cannot be observed directly. Use the two drawings in this figure to develop a model that might explain what happened during the few hours separating the two diagrams.*

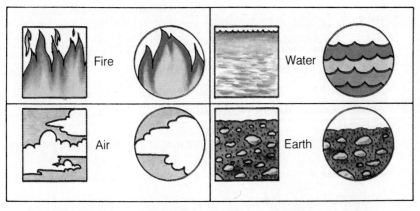

Figure 4–2 *Some ancient Greeks believed that all the matter on the earth was made of different combinations of four basic elements—fire, air, water, and earth. Which two elements do you think the Greeks believed could be combined to make steam?*

pieces forever or was there a limit to the number of times a piece of matter could be divided?

After much observation and questioning, Democritus concluded that matter could not be divided into smaller and smaller pieces forever. Eventually the smallest possible piece would be obtained. This piece would be indivisible. Democritus named this smallest piece of matter an **atom.** The word *atom* comes from the Greek word *atomos,* meaning "not to be cut" or "indivisible."

The Greek philosophers who shared Democritus' belief about the atom were called atomists. The atomists had no way of knowing what atoms were or how they looked. But they hypothesized that atoms were small, hard particles that were all made of the same material but were of different shapes and sizes. Also, they were infinite in number, always moving, and capable of joining together.

Although Democritus and the other atomists were on the right trail, the theory of atoms was ignored and forgotten. Very few people believed the idea. In fact, it took almost 2100 years before an atomic model of matter was accepted.

Dalton's Model

In the early 1800s, the English chemist John Dalton did a number of experiments that eventually led to the acceptance of the idea of atoms. Dalton had long been interested in meteorology, the study of weather. His observations about the composition of air led him to investigate the properties of gases. He discovered that gases combine as if they were made of individual particles. These particles were the atoms of Democritus.

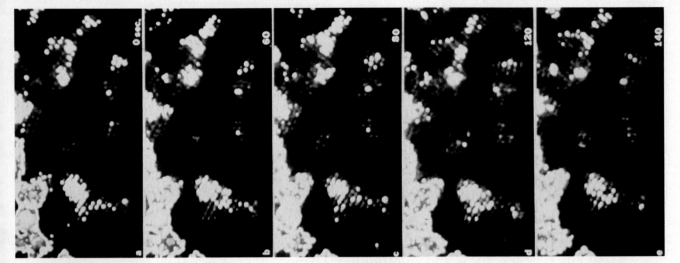

Figure 4–3 *These photographs of uranium atoms were taken by scientists at the University of Chicago. The blue spots are uranium atoms magnified more than 5 million times. The yellow areas represent a second layer of uranium atoms, and the reddish areas represent third layers. You can detect atom motion by the change in position of the colors.*

Dalton's Atomic Theory

In 1803, Dalton combined the results of his experiments with other observations about matter and proposed an atomic theory. The basic ideas of Dalton's atomic theory are as follows:

All elements are composed of atoms. Atoms are indivisible and indestructible particles.

Atoms of the same element are exactly alike.

Atoms of different elements are different.

Compounds are formed by the joining of atoms of two or more elements.

Dalton's atomic theory of matter became one of the foundations of chemistry. But like many scientific theories, Dalton's theory had to be modified as scientists gained more information about the structure of matter.

SECTION REVIEW

1. What is indirect evidence? Why is it important?
2. How did Democritus contribute to the development of an atomic model?
3. How did Dalton's atomic theory differ from the atomists' concept of the atom?
4. What type of information might scientists gather that would make it necessary to modify Dalton's atomic theory?

4–2 A Divisible Atom

Was Dalton correct? Is an atom indivisible? In 1897, the work of the English scientist J. J. Thomson provided the first hint that an atom is made of even smaller particles. Thomson was studying the passage of an electric current through a gas. The gas gave off rays that Thomson showed were made of negatively charged particles. But Thomson knew the gas was made of uncharged atoms. So where had the negatively charged particles come from? From within the atom, Thomson concluded. A particle smaller than the atom had to exist. The atom was divisible! Thomson called the negatively charged particles "corpuscles." Today, they are known as **electrons.**

Thomson's Model

As often happens in science, Thomson's discovery of electrons created a new problem to solve. The atom was known to be neutral, or uncharged. But if electrons in the atom were negatively charged, what balanced the negative charge? Thomson's answer was that there had to be a positive charge. The atom had to contain positively charged particles to balance the negative charge of the electrons.

In all his experiments, Thomson was never able to find these positively charged particles. But he was certain they existed. So he proposed a model of the atom that is sometimes called the "plum pudding" model. Each atom was pictured as being made of a puddinglike, positively charged material. Scattered throughout this material, like plums in a pudding, were the negatively charged electrons. Figure 4–5 shows Thomson's proposed atomic model.

Rutherford's Model

Although Thomson's model was far from correct, it was an important step toward understanding the structure of the atom. The next step was taken by the British physicist Ernest Rutherford. In 1908, Rutherford devised an experiment to test Thomson's model. He fired a stream of tiny positively

Figure 4–4 *Artist-physicist Bill Parker created this "electric art" by passing an electric current through a glass sphere containing certain gases. The light is produced when electrons in the gases absorb energy and then release it in the form of light. Who is credited with the discovery of the electron?*

Figure 4–5 *Thomson's model of the atom pictured a "pudding" of positively charged material throughout which negatively charged electrons were scattered. What is the overall charge on this atom? How can you tell?*

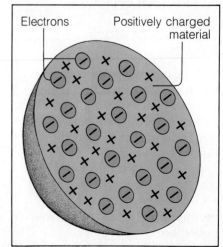

Electrons   Positively charged material

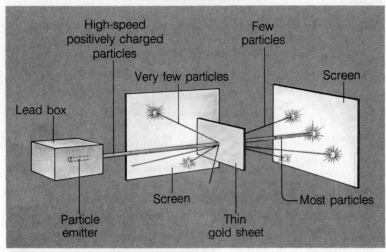

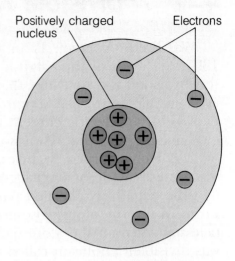

Figure 4–6 *In Rutherford's experiment, most of the positively charged particles passed right through the gold sheet (left). A few particles were slightly deflected, and a very few bounced straight back. From these observations, Rutherford concluded that the atom was mostly empty space with a dense, positively charged nucleus in the center (right).*

Sharpen Your Skills

Constructing Atomic Models

1. Using materials such as cardboard, construction paper, colored pencils, string, and cotton, construct models of the Thomson atom and the Rutherford atom.

2. Label the models and display them for your class. Write a brief description of the experiment that each model was based on.

charged particles at a very thin sheet of gold foil. Although the gold foil was hammered very thin, it was still two thousand atoms thick! Surrounding the foil was a screen coated with a material that glowed whenever a positively charged particle hit it. Using a microscope to detect the flashes of light made by the positively charged particles as they hit the screen, Rutherford was able to prove that Thomson's model was incorrect.

If Thomson's model were correct and positive and negative particles were spread evenly throughout the atom, then all the particles that were fired would pass through the foil as easily as bullets through tissue paper. The positively charged "bullets" would be only slightly deflected by the electrons scattered throughout the puddinglike material.

What actually happened was quite a surprise to Rutherford. Most of the particles passed through the foil with *no* deflection at all. But some of the particles were greatly deflected. In fact, a few bounced almost straight back from the foil, as if they had hit something solid. How was Rutherford to interpret these results?

Rutherford knew that positive charges repel other positive charges. So he proposed that an atom had a small, dense, positively charged center, which he called the **nucleus** (NOO-klee-uhs; plural: nuclei, NOO-klee-igh). The nucleus is tiny compared to the atom as a whole. To get an idea of the size of the nucleus in an atom, think of a marble in a baseball stadium!

Rutherford reasoned that all of an atom's positively charged particles were contained in the nucleus. The negatively charged electrons were scattered outside the nucleus around the atom's edge. This arrangement meant that atoms were not a pudding filled with positively charged material, as Thomson had proposed. Atoms were mostly empty space! Although this model was useful in many ways, it did not adequately explain the arrangement of the electrons. It would be the job of future scientists to improve on Rutherford's atomic model.

The Bohr Model

Rutherford's model proposed that negatively charged electrons were held in an atom by the attraction between them and the positively charged nucleus. But where exactly were the electrons in the atom? In 1913, the Danish scientist Niels Bohr proposed an improvement to the Rutherford model that placed each electron in a specific energy level. According to Bohr's atomic model, electrons move in definite orbits around the nucleus, much like planets circle the sun. These orbits, or energy levels, are located at certain distances from the nucleus.

Figure 4–7 *If you could stand on the nucleus of an atom, the nearest electron would appear as far away as a distant star appears from the earth. How would you describe the region of an atom between the nucleus and the nearest electron?*

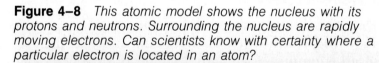

Figure 4–8 *This atomic model shows the nucleus with its protons and neutrons. Surrounding the nucleus are rapidly moving electrons. Can scientists know with certainty where a particular electron is located in an atom?*

Maria Goeppert Mayer

Using reference materials in the library, find out about physicist Maria Goeppert Mayer. Write a report on her life in which you include the following information:

1. For what work did she win a Nobel prize? In what year?

2. Why was she denied a scientific position during most of her life?

The Wave Model

Bohr's model worked well in explaining the structure and behavior of simple atoms such as hydrogen. But it did not explain more complex atoms.

Today's atomic model is based on the principles of wave mechanics. The basic ideas of wave mechanics are complicated and involve complex mathematical equations. Some of the conclusions of this theory, however, will help you understand the arrangement of electrons in an atom.

According to the theory of wave mechanics, electrons do not move about an atom in a definite path like planets about the sun. In fact, it is impossible to determine the exact location of an electron. Scientists can only predict where an electron is most likely to be found. The probable location of an electron is based on how much energy the electron has.

As you can see, the modern atomic model is based on the models of Rutherford and Bohr, and on the principles of wave mechanics. **According to the modern atomic model, an atom has a small, positively charged nucleus surrounded by a large region in which there are enough electrons to make the atom neutral.**

SECTION REVIEW

1. Describe Thomson's model of the atom.
2. How did Rutherford discover that most of the atom is empty space with a small, positively charged nucleus in the center?
3. How does the Bohr model of the atom differ from the wave model?
4. Explain why the Bohr concept of the atom is still used as a basic model, despite its shortcomings.

4–3 Subatomic Particles

When Thomson performed his experiments, he was hoping to find a single particle smaller than an atom. This task is similar to finding a particular grain of sand among the grains of sand making up all the beaches of the earth. If Thomson were alive today, he certainly would be surprised to learn that scientists know about the existence of at least two hundred different kinds of such particles! Because these particles are smaller than an atom, they are called **subatomic particles.**

At this time, you need to know about only three of these subatomic particles. **The three main subatomic particles are the proton, neutron, and electron.** As you read about these particles, note the location, mass, and charge of each. In this way, you will gain an understanding of the modern atomic theory.

The Nucleus

The nucleus is the center of the atom. Although the nucleus is about a hundred thousand times smaller than the entire atom, it accounts for 99.9 percent of the mass of an atom. Two different kinds of subatomic particles are found in the nucleus.

PROTONS One of the particles that makes up the nucleus is the **proton.** A proton is a positively charged particle. All protons are identical, regardless of the element in which they are found.

Figure 4–9 *When subatomic particles collide inside a particle accelerator, new and unusual particles may be produced. By studying the tracks made by these particles in a bubble chamber, scientists can learn more about the nature and interactions of subatomic particles.*

CAREER   *Particle Physicist*

HELP WANTED: PARTICLE PHYSICIST to join a team of physicists as a junior researcher. Advanced degree in physics required. Research experience and familiarity with particle accelerators helpful.

From the air, the underground laboratory looks as if it is covered by a circular race track. But the fastest racers on the earth could never match the speeds achieved by subatomic particles as they circle through the 6.3-kilometer tunnel at Fermilab in Illinois. Here **particle physicists** perform experiments designed to explore the structure and nature of subatomic particles. Protons, neutrons, and electrons, as well as nearly 200 other subatomic particles, are the concern of a particle physicist.

A particle physicist works with particle accelerators in which one kind of element may be changed into another element or new elements may be created.

Particle physicists work in private or government-run laboratories and in university research facilities. If you would like to learn more about a career as a particle physicist, write to the American Institute of Physics, Public Information Division, 335 East 45th Street, New York, NY 10017.

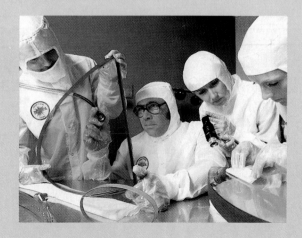

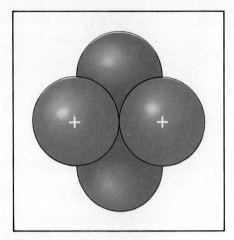

Figure 4–10 *This illustration shows the nucleus of a helium atom. The helium atom contains 2 protons and 2 neutrons. What is its atomic mass in amu's? What is its atomic number?*

The mass of a subatomic particle is very small. So scientists use a special unit to measure the mass. This unit is an **atomic mass unit,** or **amu.** A proton has a mass of 1 amu. To get an idea of how small 1 amu is, imagine the number 6 followed by 23 zeros. That is how many protons it would take to equal a mass of just 1 gram!

NEUTRONS The other particle that makes up the nucleus is the **neutron.** A neutron is an electrically neutral particle. It has no charge. Like protons, all neutrons are identical. A neutron has slightly more mass than a proton. But the mass of a neutron is still considered to be 1 amu.

Atomic Number

You learned that atoms of different elements are different. But if all protons are identical and all neutrons are identical, then what accounts for this

Figure 4–11 *The nuclei of helium, beryllium, and neon atoms all contain protons and neutrons. Yet helium, beryllium, and neon are very different elements. What accounts for this difference?*

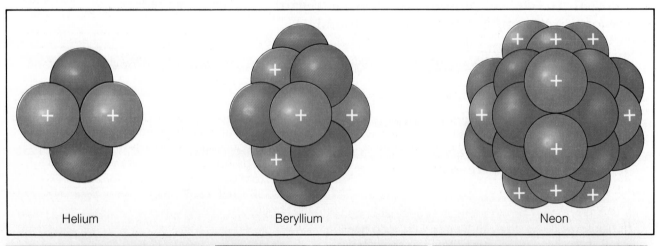

Helium

Beryllium

Neon

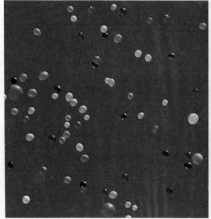

difference? The answer is that the number of protons in a nucleus determines what the element is.

The number of protons in the nucleus of an atom is called the **atomic number** of an element. The atomic number identifies the element. All hydrogen atoms—and only hydrogen atoms—have 1 proton and an atomic number of 1. Carbon atoms have 6 protons and an atomic number of 6. Oxygen has an atomic number of 8. There are 8 protons in the nucleus of every oxygen atom. How many protons does uranium, atomic number 92, have? Nitrogen, atomic number 7?

Isotopes

The atomic number of an element never changes. This means that the number of protons in the nucleus of every atom of the element is always the same. This is not the case with the number of neutrons. Atoms of the same element can have different numbers of neutrons.

Atoms of the same element that have the same number of protons but different numbers of neutrons are called **isotopes** (IGH-suh-tohps). Figure 4–13 shows three isotopes of the element hydrogen. Notice that the number of protons does not change. All three isotopes of hydrogen have the same atomic number, 1. But the number of neutrons in these three isotopes is different. How many neutrons does each isotope have? Figure 4–12 shows two isotopes of the element carbon. Each isotope has 6 protons. But one isotope has 6 neutrons and the other isotope has 8 neutrons.

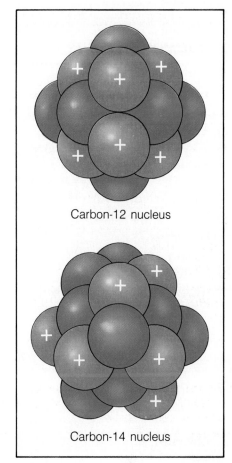

Carbon-12 nucleus

Carbon-14 nucleus

Figure 4–12 *These two isotopes of carbon have the same atomic number—6. What is the difference between the two isotopes?*

Figure 4–13 *The three isotopes of hydrogen are protium, deuterium, and tritium. Which isotope contains 2 neutrons? What is the atomic number of each isotope?*

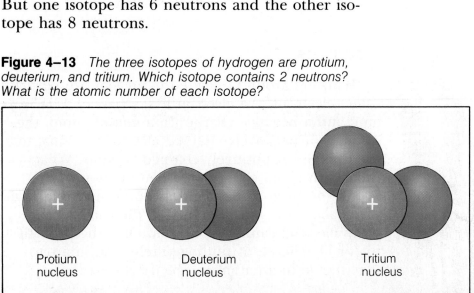

Protium
nucleus

Deuterium
nucleus

Tritium
nucleus

Mass Number and Atomic Mass

All atoms have a **mass number.** The mass number of an atom is the sum of the protons and neutrons in its nucleus. The mass number of the carbon isotope with 6 neutrons is 6 (protons) + 6 (neutrons), or 12. The mass number of the carbon isotope with 8 neutrons is 6 (protons) + 8 (neutrons), or 14. To distinguish one isotope from another, the mass number is given along with the element's name.

Two common isotopes of the element uranium are uranium-235 and uranium-238. The atomic number, or number of protons, of uranium is 92. Since the mass number is equal to the number of protons plus the number of neutrons, the number of neutrons can easily be determined. The number of neutrons is determined by subtracting the atomic number from the mass number. How many neutrons are there in each uranium isotope?

Any sample of an element as it occurs in nature will contain a mixture of isotopes. As a result, the **atomic mass** of the element will be the average of the masses of all the atoms in the sample. The atomic mass of an element refers to the average mass of all the isotopes of that element as they occur in nature. For this reason, the atomic mass of an element is not usually a whole number. The atomic mass of carbon is 12.011. This number indicates that in any sample of carbon there are more atoms of carbon-12 than there are atoms of carbon-14. How do you know this to be true?

Electrons

Whirling around outside the nucleus are particles called electrons. An electron has a mass of 1/1836 amu and a negative charge. In a neutral atom, the number of negatively charged electrons is equal to the number of positively charged protons. What, then, is the total charge on a neutral atom?

As you have read, electrons do not move in fixed paths about the nucleus. In fact, the exact location of an electron cannot be known. Only the probability, or likelihood, of finding an electron in a particular region in an atom can be determined.

COMMON ELEMENTS

Name		Atomic Number	Mass Number
Hydrogen	H	1	1
Helium	He	2	4
Carbon	C	6	12
Nitrogen	N	7	14
Oxygen	O	8	16
Fluorine	F	9	19
Sodium	Na	11	23
Aluminum	Al	13	27
Sulfur	S	16	32
Chlorine	Cl	17	35
Calcium	Ca	20	40
Iron	Fe	26	56
Copper	Cu	29	64
Zinc	Zn	30	65
Silver	Ag	47	108
Gold	Au	79	197
Mercury	Hg	80	201
Lead	Pb	82	207

Figure 4–14 *This chart shows the symbol, atomic number, and mass number for some common elements. Why is the mass number of an element always a whole number while the atomic mass is usually not?*

SUBATOMIC PARTICLES

Particle	Mass *(amu)*	Charge	Location
Proton	1	+	Nucleus
Neutron	1	Neutral	Nucleus
Electron	1/1836	–	Electron cloud

Figure 4–15 *The mass, charge, and location of the three basic subatomic particles are shown in this chart. Which subatomic particle has a neutral charge and a mass of 1 amu? Where is it located?*

The space in which electrons are *likely* to be found is called the **electron cloud.** The electron cloud is somewhat like the area around a beehive in which the bees move. Sometimes the electrons are near the nucleus. Sometimes they are farther away from it. In a hydrogen atom, one electron "fills" the cloud. It fills the cloud in the sense that it can be found almost anywhere within the space.

Although electrons whirl about the nucleus billions of times in one second, they do not do so in a random way. Each electron seems to be located in a certain area in the electron cloud. The location of an electron in the cloud depends upon how much energy the electron has.

According to modern atomic theory, electrons are arranged in **energy levels.** An energy level represents the most likely location in the electron cloud in which an electron can be found. Electrons with the lowest energy are found in the energy level closest to the nucleus. Electrons with higher energy are found in energy levels farther from the nucleus.

Each energy level within an atom can hold only a limited number of electrons. The energy level closest to the nucleus—the lowest energy level—can never hold more than 2 electrons. The second and third energy levels can each hold 8 electrons. See Figure 4–16 on page 102. The chemical properties of different elements depend on how many electrons are in the various energy levels of its atoms, or the electron arrangement of its atoms.

Sharpen Your Skills

Atomic Math

Calculate the atomic number of element X by doing the following arithmetic:

1. Multiply the atomic number of hydrogen by the number of electrons in mercury, which has an atomic number of 80.

2. Divide this number by the number of neutrons in helium, atomic number 2, mass number 4.

3. Add the number of protons in potassium, atomic number 19.

4. Add the mass number of the most common isotope of carbon.

5. Subtract the number of neutrons in sulfur, atomic number 16, mass number 32.

6. Divide by the number of electrons in boron, atomic number 5, mass number 11.

You now have the atomic number of element X. Which of the following elements is X?

fluorine: atomic number 9
neon: atomic number 10
sodium: atomic number 11

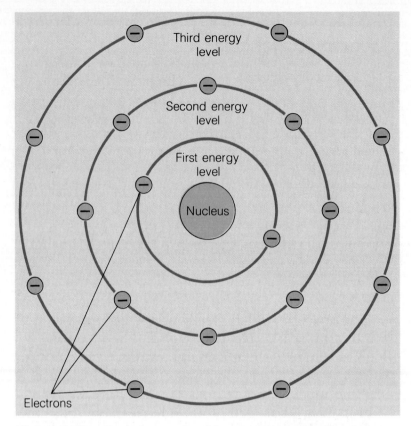

Figure 4–16 *Each energy level in an atom can hold only a certain number of electrons. How many electrons are there in the first, second, and third energy levels shown here?*

Sharpen Your Skills

Probability: Finding Your Friend

The following situation might help you understand the concept of probability.

1. You are trying to locate a friend on a sunny Saturday afternoon. Although you cannot say with absolute certainty where your friend is, you can estimate the chances of finding your friend in various places. Your estimates are based on past experiences.

2. Construct a table listing at least seven possible locations for your friend. Next to each location, give the probability in percent. Remember that your total probability should equal 100 percent.

3. Would a change in the weather affect your probability determination? How about a change in the day of the week?

4. How does this activity relate to an electron's location in an atom?

According to modern atomic theory, electrons can move from one energy level to another. Such a move involves either the gain or the loss of energy. In order to move to a higher energy level farther from the nucleus, an electron must absorb a *specific* amount of energy. When an electron has absorbed the amount of energy required to move to a higher energy level, the electron is said to be excited. See Figure 4–17.

An electron also can lose energy and move to a lower energy level closer to the nucleus. Here again, an electron must lose a *specific* amount of energy. In addition, an electron can move to a lower energy level only if that level is not filled. For example, if the first energy level contains 2 electrons, it is filled. An electron from a higher energy level cannot move into this first energy level because the maximum number of electrons is already there. You can now understand why atoms do not collapse.

Figure 4–17 *An electron jumps to a higher energy level when it absorbs a specific amount of energy. What happens to an electron when it loses a specific amount of energy?*

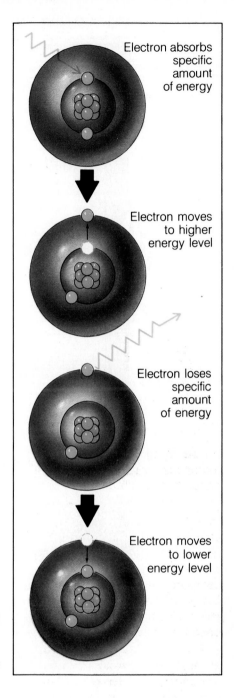

Electron absorbs specific amount of energy

Electron moves to higher energy level

Electron loses specific amount of energy

Electron moves to lower energy level

Can the atom be "cut"? The existence of protons, neutrons, and electrons proves it can. In fact, protons and neutrons can be separated into even smaller particles. It is now believed that a new kind of particle makes up all the other known particles in the nucleus. This particle is called the **quark** (kwahrk). There are a number of different kinds of quarks. All nuclear particles are thought to be combinations of three quarks. One group of three quarks will produce a neutron. Another group of three quarks will produce a proton. If protons are accelerated so that they collide with other particles, different groups of three quarks may form. Each different group will produce a different subatomic particle.

SECTION REVIEW

1. Classify the three main subatomic particles according to location, charge, and atomic mass.
2. Why does the nucleus account for 99.9 percent of the mass of an atom?
3. What is the atomic number of an element? What is its significance?
4. Nitrogen-14 and nitrogen-15 are isotopes of the element nitrogen. Describe how atoms of these isotopes would differ from each other.
5. Why must scientists consider the concept of probability in describing the location of electrons?
6. Suppose the element sodium has only one naturally occurring isotope. How will the atomic mass of this isotope compare with the mass number?

4–4 Forces Within the Atom

What keeps an atom together? Why don't the electrons fly out of their orbits around the nucleus? Why don't the protons move away from each other? Why don't all the atoms in the universe explode?

Section Objective

To identify the four forces associated with atomic structure

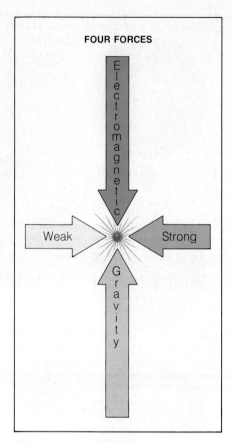

FOUR FORCES

Electromagnetic

Weak   Strong

Gravity

Figure 4–18 *The four known forces that govern all the interactions of matter and energy are the strong force, electromagnetic force, weak force, and gravity. Which of these four forces is the weakest?*

The answers lie in the forces within the atom. **The four forces that account for the behavior of subatomic particles are the electromagnetic force, strong force, weak force, and gravity.**

The **electromagnetic force** can either attract or repel the particles on which it is acting. If the particles have the same charge, such as two protons, the electromagnetic force is a force of repulsion. If the particles have opposite charges—such as an electron and a proton—the electromagnetic force is a force of attraction.

Electrons are kept in orbit around the nucleus by the electromagnetic force. The negatively charged electrons are attracted to the positively charged nucleus.

The electromagnetic force acts in the nucleus as a force of repulsion between positively charged protons. What keeps the protons from repelling each other and causing the explosion of the atom?

The **strong force** opposes the electromagnetic force of repulsion between protons. The strong force "glues" protons together to form the nucleus. Without the strong force, there would be no atoms. The strong force works only when protons are very close together, however. Although the strong force

Figure 4–19 *The strong force opposes the electromagnetic force of repulsion between two protons (top). The strong force becomes powerful enough to overcome the repulsive force and bind protons in the nucleus only when the protons are very close together (bottom).*

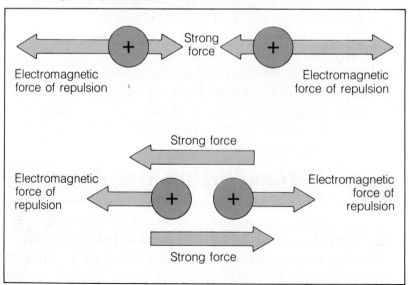

Strong force

Electromagnetic force of repulsion

Electromagnetic force of repulsion

Strong force

Electromagnetic force of repulsion

Electromagnetic force of repulsion

Strong force

is the greatest of the four forces, it has a very limited range. See Figure 4–19.

The **weak force** is the key to the power of the sun. It is responsible for a process known as radioactive decay. During radioactive decay, a neutron in the nucleus changes into a proton and an electron.

The final force, **gravity,** is by far the weakest force known in nature. Yet it is probably the force most familiar to you. Gravity is the force of attraction exerted between all objects in nature. Gravity causes apples to fall from a tree and planets to remain in orbit around the sun. The effects of gravity are most easily observed in the behavior of large objects. Inside the nucleus of an atom, the effect of gravity is very small compared to the effects of the other forces. The role of gravity in the atom is not well understood.

As you can see, the four forces—electromagnetic, strong, weak, and gravity—are very different. Yet physicists have tried to develop a single principle that would account for the differences between these forces. Such a principle would explain all four forces in terms of one fundamental force and all varieties of particles in terms of one basic particle.

And that is where physicists such as Fiorini, Sulak, and Koshiba enter the picture. They are seeking to determine if the proton decays. For if all forces and particles are really the same, then the disintegration of protons in the nucleus must mean that matter is disappearing! If these physicists can discover the "death" of protons, they will be one step closer to predicting the fate of the universe.

Figure 4–20 *New stars are forming within the hydrogen and helium gas that makes up the Dumbbell Nebula. All of the natural elements heavier than hydrogen and helium are created within stars. What will be the future of these elements if the proton is found to decay?*

SECTION REVIEW

1. What four forces govern the behavior of subatomic particles?
2. Which two forces are responsible for holding the atom together?
3. In what way does the electromagnetic force differ from the other three forces?
4. Why is gravity a relatively ineffective force within the nucleus?
5. Although gravity is the weakest of the four forces within the atom, explain why it is one of the most easily observed forces in your daily life.

Shoe-Box Atoms

Problem

How can indirect evidence be used to build a model?

Materials *(per group)*

shoe box, numbered and taped shut,
    containing unidentified objects
balance
magnet
meterstick

Procedure

1. Your teacher will give you a shoe box with an object(s) inside. Do not open or damage the box.
2. Use a magnet to determine if the contents have any magnetic properties.
3. Determine the mass of an empty shoe box. Then determine the mass of your shoe box. The difference between the two masses is the mass of the object(s) inside your shoe box.
4. By tilting the box you can determine something about the object's shape. Does it slide? (flat) Does it roll? (rounded) Does it collide inside? (more than one object)
5. Shake the box up and down to determine if the object bounces. How hard does it bounce? Does it flip?
6. For each test you perform, record your observations in a data table similar to the one shown here.

Observations

1. How many objects are in your shoe box?
2. Is the object soft? Metallic? Fragile?
3. Is the object flat or rounded?

Conclusions

1. Make a sketch of what you think is in your shoe box. Draw the objects so that they show relative sizes.
2. What other indirect evidence did you gather to help you make the drawing?
3. How does your sketch compare with the actual contents, as reported by your teacher? Make a sketch of the actual contents.
4. Describe how you can develop a model of an object without directly observing the object.

Test Performed	Results	
	Trial 1	Trial 2
Magnet brought near		
Mass of object(s) determined		
Box tilted		
Box shaken		

CHAPTER REVIEW

SUMMARY

4-1 Development of an Atomic Model

❏ A model is important to scientists because it explains observed facts and can be modified.

❏ More than 2400 years ago, the Greek philosopher Democritus theorized the existence of the atom, the smallest piece of matter.

❏ John Dalton's atomic theory was based on experimental evidence about the behavior of matter. His theory stated that all matter is made of indivisible particles, or atoms.

4-2 A Divisible Atom

❏ The discovery of the electron by J. J. Thomson proved that the atom is divisible.

❏ Thomson's model pictured the atom as being made of a positively charged, puddinglike material throughout which negatively charged electrons were scattered.

❏ Rutherford's experiments with gold foil and positively charged "bullets" led him to conclude that an atom has a small, dense, positively charged nucleus surrounded by negatively charged electrons.

❏ The Bohr model of the atom pictured electrons as moving in definite orbits, or energy levels, around the nucleus.

❏ According to the theory of wave mechanics, electrons do not move about an atom in definite orbits. The exact location of an electron in an atom is impossible to determine.

4-3 Subatomic Particles

❏ Protons and neutrons are found in the nucleus. The nucleus accounts for 99.9 percent of an atom's mass.

❏ Protons have a positive charge and a mass of 1 amu.

❏ Neutrons are electrically neutral and have a mass of 1 amu.

❏ The number of protons in the nucleus of an atom is called the atomic number.

❏ Atoms of the same element that have the same number of protons but different numbers of neutrons are called isotopes.

❏ The mass number of an atom is the sum of the protons and neutrons in its nucleus.

❏ The atomic mass of an element is the average mass of all the naturally occurring isotopes of that element.

❏ Electrons have a negative charge and a mass of 1/1836 amu.

❏ Within the electron cloud, electrons are arranged in energy levels.

❏ Subatomic particles in the nucleus are made up of quarks.

4-4 Forces Within the Atom

❏ The forces that govern the behavior of subatomic particles are electromagnetic, strong, weak, and gravity.

VOCABULARY

Define each term in a complete sentence.

amu	electromagnetic force	isotope	quark
atom	electron	mass number	strong force
atomic mass	electron cloud	matter	subatomic particle
atomic mass unit	energy level	neutron	weak force
atomic number	gravity	nucleus	
		proton	

CONTENT REVIEW: MULTIPLE CHOICE

On a separate sheet of paper, write the letter of the answer that best completes each statement.

1. The name that Democritus gave to the smallest possible piece of matter is
   a. molecule.   b. atom.   c. electron.   d. proton.

2. Which of the following is not one of the basic ideas of Dalton's atomic theory?
   a. Compounds are formed by the joining of atoms of two or more elements.
   b. Atoms of the same element are exactly alike.
   c. Atoms of different elements are exactly alike.
   d. All elements are composed of atoms.

3. The scientist J. J. Thomson discovered the
   a. proton.   b. electron.   c. neutron.   d. nucleus.

4. Rutherford's atomic model pictured a positively charged center, or
   a. electron.   b. neutron.   c. nucleus.   d. quark.

5. Particles smaller than the atom are called
   a. molecules.   b. elements.   c. ions.   d. subatomic particles.

6. The nucleus of an atom contains
   a. protons and neutrons.   b. protons and electrons.
   c. neutrons and electrons.   d. protons, neutrons, and electrons.

7. The number of protons in an atom with an atomic number of 18 is
   a. 10.   b. 36.   c. 18.   d. 8.

8. An isotope of oxygen, atomic number 8, could have
   a. 8 protons and 10 neutrons.   b. 10 protons and 10 neutrons.
   c. 10 protons and 8 electrons.   d. 6 protons and 8 neutrons.

9. All nuclear particles are thought to be made of a combination of three
   a. electrons.   b. isotopes.   c. molecules.   d. quarks.

10. Which of the following forces within the atom is responsible for keeping electrons in orbit around the nucleus?
   a. electromagnetic   b. strong   c. weak   d. gravity

CONTENT REVIEW: COMPLETION

On a separate sheet of paper, write the word or words that best complete each statement.

1. Elements are composed of _____.
2. Negatively charged subatomic particles are called _____.
3. Rutherford is credited with the discovery of the _____.
4. _____ that have a positive charge and a mass of 1 amu.
5. Atoms of the same element that have the same atomic number but different atomic masses are _____.
6. An atom's _____ is the sum of the protons and neutrons in its nucleus.
7. The _____ has a negative charge and a mass almost equal to zero.
8. The negative particles in an atom are arranged in _____.
9. The _____ now thought to make up all other nuclear particles.
10. The force that holds the protons of an atom together is the _____.

108

CONTENT REVIEW: TRUE OR FALSE

Determine whether each statement is true or false. Then on a separate sheet of paper, write "true" if it is true. If it is false, change the underlined word or words to make the statement true.

1. The idea that matter was made of indivisible particles called atoms was proposed by <u>Aristotle</u>.
2. In the early 1800s, <u>Dalton</u> developed a theory of atomic structure that was based on chemical experiments.
3. In Thomson's experiment, the gas in the tube gave off rays that were made of negatively charged particles called <u>neutrons</u>.
4. In Rutherford's experiment, some of the positively charged "bullets" were deflected by a <u>negatively</u> charged center.
5. Most of the mass of the atom is located in the <u>electron cloud</u>.
6. Subatomic particles that have a mass of 1 amu and no electric charge are called <u>protons</u>.
7. Chlorine has an atomic number of 17. It has <u>17</u> protons in its nucleus.
8. In order to distinguish one isotope of an element from another isotope of the same element, the <u>atomic number</u> of the isotope is given with the element's name.
9. Electrons having the least amount of energy are found <u>closest to</u> the nucleus.
10. The <u>weak force</u> is responsible for a process known as radioactive decay.

CONCEPT REVIEW: SKILL BUILDING

Use the skills you have developed in the chapter to complete each activity.

1. **Applying definitions** If the letter Z represents the atomic number of a neutral atom and the letter A represents the mass number, explain how you could use these symbols to find the number of electrons, number of protons, number of neutrons.
2. **Applying concepts** In his experiment, Rutherford used positively charged helium nuclei as the "bullets" he fired at the gold foil. How do you account for the fact that a helium nucleus is positively charged? What is the mass of the nucleus?
3. **Relating concepts** In an experiment, a scientist passes an electric current through a container of water that has been mixed with a small amount of acid. The water seems to disappear while two cylinders on opposite sides of the container fill with gas. A simple test determines that one cylinder contains oxygen and the other contains hydrogen. How does this experiment support Dalton's atomic theory?

CONCEPT REVIEW: ESSAY

Discuss each of the following in a brief paragraph.

1. A certain element contains 80 percent of an isotope of mass number X and 20 percent of an isotope of mass number Y. Is the atomic mass of this element closer to X or to Y? Explain your answer.
2. Describe the electron configuration of each element based on atomic number: sulfur, 16; fluorine, 9; argon, 18; lithium, 3.
3. Describe the four forces and explain their role in the structure of an atom.

The Periodic Law   5

CHAPTER SECTIONS

5–1 Development of a Periodic Table

5–2 The Modern Periodic Table

5–3 Using the Periodic Table

5–4 Periodic Properties of the Elements

CHAPTER OBJECTIVES

After completing this chapter, you will be able to

5–1 Explain how Mendeleev developed his periodic table.

5–1 Define periodic properties.

5–2 Compare the modern periodic table with Mendeleev's table.

5–2 State the periodic law.

5–3 Describe how the periodic table can be used to determine properties of the elements.

5–4 Identify some periodic properties of the elements.

Hidden away in some dark corner of a medieval castle, an alchemist peers anxiously into a huge iron pot. Strange vapors fill the room as a peculiar mixture bubbles and brews. The alchemist gently strokes a piece of gold as he tends the pot. Visions of mountains of gold crowd his mind as he dreams of becoming the richest man in the world.

Alchemists, sometimes considered to be the earliest scientists, believed they could turn common metals into gold. Hoping to profit from such discoveries, many kings and princes housed their own personal alchemists in their castles.

Many alchemists were quite clever. They learned to change the color of copper so that it looked like gold. They removed impurities from lead so that it resembled silver. But, alas, the physical appearance of the metal was the only property they managed to change! Copper was still copper and lead was still lead. No alchemist ever succeeded in changing a common metal into a precious one.

Today, scientists know what the alchemists did not: Every element is unique and has its own set of physical and chemical properties. Elements can combine with each other, but under ordinary circumstances, one element cannot change into another.

In this chapter, you will learn how the study of elements and their properties led to the development of a valuable scientific tool. You will read about a nineteenth-century Russian chemist who became very famous—not by changing lead into gold, but by performing a different kind of scientific "magic." He predicted the existence and properties of elements that had not even been discovered!

Surrounded by an odd assortment of materials and tools, the alchemist labored long hours in the hope of changing common metals into gold.

5–1 Development of a Periodic Table

To trace the development of Mendeleev's periodic table.

Imagine that you are a detective with a great mystery to solve. You know that scattered throughout the earth are 63 unique and fascinating substances called elements. Some of the substances are rare and valuable solids; others are strange gases; still others are needed to support human life.

Your task is to track down these elements and determine how they are related. You suspect that there is a grand design, a pattern that explains everything. You want to find it. You even believe that if you can solve this mystery, you can predict the existence of elements yet to be discovered.

This story is more than a fictional detective tale. It is actually the story of the Russian chemist Dmitri Mendeleev (D'MEE-tree mehn-duh-LAY-ehf). In the mid-1800s, Mendeleev became quite famous for discovering one of the basic principles of chemistry.

Mendeleev was writing a book called *Principles of Chemistry*. He had collected thousands of facts about the 63 elements that had already been discovered. Several scientists working before Mendeleev had come to the conclusion that groups of elements had similar chemical and physical properties.

Mendeleev's hunch was that a certain pattern or order must exist among *all* the elements. He was

Figure 5–1 *Each element has its characteristic chemical and physical properties. Potassium is a soft silvery metal that reacts explosively with water (left). Aluminum, also a silvery metal, does not easily combine with oxygen in water or in the air (right). Thus, aluminum can be used in electronic devices, household items, and building materials.*

Figure 5–2 *Mendeleev recognized that the properties of elements are repeated in a periodic way. Thus, certain elements have similar properties. Silver (left), gold (center), and copper (right) are all shiny hard elements that are good conductors of electricity. What are some uses of these elements?*

convinced that he could find a way of arranging the elements so that those with similar properties were grouped together. He set about testing his hypothesis by using the scientific method. Do you remember the basic steps of the scientific method?

Mendeleev already had enough information about the elements, but he needed to organize his data. So he made a card for each of the known elements. On the card he listed the properties of that element, such as atomic mass, density, color, and melting point. He also included the element's valence, or bonding ability. The valence number indicates the number of electrons involved in bonding.

Looking for a pattern, Mendeleev decided to arrange the cards in order of increasing atomic mass. If he started with lithium, the next element would be beryllium. Then would come boron, carbon, nitrogen, oxygen, and fluorine. When the cards were arranged, Mendeleev made an important observation. The valence numbers always occurred in the pattern 1 2 3 4 3 2 1. Then Mendeleev saw something else equally remarkable. When he arranged the elements in rows of seven, they fell into columns, one under the other. All the elements in a column had the same valence! All the elements in a column showed similar chemical and physical properties!

As Mendeleev analyzed his results, he thought about the concept of **periodic** properties. When used this way, the word periodic means "repeating according to some pattern." The days of the week

Figure 5–3 *The periodic table was Mendeleev's greatest contribution to science—but not his only one. In 1887, Mendeleev attempted to study solar eclipses by traveling aloft in a hot air balloon. What property of elements did Mendeleev base his periodic table on?*

Mendeleev—Chemical Superstar

When Mendeleev made his astonishing predictions about undiscovered elements, there was no radio, television, or newspaper and magazine coverage of the event.

1. Get together with four or five of your classmates and discuss how Mendeleev's work might be covered by the news media today.

2. Plan and stage at least two "media events" that would bring Mendeleev's discoveries to the attention of the public. For example, you might want to produce a television interview of Mendeleev or write an article that would appear in a popular science magazine.

are periodic because every seven days the pattern recurs. The notes of the musical scale are periodic, repeating a pattern with every eighth tone. Can you explain why the months of the year are periodic?

Mendeleev concluded that he had found a periodic relationship among the elements. After listing each series of seven elements in order of increasing atomic mass, the same properties showed up again. Mendeleev stated that "the properties of the elements are periodic functions of their atomic masses."

Mendeleev designed a periodic table in which the elements were arranged in order of increasing atomic mass. As he constructed this table, every so often he left blank spaces in order to make the known elements fit in the correct columns. Then he boldly announced that these blank spaces represented elements that had not yet been discovered. He even went so far as to predict the properties of these missing elements! He based his predictions on the properties of the elements above and below the spaces in the table.

Surely enough, Mendeleev was right. Three elements discovered in his lifetime had properties

Figure 5–4 *The discovery of the element germanium in 1886 made Mendeleev the most famous chemist of the time. As you can see, his predictions about the properties of element 32, or "ekasilicon," were extremely close to the actual properties. Why do you think Mendeleev named element 32 "ekasilicon"?*

MENDELEEV'S PREDICTIONS AND ACTUAL PROPERTIES OF ELEMENT 32

"Ekasilicon"		Germanium	
Date predicted	1871	Date discovered	1886
Atomic mass	72	Atomic mass	72.6
Density	5.5 g/cm^3	Density	5.47 g/cm^3
Bonding power	4	Bonding power	4
Color	Dark gray	Color	Grayish-white

that agreed with those he had predicted. It is no wonder that Mendeleev became the most famous chemist of his time. Figure 5–4 shows how closely Mendeleev's predictions approached the actual properties of one of the "missing" elements.

SECTION REVIEW

1. What relationship among the elements did Mendeleev discover?
2. What is meant by the word periodic?
3. How did Mendeleev predict the existence of undiscovered elements?
4. State in your own words the way Mendeleev followed the basic steps of the scientific method.

SEPTEMBER

S	M	T	W	Th	F	S
1	2	3	4	5	6	7
8	9	10	11	12	13	14
15	16	17	18	19	20	21
22	23	24	25	26	27	28
29	30					

Figure 5–5 *The days of the month are periodic because every seven days the pattern recurs. What does periodic mean?*

5–2 The Modern Periodic Table

Section Objective

To describe the design of the modern periodic table

Despite the importance of Mendeleev's work, his periodic table was not perfect. When the elements are arranged in order of increasing atomic mass, several elements appear to be misplaced in terms of their properties. Mendeleev assumed that this was because the atomic masses of these elements had been incorrectly measured. Yet new measurements continued to confirm the original masses. What could be the problem?

A New Periodic Law

It was not until fifty years after Mendeleev had developed his table that the answer to the problem became apparent. It was then that the British scientist Henry Moseley determined for the first time the atomic numbers of the elements. The atomic number of an element is the number of protons contained in the nucleus of each atom of that element.

University of Oxford, Museum of The History of Science, Courtesy AIP Niels Bohr Library.

Figure 5–6 *Henry Gwyn-Jeffreys Moseley's discovery of atomic number led to a major improvement of Mendeleev's periodic table. Elements were now arranged in order of increasing atomic number. In 1915, this brilliant scientist enlisted in the English Army. Several months later, at the age of 27, Moseley was killed during the famous World War I battle of Gallipoli.*

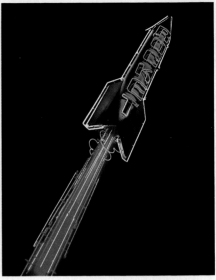

Figure 5–7 *Elements within the same family have similar properties. Both helium and neon are extremely unreactive gases. Helium is used in blimps (left), and neon is used in colored lights (right). What does unreactive mean?*

The discovery of atomic numbers led to an important change in Mendeleev's periodic table. It turns out that when the elements are arranged in order of *increasing atomic number,* elements with similar physical and chemical properties fall into place without exception. Thus, Mendeleev's periodic table was replaced by the modern periodic table. The **periodic law** forms the basis of the modern periodic table. **The periodic law states that the physical and chemical properties of the elements are periodic functions of their atomic numbers.**

Columns of the Table

Look at the periodic table of the elements found on pages 118–119. You will notice that the table consists of vertical columns of elements. Each column is labeled with a number and a letter. There are eight main columns of elements.

Columns of elements in the periodic table are called **groups** or **families.** Elements within the same family have similar but not identical properties. For

Lithium (Li)

Sodium (Na)

Potassium (K)

Figure 5–8 *Elements in the same family of the periodic table have similar properties. Here you see the electron arrangement of the elements lithium, sodium, and potassium. How is the electron arrangement in each element the same?*

example, lithium (Li), sodium (Na), potassium (K), and the other members of Family IA are all soft silver-white shiny metals. They are also all highly reactive elements. Fluorine (F), chlorine (Cl), bromine (Br), and iodine (I) make up Family VIIA. These elements are also very much alike. Fluorine and chlorine are gases. Bromine is a liquid, and iodine a solid. But both bromine and iodine become gases very easily. All four elements react to form the same kinds of compounds. You will learn more about each family and its properties in Chapter 6.

Rows of the Table

Each horizontal row of elements in the periodic table is called a **period.** Unlike the elements in a family, the elements in a period are not alike in properties. In fact, the properties of the elements change greatly across any given row.

But there is a pattern to the properties of the elements as one moves across a period from left to right. The first element in a period is always a very active solid. The last element in a period is always a very inactive gas. You can see this pattern by looking at Period 4 of the periodic table. The first element, potassium (K), is an active solid. The last element, krypton (Kr), is an inactive gas.

Sharpen Your Skills

Classifying Objects

Mendeleev's table and the modern periodic table are systems of classifying the elements based on similar and different physical and chemical properties.

Choose a set of objects familiar to you, such as coins, stamps, marbles, leaves, playing cards, or jelly beans. Devise your own system of classifying the objects. Put your results in a table.

Figure 5–9 *The properties of elements in the same period are not alike. Reading from left to right are the elements potassium, calcium (top), gallium, arsenic, and bromine (bottom). In what ways do the properties change across the period?*

PERIODIC TABLE

1 —**New designation**

IA —**Original designation**

Key

6	Atomic number
C	Element's symbol
Carbon	Element's name
12.011	Atomic mass

1

1
H
Hydrogen
1.00794

2

IIA

Transition Metals

3		4	5	6	7	8	9

2

3	4
Li	**Be**
Lithium	Beryllium
6.941	9.0122

3

11	12	3	4	5	6	7	8	9
Na	**Mg**	IIIB	IVB	VB	VIB	VIIB		VIIIB
Sodium	Magnesium							
22.990	24.305							

4

19	20	21	22	23	24	25	26	27
K	**Ca**	**Sc**	**Ti**	**V**	**Cr**	**Mn**	**Fe**	**Co**
Potassium	Calcium	Scandium	Titanium	Vanadium	Chromium	Manganese	Iron	Cobalt
39.098	40.08	44.956	47.88	50.94	51.996	54.938	55.847	58.9332

5

37	38	39	40	41	42	43	44	45
Rb	**Sr**	**Y**	**Zr**	**Nb**	**Mo**	**Tc**	**Ru**	**Rh**
Rubidium	Strontium	Yttrium	Zirconium	Niobium	Molybdenum	Technetium	Ruthenium	Rhodium
85.468	87.62	88.9059	91.224	92.91	95.94	(98)	101.07	102.906

6

55	56	57 to 71	72	73	74	75	76	77
Cs	**Ba**		**Hf**	**Ta**	**W**	**Re**	**Os**	**Ir**
Cesium	Barium		Hafnium	Tantalum	Tungsten	Rhenium	Osmium	Iridium
132.91	137.33		178.49	180.95	183.85	186.207	190.2	192.22

7

87	88	89 to 103	104	105	106	107	108	109
Fr	**Ra**		**Unq**	**Unp**	**Unh**	**Uns**	**Uno**	**Une**
Francium	Radium		Unnilquadium	Unnilpentium	Unnilhexium	Unnilseptium	Unniloctium	Unnilennium
(223)	226.025		(261)	(262)	(263)	(262)	(265)	(266)

The new Group designations are those assigned by IUPAC in 1984.

Lanthanoid Series

Actinoid Series

Rare-Earth Elements

57	58	59	60	61	62
La	**Ce**	**Pr**	**Nd**	**Pm**	**Sm**
Lanthanum	Cerium	Praseodymium	Neodymium	Promethium	Samarium
138.906	140.12	140.908	144.24	(145)	150.36

89	90	91	92	93	94
Ac	**Th**	**Pa**	**U**	**Np**	**Pu**
Actinium	Thorium	Protactinium	Uranium	Neptunium	Plutonium
227.028	232.038	231.036	238.029	237.048	(244)

Figure 5–10 *The modern periodic table of the elements is shown here.*

OF THE ELEMENTS

C	Solid
Br	Liquid
H	Gas

Nonmetals

					18 VIIIA
13 IIIA	**14** IVA	**15** VA	**16** VIA	**17** VIIA	2 **He** Helium 4.003
5 **B** Boron 10.81	6 **C** Carbon 12.011	7 **N** Nitrogen 14.007	8 **O** Oxygen 15.999	9 **F** Fluorine 18.998	10 **Ne** Neon 20.179
13 **Al** Aluminum 26.98	14 **Si** Silicon 28.086	15 **P** Phosphorus 30.974	16 **S** Sulfur 32.06	17 **Cl** Chlorine 35.453	18 **Ar** Argon 39.948

10	**11** IB	**12** IIB
28 **Ni** Nickel 58.69	29 **Cu** Copper 63.546	30 **Zn** Zinc 65.39
46 **Pd** Palladium 106.42	47 **Ag** Silver 107.868	48 **Cd** Cadmium 112.41
78 **Pt** Platinum 195.08	79 **Au** Gold 196.967	80 **Hg** Mercury 200.59

31 **Ga** Gallium 69.72	32 **Ge** Germanium 72.59	33 **As** Arsenic 74.922	34 **Se** Selenium 78.96	35 **Br** Bromine 79.904	36 **Kr** Krypton 83.80
49 **In** Indium 114.82	50 **Sn** Tin 118.71	51 **Sb** Antimony 121.75	52 **Te** Tellurium 127.60	53 **I** Iodine 126.905	54 **Xe** Xenon 131.29
81 **Tl** Thallium 204.383	82 **Pb** Lead 207.2	83 **Bi** Bismuth 208.98	84 **Po** Polonium (209)	85 **At** Astatine (210)	86 **Rn** Radon (222)

The symbols shown here for elements 104-109 are being used temporarily until names for these elements can be agreed upon.

Metals

Mass numbers in parentheses are those of the most stable or common isotope.

63 **Eu** Europium 151.96	64 **Gd** Gadolinium 157.25	65 **Tb** Terbium 158.925	66 **Dy** Dysprosium 162.50	67 **Ho** Holmium 164.93	68 **Er** Erbium 167.26	69 **Tm** Thulium 168.934	70 **Yb** Ytterbium 173.04	71 **Lu** Lutetium 174.967
95 **Am** Americium (243)	96 **Cm** Curium (247)	97 **Bk** Berkelium (247)	98 **Cf** Californium (251)	99 **Es** Einsteinium (252)	100 **Fm** Fermium (257)	101 **Md** Mendelevium (258)	102 **No** Nobelium (259)	103 **Lr** Lawrencium (260)

There are seven periods of elements. Look at Periods 6 and 7. You will notice that in each of these periods a row has been separated out and displayed under the main table. These two rows are part of the periodic table. They have been separated out to make the table shorter and easier to read. Elements in these two rows are rare-earth elements.

SECTION REVIEW

1. How does the arrangement of elements in the modern periodic table differ from that in Mendeleev's table?
2. What important feature of an atom did Moseley determine?
3. In the modern periodic table, what is a family? A period?
4. Chlorine is often added to swimming-pool water to kill germs. According to the periodic law, what other element might be used to do the same job?

5–3 Using the Periodic Table

The periodic table is one of the most important tools of a chemist. A great deal of information about an element can be gathered by using the periodic table correctly. As you read this section, refer often to the periodic table on pages 118–119.

Element Key

Look closely at the periodic table. Each element is found in a separate square. **Important information about an element is given in each square of the periodic table: its atomic number, chemical symbol, name, and atomic mass.**

The number at the top of each square is the *atomic number* of the element. Remember that the atomic number of an element is unique. No two elements have the same atomic number. As you look at the table, you can see that the elements are arranged in order of increasing atomic number.

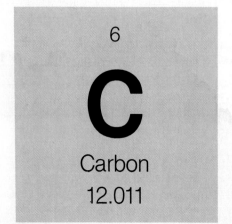

6

C

Carbon

12.011

Figure 5–11 *Four important facts about an element are supplied in each square of the periodic table: the symbol, name, atomic number, and atomic mass of that element.*

HELP WANTED: MATERIALS SCIENTIST to develop new materials for use in automobile and airplane construction. College degree in chemistry or engineering required.

The airplane you see here looks as if it is flying backwards! But the plane, called the X-29, cuts through the air on its forward-swept wings with grace and speed.

Airplane designers have known since 1935 that forward-swept wings would be more aerodynamically efficient for high-speed airplanes. But early forward-swept wings made from steel tended to break off at high speeds.

Finally, in the 1970s, **materials scientists** developed a new material that makes forward-swept wings possible. They discovered that graphite, which is a form of carbon, can be sandwiched with plastic. The combination is stronger and more flexible than steel yet lighter in weight than metals.

A materials scientist works with metals, such as iron and aluminum, and with other materials, such as graphite, plastics, and ceramics. Products developed by materials scientists are all around you. The glue that holds this book together, rocket engines, and bicycle tires are just a few of the many products that materials scientists have helped to develop.

In order to join the exciting world of materials science, you should be interested in science, curious about the chemical composition of matter, and have some mechanical ability. If you would like to find out more about becoming a materials scientist, write to the American Society for Metals, Chapter and Membership Development, Metals Park, OH 44073.

Just below the atomic number, near the center of the square, is the *chemical symbol* for the element. Below the chemical symbol, the *name* of the element is spelled out. The number near the bottom of the square is the *atomic mass* of the element.

Now practice using what you have just learned. Locate the element boron in the periodic table. What is its atomic number? Its symbol? What element has the symbol Cd? What element has an atomic number of 38? What is the atomic mass of magnesium? Of bromine?

Metals and Nonmetals

When you hear the word **metal,** you probably think of a familiar substance such as silver, iron, or copper. These elements are indeed metals. But substances you may not have thought of as metals—such as calcium, sodium, and potassium—are also classified as metals.

Sharpen Your Skills

Metals and Nonmetals

1. See how many different metallic elements and non-metallic elements you can find around your home. Remember that you are looking for elements. Materials such as glass and plastic are not elements.

2. How many metals did you find? What are they? How are they used in your home?

3. How many nonmetals did you find? What are they? How are they used in your home?

What reasons can you give for the difference between the number of metals and nonmetals you found?

To a scientist, an element is a metal if it has certain properties. Metals are good conductors of heat and electricity. Metals are shiny and have high melting points. Metals are **ductile,** which means they can be drawn into thin wires. They are **malleable,** which means they can be hammered into thin sheets.

Of the 109 known elements, 88 are metals. If you look at the periodic table, you will see a dark, zigzag line running like steps down the right side of the table. Elements to the left of the line are metals.

Nonmetals, which are the elements to the right of the dark line, do not have the properties metals have. Nonmetals are poor conductors of heat and electricity. They usually have dull surfaces and low melting points. Those nonmetals that are solids tend to be brittle and break easily. Carbon and phosphorus are examples of nonmetals that are solids at room temperature. Bromine is a liquid nonmetal. Nonmetals that are gases include oxygen, nitrogen, and chlorine. Using the periodic table, can you name some other nonmetals?

The dividing line between metals and nonmetals is not quite as definite as it appears. For along each side of the dark line are elements that have properties of both metals and nonmetals. These elements are called **metalloids** (MEHT-uhl-oidz). Metalloids may be shiny or dull. They conduct heat and electricity better than nonmetals but not as well as metals. The metalloids include boron, silicon, germanium, arsenic, antimony, tellurium, polonium, and astatine.

Figure 5–12 *Iodine (left) and sulfur (right) are two typical nonmetals. They are characteristically dull and brittle. Where on the periodic table are nonmetals located?*

Figure 5–13 *Metalloids are elements that have properties of both metals and nonmetals. The metalloid silicon (left) is important in the manufacture of computer chips. Entire computer circuits can be arranged on just one silicon chip. Antimony (right), another metalloid, is used to make alloys. What are some other metalloids?*

SECTION REVIEW

1. What information is given in the square that is assigned to each element?
2. What is the position on the periodic table of those elements that are called metals? Nonmetals?
3. What are some characteristic properties of metals? Of nonmetals?
4. What are metalloids?
5. Suppose that you have a sample of an unknown element. You notice that the element is shiny and that its melting point is fairly high. However, the element does not conduct heat well. Which of the following elements might the sample be—iodine, aluminum, iron, or silver? Explain your answer.

5–4 Periodic Properties of the Elements

Section Objective

To identify periodic trends in the elements

You have learned several ways in which the periodic table provides important information about the elements. Elements in the same family, or vertical column, have similar properties. Elements on the left of the table are metals. Elements on the right are nonmetals. Metalloids, which show properties of both metals and nonmetals, are located on either side of the dark zigzag line.

Figure 5–14 *The properties of elements vary in a regular way from left to right across a period. Sodium, an extremely reactive metal, is used in its vapor phase in street lights (right). Sodium vapor lamps provide bright-yellow light. Argon, an extremely unreactive gas, is used to make glowing works of art (left). How does the electron arrangement of each element account for its reactivity?*

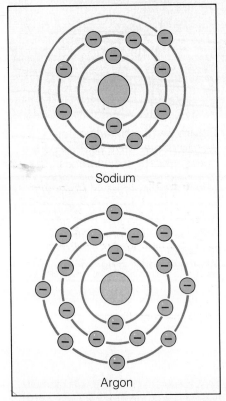

Sodium

Argon

Additional information about the elements can be obtained from their location in a period, or horizontal row. **Certain properties of elements vary in a regular way from left to right across a period.** These properties include electron arrangement, reactivity, atomic size, and metallic properties.

The valence number of an element is related to the electrons in the outermost energy level of an atom of that element. It is these electrons that are involved in the chemical combining of elements to form compounds.

Starting at the left of each period, the pattern of valence numbers is 1 2 3 4 3 2 1 0. An element with a valence of 1 will gain, lose, or share 1 electron in a chemical combination. An element with a valence of 4 will gain, lose, or share 4 electrons. What is true about an element with a valence of 0? How reactive is such an element?

Elements to the left in a period tend to lose electrons easily when they combine with other elements. You know that elements on the left of the table are metals. So another property of metals is that they lose electrons in chemical combinations. Elements to the right in a period tend to gain electrons easily when they combine with other elements. What kind of elements are these?

The amount of energy needed to remove an electron from an atom shows a periodic increase from left to right across a period. Since atoms of elements on the left in a period tend to lose electrons, removing an electron from such an atom re-

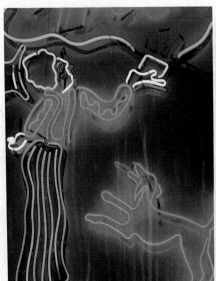

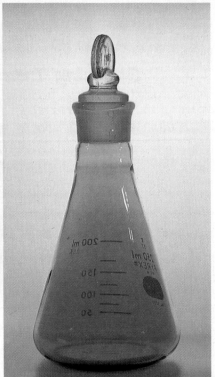

Figure 5–15 *Metallic properties of the elements also are periodic. Chromium is a shiny hard metal often used as automobile trim (left). Bromine is a dull-brown liquid at room temperature (right). What is true about the number of electrons in the outermost energy level of atoms across a period? About the metallic properties?*

quires a small amount of energy. Removing an electron from an atom of an element on the right in a period requires a large amount of energy. Why?

Another property of elements that varies periodically is atomic size. From left to right across a period, atomic size decreases. This decrease can be explained in terms of electron arrangement. As the atomic number increases across a period, one electron is added to each successive element. But this electron is still in the same energy level. The increase in the number of electrons in the energy level and the number of protons in the nucleus produces a stronger attraction between these oppositely charged particles. The electrons are pulled closer to the nucleus. The size of the atom decreases. Can you explain why atomic size increases from top to bottom in a family?

Metallic properties of the elements are also periodic. From left to right across a period, elements become less metallic in nature.

SECTION REVIEW

1. What properties are periodic in nature?
2. What is the pattern of valences from left to right across a period?
3. How does atomic size change across a period? Down a family?
4. Why does the amount of energy needed to remove an electron from an atom decrease from top to bottom in a family?

Sharpen Your Skills

Predicting Formulas

Zinc (Zn), cadmium (Cd), and mercury (Hg) are in the zinc subgroup of the periodic table. Predict the formulas of the corresponding compounds of cadmium and mercury based on the fact that zinc forms the following compounds:

$ZnCl_2$ (zinc chloride)

ZnO (zinc oxide)

ZnS (zinc sulfide)

$Zn(NO_3)_2$ (zinc nitrate)

5 LABORATORY INVESTIGATION

Graphing Trends in the Periodic Table

	IA	IIA	IIIA	IVA	VA	VIA	VIIA	VIIIA
2	3 **Li** 1.23 124	4 **Be** 0.89 215	5 **B** 0.80 191	6 **C** 0.77 260	7 **N** 0.70 335	8 **O** 0.66 314	9 **F** 0.64 402	10 **Ne** 0.67 497
3	11 **Na** 1.57 119	12 **Mg** 1.36 176	13 **Al** 1.25 138	14 **Si** 1.17 188	15 **P** 1.10 242	16 **S** 1.04 239	17 **Cl** 0.99 299	18 **Ar** 0.98 363
4	19 **K** 2.03 100	20 **Ca** 1.74 141						
5	37 **Rb** 2.16 96	38 **Sr** 1.91 131						
6	55 **Cs** 2.35 90	56 **Ba** 1.98 120						

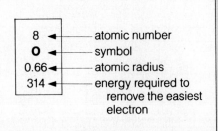

Problem

Are certain properties of elements periodic functions of their atomic numbers?

Materials (per student)

2 sheets of graph paper
2 colored pencils (different colors)
straight edge

Procedure

1. For elements 3–20, make a graph of atomic radius as a function of atomic number. Plot atomic number on the X axis and atomic radius on the Y axis. Make sure each scale is uniform and covers the range of numbers to be plotted. Label the graph. Include a title and labels for each axis.
2. For elements in Family IA, make a graph of atomic radius as a function of atomic number. On the same graph, use a different color to do the same for elements in Family IIA. Label the graph.
3. For elements 3–20, make a graph of the energy required to remove the easiest electron as a function of atomic number. Plot atomic number on the X axis and energy on the Y axis. Label the graph.
4. For elements in Family IA, make a graph of the energy required to remove the easiest electron as a function of atomic num-

ber. On the same graph, use a different color to do the same for elements in Family IIA. Label the graph.

Observations

1. What happens to the atomic radius as the atomic number increases across a period? Down a family?
2. What happens to the energy needed to remove an electron as the atomic number increases across a period? Down a family?

Conclusions

1. What properties of the elements are periodic functions of their atomic numbers?
2. Why does atomic radius change as it does?
3. Why does energy required to remove an electron change as it does?

CHAPTER REVIEW

SUMMARY

5–1 Development of a Periodic Table

❑ Mendeleev arranged the elements in order of increasing atomic mass. All the elements in a column had the same valence and showed similar chemical and physical properties.

❑ Empty spaces in Mendeleev's periodic table proved to be undiscovered elements.

5–2 The Modern Periodic Table

❑ Moseley's discovery of atomic number altered Mendeleev's periodic table.

❑ In the modern periodic table, elements are arranged in order of increasing atomic number.

❑ The periodic law states that the physical and chemical properties of the elements are periodic functions of their atomic numbers.

❑ Vertical columns in the periodic table are called groups or families.

❑ Horizontal rows in the periodic table are called periods.

5–3 Using the Periodic Table

❑ Each element occupies one square in the table.

❑ Each square contains the element's atomic number, symbol, name, and atomic mass.

❑ The elements can be classified as metals, nonmetals, or metalloids.

❑ Metals are good conductors of heat and electricity. They are shiny and have high melting points. They are ductile and malleable.

❑ Nonmetals are poor conductors of heat and electricity. They usually have dull surfaces and low melting points. Solid nonmetals are brittle.

❑ Metalloids have properties of both metals and nonmetals.

5–4 Periodic Properties of the Elements

❑ Periodic properties of the elements include electron arrangement, reactivity, atomic size, and metallic properties.

VOCABULARY

Define each term in a complete sentence.

ductile	**group**	**metal**	**nonmetal**	**periodic**
family	**malleable**	**metalloid**	**period**	**periodic law**

CONTENT REVIEW: MULTIPLE CHOICE

On a separate sheet of paper, write the letter of the answer that best completes each statement.

1. In finding a relationship among the elements, Mendeleev
   a. used the scientific method.
   b. stumbled upon his discovery by accident.
   c. made his discovery while looking for something else.
   d. carried out many experiments to test the properties of elements.
2. In his periodic table, Mendeleev placed one element to the right of another because it had
   a. similar properties to the previous element.
   b. the next largest atomic number.
   c. the next largest atomic mass.
   d. the same valence number as the previous element.

3. Moseley was able to determine each element's
   a. atomic mass.   b. atomic number.   c. symbol.   d. brittleness.

4. The periodic law states that the properties of elements are periodic functions of their
   a. atomic mass.   b. symbol.   c. atomic number.   d. valence.

5. The term group refers to elements
   a. in the same row.
   b. in the same column.
   c. that were missing in Mendeleev's original table.
   d. that are metalloids.

6. If a metal can be hammered or rolled into thin sheets, the metal is
   a. ductile.   b. malleable.   c. brittle.   d. active.

7. A brittle element that is not a very good conductor of heat and electricity is
   a. inert.   b. a metal.   c. ductile.   d. a nonmetal.

8. In the periodic table, elements known as metals are
   a. in one row.   b. in one column.   c. on the left side.   d. on the right side.

9. Each period of the table begins on the left with a
   a. very active metal.   b. metalloid.   c. rare-earth element.   d. nonmetal.

10. In a given period, as atomic number increases, the size of the atom
   a. increases.   b. decreases.   c. stays the same.   d. equals zero.

CONTENT REVIEW: COMPLETION

On a separate sheet of paper, write the word or words that best complete each statement.

1. An element's _____ are those characteristics that can be used to identify the element.

2. A word that means "to repeat according to some pattern" is _____.

3. The number of protons in the nucleus of each atom of an element is called the _____ of the element.

4. The person who devised the first periodic table was _____.

5. In the modern periodic table, elements are arranged in order of increasing _____.

6. A vertical column in the periodic table is called a (an) _____ or group.

7. A horizontal row in the periodic table is called a (an) _____.

8. Elements that are found within the same _____ of the periodic table have similar properties.

9. Elements that are good conductors of heat and electricity are classified as _____.

10. Elements that have properties of both metals and nonmetals are called _____.

CONTENT REVIEW: TRUE OR FALSE

Determine whether each statement is true or false. Then on a separate sheet of paper, write "true" if it is true. If it is false, change the underlined word or words to make the statement true.

1. Mendeleev knew of <u>92</u> elements when he began work on his periodic table.

2. Mendeleev noticed a definite pattern in the <u>valence numbers</u> of the elements.

3. The word <u>ductile</u> means "repeating according to some pattern."
4. Mendeleev's periodic table was arranged in order of increasing <u>atomic number</u>.
5. Sodium, a member of Family IA, is a very <u>active</u> element.
6. The <u>atomic mass</u> is the number of protons in the nucleus of an atom.
7. High melting point is a property of <u>metals</u>.
8. <u>Nonmetals</u> are usually poor conductors of heat and electricity.
9. Elements to the left in a period tend to <u>lose</u> electrons easily.
10. From top to bottom in a given family, the atomic number increases and the size of the atom <u>decreases</u>.

CONCEPT REVIEW: SKILL BUILDING

Use the skills you have developed in the chapter to complete each activity.

1. **Classifying elements** Classify the following elements as metals, nonmetals, or metalloids: arsenic, bromine, argon, beryllium, manganese, cadmium, astatine, germanium, lithium, helium, mercury.
2. **Sequencing** Arrange the following elements in order of increasing atomic mass: sulfur, boron, copper, iron, gold, lead, sodium, hydrogen, strontium, zinc.
3. **Making a diagram** Using the element mercury, make a drawing of its square on the periodic table. Label each piece of information given.
4. **Applying concepts** Determine the identity of the following elements:
   a. This metal has a valence of 3, properties similar to aluminum, and an atomic mass slightly less than tin.
   b. This highly active element is the only liquid nonmetal. It has a valence of 1 and an atomic number of 35.
   c. This element, with a valence of 4, shows properties of metals and nonmetals and has 32 protons in the nucleus of each atom.
5. **Applying concepts** Explain why elements with the same valence number have similar properties.
6. **Making comparisons** Compare the properties of element 56, barium, with those of element 86, radon. How do you account for the difference in properties?
7. **Applying concepts** Suppose that in another galaxy, a completely different set of elements exists. These elements, which number 26, have been assigned symbols corresponding to the letters of the alphabet by the inhabitants of the galaxy. The symbols run in order of increasing atomic number. The following elements have been found to closely resemble one another in their physical and chemical properties:

   A, C, G, K, Q, and Y
   B, F, J, P, and X

   Develop a periodic table of these elements, using this information.

CONCEPT REVIEW: ESSAY

Discuss each of the following in a brief paragraph.

1. Suppose that element number 114 is discovered. Which known element will it most resemble? Explain your answer.
2. According to the periodic table, what two elements most resemble silver (Ag)?
3. How was Mendeleev able to tell that there were elements not yet discovered?
4. Compare the properties of metals, nonmetals, and metalloids. Use examples.
5. Why are elements with valences of 1 the most active metals or nonmetals?
6. How is the number assigned to a family related to the electron configuration of each element in that family?

Families of Elements 6

CHAPTER SECTIONS

6–1 Properties of Metals and Nonmetals

6–2 Active Metals

6–3 Transition Metals

6–4 From Metals to Nonmetals

6–5 Halogens

6–6 Noble Gases

6–7 Rare-Earth Elements

CHAPTER OBJECTIVES

After completing this chapter, you will be able to

6–1 Compare the properties of metals, nonmetals, and metalloids.

6–2 Name and describe the most active metals.

6–3 Describe the characteristics of the transition metals.

6–4 Explain the change in properties across the periodic table.

6–5 Describe the properties of the halogen family.

6–6 Describe the properties of the noble gases.

6–7 Identify the rare-earth elements.

Displaying every color of the rainbow, these finely ground particles were once valued as semiprecious stones. Traders in the ancient world carried the rarest of them across continents, hoping to bring the brightest and most exotic to the palaces of kings.

Chemists today observe these particles carefully, noting size, shape, and texture. They analyze their colors with a special instrument. Then they test the particles to see how well they can withstand exposure to heat, light, moisture, and air pollution.

Can you guess what these unique particles are? You may be surprised to know that they are *pigments*—the powderlike materials that give color to paint. When suspended in oil or other flowing substances, pigments can be splashed on canvas to capture the beauty of a sunset or to reveal the complex coloration of the human face.

A list of pigments reads like a chemistry book—zinc white, cadmium yellow, cobalt blue, iron oxide red, chromium green. All these pigments are made from a group of elements known as the transition metals. In this chapter you will read about the transition metals and about many other groups of elements. Each group has its own special set of properties and its own interesting—and sometimes surprising—practical uses.

The paints on this artist's palette are made from compounds called pigments. Pigments are composed of a group of elements known as transition metals.

6–1 Properties of Metals and Nonmetals

Section Objective

To compare the properties of metals and nonmetals

Consider some familiar elements—gold, copper, oxygen, carbon, iron, silver, and sulfur. If you had to divide these elements into two groups based on similar properties, how would you do it?

Most likely you would classify each element as a metal or a nonmetal. For hundreds of years scientists have been able to distinguish between these two groups. **Metals and nonmetals have many easily observed physical properties that make them distinctly different from each other.** Today, chemists believe that these properties depend upon the way electrons are arranged in the atoms of the elements.

Physical Properties of Metals

The physical properties of metals make them easy to recognize. One such property is **luster,** or shininess. Most metals also allow heat and electricity to move through them easily. So metals are good conductors of heat and electricity. Metals generally have a high density. This means that they are heavy for their size. And metals usually have fairly high melting points. With these properties in mind, can you name some objects around you that are metals?

There are two other physical properties that are common to many metals. Most metals are ductile—they can be drawn into thin wire. Most metals are malleable—they can be hammered into thin sheets.

Figure 6–1 *The physical properties of metals make them easy to recognize and useful for certain purposes. Copper (left) is a good conductor of electricity and is used in the armatures of electric motors. Magnesium (center) is used to make baseball bats because it is lightweight yet durable. Silver (right), also a good conductor of electricity, has a high melting point. What other property of metals is visible from these photos?*

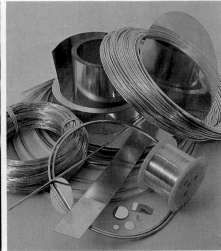

Chemical Properties of Metals

The chemical properties of metals are not quite as easy to observe as the physical properties. The chemical properties depend on the way the electrons are arranged in the atoms of the metals. An atom of a metal can have one, two, three, or four electrons in its outermost energy level. You will recall that the electrons in the outermost energy level of an atom are called valence electrons. The valence electrons in atoms of metals are rather weakly held. So metals are elements that tend to lose their outermost electrons. What happens to an atom when it loses one or more electrons?

Because they tend to lose electrons, most metals will react with water or elements in the atmosphere. Such a chemical reaction often results in **corrosion** of the metal. Corrosion is the gradual wearing away of the metal due to a chemical reaction in which the metal element is changed into a metallic compound. The rusting of iron is an example of corrosion. When iron rusts, it combines with oxygen in the air to form the compound iron oxide. The tarnishing of silver is another example of corrosion. What compound is formed during tarnishing?

Alloys

Sometimes two metals or a metal and a nonmetal can be mixed together in the molten, or melted, state. When the mixture cools and hardens, the result is a substance called an **alloy.** An alloy is a mixture of two elements—both metals or a metal and a nonmetal—that has the properties of a metal.

Steel, an alloy of iron and carbon, is harder and stronger than iron alone. Adding nickel or chromium to the steel makes stainless steel, an alloy that is very resistant to rusting. Brass, an alloy of copper and zinc, has properties that are very different from either of the metals from which it is made.

Physical Properties of Nonmetals

In general, the physical properties of nonmetals are just the opposite of the physical properties of metals. Nonmetals usually have no luster and are dull in appearance. Nonmetals do not conduct heat and electricity very well. Nonmetals are brittle and

COMMON ALLOYS

Alloy	Uses
Alnico (Al, Ni, Co, Fe, Cu)	Magnets
Brass (Cu, Zn)	Jewelry, ornaments, musical instruments
Bronze (Cu, Sn)	Jewelry, nuts, bolts, ornaments
Gold, 14 carat (Au, Cu, Ag)	Jewelry, coins
Solder (Pb, Sn)	Electric wire, solderings, welding
Stainless steel (Fe, Cr, Ni)	Surgical instruments, cutlery, pots and pans, building materials, boats, cars
Dentist's amalgam (Hg, Ag)	Dental fillings
Wrought iron (Fe, C, Mn)	Ornaments, furniture, railings

Figure 6–2 *Some common alloys and their uses are shown in this table. Alloys are mixtures of two elements—both metals or a metal and a nonmetal. What elements make up the alloy brass? Solder? What alloy contains a solid metal combined with a liquid metal?*

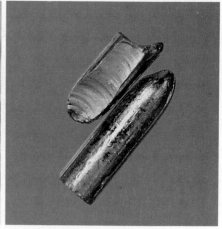

Figure 6–3 *Nonmetals have no luster and are dull in appearance. They are not ductile or malleable. Here you see three typical nonmetals: sulfur (left), phosphorus (center), and selenium (right). What are two other properties of nonmetals?*

break easily. They cannot be made into wire or hammered into thin sheets. In other words, nonmetals are not ductile or malleable. Nonmetals usually have lower densities than metals. And nonmetals generally have lower melting points.

Nonmetals are not as easy to recognize as a group as are metals. Nonmetals can be very different from one another. Bromine is a brown liquid, oxygen is a colorless gas, sulfur is a yellow solid.

Chemical Properties of Nonmetals

The chemical properties of nonmetals also tend to be opposite those of metals. Metals tend to lose electrons; nonmetals tend to gain electrons. Atoms of most nonmetals have five, six, seven, or eight electrons in their outermost energy level. Atoms with eight valence electrons have a complete outermost energy level. Atoms with five, six, or seven valence electrons gain three, two, or one electron to achieve a complete outermost energy level. Why do you think a particular nonmetal gains two electrons rather than loses six electrons?

Metalloids

Some elements display properties of both metals and nonmetals. These elements are called metalloids. The word metalloid means "metallike."

All of the metalloids are solids. They look very much like metals but are not quite as shiny. Like metals, they are usually white or gray in color. For example, the metalloid silicon has a luster that makes it look like a metal.

Most metalloids conduct heat and electricity, but not as well as metals. Metalloids are ductile and malleable. In addition to silicon, elements that are metalloids include boron, germanium, arsenic, antimony, tellurium, and polonium.

SECTION REVIEW

1. What are some physical and chemical properties of metals? Of nonmetals?
2. What is an alloy? A metalloid?
3. Why would coating a metal object with a nonmetallic substance prevent corrosion?

6–2 Active Metals

To identify the most active metals

All through history, metals such as gold, silver, iron, and copper have been valued and used. You probably are familiar with these metals. Yet there are two families of metals whose names might be unfamiliar to you. The metals in these two families are the most active metals. **The most active metals are found in Group IA and Group IIA of the periodic table.**

Alkali Metals

The elements in Group IA of the periodic table are the **alkali metals.** The members of the alkali metal family are lithium (Li), sodium (Na), potassium (K), rubidium (Rb), cesium (Cs), and francium (Fr). All six elements have the properties of metals except they are softer and less dense. The alkali metals can be cut with a knife. Because they are metals, what other physical properties do they have?

The alkali metals are the most reactive of all the metals. They are so reactive, in fact, that they are always found in nature combined with other elements, never as free elements. In pure form, the alkali metals are stored under oil to keep them from reacting with oxygen or water vapor in the air. When the alkali metals do react with water, the reaction is violent. Hydrogen gas is produced, as well as extreme heat. Because of the extreme heat, the hydrogen gas can begin to burn and can possibly

IA

| 3 |
| **Li** |
| Lithium |
| 6.941 |

| 11 |
| **Na** |
| Sodium |
| 22.990 |

| 19 |
| **K** |
| Potassium |
| 39.098 |

| 37 |
| **Rb** |
| Rubidium |
| 85.468 |

| 55 |
| **Cs** |
| Cesium |
| 132.91 |

| 87 |
| **Fr** |
| Francium |
| (223) |

Figure 6–4 *Group IA metals, or the alkali metals, are shown. How many electrons are in the outermost energy level of each of the alkali metals?*

explode. The reaction of an alkali metal with water also produces a compound known as an alkali, or a base. It is for this reason that Group IA metals are called alkali metals. You will learn more about alkalis, or bases, in Chapter 9.

The alkali metals have only one electron in their outermost energy level. This electron is easily lost. So alkali metals form positive ions. Ions are charged atoms. The tendency of alkali metals to lose their valence electron easily makes them very reactive.

Alkali metals can be identified by the characteristic color each produces in a flame test. See Figure 6–6. When a sample of an alkali metal is heated, some of the electrons in its atoms gain energy and move to a higher energy level. When these electrons fall back to their original position, they lose the energy in the form of light.

Although the alkali metals themselves have very few familiar uses, the compounds they form are

Figure 6–5 *This table shows some of the properties of the alkali metals and the uses of their compounds. Which alkali metal has radioactive isotopes?*

ALKALI METALS

Element	Properties	Uses of Compounds
Lithium (Li)	m.p. 179°C b.p. 1336°C Soft, silvery; reacts violently with water	Medicine; metallurgy
Sodium (Na)	m.p. 97.8°C b.p. 883°C Soft, silvery-white; reacts violently with water	Soap; table salt; lye
Potassium (K)	m.p. 62.5°C b.p. 758°C Soft, silvery-white; reacts violently with moisture	Fertilizer; medicine; photography
Rubidium (Rb)	m.p. 39.0°C b.p. 700°C Soft, lustrous; reacts violently with moisture	Space vehicle engines; photocells
Cesium (Cs)	m.p. 28.6°C b.p. 670°C Silvery-white, ductile; reacts with moisture	Photocells
Francium (Fr)	Extremely rare; radioactive isotopes	Not widely used

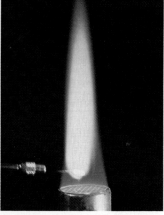

some of the most important substances you use every day. Table salt, baking soda, and soap are just a few of the compounds made from the alkali metals. The properties and uses of the alkali metals and their compounds are shown in Figure 6–5.

Alkaline Earth Metals

The elements in Group IIA of the periodic table are the **alkaline earth metals.** The members of the alkaline earth family are beryllium (Be), magnesium (Mg), calcium (Ca), strontium (Sr), barium (Ba), and radium (Ra). These elements, which are harder and denser than the alkali metals, also have higher melting points and boiling points. They are highly reactive, but not as reactive as the alkali metals. Like the alkali metals, the alkaline earth metals are never found free in nature.

Two of the alkaline earth metals are well known. Magnesium is often combined with aluminum to make alloys that are lightweight and strong. Magnesium compounds are used in medicines, photographic flashbulbs, and flares. Calcium is abundant in the earth in the form of marble and limestone rocks. Calcium is an essential part of the human body, especially in teeth and bones. The properties and uses of the alkaline earth metals and their compounds are shown in Figure 6–8 on page 138.

The alkaline earth metals have two electrons in their outermost energy level. Because their atomic size is smaller than that of the alkali metals, the alkaline earth metals hold their outer electrons more tightly. So although they are highly reactive, they

IIA

4
Be
Beryllium
9.0122

12
Mg
Magnesium
24.305

20
Ca
Calcium
40.08

38
Sr
Strontium
87.62

Figure 6–7 *Group IIA metals, or the alkaline earth metals, are shown. What type of ions do alkaline earth metals form?*

56
Ba
Barium
137.33

88
Ra
Radium
226.025

137

ALKALINE EARTH METALS

Element	Properties	Uses of Compounds
Beryllium (Be)	m.p. 1285°C b.p. 2970°C Poisonous	Radio parts; steel
Magnesium (Mg)	m.p. 650°C b.p. 1117°C Burns with very bright flame; strong but not dense	Medicine; photographic flashbulbs; auto parts; space vehicle parts; flares
Calcium (Ca)	m.p. 851°C b.p. 1487°C Silvery; important part of bones and teeth; tarnishes in moist air	Plaster and plasterboard; mortar and cement; water softeners; metal bearings
Strontium (Sr)	m.p. 774°C b.p. 1366°C Least abundant alkaline earth metal; reactive in air	Fireworks; flares
Barium (Ba)	m.p. 850°C b.p. 1537°C Extremely reactive in air	Medicine; paints; glassmaking
Radium (Ra)	m.p. (700°C) b.p. (1525°C) Silvery-white but turns black in air; radioactive	Treatment of cancer; medical research

Values in parentheses are physical properties of the most stable isotope.

Figure 6–8 *This table shows some of the properties of alkaline earth metals and the uses of their compounds. Which alkaline earth metal is essential to strong bones and teeth?*

are less so than the alkali metals. Can you explain why the electrons of a smaller atom are more tightly held than the electrons of a larger atom? Alkaline earth metals form positive ions.

SECTION REVIEW

1. What name is given to the elements that make up Group IA of the periodic table? Group IIA? What are the members of each group?
2. Which group is the most active? Why?
3. Why are the alkaline earth metals less reactive than the alkali metals?
4. What would be the formula for a compound formed between the element X with seven valence electrons and the alkali metal sodium? Between the element X and the alkaline earth metal calcium?

6-3 Transition Metals

To describe the properties of the transition metals

Turn to the periodic table on pages 118–119. Look between Group IIA and Group IIIA. What do you see? You should see 30 elements that do not seem to fit into any of the eight families. These elements are called the **transition metals.** Common transition elements include nickel, copper, zinc, platinum, and gold.

The transition metals have properties similar to one another and to other metals, but their properties do not fit in with those of any other family. Most transition metals are excellent conductors of heat and electricity. Most have high melting points and are hard. Unlike metals, however, some transition elements are brittle.

Transition metals are much less active than the alkali and alkaline earth metals. Many transition metals combine chemically with oxygen to form compounds called oxides. Many transition metals have more than one oxidation number. The oxidation number of an element is the number of electrons an atom of that element gains, loses, or shares when it chemically combines with another element. If an atom gains electrons, it will have a negative oxidation number. If an atom loses electrons, it will have a positive oxidation number.

Iron, for example, can have an oxidation number of 2+ or 3+. This means an atom of iron can lose either 2 or 3 electrons. Tin can have an oxidation number of 2+ or 4+. The oxidation number of manganese can range from 2+ to 7+.

Transition metals form compounds that are brightly colored. Particular compounds of the transition metals cobalt and cadmium are used as pigments in paint. Have you ever heard of cobalt blue or cadmium yellow? Transition metals have many practical uses. Figure 6–9 shows some of them.

Figure 6–9 *The transition elements have many common uses. Which transition element is liquid at room temperature?*

TRANSITION ELEMENTS	
Element	**Uses**
Iron (Fe)	Manufacturing; building materials; dietary supplement
Cobalt (Co)	Magnets; heat-resistant tools
Nickel (Ni)	Coins; batteries; jewelry; plating
Copper (Cu)	Electric wiring; plumbing; motors
Silver (Ag)	Jewelry; dental fillings; mirror backing; electric conductor
Gold (Au)	Jewelry; base for money systems; coins; dentistry
Zinc (Zn)	Paints; medicines; coat metals
Cadmium (Cd)	Plating; batteries; nuclear reactors
Mercury (Hg)	Liquid in thermometers, barometers, electric switches; dentistry; paints

SECTION REVIEW

1. What are the transition metals?
2. Why are the transition metals in a separate group?
3. What common metals are transition elements?
4. What are some physical and chemical properties of the transition metals?

6-4 From Metals to Nonmetals

IIIA

5
B
Boron
10.81

13
Al
Aluminum
26.98

31
Ga
Gallium
69.72

49
In
Indium
114.82

81
Tl
Thallium
204.383

Figure 6–10 Group IIIA elements are also called the boron family. What is true about the properties of these elements as you go down the group?

As you move from left to right across the periodic table, the properties of the elements become more nonmetallic. **It is in Groups IIIA to VIA of the periodic table that the properties of elements change from metallic to nonmetallic.** These groups include the boron family, carbon family, nitrogen family, and oxygen family.

If you look at Groups IIIA, IVA, VA, and VIA on the periodic table, you will notice that the zigzag line that divides metals and nonmetals runs right through these groups. Do you remember the name for elements on either side of this line? How many of these special elements are present in each of the four families?

The Boron Family

Boron (B), the first element in the boron family, is a metalloid. Aluminum (Al), which is right beneath boron, is by its position a metalloid. But the properties of aluminum are usually those of metals. The other members of the boron family—gallium (Ga), indium (In), and thallium (Th)—are metals.

Boron, which is hard and brittle, is never found in nature in the free state. It is usually found combined with oxygen. The compound boric oxide is important in making heat-resistant glass. Boric acid is commonly used as an eyewash and antiseptic. The compound borax is useful as a cleaning agent and water softener.

Aluminum is the most abundant metal and the third most abundant element in the earth's crust. Aluminum is found as aluminum oxide in the ore called bauxite. Aluminum is extremely valuable in industry. It is light, strong, and does not tarnish in air. It is an excellent reflector of light and a good conductor of heat and electricity. Aluminum is used in pots and pans, electric wiring, airplane parts, and the manufacture of alloys. Because aluminum is very malleable, it is used to make the familiar household product aluminum foil. Can you explain why it would take a very malleable metal to make aluminum foil?

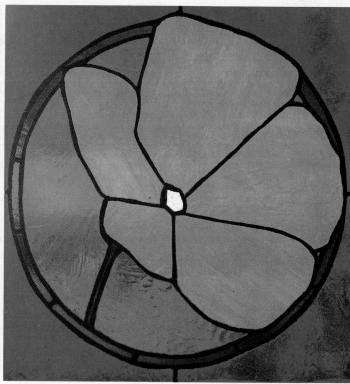

The Carbon Family

The carbon family includes the elements carbon (C), silicon (Si), germanium (Ge), tin (Sn), and lead (Pb). Carbon can combine with other elements in a great variety of ways. As a result, millions of carbon-containing compounds exist. Most compounds that contain carbon are called **organic compounds.** Carbon has often been called "the basis for life" because all living things contain organic compounds. You will learn more about organic compounds in Chapter 10.

Silicon is the second most abundant element in the earth's crust. Silicon is used in glass and in cement. It is also used in solar cells. Solar cells convert the energy of sunlight into electric energy.

Germanium is a metalloid used in transistors. Transistors are devices found in many electronic instruments, such as radios and televisions. Tin is a metal. Tin resists rusting and corrosion, so it is used in making cans for food. The common tin can is really a steel can with a coating of tin on the inside.

The densest element in the carbon family is the metal lead. Until recently, lead was used in paints and gasoline. But because lead is poisonous, it is being removed from many compounds.

IVA

6
C
Carbon
12.011

14
Si
Silicon
28.086

32
Ge
Germanium
72.59

Figure 6–12 *The carbon family is Group IVA of the periodic table. What two elements in this family are metalloids?*

50
Sn
Tin
118.71

82
Pb
Lead
207.2

VA	VIA
7 **N** Nitrogen 14.007	8 **O** Oxygen 15.999
15 **P** Phosphorus 30.974	16 **S** Sulfur 32.06
33 **As** Arsenic 74.922	34 **Se** Selenium 78.96
51 **Sb** Antimony 121.75	52 **Te** Tellurium 127.60
83 **Bi** Bismuth 208.98	84 **Po** Polonium (209)

Figure 6–13 *Group VA elements are also called the nitrogen family. Which element in this family shows the most metallic properties? The oxygen family is Group VIA. Which member of this family is a gas?*

The Nitrogen Family

The nitrogen family consists of nitrogen (N), phosphorus (P), arsenic (As), antimony (Sb), and bismuth (Bi). Nitrogen and phosphorus are nonmetals. Arsenic is a metalloid with mostly nonmetallic properties. Antimony is a metalloid with mostly metallic properties. Bismuth is the most metallic element in the family.

All members of the nitrogen family have five electrons in their outermost energy level. In the heavier elements, the outermost electrons are very far from the nucleus. They are more easily lost. This ease of losing valence electrons explains why the properties shift from nonmetallic to metallic as you move down this group.

Nitrogen, the most abundant element in the earth's atmosphere, is highly stable and does not combine easily with other elements. Nitrogen is used in the production of fertilizers, explosives, drugs, and dyes. Ammonia, a compound made of nitrogen and hydrogen, is a common household cleaning agent.

Phosphorus is a nonmetal that is too active to be found free in nature. One of its main uses is in making the tips of matches. Arsenic is an important ingredient in many insecticides. Both antimony and bismuth are used in making alloys.

The Oxygen Family

The oxygen family includes oxygen (O), sulfur (S), selenium (Se), tellurium (Te), and polonium (Po). All these elements have six electrons in their outermost energy level. Like the nitrogen family, their properties go from nonmetallic in oxygen and sulfur to metalloid in selenium and tellurium to metallic in polonium.

Oxygen, the most abundant element in the earth's crust, is very reactive and combines with almost every other element. Oxygen is a gas. It is necessary to most forms of life. The processes of respiration in plants and animals and photosynthesis in green plants require oxygen. At elevated temperatures, oxygen combines rapidly with other substances in a process called combustion. The burning of wood is a familiar example of combustion. Oxygen itself does not burn. But it is necessary for the burning of other substances. This means that oxygen supports combustion.

Sulfur, selenium, and tellurium are brittle solids at room temperature. They all combine with oxygen to form dioxides and also combine with metals and hydrogen.

Sulfur is used in the manufacture of such products as drugs, insecticides, matches, gunpowder, and rubber. Selenium is used in making red glass and enamels. Tellurium is useful in making alloys. Polonium is a very rare radioactive element.

SECTION REVIEW

1. What elements are in the boron family? The carbon family?
2. What is an organic compound?
3. What elements are in the nitrogen family? The oxygen family?
4. Why do the properties of elements in the nitrogen and oxygen families shift from nonmetallic to metallic down the group?

Figure 6–14 *This brush fire burns because of the presence of the element oxygen. Oxygen is a Group VIA nonmetal that supports combustion. What other elements belong to the oxygen family?*

6–5 Halogens

Elements in Group VIIA are called **halogens** (HAL-uh-juhn). The halogens are strongly nonmetallic. They tend to gain electrons and form negative ions. **The halogens—which include the elements fluorine (F), chlorine (Cl), bromine (Br), iodine (I), and astatine (At)—are the most active nonmetals.** As a result, they are never found free in nature. They are always found combined in a compound.

The chemical reactivity of the halogens is due to the number of electrons in the outermost energy levels of their atoms. Each halogen atom has 7 valence electrons. Atoms of the halogens need to gain only 1 electron to fill their outermost level.

Fluorine is the most active halogen. Fluorine and chlorine are gases. Bromine is a liquid. Iodine and astatine are solids. Astatine is radioactive. See Figure 6–17 on page 144.

Like most nonmetals, halogens have low melting points and boiling points. In the gas phase, halogens exist as diatomic elements. A diatomic element always contains two atoms of that element in one

Section Objective

To describe the properties of the halogens

VIIA

9
F
Fluorine
18.998

17
Cl
Chlorine
35.453

35
Br
Bromine
79.904

53
I
Iodine
126.905

85
At
Astatine
(210)

Figure 6–15 *Group VIIA elements are called the halogens. Which halogen is the most active nonmetal?*

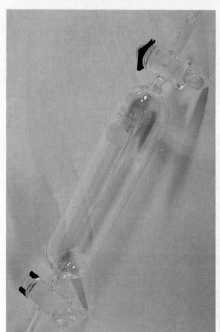

Figure 6–16 *Three members of the halogens, or Group VIIA elements, are shown here. Chlorine is a greenish-yellow gas (left). Bromine is a brown liquid (center), one of the few liquid elements. Iodine is a purple-black solid (right) that sublimes to produce a purple vapor. What is the most active halogen?*

Figure 6–17 *Because of their chemical reactivity, the halogens have many uses.*

HALOGENS

Element	Uses
Fluorine (F)	Etching glass; refrigerants; nonstick utensils; preventing tooth decay
Chlorine (Cl)	Bleaching agent; disinfectant; water purifier
Bromine (Br)	Medicine; dyes; photography
Iodine (I)	Medicine; disinfectant; dietary supplement in salt
Astatine (At)	Rare element

molecule. What is the formula for a molecule of fluorine? Chlorine?

The halogens combine readily with metals to form a class of compounds known as salts. In fact, the word "halogen" comes from the Greek words *halos* and *genos*, which mean "salt formers." Table salt, which is sodium chloride, is one example of a salt. Perhaps you have heard of sodium fluoride, which is used to fluoridate water, or calcium chloride, which is used to melt ice on streets and sidewalks. Silver bromide, another salt, is used in photographic film.

SECTION REVIEW

1. Are the halogens strongly metallic or nonmetallic?
2. What elements make up the halogen family?
3. What does the word "halogen" mean in Greek? Why is this an appropriate name for the elements in this family?
4. Why are the halogens highly reactive?
5. What name would you give to a salt formed when chlorine reacts with zinc? When iodine reacts with potassium?

6–6 Noble Gases

Section Objective

To relate electron configuration to the behavior of the noble gases

The six elements that make up the last family of the periodic table, or Group VIIIA, are called the **noble gases.** All the elements in this family are colorless gases that are extremely unreactive. Because they do not readily combine with other elements to form compounds, the noble gases are called **inert.**

The family of noble, or inert, gases includes helium (He), neon (Ne), argon (Ar), krypton (Kr), xenon (Xe), and radon (Rn). All the noble gases are found in small amounts in the earth's atmosphere. Argon, the most common of the noble gases, makes up about 1 percent of the atmosphere. Because they are so scarce and so unreactive, the noble gases were not discovered until the end of the nineteenth century. This was almost 50 years after Mendeleev had set up the periodic table.

The most striking property of the noble gases is their inactivity. It is only under special laboratory conditions that the noble gases can be made to combine chemically with other elements. In fact, atoms

Figure 6–18 *Group VIIIA elements are known as the noble gases. Why are these gases also called inert?*

VIIIA

2
He
Helium
4.003

10
Ne
Neon
20.179

18
Ar
Argon
39.948

36
Kr
Krypton
83.80

54
Xe
Xenon
131.29

86
Rn
Radon
(222)

Figure 6–19 *Crystals of xenon tetrafluoride such as these were first prepared in 1962 (left). Before that time, it was believed that noble gases could not take part in chemical reactions to form compounds. One of the most common uses of the noble gases is in colored lights. These tubes are filled with neon, which gives off a bright red light when electricity passes through it (right). Why are Group VIIIA gases so unreactive?*

HELP WANTED: JEWELER'S ASSIST-ANT willing to learn the trade of jewelry making from a busy shop owner. High school diploma or some technical training helpful, but a patient beginner with an interest in art and beauty may apply.

For thousands of years, people have adorned themselves with jewelry made from precious metals, stones, and other materials. Jewelry is admired and cherished for its beauty and value. **Jewelers** design and create stylish and attractive jewelry for their customers. They are experts in the qualities of metals and nonmetals, such as gold, silver, diamonds, and other gems.

Jewelers who own shops are usually responsible for the many facets of the jewelry business. These include designing jewelry, shaping, molding, or soldering metal pieces, cutting and setting stones, dealing with customers, and repairing broken jewelry.

Most jewelers learn their trade from more experienced jewelers or by attending technical schools, where they learn how to use jewelers' hand tools and machines. Frequently, jewelry making and repair require precise and delicate

work on small objects. So dexterity, coordination, patience, and the ability to concentrate are required to pursue a career as a jeweler. Artistic ability is also a valuable asset, especially if you would one day like to design jewelry or own your own shop.

If you would like to learn more about a career as a jeweler, contact: Jewelers of America, Time-Life Building, Suite 650, 1271 Avenue of the Americas, New York, NY 10020.

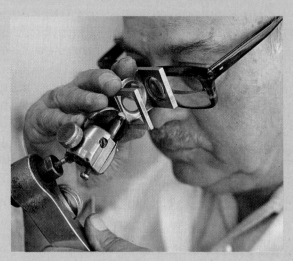

Sharpen Your Skills

Deep-Sea Danger

One of the dangers of deep-sea diving is a condition known as "the bends." Using books and other reference materials in the library, find out what element causes the bends. Which of the noble gases can be used to help prevent the bends? Write a report in which you describe your findings.

of a noble gas do not even combine with each other to form diatomic molecules.

The inactivity of the noble gases can be explained in terms of the electron configurations of their atoms. Atoms of noble gases already have complete outermost energy levels. They do *not* need to bond to other atoms in order to fill their energy levels and achieve stability. Among the noble gases, helium has 2 valence electrons; and neon, argon, krypton, xenon, and radon each have 8 electrons.

Some common uses of the inert gases probably are quite familiar to you. You no doubt have watched a balloon filled with helium float in the air. And you have seen neon-filled, brightly colored signs above theaters, restaurants, and stores. Some of the uses of the noble gases may be less familiar to you—radon to treat cancer, argon in light bulbs, and xenon in photographic lamps.

SECTION REVIEW

1. Which elements make up the family of noble gases?
2. What is the most striking property of the noble gases?
3. What is another name for the noble gases? Why is this an appropriate name?
4. Why are the noble gases so unreactive?

6–7 Rare-Earth Elements

Have you ever wondered why two rows of elements stand alone at the bottom of the periodic table? The 30 elements in these two rows are called the rare-earth elements. **The rare-earth elements are so similar to one another that, in a sense, they really do belong in the same squares of the periodic table.** They have been separated out and displayed under the main table to make the table shorter and easier to read.

The first row, called the **lanthanoid series,** is made up of soft, malleable metals that have a high luster and conductivity. The primary oxidation number of the lanthanoid series is 3+. The lanthanoids are used in industry to make various alloys and high-quality glass.

The elements in the second row make up the **actinoid series.** All the actinoids are radioactive. With the exception of three elements, all the actinoids are synthetic, or made in the laboratory. Like the lanthanoids, the primary oxidation number of the actinoids is 3+. The best-known actinoid is uranium, which is used as a nuclear fuel.

SECTION REVIEW

1. Where on the periodic table are the lanthanoid series and the actinoid series located?
2. What are two uses of lanthanoids?
3. What is the best-known element in the actinoid series?
4. Based on the position of the rare-earth elements in the periodic table, what can you predict about their properties?

6 LABORATORY INVESTIGATION

Flame Tests

Problem

Can elements be identified by using a flame test?

Materials *(per group)*

nichrome or platinum wire
cork
Bunsen burner
dilute hydrochloric acid
distilled water
8 test tubes
test tube rack
8 chloride test solutions
safety goggles

Procedure

1. Label each of the test tubes with one of the following compounds: LiCl, CaCl$_2$, KCl, CuCl$_2$, SrCl$_2$, NaCl, BaCl$_2$, unknown.
2. Pour 5 mL of each test solution in the correctly labeled test tube. Be sure to put the correct solution in each labeled test tube.
3. Push one end of a piece of nichrome or platinum wire into a cork. Then bend the other end of the wire into a tiny loop.
4. Put your safety goggles on. Clean the wire by dipping it into dilute hydrochloric acid and then into distilled water. Holding the cork, heat the wire in the blue flame of a burner until the wire is glowing and no longer colors the burner flame.
5. Dip the clean wire into the first test solution. Hold the wire at the tip of the inner cone of the burner flame. Record on a data table like the one shown here the color given to the flame.
6. Clean the wire by repeating step 4.
7. Repeat step 5 for the other six known test solutions. Remember to clean the wire after testing each solution.
8. Obtain an unknown solution from your teacher. After cleaning the wire, repeat the flame test for this compound.

Observations

1. What flame colors are produced by each compound?
2. What flame color is produced by your unknown?

Conclusions

1. Is the flame color a test for the metal or for the chloride in each compound? Explain your answer.
2. Why is it necessary to carefully clean the wire before testing each solution?
3. What metal is present in your unknown? How do you know?
4. How can you identify a metal using a flame test?
5. What do you think would happen if your test solution were a mixture of two metals? Could each metal be identified?

Compound	Color of Flame
Lithium chloride LiCl	
Calcium chloride CaCl$_2$	

CHAPTER REVIEW

SUMMARY

6–1 Properties of Metals and Nonmetals

❏ Among the physical properties of metals are luster, good conductivity of heat and electricity, high density, high melting point, ductility, and malleability.

❏ Metals form positive ions.

❏ An alloy is a mixture of two or more metals or a metal and a nonmetal. An alloy has the properties of a metal.

❏ Nonmetals have physical properties that are, in general, just the opposite of metals.

❏ Nonmetals form negative ions.

❏ Elements with some metallic and some nonmetallic properties are called metalloids.

6–2 Active Metals

❏ The metals of Group IA, called alkali metals, are very active.

❏ Group IIA metals, called alkaline earth metals, are active metals.

6–3 Transition Metals

❏ The transition metals are the three rows of elements found between Group IIA and Group IIIA of the periodic table.

❏ Transition metals have properties similar to each other, but not much like any other family.

6–4 From Metals to Nonmetals

❏ Properties of the elements change from metallic to nonmetallic in the boron, carbon, nitrogen, and oxygen families.

❏ The most abundant member of the boron family is the widely used metal aluminum.

❏ Carbon is the most important member of the carbon family because all living things contain carbon.

❏ The nitrogen and oxygen families each contain five elements whose properties range from nonmetallic to metalloid to metal.

6–5 Halogens

❏ The members of the halogen family are active, strongly nonmetallic elements that react readily with metals to form salts.

6–6 Noble Gases

❏ The noble, or inert, gases are unreactive and do not combine with other elements except under specially controlled conditions.

6–7 Rare-Earth Elements

❏ The rare-earth elements make up the two rows at the bottom of the periodic table. There are two series—the lanthanoids and the actinoids.

VOCABULARY

Define each term in a complete sentence.

actinoid series	lanthanoid series
alkali metal	luster
alkaline earth metal	noble gas
alloy	organic compound
corrosion	transition metal
halogen	
inert	

CONTENT REVIEW: MULTIPLE CHOICE

On a separate sheet of paper, write the letter of the answer that best completes each statement.

1. Some metals are very heavy for their size. This property is referred to as high
   a. ductility.   b. luster.   c. density.   d. malleability.

2. When an element combines with oxygen, the resulting compound is known as a (an)
   a. alloy.   b. allotrope.   c. salt.   d. oxide.

3. In the periodic table, the metallic character of the elements increases as you move
   a. down and to the right.   b. up and to the right.
   c. down and to the left.   d. up and to the left.

4. Elements that display properties of both metals and nonmetals are called
   a. transition metals.   b. alkaline earths.   c. salts.   d. metalloids.

5. Which of the following is an alkali metal?
   a. sodium   b. gold   c. neon   d. chlorine

6. Which of the following is a transition metal?
   a. sodium   b. gold   c. neon   d. chlorine

7. Which of the following is a halogen?
   a. sodium   b. gold   c. neon   d. chlorine

8. Which of the following is a noble gas?
   a. sodium   b. gold   c. neon   d. chlorine

9. Which element is called "the basis of life"?
   a. iron   b. oxygen   c. carbon   d. silicon

10. When a metal combines with a halogen, the kind of compound formed is called a (an)
    a. organic compound.   b. salt.   c. actinoid.   d. oxide.

CONTENT REVIEW: COMPLETION

On a separate sheet of paper, write the word or words that best complete each statement.

1. Metals are shiny, or have a high _____.

2. When two molten metals are mixed, the substance formed when the molten material cools and hardens is called a (an) _____.

3. The elements in Group IA are called _____.

4. If a metal is _____, it means it can be hammered into thin sheets.

5. A characteristic of transition metals is that their _____ can vary.

6. _____ is the most abundant element in the earth's crust.

7. Organic compounds are those compounds that contain the element _____.

8. In the Greek language, the word _____ means "salt former."

9. The noble gas that can make a balloon float is _____.

10. All of the actinoids are _____ elements.

Determine whether each statement is true or false. Then on a separate sheet of paper, write "true" if it is true. If it is false, change the underlined word or words to make the statement true.

1. The property of metals that means they can be drawn into thin wire is called <u>luster</u>.
2. Nonmetals tend to <u>lose</u> electrons.
3. In general, the <u>nonmetallic</u> character of the elements increases as you go up and to the right in the periodic table.
4. Sodium belongs to the <u>transition</u> metals.
5. Calcium is a <u>metal</u> that belongs to the alkaline earth family.
6. Gold is a <u>transition metal</u>.
7. <u>Aluminum</u> is a member of the boron family.
8. Compounds that contain carbon are known as <u>inorganic</u> compounds.
9. All members of the nitrogen family have <u>five</u> electrons in their outermost energy level.
10. The most striking property of the noble gases is their extreme <u>inactivity</u>.

Use the skills you have developed in the chapter to complete each activity.

1. **Designing an experiment** Describe the laboratory procedure you would follow to determine whether an unknown element is a metal or a nonmetal.
2. **Making diagrams** Draw a diagram to show the arrangement of electrons in the outermost energy level of an atom in each family of the periodic table.
3. **Applying concepts** Explain why metals are easily corroded.
4. **Applying concepts** In what ways does the position of an element in the periodic table tell you how it may combine with other elements to form compounds?
5. **Identifying patterns** Predict what will happen when the elements in each of the following pairs are brought together in a chemical reaction:

   a. lithium and bromine
   b. magnesium and chlorine
   c. calcium and oxygen
   d. potassium and neon

6. **Classifying elements** Classify each of the following elements as very active, moderately active, fairly inactive, or inert: magnesium, mercury, fluorine, krypton, helium, gold, potassium, calcium, bromine.
7. **Making inferences** Why were the noble gases difficult to discover?
8. **Making and interpreting graphs** Make a graph of melting point as a function of mass number for elements of the alkali metal family. Describe the graph. What relationship between melting point and mass number does your graph suggest?

Discuss each of the following in a brief paragraph.

1. Why do atoms of the alkali metals readily lose 1 electron?
2. Why do nonmetals tend to gain electrons?
3. What accounts for the extreme unreactivity of the noble gases?
4. Sodium never occurs in nature as a free element, and platinum seldom occurs in compounds. How are these observations related to the chemical properties of these two metals?

Adventures in Science

STEPHEN HAWKING: Changing Our View of the Universe

Scientists have long struggled to find the connection between two branches of physics. One of these branches deals with the forces that rule the world of atoms and subatomic particles. The other branch deals with gravity and its role in the universe of stars and galaxies. Physicist Stephen Hawking has set himself the task of discovering the connection. Leading theoretical physicists agree that if anyone can discover a unifying principle, it will certainly be this extraordinary scientist.

Dr. Hawking's goal, as he describes it, is simple. "It is complete understanding of the universe, why it is as it is and why it exists at all." In order to achieve such an understanding, Dr. Hawking seeks to "quantize gravity." Quantizing gravity means combining the laws of gravity and the laws of quantum mechanics into a single universal law. Dr. Hawking and other theoretical physicists believe that with such a law, the behavior of all matter in the universe, and the origin of the universe as well, could be explained.

Dr. Hawking's search for a unifying theory has led him to study one of science's greatest mysteries: black holes. A black hole is an incredibly dense region in space whose gravitational pull attracts all nearby objects, virtually "swallowing them up." A black hole is formed when a star uses up most of the nuclear fuel that has kept it burning. During most of its life as an ordinary star, its nuclear explosions exert enough outward force to balance the powerful inward force of gravity. But when the star's fuel is used up, the outward force ceases to exist. Gravity takes over and the star collapses into a tiny core of extremely dense material, possibly no bigger than the period at the end of this sentence.

Hawking has already proved that a black hole can emit a stream of electrons. Prior to this discovery, scientists believed that nothing, not even light, could escape from a black hole. So scientists have hailed Hawking's discovery as "one of the most beautiful in the history of physics."

Probing the mysteries of the universe is no ordinary feat. And Stephen Hawking is no ordinary man. Respected as one of the most brilliant physicists in the world, Hawking is also considered one of the most remarkable. For Dr. Hawking suffers from a serious disease of the nervous system that has confined him to a wheelchair, barely able to move or to speak. Although Dr. Hawking gives numerous presentations and publishes countless articles and papers, his addresses must be translated and his essays written down by other hands.

Hawking became ill during his first years at Cambridge University in England. The disease progressed quickly and left the young scholar quite despondent. He even considered giving up his research, as he thought he would not live long enough to receive his Ph.D. But in 1965, Hawking's life changed. He married Jane Wilde, a fellow student and language scholar. Suddenly life took on new meaning. "That was the turning point," he says. "It made me determined to live, and it was about that time that I began making professional progress." Hawking's health and spirits improved.

His studies continued and reached new heights of brilliance. Today, Dr. Hawking is professor of mathematics at Cambridge University and a husband and father who leads a full and active life.

Dr. Hawking believes that his illness has benefited his work. It has given him more time to think about physics. So although his body is failing him, his mind is free to soar. Considered to be one of the most brilliant physicists of all times, Dr. Hawking has taken some of the small steps that lead science to discovery and understanding. With time to ponder the questions of the universe, it is quite likely that Stephen Hawking will be successful in uniting the world of the tiniest particles with the world of stars and galaxies.

Stephen Hawking, shown here with his family, is Lucasian professor of mathematics at Cambridge University—a position once held by Isaac Newton. Hawking has received numerous prizes for his work.

Issues in Science

THE FIFTH FORCE: IS IT WITH US?

According to legend, in the late 1500s the famous Italian scientist Galileo climbed to the top of the Leaning Tower of Pisa in Italy and dropped two cannonballs at exactly the same time. One cannonball weighed ten times as much as the other. Popular scientific theories of Galileo's day predicted that the heavier ball would land first. But both of Galileo's cannonballs hit the ground at exactly the same time!

Although this story may be only legend, Galileo's experiments did prove an important scientific fact: all falling objects, regardless of their masses, accelerate at the same rate and thus fall at the same speed in a vacuum. The force that causes falling objects to accelerate at the same rate is gravity.

Now, nearly 300 years later, a new theory is shaking the very roots of physics. Unleashing a flurry of new experiments and sharp debate, the theory suggests the existence of a new force in nature. If indeed this theory is correct, it might prove the teachings of Galileo, Newton, and even Einstein wrong, by proving that there is a force that works against gravity.

Until recently, practically all scientists would have said there is no force that works against gravity. Now, however, some scientists are not so sure. In fact, these scientists have even suggested the existence of such a force.

Ephraim Fischbach of the University of Washington; Daniel Sudarsky, Aaron Szafer, and Carrick Talmadge of Purdue University; and Samuel Aronson of Brookhaven National Laboratory say they have found evidence of a force that under certain circumstances works against gravity. They call it the force of hypercharge. Many other people call it "the fifth force."

Most physicists believe in the existence of four basic forces in nature. These four forces are gravity, electromagnetism, the strong nuclear force, and the weak nuclear force.

Gravity is the force of attraction between all objects in the universe. The earth and a falling apple have a gravitational attraction for each other. So they pull on each other. Because the earth is more massive, its pull on the apple is greater, and thus noticeable.

According to Dr. Fischbach, hypercharge is a relatively weak force that works against gravity when objects are within about 200 meters of each other. Since this countergravitational force is much weaker than the pull of gravity, it is hardly noticeable.

Fischbach and his associates began to suspect the existence of a fifth force when they observed some strange results in gravity experiments they performed. After reexamining the results of many previous experiments, they concluded that as the force of gravity draws two objects together, another weaker force repels the objects. This force is hypercharge.

The magnitude of the hypercharge force is in part determined by the binding energy of an atomic nucleus. Since binding energy in various atomic nuclei is not the same, atoms would differ in the amount of fifth force they generate. As a result of differences in hypercharge, all objects would not obey Galileo's theory of gravitational acceleration and would not fall to the earth at the same speed. One object would fall more slowly than another!

Does the fifth force exist? Several leading scientists are doubtful. Nobel prize winner Richard Feynman believes that if the force is as strong as described, "it would have had effects in other experiments...." Dr. Feynman questions the validity of the tests that claim to show evidence of a new force.

Dr. Leon Lederman of Fermilab says of the fifth force, "My prediction is that the whole thing will go away."

Gravitational expert Robert Dicke of Princeton University explains, "The statistical evidence is not overwhelmingly convincing. I'd call it moderately persuasive. I put the chances of its being right at fifty percent or slightly better."

Many experiments are planned to test the theory of a fifth force. But scientists warn that it may be difficult to get valid results from the experiments.

If a fifth force exists, it will have a significant impact on the science of physics. But even with that prospect, some scientists are excited by the challenge of proving the existence of a new force. Even Nobel prize winner Dr. Sheldon Glashow of Harvard University admits, "It would be fun if it were true."

Could it be that Superman and Lois Lane have known about the fifth force all this time?

◄ As this juggler knows, all things that go up must come down. Or must they?

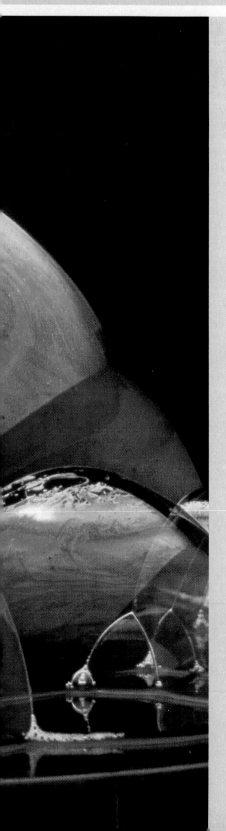

Interactions of Matter

See if you can solve this puzzle by determining what you would make if you performed the following steps. First, treat a fat called palmitin with an alkali such as sodium hydroxide in a process called saponification. The fat will break down to produce the substances sodium palmitate and glycerin. Discard the glycerin. Then add the sodium palmitate to a wetting compound to form a solution. Now dip a thin-sided ring, preferably one with a handle, into the liquid. Finally, apply a gentle stream of air to the film on the ring.

Here is what you actually did. When you saponified the palmitin, you made soap. Then you added it to water to make a solution. Blowing on the ring created a bubble.

Chemical reactions such as saponification may not be familiar to you. Yet chemical reactions are occurring all around you and even in your body at this very moment. As you read the chapters in this unit, you will learn about the interactions of matter that can occur in a test tube, in nature, and even inside yourself!

CHAPTERS

7 Atoms and Bonding

8 Chemical Reactions

9 Solution Chemistry

10 Carbon Chemistry

11 Nuclear Chemistry

Saponification is the chemical process by which soap is made. As light passes through these soap bubbles, a lovely pattern of colors is produced.

Atoms and Bonding 7

CHAPTER SECTIONS

7–1 Chemical Bonding

7–2 Ionic Bonds

7–3 Covalent Bonds

7–4 Metallic Bonds

7–5 Predicting Types of Bonds

CHAPTER OBJECTIVES

After completing this chapter, you will be able to

7–1 Explain chemical bonding on the basis of unfilled energy levels.

7–2 Describe the formation of ions and ionic bonds.

7–2 Relate ionic bonding to the properties of ionic compounds.

7–3 Describe the formation of covalent bonds.

7–3 Define a molecule.

7–3 Draw and interpret electron-dot diagrams.

7–4 Relate metallic bonding to the properties of metals.

7–5 Predict bond types on the basis of the positions of atoms in the periodic table.

Trapped in a tangle of twisted metal and broken glass, the driver of the mangled car cries out in pain. Within moments, the rescue squad arrives and quickly checks the driver's injuries. The emergency medical technician begins treatment by injecting the powerful pain-killing drug morphine into the victim's arm. In seconds, the drug begins to ease the pain.

At the same time, in a nearby home, a parent uses cough medicine to relieve the hacking, choking cough of a sick child. The threat of pneumonia had convinced the child's doctor that prescribing a cough medicine containing codeine was necessary. Soon the child is resting comfortably.

Although morphine and codeine are used for different purposes, they are similar in many ways. Both of these products are made from the same plant. Both are valuable drugs that ease suffering. And both can be dangerous if they are not used properly.

Morphine and codeine are similar for another reason. They are made of the same elements: carbon, oxygen, hydrogen, and nitrogen. These four elements make up many of the chemical substances found in all plants and animals, including you! If so many substances contain the same four elements, what makes them different from each other? The answer lies in the way in which these elements combine to form various substances. In this chapter you will learn how and why elements combine and what important products they form. Turn the page for a look into the world of substances and their structures.

This computer-generated photo of a morphine molecule shows the way in which carbon, oxygen, hydrogen, and nitrogen atoms combine to form this unique compound. You actually are seeing five images of the molecule. Carbon atoms are light blue; oxygen, red; hydrogen, gray; and nitrogen, dark blue.

*To relate electron
arrangement to chemical
bonding*

7–1 Chemical Bonding

Every object, regardless of its size, is made up of an incredible number of tiny particles called atoms. Atoms, the basic building blocks of matter, make up all of the substances in the universe.

If you were to try to list all of these different substances, your list would probably be endless. Scientists know there are hundreds of thousands of different substances in nature. Yet there are only 109 different types of elements! How can just these 109 different elements form so many different substances?

The 109 elements are each made of specific types of atoms. Atoms of elements combine with one another to produce new and different substances called compounds. You are already familiar with several compounds: water, sodium chloride, sugar, carbon dioxide, and ammonia. Compounds contain more than one kind of atom chemically joined together.

The combining of atoms of elements to form new substances is called **chemical bonding.** Chemical bonds are formed in very definite ways. The atoms combine according to certain rules. Such rules are determined by the structure of the atom.

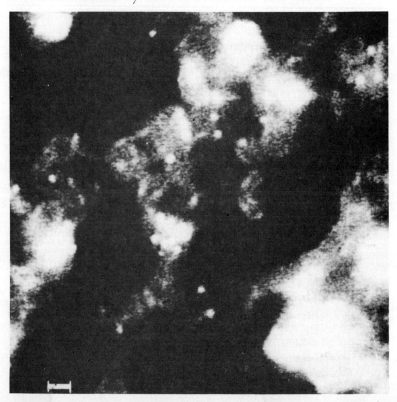

Figure 7–1 *Just how small are atoms? These uranium atoms have been magnified more than five million times by an electron microscope. The small bright spots are single uranium atoms. The larger spots are groups of atoms.*

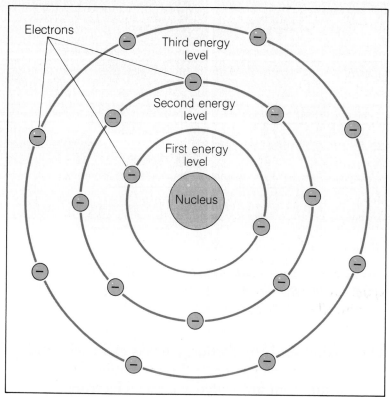

Figure 7–2 *Within the electron cloud, electrons are arranged in energy levels. Each energy level can hold only a certain number of electrons. When an energy level is holding its maximum number of electrons, it is complete. How many electrons can the first energy level hold? The second? The third?*

In the diagram:
- Electrons
- Third energy level
- Second energy level
- First energy level
- Nucleus

Electrons and Energy Levels

The atom contains a positively charged center called the nucleus. Located outside the nucleus are negatively charged particles called electrons. The negative charge of the electrons balances the positive charge of the nucleus. The atom as a whole is neutral. It has no net charge.

The negatively charged electrons of an atom are attracted by the positively charged nucleus of that atom. This electron–nucleus attraction holds the atom together. The electrons, however, are not pulled into the nucleus. They remain in a region outside the nucleus called the electron cloud.

The electron cloud is made up of a number of different energy levels. Electrons within an atom are arranged in energy levels. Each energy level can hold only a certain number of electrons. The first, or innermost, energy level can hold only 2 electrons.

Figure 7–3 *An atom contains a positively charged center called the nucleus. Located outside the nucleus are negatively charged electrons. This atom shows 2 positively charged protons and 2 neutral neutrons in the nucleus. How many electrons are in this atom? What is true about the number of protons and electrons in an atom?*

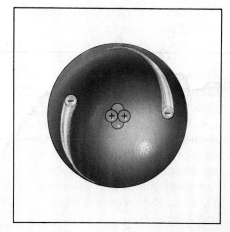

Figure 7–4 *These balloons are filled with helium, a highly unreactive element (left). Neon gas, another unreactive element, is used in neon lights such as these (center). Argon, shown here as a laser made visible through smoke, is also highly unreactive (right). What is it about their electron configurations that makes these elements unreactive?*

The second and third energy levels can each hold 8 electrons. The electrons in the outermost energy level of an atom are called **valence electrons.**

When the outermost energy level of an atom contains the maximum number of electrons, the level is full, or complete. Atoms that have filled outermost energy levels are very stable, or unreactive. Such atoms usually do not combine with other atoms to form compounds. They do not form chemical bonds.

The atoms of elements such as helium, neon, and argon do not form chemical bonds. If you look at the periodic table on pages 118–119, you will see that these atoms are all in Family VIIIA. This family contains all the atoms that have filled outermost energy levels. Remember that if the first energy level is also the outermost, it needs only 2 electrons to make it complete. Which element in Family VIIIA has only 2 valence electrons?

Electrons and Bonding

The electron arrangement of the outermost energy level of an atom determines whether or not the atom will form chemical bonds. Atoms of elements of Family VIIIA have complete outermost energy levels. These atoms generally do not form chemical bonds.

Atoms of elements other than those of the helium family (VIIIA) do not have filled outermost energy levels. Their outermost energy level lacks one or more electrons to be complete. Some of these atoms tend to gain electrons in order to fill the outermost energy level. Fluorine, which has 7 valence electrons, gains 1 electron to fill its outer energy level. Other atoms tend to lose their valence electrons and are left with only filled energy levels. For what was the filled next-to-the-outermost energy level is now the outermost energy level. Sodium, which has 1 valence electron, loses 1 electron.

In order to achieve stability, an atom will either gain or lose electrons. In other words, an atom will bond with another atom if the bonding gives both atoms complete outermost energy levels. In the next section, you will learn how bonding takes place.

SECTION REVIEW

1. What is chemical bonding?
2. Where are the electrons that are involved in bonding located in an atom?
3. What is the maximum number of electrons that can be held in the first energy level of an atom? In the second level? In the third level?
4. Explain why elements such as krypton (Kr) and xenon (Xe) do not readily react to form compounds.

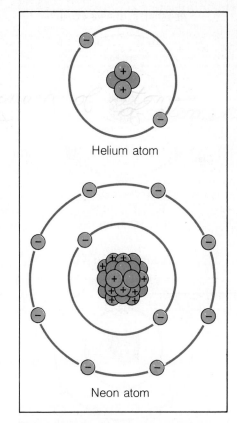

Figure 7–5 *The outermost energy level of a helium atom contains the maximum number of electrons—2. In a neon atom, the outermost energy level is the second energy level. It contains the maximum 8 electrons. What chemical property do these elements share?*

7–2 Ionic Bonds

Section Objective

To describe an ionic bond

A complete outermost energy level can be achieved by the transfer of electrons from one atom to another. Bonding that involves a transfer of electrons is called **ionic bonding.** Ionic bonding, or electron-transfer bonding, gets its name from the word **ion,** which means "charged particle." Ions are formed when ionic bonding occurs.

Because ionic bonding involves the transfer of electrons, one atom gains electrons and the other atom loses electrons. Within each atom the negative and positive charges no longer balance. The atom that has gained electrons has gained a negative

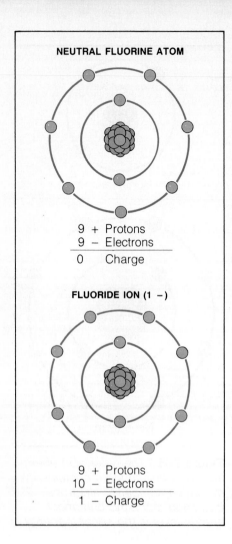

NEUTRAL FLUORINE ATOM

9 + Protons
9 − Electrons
0   Charge

FLUORIDE ION (1 −)

9 + Protons
10 − Electrons
1 − Charge

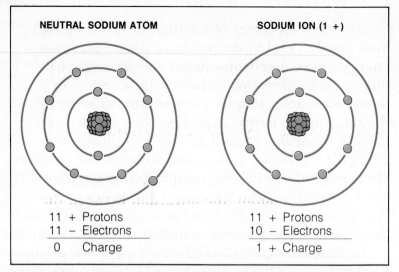

NEUTRAL SODIUM ATOM   **SODIUM ION (1 +)**

11 + Protons   11 + Protons
11 − Electrons   10 − Electrons
0   Charge   1 + Charge

Figure 7–6 *The formation of a negative fluoride ion involves the gain of an electron by a fluorine atom. How many valence electrons does a fluorine atom have? The formation of a positive sodium ion involves the loss of an electron by a sodium atom. What is the symbol for a fluoride ion? A sodium ion?*

charge. It is a negative ion. For example, fluorine (F) has 7 valence electrons. To complete its outermost energy level, the fluorine atom gains 1 electron. In gaining 1 negatively charged electron, the fluorine atom becomes a negative ion. The symbol for the fluoride ion is F^-.

The sodium atom (Na) has 1 valence electron. When a sodium atom loses this valence electron, it is left with an outermost energy level containing 8 electrons. In losing 1 negatively charged electron, the sodium atom becomes a positive ion. The symbol for the sodium ion is Na^+.

In nature, it is a general rule that opposites attract. Since the two ions Na^+ and F^- have opposite charges, they attract each other. The strong attraction between oppositely charged ions that have been

Figure 7–7 *The general rule that opposites attract is responsible for the formation of the ionic bond between a positive sodium ion and a negative chloride ion. Notice the transfer of an electron during the ionic bonding. What is the formula for the resulting compound?*

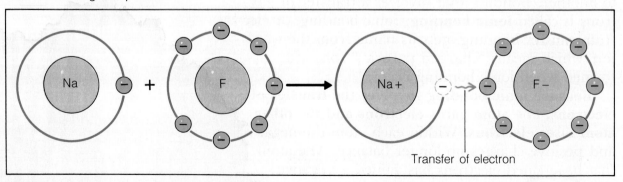

Transfer of electron

formed by the transfer of electrons holds the ions together in an ionic bond. The formation of the ionic bond results in the formation of the compound sodium fluoride, NaF.

Ionization Energy and Electron Affinity

In order for the outermost electron to be removed from an atom, the attraction between the negatively charged electron and the positively charged nucleus must be overcome. The process of removing an electron and forming ions is called **ionization.** Energy is needed for ionization. This energy is called **ionization energy.**

The ionization energy for atoms that have few valence electrons is low. Only a small amount of energy is needed to remove electrons from the outermost energy level. As a result, these atoms tend to lose electrons easily and to become positive ions. What elements have low ionization energies?

The ionization energy for atoms with many valence electrons is very high. These atoms do not lose electrons easily. As a matter of fact, these atoms usually gain electrons. The tendency of an atom to attract electrons is called **electron affinity.** Atoms such as fluorine are said to have a high electron affinity because they attract electrons very easily. What other atoms have a high electron affinity?

Figure 7–8 *During ionization, an electron is removed from an atom and an ion forms. Energy is absorbed during ionization. Energy is released when an atom gains an electron and forms an ion. What is the tendency of an atom to gain electrons called?*

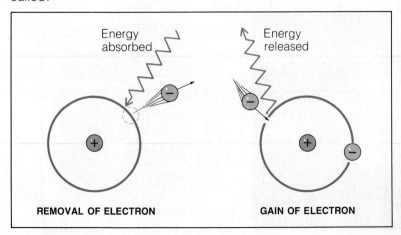

REMOVAL OF ELECTRON   GAIN OF ELECTRON

1. Make a small sliding loop in the end of a 10-cm length of thin plastic fishing line. Attach the loop to a small crystal of sea salt (NaCl).

2. In a beaker containing 200 mL of very hot water, dissolve by stirring as much sea salt as the water will hold.

3. Suspend the fishing line containing the loop and crystal in the beaker. Tie the other end of the line to a pencil. Lay the pencil across the top of the beaker to support the line. The crystal should be suspended about halfway down in the liquid.

4. Allow the liquid to cool slowly. Observe the growing crystals each day for 3 days. Draw what you see. Explain your observations in terms of ionic bonding.

Arrangement of Ions in Ionic Compounds

Ions of opposite charge strongly attract each other. Ions of like charge strongly repel each other. As a result, the ions in an ionic compound are arranged in a specific way. Positive ions tend to be near negative ions and farther from other positive ions.

The placement of ions in an ionic compound results in a regular, repeating arrangement called a **crystal lattice.** A crystal lattice is made up of huge numbers of ions grouped together in a regular, repeating pattern. A crystal lattice gives the compound great stability and accounts for certain physical properties. For example, ionic solids tend to have high melting points because a great deal of energy is needed to overcome the strong ion attractions within the lattice. Figure 7–9 shows the crystal lattice structure of sodium chloride.

Ionic compounds are made up of nearly endless arrays of ions. A chemical formula shows the *ratios* of ions present in the crystal lattice. For example, sodium chloride has the formula NaCl because it has one Na^+ for each Cl^- ion. What is the ratio of potassium ions to bromide ions in the ionic compound KBr?

Each ionic compound has a characteristic crystal lattice arrangement. This lattice arrangement gives a

Figure 7–9 *These crystals of sodium chloride have a characteristic crystal lattice, which gives them their shape (left). In the drawing of the crystal, you can see the arrangement of the sodium and chloride ions (right). What is the common name for this crystal?*

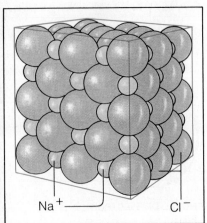

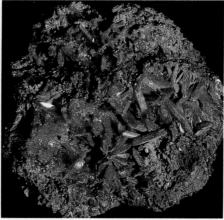

Figure 7–10 *Ionic crystals often have beautiful and unusual shapes. Here you see six-sided snowflake crystals surrounded by frost crystals (left), crystals of the mineral crocoite (center), and crystals of the mineral aragonite (right).*

particular shape to the crystals of the compound. For example, sodium chloride forms cubic crystals. Other ionic compounds form crystals of other shapes. Figure 7–10 shows some of the unusual shapes that result from ionic bonding.

SECTION REVIEW

1. What happens to electrons during ionic bonding?
2. What is an ion?
3. What is ionization energy? Electron affinity?
4. What is a crystal lattice? What holds a crystal lattice together?
5. What happens when an atom of potassium (K) bonds with an atom of iodine (I)?

7–3 Covalent Bonds

Section Objective

To describe a covalent bond

Bonding in which electrons are shared rather than transferred is called **covalent bonding.** Covalent bonding usually occurs between atoms that have high ionization energies and high electron affinities. In other words, neither atom loses electrons easily, but both atoms attract electrons.

By sharing electrons, each atom fills up its outermost energy level. So the shared electrons are in the outermost energy level of both atoms at the same time.

167

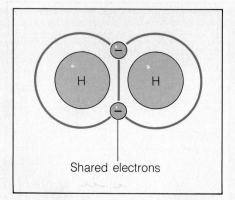

Shared electrons

Figure 7–11 *The covalent bond between 2 atoms of hydrogen results in a molecule of hydrogen. In a covalent bond, the electrons are shared. How many valence electrons does each hydrogen atom have?*

Nature of the Covalent Bond

In covalent bonding, the positively charged nucleus of each atom simultaneously attracts the negatively charged electrons that are being shared. The electrons spend most of their time between the atoms. The attraction between the nucleus and shared electrons holds the atoms together.

The simplest kind of covalent bond is formed between two hydrogen atoms. Each hydrogen atom has 1 valence electron. By sharing their valence electrons, both hydrogen atoms fill their outermost energy level. Remember that the outermost energy level of a hydrogen atom is complete with 2 electrons. The two atoms are now joined in a covalent bond. See Figure 7–11.

The electron-sharing that takes place in a covalent bond can be represented by an **electron-dot diagram.** In such a diagram, the chemical symbol of an element represents the nucleus and inner energy levels of the atom. Dots surrounding the symbol represent valence electrons.

A hydrogen atom has only 1 valence electron. An electron-dot diagram of a hydrogen atom would look like this:

H·

The covalent bond between 2 hydrogen atoms shown in Figure 7–11 can be represented in an electron-dot diagram like this:

H:H

The two hydrogen atoms are sharing a pair of electrons. Each hydrogen atom achieves a complete outermost energy level. Although different colors are used here to represent different hydrogen atoms, there is really no difference between the atoms or the electrons. Color is used only to show that each hydrogen atom contributes 1 electron to the pair being shared.

Chlorine has 7 valence electrons. An electron-dot diagram of a chlorine atom looks like this:

:C̈l·

The chlorine atom needs one more electron to complete its outermost energy level. If it bonds with another chlorine atom, the two atoms could share a pair of electrons. The electron-dot diagram for this covalent bond would look like this:

$$:\!\ddot{\text{C}}\text{l}\!:\!\ddot{\text{C}}\text{l}\!:$$

Covalent bonding often takes place between atoms of the same element. In addition to hydrogen and chlorine, the elements oxygen, fluorine, bromine, iodine, and nitrogen bond in this way. These elements are called **diatomic elements.** When found in nature, diatomic elements always exist as two atoms covalently bonded.

The chlorine atom, with its 7 valence electrons, can also bond covalently with an unlike atom. For example, a hydrogen atom can combine with a chlorine atom to form the compound hydrogen chloride. See Figure 7–13. The electron-dot diagram for this covalent bond is

$$\text{H}\!:\!\ddot{\text{C}}\text{l}\!:$$

You can see from this electron-dot diagram that by sharing electrons each atom completes its outermost energy level.

The following electron-dot diagrams show the compounds water, H_2O, and ammonia, NH_3.

$$\begin{array}{cc} \text{H} & \text{H}\\ :\!\ddot{\text{O}}\!:\text{H} & \text{H}\!:\!\ddot{\text{N}}\!:\\ & \text{H} \end{array}$$

In each compound, both kinds of atoms have completed their outermost energy levels.

Formation of Molecules

In a covalent bond, a relatively small number of atoms are involved in the sharing of electrons. The combination of atoms that results forms a separate unit rather than the large crystal lattices characteristic of ionic compounds.

The combination of atoms formed by a covalent bond is called a **molecule.** A molecule is the smallest particle of a covalently bonded substance that has all

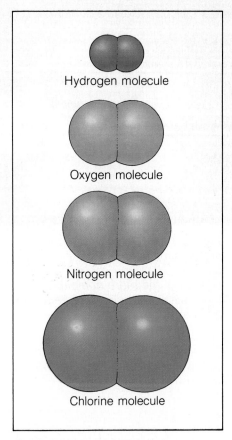

Figure 7–12 *Diatomic elements include hydrogen, oxygen, nitrogen, and chlorine. How many valence electrons does an atom of each element have?*

Figure 7–13 *By sharing their valence electrons, hydrogen and chlorine form a molecule of the compound hydrogen chloride. What kind of bond is this?*

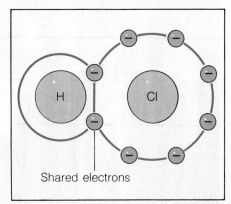

Shared electrons

169

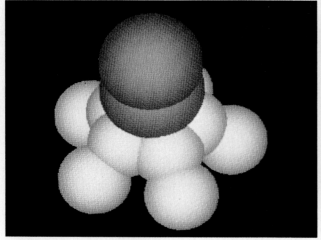

Figure 7–14 *Not all molecules are as simple as hydrogen chloride. Here you see computer images of the more complex molecules of a body fluid (left) and a virus (right).*

the properties of that substance. Molecules are represented by chemical formulas. A chemical formula contains the symbol of each element involved in the bond and subscripts that show the number of atoms of each element. When there is only 1 atom of an element, the subscript 1 is not written. It is understood to be 1. Thus, a hydrogen chloride molecule has the formula HCl. What would be the formula for a molecule that has 1 carbon (C) atom and 4 chlorine (Cl) atoms?

Covalently bonded solids tend to have low melting points. Although there are attractions between the molecules of the solid, the attractions are relatively weak. So only a small amount of energy is needed to separate the molecules from one another.

Some covalent substances, however, do not have low melting points. Molecules of these substances are very large because the atoms involved continue to bond to one another. These substances are called **network solids.** Carbon in the form of graphite and silicon dioxide are examples of network solids.

Figure 7–15 *Diamond, shown here in its natural state, is a network solid (left). So too is an extremely strong glue (right). Network solids contain bonds that are difficult to break. What is true about the melting point of most network solids?*

Certain glues also form networks of atoms whose bonds are difficult to break. This accounts for the holding properties of such glues.

Polyatomic Ions

Certain ions are made up of covalently bonded atoms that tend to stay together as if they were a single atom. A group of covalently bonded atoms that acts like a single atom when combining with other atoms is called a **polyatomic ion.** Although the bonds within the polyatomic ion are covalent, the polyatomic ion usually forms ionic bonds with other atoms.

The ammonium ion, NH_4^+, is a polyatomic ion. The bonds between nitrogen and hydrogen atoms are covalent.

$$\begin{matrix} & H & \\ & \ddot{\cdot} & \\ H\!:\!\!\underset{\cdot\cdot}{N}\!:\!H & & + \\ & H & \end{matrix}$$

When the ammonium ion combines with the chloride ion, it forms an ionic bond.

$$\left[\begin{matrix} & H & \\ & \ddot{\cdot} & \\ H\!:\!\!\underset{\cdot\cdot}{N}\!:\!H \\ & H & \end{matrix}\right]^+ \quad Cl^-$$

SECTION REVIEW

1. What is a covalent bond?
2. What is a molecule?
3. What is a polyatomic ion?
4. What elements and how many atoms of each are represented in the following chemical formulas: Na_2CO_3, $Ca(OH)_2$, $Mg(C_2H_3O_2)_2$?

POLYATOMIC IONS

Name	Formula
ammonium	NH_4^{1+}
acetate	$C_2H_3O_2^{1-}$
chlorate	ClO_3^{1-}
hydrogen carbonate	HCO_3^{1-}
hydroxide	OH^{1-}
nitrate	NO_3^{1-}
nitrite	NO_2^{1-}
carbonate	CO_3^{2-}
sulfate	SO_4^{2-}
sulfite	SO_3^{2-}
phosphate	PO_4^{3-}

Figure 7–16 *The name and formula of some common polyatomic ions are shown here. Which polyatomic ion has a positive charge?*

Figure 7–17 *A polyatomic ion is a group of covalently bonded atoms that act like a single atom when combining with other atoms.*

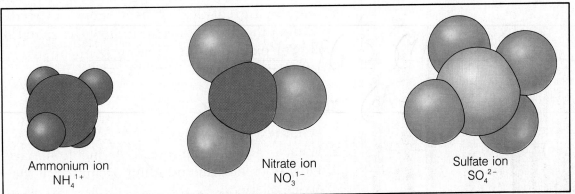

Ammonium ion
NH_4^{1+}

Nitrate ion
NO_3^{1-}

Sulfate ion
SO_4^{2-}

7–4 Metallic Bonds

Iron, copper, silver, and gold are familiar examples of metals. Metals are elements that tend to give up electrons easily. In metallic solids, however, only atoms of the metals are present. There are no other atoms to accept the electrons the metals give up. How, then, do the atoms of metals bond?

The atoms of metals form **metallic bonds.** In a metallic bond, the outer electrons of the atoms form a common electron cloud. This common distribution of electrons occurs throughout a metallic crystal. In a sense, the electrons become the property of all the atoms. These electrons are often described as a "sea of electrons." **The positive nuclei of atoms of metals are surrounded by free-moving, or mobile, electrons that are all attracted by the nuclei at the same time.**

The sea of mobile electrons in a metallic crystal accounts for many of the properties of metals. Metals are malleable, which means they can be hammered into thin sheets without breaking. Metals are also ductile—they can be drawn into thin wire. The flexibility of metals results from the fact that the metal ions can slide by each other and the electrons are free to flow. Yet the attractions between the ions and the electrons hold the metal together even when it is being hammered or drawn into wire.

The ability of the electrons to flow freely also accounts for the high electric conductivity of metals. Electricity flows easily through metals. What metals are good conductors of electricity?

Metallic bonding also accounts for the high melting point of most metals. The attractions between the ions and the free-moving electrons are fairly strong. So a great deal of heat energy is needed to overcome the attractions and allow the metal to melt. For example, the melting point of silver is 961.9°C and of gold, 1064.4°C.

Figure 7–18 *The metal platinum has a very high melting point, which makes it extremely useful in heat-resistant containers. What type of bond holds platinum atoms together?*

Figure 7–19 *In a metallic bond, the outer electrons of the metal atoms form a "sea of mobile electrons." What properties of metals does a metallic bond explain?*

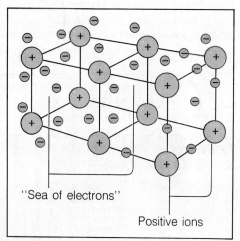

"Sea of electrons"

Positive ions

SECTION REVIEW

1. What is a metallic bond?
2. What is a malleable metal? A ductile metal?
3. How does metallic bonding account for the properties of metals?

7-5 Predicting Types of Bonds

Section Objective

To predict bond type based on oxidation number

The placement in the periodic table of the elements involved in bonding often indicates whether the bond will be ionic, covalent, or metallic. Look at the periodic table on pages 118–119. Elements at the left and in the center of the periodic table are metals. These elements have metallic bonds.

Compounds formed between elements that lose electrons easily and those that gain electrons easily will have ionic bonds. You know that elements at the left and in the center of the periodic table tend to lose valence electrons easily. These elements are metals. Elements at the right tend to gain electrons readily. These elements are nonmetals. A compound formed between a metal and a nonmetal will thus have ionic bonds.

Compounds formed between elements that have similar tendencies to gain electrons will have covalent bonds. Bonds between nonmetals, which are at

CAREER   *Environmental Analyst*

HELP WANTED: ENVIRONMENTAL ANALYST to conduct surveys of areas affected by known and unknown pollutants. Must be familiar with chemical mixtures and compounds. Advanced degree in environmental science required.

The campers pile into a van, talking excitedly about the mountain lake they will reach by evening. Finally, the van stops and the happy campers tumble out. But everyone's smile disappears at the sight and smell of dead fish on the lake's rocky shore. Many dead trees stand in the once-lush forest.

These types of destruction may be caused by pollution. Towns with problems such as these may hire an **environmental analyst** to find what is affecting the area. Environmental analysts use chemical testing of air, water, and soil to discover the causes of environmental problems.

Pollutants from industry, waste disposal, agricultural runoff, or other sources may combine chemically with natural elements. The result may be a combination of chemicals that are harmful or deadly to the environment.

After analyzing the situation, the analyst may suggest ways to control the pollution problems. Some analysts are qualified to run cleanup operations in polluted areas.

If you would like to learn more about a career as an environmental analyst, contact the Environmental Protection Agency, Public Information Center, East Tower Basement, Mail Code PM-211B, 401 M Street SW, Washington, DC 20460.

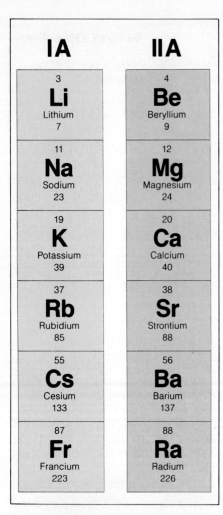

IA	IIA
3 **Li** Lithium 7	4 **Be** Beryllium 9
11 **Na** Sodium 23	12 **Mg** Magnesium 24
19 **K** Potassium 39	20 **Ca** Calcium 40
37 **Rb** Rubidium 85	38 **Sr** Strontium 88
55 **Cs** Cesium 133	56 **Ba** Barium 137
87 **Fr** Francium 223	88 **Ra** Radium 226

Figure 7–20 *The elements in Family IA and IIA are active metals. What is the oxidation number of atoms of Family IA elements? Of atoms of Family IIA elements?*

the right of the periodic table, will be covalent. What type of bonding would you expect between magnesium (Mg) and fluorine (F)? Between oxygen (O) and chlorine (Cl)? In a sample of zinc (Zn)?

Combining Capacity of Atoms

The number of electrons in the outermost energy level of an atom, or the valence electrons, determines how an atom will combine with other atoms. If you know the number of valence electrons in an atom, you can calculate the number of electrons that atom needs to gain, lose, or share in forming a compound. The number of electrons an atom gains, loses, or shares when it forms chemical bonds is called its **oxidation number.** The oxidation number of an atom describes its combining capacity.

An atom of sodium has 1 valence electron. It loses this electron when it combines with another atom. In so doing, it forms an ion with a 1+ charge, Na^+. The oxidation number of sodium is 1+. A magnesium atom has 2 valence electrons, which it will lose when it forms a chemical bond. The magnesium ion is Mg^{2+}. The oxidation number of magnesium is 2+.

An atom of chlorine has 7 valence electrons. It will gain 1 electron when it bonds with another atom. The ion formed will have a 1− charge, Cl^-.

Figure 7–21 *This is the first photograph ever taken of atoms and their bonds. The bright round objects are single atoms. The fuzzy areas between atoms represent bonds.*

The oxidation number of chlorine is 1−. Oxygen has 6 valence electrons. How many electrons will it gain? What is its oxidation number?

Some elements have more than one oxidation number. Copper can have oxidation numbers of 1+ or 2+. Iron can have oxidation numbers of 2+ or 3+. Carbon, which has 4 valence electrons, can either lose or gain 4 electrons. Carbon can have oxidation numbers of 4+ or 4−, depending on the other atoms with which it bonds. You can determine the oxidation number of any atom by knowing the number of electrons in its outermost energy level.

Using Oxidation Numbers

You can use the oxidation numbers of atoms to predict how atoms will combine and what the formula for the resulting compound will be. In order to do this, you must follow one important rule: *The sum of the oxidation numbers of the atoms in a compound must be zero.*

Sodium has an oxidation number of 1+. Chlorine has an oxidation number of 1−. One atom of sodium will bond with 1 atom of chlorine to form NaCl. Magnesium has an oxidation number of 2+. When magnesium bonds with chlorine, 1 atom of magnesium must combine with 2 atoms of chlorine, since each chlorine atom has an oxidation number of 1−. In other words, 2 atoms of chlorine are needed to gain the electrons lost by 1 atom of magnesium. The compound formed, magnesium chloride, contains 2 atoms of chlorine for each atom of magnesium. Its formula is $MgCl_2$. What would be the formula for calcium bromide? For sodium oxide? Remember the rule of oxidation numbers!

SECTION REVIEW

1. How can the periodic table be used to predict bond types?
2. What is an oxidation number?
3. How can the oxidation number of an atom be determined?
4. What rule of oxidation numbers must be followed in writing chemical formulas?
5. Predict the type of bond for each combination: Ca–Br, C–Cl, Ag–Ag, K–OH, SO_4^{2-}.

Figure 7–22 *The elements in Family VIIA are active nonmetals. What is the oxidation number of atoms of these elements? What type of bonds do these elements form when they combine with active metals?*

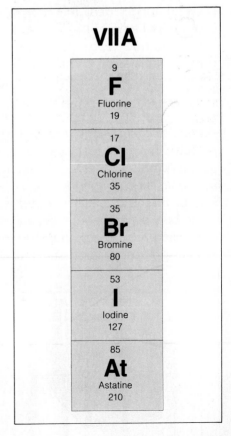

VIIA
9 **F** Fluorine 19
17 **Cl** Chlorine 35
35 **Br** Bromine 80
53 **I** Iodine 127
85 **At** Astatine 210

7 LABORATORY INVESTIGATION

Properties of Ionic and Covalent Compounds

Problem

Do covalent compounds have different properties from ionic compounds?

Materials *(per group)*

salt	glass-marking pencil	vegetable oil
sugar	light bulb	distilled water (100 mL)
4 medium-sized test tubes	light bulb socket	timer
test tube tongs	3 connecting wires	safety goggles
Bunsen burner	2 100-mL beakers	
dry-cell battery	stirring rod	

Procedure

1. Place a small sample of salt in a test tube. Label the test tube. Place an equal amount of sugar in another test tube. Label that test tube.
2. Using tongs, heat the test tube of salt over the flame of the Bunsen burner. Determine how long it takes for the salt to melt. Immediately stop heating when melting begins. Record the time.
3. Repeat step 2 using the sugar.
4. Half fill a test tube with vegetable oil. Place a small sample of salt in the test tube. Shake the test tube gently for about 10 seconds. Observe the results.
5. Repeat step 4 using sugar.
6. Pour 50 mL of distilled water into a 100-mL beaker. Add some salt and stir until it is dissolved. To another 100-mL beaker add some sugar and stir until dissolved.

7. Using the beaker of salt water, set up a circuit as shown. Observe the results. Repeat the procedure using the beaker of sugar water.

Observations

1. Does the salt or the sugar take a longer time to melt?
2. Does the salt dissolve in the vegetable oil? Does the sugar?
3. Which compound is a better conductor of electricity? Explain your answer.

Conclusions

1. Which substance do you think has a higher melting point? Explain.
2. Vegetable oil is a covalent compound. If "like dissolves in like," predict the type of bonding in salt. In sugar.
3. How do the properties of each type of compound relate to their bonding?

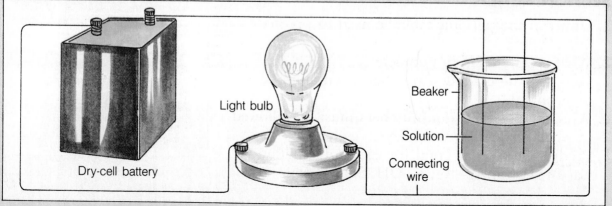

Light bulb

Beaker

Solution

Dry-cell battery

Connecting wire

CHAPTER REVIEW

SUMMARY

7-1 Chemical Bonding

❏ Chemical bonding is the combining of elements to form new substances.

❏ The first energy level can hold a maximum of 2 electrons. The second and third energy levels can each hold 8 electrons.

❏ Electrons in the outermost energy level are called valence electrons.

❏ Bonding involves the incomplete outermost energy level of an atom.

7-2 Ionic Bonds

❏ Ionic bonding involves a transfer of electrons and a formation of ions. An ion is a charged particle.

❏ Ionization energy is the amount of energy needed to remove an electron from a neutral atom. Electron affinity is the tendency of an atom to attract electrons.

7-3 Covalent Bonds

❏ Covalent bonding involves a sharing of electrons. The shared electrons are simultaneously attracted by the nuclei of the atoms involved in the bond.

❏ Diatomic elements always exist in nature as two atoms covalently bonded.

❏ A molecule is the smallest unit of a covalently bonded substance that has all the properties of that substance.

❏ Network solids are substances whose molecules are very large because the atoms in the substance continue to bond to one another.

❏ A polyatomic ion is a group of covalently bonded atoms that acts like a single atom when combining with other atoms.

7-4 Metallic Bonds

❏ Metals are elements that tend to give up electrons easily.

❏ The basis of metallic bonding is the sea of mobile electrons that surrounds the nuclei and is simultaneously attracted by them.

❏ Metals demonstrate high electric conductivity because of the sea of mobile electrons.

7-5 Predicting Types of Bonds

❏ The position of elements in the periodic table indicates whether the bonds they form will be ionic, covalent, or metallic.

❏ The oxidation number, or combining capacity, of an atom refers to the number of electrons the atom gains, loses, or shares when it forms chemical bonds.

❏ The oxidation number of any atom can be determined by knowing the number of electrons in its outermost level.

❏ In a chemical formula, the sum of the oxidation numbers of the atoms in a compound must be zero.

VOCABULARY

Define each term in a complete sentence.

chemical bonding	ductile	ionization	oxidation number
covalent bonding	electron affinity	ionization energy	polyatomic ion
crystal lattice	electron-dot diagram	malleable	valence electron
diatomic element	ion	metallic bond	
	ionic bonding	molecule	
		network solid	

CONTENT REVIEW: MULTIPLE CHOICE

On a separate sheet of paper, write the letter of the answer that best completes each statement.

1. Chemical bonding is the combining of elements to form new
   a. atoms.   b. energy levels.   c. substances.   d. electrons.
2. The center of an atom is called the
   a. electron.   b. energy level.   c. octet.   d. nucleus.
3. The maximum number of electrons in the second energy level is
   a. 1.   b. 2.   c. 8.   d. 18.
4. Bonding that involves a transfer of electrons is called
   a. metallic.   b. covalent.   c. ionic.   d. network.
5. Atoms that readily lose electrons have
   a. low ionization energy and low electron affinity.
   b. high ionization energy and low electron affinity.
   c. low ionization energy and high electron affinity.
   d. high ionization energy and high electron affinity.
6. Bonding that involves sharing of electrons within a molecule is called
   a. metallic bonding.   b. covalent bonding.
   c. ionic bonding.   d. crystal bonding.
7. The combination of atoms formed by covalent bonds is called a (an)
   a. element.   b. ion.   c. molecule.   d. crystal.
8. An example of a polyatomic ion is
   a. SO_4^{2-}.   b. Ca^{2-}.   c. NaCl.   d. O_2.
9. A sea of electrons is the basis of bonding in
   a. metals.   b. nonmetals.
   c. ionic substances.   d. covalent substances.
10. Bonding between atoms on the left and right sides of the periodic table tends to be
   a. covalent.   b. ionic.   c. metallic.   d. impossible.

CONTENT REVIEW: COMPLETION

On a separate sheet of paper, write the word or words that best complete each statement.

1. Electrons in the outermost energy level are called _____.
2. A charged particle is a (an) _____.
3. The tendency of an atom to attract electrons is called _____.
4. A regular, repeating arrangement of ions is called a (an) _____.
5. Bonding in which electrons are shared is called _____.
6. Elements that exist as two covalently bonded atoms are _____.
7. A group of covalently bonded atoms that acts like a single atom when combining is called a (an) _____.
8. Metals that can be hammered into thin sheets are said to be _____.
9. Compounds formed between metals and nonmetals will have _____ bonds.
10. The combining capacity of an atom is described by its _____.

178

CONTENT REVIEW: TRUE OR FALSE

Determine whether each statement is true or false. Then on a separate sheet of paper, write "true" if it is true. If it is false, change the underlined word or words to make the statement true.

1. Helium is an example of an element that does not tend to form chemical bonds.
2. An atom that has lost an electron is negatively charged.
3. Ionization energy is needed for an atom to gain an electron.
4. Bonding in which electrons are transferred is called covalent bonding.
5. Bromine is a diatomic element.
6. A covalent bond forms a crystal.
7. In a metallic bond, the outer electrons of the atoms form a common electron cloud.
8. A substance that can be drawn into thin wire is said to be ductile.
9. Compounds formed between a metal and a nonmetal will have ionic bonds.
10. It is impossible for an element to have more than one oxidation number.

CONCEPT REVIEW: SKILL BUILDING

Use the skills you have developed in the chapter to complete each activity.

1. **Making predictions** Predict the type of bond formed by each pair of atoms. Explain your answers. a. Mg and Cl b. S and Br c. Na and Na d. I and I e. Li and I
2. **Identifying patterns** Use the periodic table to predict the ion that each atom will form when bonding. a. sulfur (S) b. rubidium (Rb) c. argon (Ar) d. astatine (At) e. sodium (Na) f. aluminum (Al)
3. **Making diagrams** Draw the electron configuration for a Period 2 atom from each of the eight families of the periodic table.
4. **Drawing a conclusion** Draw an electron-dot diagram for the following molecules and explain why both molecules are stable.
   a. F_2 b. NF_3
5. **Making predictions** Use the periodic table to predict the formulas for the compounds formed by each of the following pairs of atoms. a. K and S b. Li and F c. Ba and S d. Mg and N
6. **Applying concepts** Predict the formulas for compounds formed by each of the following pairs of polyatomic ions.
   a. NH_4^+ and NO_3^-
   b. NH_4^+ and SO_4^{2-}
   c. NH_4^+ and OH^-

CONCEPT REVIEW: ESSAY

Discuss each of the following in a brief paragraph.

1. a. What is the difference between ionization energy and electron affinity?
   b. Why do atoms of high electron affinity tend to form ionic compounds with atoms of low ionization energy?
2. Define the following structures that result from chemical bonds. Give one physical property of each. a. crystal lattice b. network solid c. covalently bonded solid
3. List the three types of chemical bonds and explain the differences among them.
4. Explain why the elements of Family VIIIA do not tend to form chemical bonds.
5. What are four properties of metals? How does the bonding in metals account for these properties?
6. How can you use the oxidation number of an atom to predict how it will bond?

Chemical Reactions 8

CHAPTER SECTIONS

8–1 Nature of Chemical Reactions

8–2 Chemical Equations

8–3 Types of Chemical Reactions

8–4 Energy of Chemical Reactions

8–5 Rates of Chemical Reactions

CHAPTER OBJECTIVES

After completing this chapter, you will be able to

8–1 Describe the characteristics of chemical reactions.

8–1 Explain the basis of chemical reactions.

8–2 Interpret, write, and balance chemical equations.

8–3 Classify types of chemical reactions.

8–4 Describe the role of energy in exothermic and endothermic reactions.

8–4 Relate activation energy to chemical reactions.

8–5 Apply the collision theory to factors that affect reaction rate.

Fireworks flash brilliantly in the night sky over the dark waters of the harbor. It is Independence Day, July 4, 1986. It is a day of celebration in honor of a very special lady. She towers above the waters, the torch in her upraised hand reaching high into the sky. She is a symbol of freedom, justice, and the brotherhood of people of all nations. Her name is Liberty.

She has stood there for a century. But the passage of time had not been very kind to her. The bronze of her outer structure, once bright and gleaming, had turned a dull gray-green. And the structure that supports her had begun to weaken. What caused these changes? The answer has to do with the chemistry of atoms.

This chemistry, which damaged the Statue of Liberty, also made possible the glorious restoration of this Lady in the Harbor. And the colorful fireworks lighting up the sky in honor of her birthday are also products of the chemistry of atoms.

Chemical changes take place at all times, not just on the Fourth of July. And they take place everywhere, not just in New York Harbor. In this chapter, you will learn about the nature of these chemical changes, many of which shape the world around you.

On July 4, 1986, fireworks lit up the sky in New York Harbor as the nation celebrated the one-hundredth birthday of the Statue of Liberty—symbol of freedom and brotherhood for people of all nations.

8-1 Nature of Chemical Reactions

Section Objective

To describe the characteristics of chemical reactions

Here's a chemical puzzle for you. What do the rusting of iron, the burning of gasoline, and the cooking of sugar have in common? They are all examples of **chemical reactions.** A chemical reaction is a process in which the physical and chemical properties of the original substances change as new substances with different physical and chemical properties are formed. Can you name some other examples of chemical reactions?

Characteristics of Chemical Reactions

In any chemical reaction, a new substance is formed. **When a chemical reaction takes place, there is always a change in the properties and in the energy of the substances involved in the chemical reaction.** Both the physical and chemical properties of the substances are changed.

Figure 8–1 *Rusting is a chemical reaction in which iron combines with oxygen to form the compound iron oxide (left). Rusting takes place very slowly, and only a very small amount of heat energy is given off. Fighting brush fires involves a chemical reaction in which noncombustible products are formed (right). This chemical reaction occurs rapidly. What two things always change in a chemical reaction?*

For example, inside a flashbulb is a small coil of shiny gray metal. This metal is magnesium. The bulb is also filled with the invisible gas oxygen. When the flashbulb is set off, the magnesium combines with the oxygen in a chemical reaction. Energy is released in the form of light, and a fine white powder is produced. You can see this powder on the inside of the bulb. The powder is magnesium oxide, a compound with physical and chemical properties very different from the elements magnesium and oxygen. So a chemical reaction has occurred.

In any chemical reaction, there are always two kinds of substances: the substances that are present before the change and the substances that are formed by the change. A substance that enters into a chemical reaction is called a **reactant** (ree-AK-tehnt). A substance that is produced by a chemical reaction is called a **product.** So a general description of a chemical reaction could be stated as reactants changing into products. In the example of the flashbulb, what are the reactants? The product?

In addition to changes in properties, chemical reactions always involve a change in energy. Energy is either absorbed or released during a chemical reaction. For example, heat energy is absorbed when sugar changes into caramel. When gasoline burns, heat energy is released. Later in this chapter you

Figure 8–2 *Inside this flashbulb is a thin coil of magnesium metal and the invisible gas oxygen (top). When the flashbulb is set off, a chemical reaction takes place in which the magnesium combines with oxygen to form magnesium oxide (bottom). How can you tell a chemical reaction has occurred?*

Figure 8–3 *The ability of substances to burn fueled the Voyager 1 spacecraft on its mission to the outer planets (right). The ability of substances not to burn helped this firefighter extinguish a bog fire (left). What type of property is the ability to burn?*

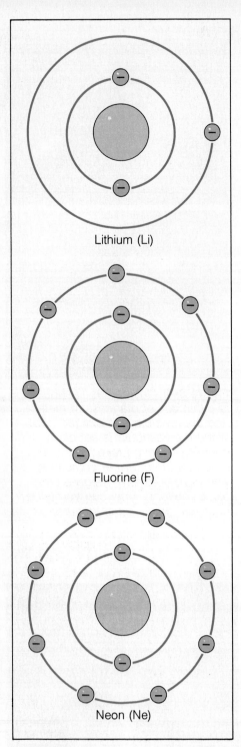

Figure 8–4 *The arrangement of electrons in an atom determines the atom's ability to undergo chemical reactions. How many valence electrons does each atom shown here have? Which atom is likely to be unreactive?*

Lithium (Li)

Fluorine (F)

Neon (Ne)

will learn more about energy changes that accompany chemical reactions.

Capacity to React

In order for a chemical reaction to occur, the reactants must have the ability to combine with other substances to form products. What accounts for the ability of different substances to undergo certain chemical reactions? In order to answer this question, you must think back to what you learned about atoms and bonding.

Atoms contain electrons, or negatively charged particles, which are located in energy levels. The electrons in the outermost energy level of an atom are called the valence electrons. It is the valence electrons that are involved in chemical bonding. An atom forms chemical bonds with other atoms in order to complete its outermost energy level. A chemical bond can be formed by the loss or gain of electrons, which is ionic bonding. Or it can be formed by the sharing of electrons, which is covalent bonding.

The arrangement of electrons in an atom determines the bonding capacity of that atom. Bonding capacity refers to the ease with which an atom will form chemical bonds. The bonding capacity of an atom determines its chemical properties, or its ability to undergo chemical reactions.

Figure 8–5 *During a chemical reaction, bonds between atoms of the reactants are broken, atoms are rearranged, and new bonds in products are formed.*

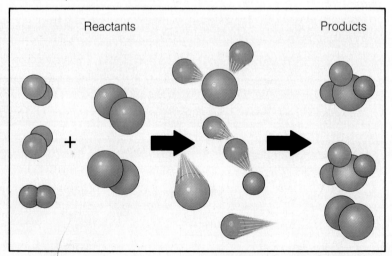

Reactants

Products

+

During a chemical reaction, atoms can form molecules, molecules can break apart to form atoms, or molecules can react with other molecules. In any case, new substances are produced as existing bonds are broken, atoms are rearranged, and new bonds are formed.

SECTION REVIEW

1. What is a chemical reaction?
2. What is a reactant? A product?
3. What is the relationship between the arrangement of electrons in an atom and the atom's chemical properties?

8–2 Chemical Equations

Chemical reactions involve rearrangements of atoms. In order to describe a chemical reaction, it is necessary to indicate the atoms that are involved in the reaction. One way of doing this is to use words. But describing a chemical reaction with words can be awkward. Many atoms may be involved, and the changes may be complicated.

For example, consider the flashbulb reaction described before. A word equation for this reaction would be stated: Magnesium combines with oxygen to form magnesium oxide and give off energy in the form of light. You could shorten this sentence a bit by saying: Magnesium and oxygen form magnesium oxide and light energy.

Chemists have developed a more convenient way to represent a chemical reaction. Using symbols to represent elements and formulas to represent compounds, a chemical reaction can be described by a **chemical equation.** A chemical equation is an expression in which symbols and formulas are used to represent a chemical reaction.

In order to write a chemical equation, you must first write the correct chemical symbols or formulas for the reactants and products. Then you need to separate these symbols or formulas with a plus sign. A "+" sign replaces the word "and." Between the reactants and products, you need to draw an arrow.

Section Objective

To balance chemical equations

Figure 8–6 *The eruption of Mt. Ngaurahoe in New Zealand is a dramatic example of a chemical reaction. Where does the energy for this reaction come from?*

This arrow, which is read "yields," takes the place of an equal sign. It also shows the direction of the chemical change. The chemical equation for the flashbulb reaction can now be written:

$$Mg + O_2 \longrightarrow MgO + energy$$
$$magnesium + oxygen \longrightarrow magnesium\ oxide + energy$$

Conservation of Mass

Chemists have long known that atoms can be neither created nor destroyed during a chemical reaction. In other words, the number of atoms of each element must be the same before and after the chemical reaction.

If the number of atoms of each element remains the same, then mass can never change in a chemical reaction. The total mass of the reactants must equal the total mass of the products. This observation that mass remains constant in a chemical reaction is known as the **law of conservation of mass.**

Balancing Chemical Equations

The law of conservation of mass must be considered when writing a chemical equation for a chemical reaction. A chemical equation must show that atoms are neither created nor destroyed. The number of atoms of each element must be the same on both sides of the equation.

An equation in which the number of atoms of each element is the same on both sides of the equation is called a balanced chemical equation. To balance a chemical equation, **coefficients** (koh-uh-FIHSH-uhnts) are placed in front of symbols and formulas. Coefficients are numbers that indicate how many atoms or molecules of each substance are involved in the reaction.

Let's go back to the chemical equation for the flashbulb reaction:

$$Mg + O_2 \longrightarrow MgO + energy$$

Is the law of conservation of mass observed?

How many magnesium atoms do you count on the left side of the equation? You should count 1.

If you were alive one hundred years ago, you probably would have spent much of your time growing and preparing your own food. What you did not grow or process yourself, you would have purchased fresh nearly every day. Packaged and canned foods were not common then. And there were no mechanical refrigerators.

Today, most people can reach into the refrigerator or cabinet for a snack or easy-to-prepare meal. Much of the food you eat has been processed for you by a food processing company. Almost every method of food processing involves chemical reactions. **Food chemists** use their knowledge of chemistry to develop these food processing methods.

Some food chemists develop new foods or new flavors. Others develop improved packaging and storage methods for foods. Food chemists might work in the plants where food is processed. Food chemists may test samples of a product to be sure that the nutrients in the food match the nutritional information printed on the package.

If you are interested in a career as a food chemist, write to the Institute of Food Technologists, Career Guidance, Suite 300, 221 North LaSalle Street, Chicago, IL 60601.

And on the right side? You should count 1. Now try the same thing for oxygen. There are 2 oxygen atoms on the left but only 1 on the right. This cannot be correct, since atoms can be neither created nor destroyed during a chemical reaction.

To balance this equation, you must represent more than 1 atom of oxygen and more than one molecule of magnesium oxide:

$$2Mg + O_2 \longrightarrow 2MgO + energy$$

If you count atoms again, you will find 2 magnesium atoms on each side of the equation, as well as 2 oxygen atoms. The equation is balanced. It can be read: 2 atoms of magnesium combine with 1 molecule of oxygen to yield 2 molecules of magnesium oxide. Notice that when no coefficient is written, such as in front of the molecule of oxygen, the number is understood to be 1. Remember that to balance a chemical equation, you can change coefficients but never symbols or formulas.

Chemical equations are easy to write and balance. Follow the rules in Figure 8–7 and on page 188.

Figure 8–7 *These are the steps to follow in balancing a chemical equation. What law must a chemical equation obey?*

BALANCING EQUATIONS

$$H_2 + O_2 \rightarrow H_2O$$

1. Write a chemical equation with correct symbols and formulas.

2. Count the number of atoms of each element on each side of the arrow.

$$2H_2 + O_2 \rightarrow 2H_2O$$

3. Balance atoms by using coefficients.

4. Check your work by counting atoms of each element.

A Balancing Act

Rewrite each of the following equations on a sheet of paper. Balance each equation, referring to the rules of balancing in Figure 8–7.

$BaCl_2 + H_2SO_4 \longrightarrow$
$\quad BaSO_4 + HCl$

$P + O \longrightarrow P_4O_{10}$

$KClO_3 \longrightarrow KCl + O_2$

$C_3H_8 + O_2 \longrightarrow CO_2 + H_2O$

$Cu + AgNO_3 \longrightarrow$
$\quad Cu(NO_3)_2 + Ag$

$$F = -32 \div 1.8 -$$

1. Write a word equation and then a chemical equation for the reaction. Make sure the symbols and formulas for reactants and products are correct.

2. Count the number of atoms of each element on each side of the arrow. If the numbers are the same, the equation is balanced.

3. If the number of atoms of each element is not the same on both sides of the arrow, you must balance the equation by using coefficients. Put a coefficient in front of a symbol or formula so that the number of atoms of that substance is the same on both sides of the arrow. Continue this procedure until you have balanced all the atoms.

4. Check your work by counting the atoms of each element to make sure they are the same on both sides of the equation.

Sample Problem

Write a balanced equation for the reaction between nitrogen and hydrogen to form ammonia.

Solution

Step 1 Write a word equation and then a chemical equation.

Nitrogen and hydrogen form ammonia
$N_2 + H_2 \longrightarrow NH_3$

Step 2 Count the number of atoms of each element on each side of the equation.

$2 \text{ N atoms} \longrightarrow 1 \text{ N atom}$
$2 \text{ H atoms} \longrightarrow 3 \text{ H atoms}$

Step 3 Balance the equation by using coefficients.

$N_2 + 3 H_2 \longrightarrow 2 NH_3$

Step 4 Check your work by counting the atoms of each element on both sides of the equation.

$2 \text{ N atoms} \longrightarrow 2(1) = 2 \text{ N atoms}$
$3(2) = 6 \text{ H atoms} \longrightarrow 2(3) = 6 \text{ H atoms}$

Practice Problems

1. Write a balanced equation for the reaction between hydrogen and oxygen to form water.

2. Write a balanced equation for the reaction between sodium sulfide, Na_2S, and silver nitrate, $AgNO_3$, to produce sodium nitrate, $NaNO_3$, and silver sulfide, Ag_2S.

SECTION REVIEW

1. What is a chemical equation?
2. State the law of conservation of mass.
3. Why must a chemical equation be balanced?
4. Write a balanced chemical equation for the reaction between sodium and oxygen to form sodium oxide, Na_2O.
5. Why can't you change symbols or formulas in order to balance a chemical equation?

8–3 Types of Chemical Reactions

Section Objective

To identify the four types of chemical reactions

There are billions of different chemical reactions. In some reactions, elements combine to form compounds. In other reactions, compounds break down into elements. And in still other reactions, one element replaces another.

Chemists have identified four general types of reactions: synthesis, decomposition, single replacement, and double replacement. In each type of reaction, atoms are being rearranged and substances are being changed in a specific way.

Synthesis Reaction

In a **synthesis** (SIHN-thuh-sihs) **reaction,** two or more simple substances combine to form a new, more complex substance. For example, the reaction between sodium and chlorine to form sodium chloride is a synthesis reaction:

$$2Na + Cl_2 \longrightarrow 2NaCl$$

sodium + chlorine $\longrightarrow$ sodium chloride

Reactions involving the corrosion of metals are synthesis reactions. The rusting of iron involves the chemical combination of iron with oxygen to form iron oxide. Here is the balanced equation for this reaction:

$$4Fe + 3O_2 \longrightarrow 2Fe_2O_3$$

iron + oxygen $\longrightarrow$ iron oxide

Sharpen Your Skills

Preventing a Chemical Reaction

1. Obtain two large nails. Paint one nail and let it dry. Do not paint the other nail.
2. Pour a little water into a jar or beaker.
3. Stand both nails in the container of water. Cover the container and let it stand for several days. Compare the appearance of the nails.

Describe what happens to each nail. Give a reason for your observations. Write a word equation for any reaction that has occurred.

Figure 8–8 *The tragic explosion of the* Hindenburg *on May 6, 1937, involved a synthesis reaction (left). Hydrogen and oxygen combined explosively to form water. A much less dramatic synthesis reaction is the corrosion of a metal such as copper, which was combined with tin to make the bronze of the Statue of Liberty (right).*

Figure 8–9 *Carbonic acid is added to liquids to give them "fizz." Carbonic acid, however, quickly decomposes into water and carbon dioxide gas. What type of a reaction is this? How do you know that a gas is produced?*

Decomposition Reaction

In a **decomposition reaction,** a complex substance breaks down into two or more simpler substances. Decomposition reactions are the reverse of synthesis reactions. When you take the cap off a bottle of soda, bubbles rise quickly to the top. Why? Carbonated beverages such as soda contain the compound carbonic acid, H_2CO_3. This compound decomposes into water and carbon dioxide gas. The CO_2 gas makes up the bubbles that are released. Here is the balanced equation for the decomposition of carbonic acid:

$$H_2CO_3 \longrightarrow H_2O + CO_2$$
carbonic acid $\longrightarrow$ **water + carbon dioxide**

Single-Replacement Reaction

In a **single-replacement reaction,** an uncombined element replaces an element that is part of a compound. For example, the very active metal sodium must be stored in oil, not water. When it comes in contact with water, it reacts explosively. The sodium replaces the hydrogen in the water and releases lots of energy. Here is the balanced equation for the reaction of sodium with water:

$$2Na + 2H_2O \longrightarrow 2NaOH + H_2$$
sodium + water $\longrightarrow$ sodium hydroxide
+ hydrogen

Most single-replacement reactions do not cause explosions. When a piece of zinc is placed in a beaker of hydrochloric acid, the zinc replaces the hydrogen in the acid and sets it free. Bubbles of hydrogen gas can be seen as the reaction progresses. Zinc chloride is the other product. Here is the balanced equation for this reaction:

$$Zn + 2HCl \longrightarrow ZnCl_2 + H_2$$
zinc + hydrochloric acid $\longrightarrow$ zinc chloride
+ hydrogen

Double-Replacement Reaction

In a **double-replacement reaction,** different atoms in two different compounds replace each other. In other words, two compounds react to form two new compounds.

If you have ever had an upset stomach, you may have taken a medicine that contained the compound magnesium carbonate. This compound reacts with

Sharpen Your Skills

Double-Replacement Reaction

1. Place a small amount of baking soda in a glass beaker or jar.
2. Pour some vinegar on the baking soda. Observe what happens.

Baking soda is sodium hydrogen carbonate, $NaHCO_3$. Vinegar is acetic acid, $HC_2H_3O_2$. Write the chemical equation for this reaction. What gas is produced? How could you test for the presence of this gas?

Figure 8–10 *Because copper is a more active metal than silver, it can replace the silver in silver nitrate. In these four photos, you can see the gradual buildup of silver metal on the coil. What type of reaction is this? What other indication is there that a chemical change is taking place?*

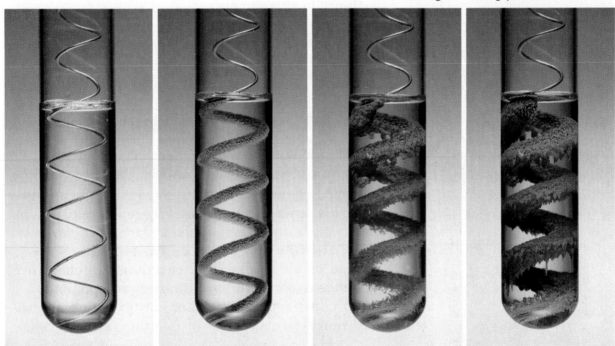

the hydrochloric acid in your stomach in the following way:

$$MgCO_3 + 2HCl \longrightarrow MgCl_2 + H_2CO_3$$

magnesium carbonate $\longrightarrow$ **magnesium chloride + hydrochloric acid + carbonic acid**

In this double-replacement reaction, the magnesium and hydrogen replace each other, or "switch partners." One product is magnesium chloride, a harmless compound. The other product is carbonic acid. Do you remember what happens to carbonic acid? It decomposes into water and carbon dioxide. Your stomachache goes away because instead of too much acid, there is now water and carbon dioxide. You owe your relief to this double-replacement reaction:

$$MgCO_3 + 2HCl \longrightarrow MgCl_2 + H_2O + CO_2$$

magnesium carbonate $\longrightarrow$ **magnesium chloride + hydrochloric acid + water + carbon dioxide**

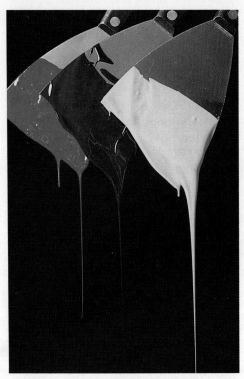

Figure 8–11 *Paints are chemical compounds produced by double-replacement reactions. Yellow paint contains cadmium sulfide, which gives it its characteristic color. Cadmium sulfide and hydrogen chloride are produced when cadmium chloride and hydrogen sulfide are combined. What is the balanced chemical equation for this reaction?*

SECTION REVIEW

1. Name the four types of reactions.
2. What is the difference between a synthesis reaction and a decomposition reaction?
3. What is a single-replacement reaction? A double-replacement reaction?
4. What type of reaction is represented by each of the following equations:
   a. $2Na + MgF_2 \longrightarrow 2NaF + Mg$
   b. $C + O_2 \longrightarrow CO_2$
   c. $2KCl + Pb(NO_3)_2 \longrightarrow 2KNO_3 + PbCl_2$

8–4 Energy of Chemical Reactions

Section Objective

To classify chemical reactions according to energy changes

When chemical reactions occur, there is always a change in energy. Sometimes energy is released, or given off, as the reaction takes place. Sometimes energy is absorbed. **Based on the type of energy change involved, chemical reactions are classified as either exothermic or endothermic reactions.**

In either type of reaction, energy is neither created nor destroyed. One of two things can happen

to the energy. It can be stored in the molecules of a reacting substance or it can be released from a reacting substance in which it was originally stored. The energy that is absorbed or released usually takes the form of heat or visible light.

Figure 8–12 *The explosion of a firecracker is an exothermic reaction (left). The cooking of pancakes is an endothermic reaction (right). What is the difference between these two types of reactions?*

Exothermic Reactions

A chemical reaction in which energy is released is an **exothermic** (ehks-uh-THER-mihk) **reaction.** A combustion reaction, or a reaction that involves burning, is an example of an exothermic reaction. For example, the combustion of methane, which occurs in a gas stove, releases a large amount of energy in the form of heat.

$$CH_4 + 2O_2 \longrightarrow CO_2 + 2H_2O + energy$$

methane + oxygen $\longrightarrow$ carbon dioxide + water + energy

The energy that is released in an exothermic reaction was originally stored in the molecules of the reactants. The molecules of the products no longer contain this stored energy. So the energy of the products is less than the energy of the reactants. An energy diagram, such as the one in Figure 8–13, on page 194 can be used to show the energy change in an exothermic reaction. Note that the reactants are higher in energy than the products are.

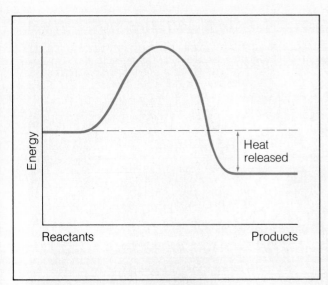
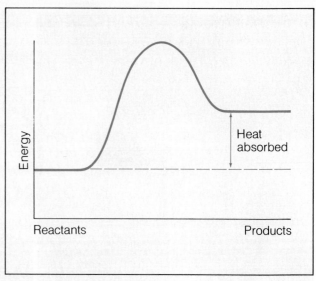

Figure 8–13 *An energy diagram for an exothermic reaction (left) indicates that heat is released during the reaction. Heat is absorbed during an endothermic reaction, as shown by its energy diagram (right). How does the heat content of products and reactants compare for each type of reaction?*

Endothermic Reactions

A chemical reaction in which energy is absorbed is an **endothermic** (ehn-duh-THER-mihk) **reaction.** The energy absorbed during an endothermic reaction is usually in the form of heat or electric energy. The decomposition of sodium chloride, or table salt, is an example of an endothermic reaction. It requires the absorption of electric energy.

$$2NaCl + energy \longrightarrow 2Na + Cl_2$$

sodium chloride + energy $\longrightarrow$ sodium
+ chlorine

The energy that is absorbed in an endothermic reaction is now stored in the molecules of the products. So the energy of the products is more than the energy of the reactants. See Figure 8–13.

Activation Energy

The total energy released or absorbed by a chemical reaction does not tell the whole story about the energy changes involved in the reaction. In order for the reactants to form products, the molecules of the reactants must combine to form a short-lived, high-energy, extremely unstable molecule. The atoms of this molecule are then rearranged to form products. This process requires energy. The molecules of the reactants must "climb" to the top of an "energy hill" before they can form products. The energy needed to "climb" to the top of the "energy hill" is called **activation energy.** After the reactants have absorbed this activation energy, they can "slide down" the energy hill to form products.

An energy diagram indicates more than whether a reaction is exothermic or endothermic. An energy diagram shows the activation energy of the reaction. Figure 8–15 shows an energy diagram for both an exothermic reaction and an endothermic reaction.

All chemical reactions require activation energy. Even an exothermic reaction such as the burning of a match requires activation energy. In order to light a match, it must first be struck. The friction of match against striking pad provides the necessary activation energy.

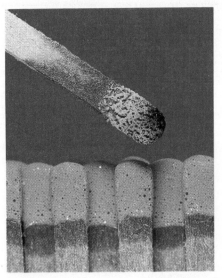

Figure 8–14 *Even though a lighted match gives off heat and the reaction is exothermic, activation energy must first be absorbed. What provides the activation energy?*

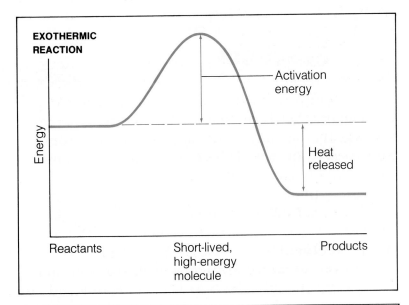

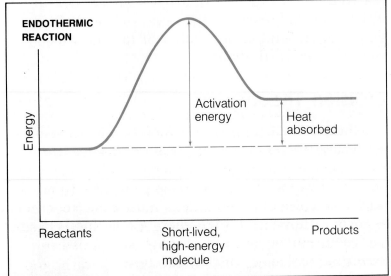

Figure 8–15 *As you can see by these energy diagrams, both an exothermic reaction and an endothermic reaction require activation energy.*

SECTION REVIEW

1. What is an exothermic reaction? An endothermic reaction?
2. On which side should the energy term be written in an equation representing an endothermic reaction? In an equation representing an exothermic reaction?
3. Compare the energy content of reactants and products in an exothermic reaction. In an endothermic reaction.
4. Compare the energy diagram of an exothermic reaction requiring a large amount of activation energy with that of an exothermic reaction requiring a small amount of activation energy.

8–5 Rates of Chemical Reactions

The complete burning of a thick log can take many hours. Yet if the log is ground into very fine sawdust, the burning can take place at dangerously high speeds. In fact, if the dust is spread through the air, the burning can produce an explosion! In both these processes, the same reaction is taking place. The various substances in wood are combining with oxygen. What, then, causes the differences in reaction times?

In order to explain differences in reaction time, chemists must study **kinetics.** Kinetics is the study of **reaction rates.** The rate of a reaction is a measure of how quickly reactants turn into products. Reaction rates depend on a number of factors, which you will now read about.

Collision Theory

Chemical reactions occur when bonds between atoms are broken, the atoms are rearranged, and new bonds are formed. In order for this process to occur, activation energy must be provided. In addition, molecules of the reactants must come together to form a short-lived, high-energy molecule. These two requirements are met through collisions between the molecules of the reactants.

The theory that relates molecular collisions to reaction rate is called the **collision theory.** According to the collision theory, reacting molecules must collide with sufficient energy if they are to form products. **The collision theory explains why the rate of a reaction is affected by four factors: concentration, surface area, temperature, and catalysts.**

Concentration

The **concentration** of a substance is a measure of the amount of that substance in a given unit of volume. A high concentration of reactants means there are a great many particles per unit volume. So there are more particles of reactants available for collisions. More collisions occur and more products are formed in a certain amount of time. What does a low concentration of reactants mean?

Generally, reactants present at high concentrations react more quickly than reactants present at low concentrations. Therefore, an increase in the concentration of reactants increases the rate of a reaction. A decrease in the concentration of reactants decreases the rate of reaction. For example, a highly concentrated solution of sodium hydroxide (NaOH), or lye, will react more quickly to clear a clogged drain than will a less concentrated lye solution. Why would the rate of burning charcoal be increased by blowing air on the fire?

Surface Area

When one of the reactants in a chemical reaction is a solid, the rate of reaction can be increased by breaking the solid into smaller pieces. This increases the surface area of the reactant. An increase in surface area increases the collisions between reacting molecules.

A given quantity of wood burns faster as sawdust than as logs. Sawdust has a much greater surface area exposed to air than do the logs. So oxygen molecules from the air can collide with more wood molecules per second. The reaction rate is increased. How does the collision theory account for the fact that fine crystals of table salt dissolve more quickly in water than do large crystals of rock salt?

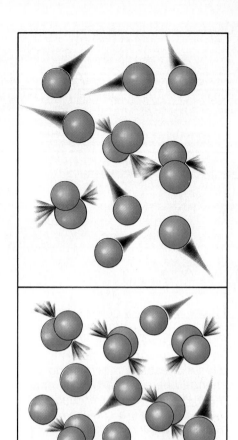

Figure 8–16 *Collisions of molecules increase when there are more molecules. The number of molecules per unit volume is called concentration. What is the relationship between concentration of reactants and reaction rate?*

197

Figure 8–17 *As bellows are pumped, more oxygen is supplied to the fire and the rate of reaction increases (left). What factor affecting reaction rate is being changed here? An explosion at a grain elevator is an ever-present danger because a chemical reaction can occur almost instantaneously (right). What reaction-rate factor is responsible for such an explosion?*

Temperature

An increase in temperature generally increases the rate of a reaction. Here again the collision theory provides an explanation for this fact. Molecules are constantly in motion. Temperature is a measure of the energy of their motion. Molecules at a high temperature have more energy of motion than molecules at a low temperature. Molecules at a high temperature move faster than molecules at a low temperature. So molecules at a high temperature collide more frequently. They also collide with greater energy. This increase in the rate and energy of collisions affects the reaction rate. More molecules of reactants are able to gain the activation energy that is needed to form products. So reaction rate is increased.

At room temperature, the rates of many chemical reactions roughly double or triple with a rise in temperature of 10°C. How does this fact explain the use of refrigeration to keep foods from spoiling?

Catalysts

Some chemical reactions take place very slowly. For such reactions, rates can be increased greatly by using a **catalyst** (KAT-uhl-ihst). A catalyst is a substance that increases the rate of a reaction but is not itself changed by the reaction.

How does a catalyst change the rate of a reaction if it is not itself changed by the reaction? The explanation again is based on the collision theory.

Sharpen Your Skills

Temperature and Reaction Rate

1. Fill one glass with cold water and another with hot water.

2. Drop a seltzer tablet into each glass of water and observe the reactions that occur.

Is there any noticeable difference in the two reactions? What effect, if any, does temperature have on this kind of reaction? Does this experiment prove that a difference in temperature always has the same effect?

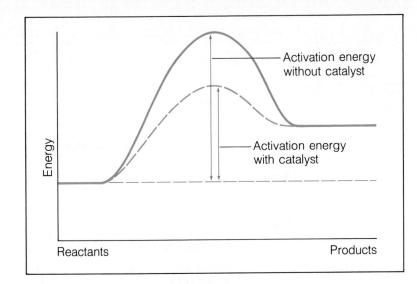

Figure 8–18 *A catalyst changes the rate of a chemical reaction without itself being changed by the reaction. According to this energy diagram, how does a catalyst affect the rate of reaction?*

Reactions often involve a series of steps. A catalyst changes one or more of the steps. A catalyst produces a different, lower energy path for the reaction. In other words, it lowers the "energy hill," or activation energy. A decrease in the activation energy needed for the reaction allows more reactant molecules to form products. Collisions need not be so energetic. Therefore, more collisions are successful at producing products.

A catalyst is usually involved in one or more of the early steps in a reaction. However, the catalyst is re-formed during a later step. This explains why a catalyst is not changed by a reaction and why it does not appear as a product of a reaction it helped to speed up.

Catalysts are used in many chemical processes. They are also used in the catalytic converters that change the harmful gases produced by automobile engines into harmless ones. Some of the most important catalysts are found in your body. These biochemical catalysts are called enzymes. Each enzyme increases the rate of a specific reaction involved in the body's metabolism. If it were not for these enzymes, digestive processes that now take a few hours would require several weeks for completion!

SECTION REVIEW

1. What is reaction rate?
2. How is reaction rate related to collision theory?
3. Name four factors that affect reaction rate.
4. How does collision theory explain the effect of a decrease in temperature on the reaction rate?

Determining Reaction Rate

Problem

How does concentration affect reaction rate?

Materials *(per group)*

3 250-mL beakers
2 graduated cylinders
stopwatch or watch with a sweep
   second hand
stirring rod
distilled water at room temperature
120 mL Solution A
90 mL Solution B
safety goggles
sheet of white paper

Procedure

1. Carefully measure 60 mL of Solution A and pour it into a 250-mL beaker. Add 10 mL of distilled water and stir.
2. Carefully measure 30 mL of Solution B and pour it into a second beaker. Place the beaker of Solution B on a piece of white paper in order to see the color change more easily.
3. Add the 70 mL of Solution A water mixture to Solution B. Stir rapidly. Record the time it takes for the reaction to occur.

4. Rinse and dry the reaction beaker.
5. Repeat the procedure using the other amounts shown in the data table.

Observations

1. What visible indication is there that a chemical reaction is occurring?
2. What is the effect of adding more distilled water on the concentration of Solution A?
3. What happens to reaction time as more distilled water is added to Solution A?
4. Make a graph of your observations by plotting time along the X axis and volume of Solution A along the Y axis.

Conclusions

1. How does concentration affect reaction rate?
2. Does your graph support your answer to question 1? Explain why.
3. What would a graph look like if time were plotted along the X axis and volume of distilled water added to Solution A were plotted along the Y axis?
4. In this investigation, what is the variable? The constant?

Solution A (mL)	Distilled Water Added to Solution A (mL)	Solution B (mL)	Reaction Time (sec)
60	10	30	
40	30	30	
20	50	30	

CHAPTER REVIEW

SUMMARY

8-1 Nature of Chemical Reactions

❑ When a chemical reaction takes place, there is always a change in the properties and in the energy of the substances.

❑ A reactant is a substance that enters into a chemical reaction. A product is a substance that is produced by a chemical reaction.

❑ An atom forms chemical bonds with other atoms in order to complete its outermost energy level. The arrangement of electrons in an atom determines the atom's bonding capacity, or its ability to undergo chemical reactions.

8-2 Chemical Equations

❑ A chemical equation is an expression in which symbols and formulas are used to represent a chemical reaction. Reactants are written to the left of the arrow in such an equation and products are written to the right.

❑ The law of conservation of mass states that matter can be neither created nor destroyed in a chemical reaction.

❑ Four basic rules should be followed in balancing equations: Write a word equation and a chemical equation, count the number of atoms of each element on each side of the arrow, use coefficients to balance the equation, check your work.

8-3 Types of Chemical Reactions

❑ In a synthesis reaction, two or more simple substances combine to form a new, more complex substance.

❑ In a decomposition reaction, a complex substance breaks down into two or more simpler substances.

❑ In a single-replacement reaction, an uncombined element replaces an element that is part of a compound.

❑ In a double-replacement reaction, different atoms in two different compounds replace each other.

8-4 Energy of Chemical Reactions

❑ When chemical reactions occur, energy can either be released or absorbed.

❑ A chemical reaction in which energy is released is called an exothermic reaction. A chemical reaction in which energy is absorbed is called an endothermic reaction.

❑ In order for reactants to form products, activation energy is needed.

8-5 Rates of Chemical Reactions

❑ The rate of a reaction is a measure of how quickly reactants turn into products.

❑ An increase in the concentration of reactants increases the rate of a reaction.

❑ An increase in the surface area of reactants increases the rate of a reaction.

❑ An increase in temperature generally increases the rate of a reaction.

❑ A catalyst is a substance that increases the rate of a reaction without itself being changed by the reaction.

VOCABULARY

Define each term in a complete sentence.

activation energy	concentration	endothermic reaction	reactant
catalyst	decomposition reaction	exothermic reaction	reaction rate
chemical equation		kinetics	single-replacement reaction
chemical reaction	double-replacement reaction	law of conservation of mass	
coefficient			synthesis reaction
collision theory		product	

CONTENT REVIEW: MULTIPLE CHOICE

On a separate sheet of paper, write the letter of the answer that best completes each statement.

1. The substances to the left of the arrow in a chemical equation are called
   a. coefficients.   b. products.   c. subscripts.   d. reactants.
2. An atom's ability to undergo chemical reactions is determined by
   a. protons.   b. neutrons.   c. innermost electrons.   d. outermost electrons.
3. In a balanced chemical equation,
   a. atoms are conserved.   b. molecules are equal.
   c. coefficients are equal.   d. energy is not conserved.
4. Two or more simple substances combine to form a new substance in a
   a. decomposition reaction.   b. double-replacement reaction.
   c. single-replacement reaction.   d. synthesis reaction.
5. A reaction in which energy is absorbed is called
   a. exothermic.   b. endothermic.   c. analytic.   d. catalytic.
6. In an exothermic reaction, heat is
   a. absorbed.   b. released.   c. destroyed.   d. conserved.
7. The energy required for reactants to form products is called
   a. energy of motion.   b. potential energy.
   c. activation energy.   d. synthetic energy.
8. The rate of a chemical reaction can be increased by
   a. decreasing concentration.   b. decreasing temperature.
   c. increasing surface area.   d. all of the above.
9. Concentration is a measure of molecular
   a. energy.   b. speed.   c. number per unit of volume.   d. temperature.
10. Adding a catalyst to a reaction increases rate by
    a. increasing molecular motion.   b. decreasing molecular motion.
    c. lowering activation energy.   d. increasing concentration.

CONTENT REVIEW: COMPLETION

On a separate sheet of paper, write the word or words that best complete each statement.

1. In a _____ change, one kind of matter is turned into another.
2. A chemical reaction is accompanied by a change in the _____ and _____ of the substances.
3. A (An) _____ means "yields."
4. According to the law of _____, matter can be neither created nor destroyed during a chemical reaction.
5. Two or more simple substances combine to form a new, more complex substance in a (an) _____ reaction.
6. An uncombined element replaces an element that is part of a compound in a (an) _____ reaction.
7. A reaction in which energy is released is called a (an) _____ reaction.
8. In an endothermic reaction, the _____ have more energy.
9. The study of reaction rates is called _____.
10. A substance that increases the rate of a chemical reaction without itself being changed is called a (an) _____.

CONTENT REVIEW: TRUE OR FALSE

Determine whether each statement is true or false. Then on a separate sheet of paper, write "true" if it is true. If it is false, change the underlined word or words to make the statement true.

1. The substances formed as a result of a chemical reaction are called <u>reactants</u>.
2. A <u>chemical equation</u> uses symbols and formulas to represent a reaction.
3. A number written in front of a chemical symbol or formula is a (an) <u>coefficient</u>.
4. To balance the following equation, the number <u>2</u> should be placed in front of O_2: $KClO_3 \longrightarrow KCl + O_2$.
5. In a <u>synthesis</u> reaction, complex substances form simpler substances.
6. The formation of carbon dioxide during combustion of a fuel is an example of a <u>decomposition</u> reaction.
7. In an exothermic reaction, products have <u>more</u> energy than reactants.
8. The <u>collision theory</u> can be used to account for the factors that affect reaction rates.
9. <u>Concentration</u> is a measure of the energy of motion of molecules.
10. Increasing surface area <u>increases</u> reaction rate.

CONCEPT REVIEW: SKILL BUILDING

Use the skills you have developed in the chapter to complete each activity.

1. **Making calculations** Balance the following equations:
   a. $PbO_2 \longrightarrow PbO + O_2$
   b. $Ca + H_2O \longrightarrow Ca(OH)_2 + H_2$
   c. $Zn + S \longrightarrow ZnS$
   d. $BaCl_2 + Na_2SO_4 \longrightarrow BaSO_4 + NaCl$
   e. $Al + Fe_2O_3 \longrightarrow Al_2O_3 + Fe$
   f. $C_{12}H_{22}O_{11} \longrightarrow C + H_2O$

   c. $4C + 6H_2 + O_2 \longrightarrow 2C_2H_6O$
   d. $2LiI + Pb(NO_3)_2 \longrightarrow 2LiNO_3 + PbI_2$
   e. $2H_2O + O_2 \longrightarrow 2H_2O_2$

2. **Classifying reactions** Identify the general type of reaction represented by each equation. Explain your answers.
   a. $NiCl_2 \longrightarrow Ni + Cl_2$
   b. $MgBr_2 + 2K \longrightarrow Mg + 2KBr$

3. **Relating cause and effect** Iron is often galvanized, or covered with the more active metal zinc, in order to protect the iron from corroding. Explain why this method is effective.

4. **Developing a model** Draw an energy diagram of an exothermic reaction that has a high activation energy. On your diagram, indicate how an increase in temperature would affect the rate of this reaction. Do the same for the addition of a catalyst.

CONCEPT REVIEW: ESSAY

Discuss each of the following in a brief paragraph.

1. Why do substances react chemically?
2. State the law of conservation of mass and explain its role in chemical reactions.
3. Use the collision theory to explain the effects on reaction rate of (a) increased concentration, (b) catalysts, and (c) increased surface area.
4. Give two reasons why collisions between molecules of reactants may *not* be effective in forming products.
5. Explain how the heat content of the products of a reaction compares with that of the reactants when the reaction is (a) exothermic or (b) endothermic.

Solution Chemistry 9

CHAPTER SECTIONS

9–1 Nature of Solutions

9–2 Making Solutions

9–3 Water—The Universal Solvent

9–4 Suspensions and Colloids

9–5 Acids

9–6 Bases

9–7 Acids and Bases in Solution: Salts

CHAPTER OBJECTIVES

After completing this chapter, you will be able to

9–1 Define a solution and describe its properties.

9–2 Identify the factors that affect rate of solution.

9–2 Describe how temperature and pressure affect solubility.

9–2 Classify solutions.

9–3 Relate the polarity of water to its use as a solvent.

9–4 Compare suspensions and colloids.

9–5 Describe the properties of acids.

9–6 Describe the properties of bases.

9–7 Relate pH number to acid–base strength.

9–7 Describe the chemical formation of salts.

Deep within the earth, many kilometers beneath its surface, one can observe the passage of time. Tens of thousands of years are visible in the breathtaking cave formations hidden beyond the reach of all but the hardiest and most dedicated explorers. Twisting up from cave floors, flowing down from cave ceilings, and jutting out from cave walls, these chemical formations range from monumental columns to tiny crystals to wispy strands thinner than a human hair.

Such complicated cave structures take thousands of years to form. In tune with nature's rules and rhythms, water, minerals, rock, and soil interact to form the most amazing sculptures. The structure that forms depends on the amount of water in the cave and the type of minerals dissolved in it. In one of the most common processes, mineral-laden water steadily drips or flows over rock that forms the cave boundaries. Carbon dioxide dissolved in the water begins to escape. The drops, heavy with excess minerals, deposit their load onto the cave surfaces.

The familiar structures known as stalactites and stalagmites represent the buildup of billions of drops of mineral-laden water over thousands of years. Even more unusual formations can be found in the hidden passages that twist and turn within the cave. Where streams no longer flow, where water trickles through cave walls, where the bones of bats are buried, nature produces some of the rarest "art" on the earth.

But nature does not work alone. In processes familiar to any scientist, minerals continually dissolve in and escape from water. In this chapter you will learn about this process and some of its more easily observed results.

Nature's solution process has produced the stalactites, stalagmites, and other unique structures found deep within the earth.

To describe the makeup of a solution

9–1 Nature of Solutions

Figure 9–1 *A variety of solutions is shown here. What substances make up the ice cream soda solution (top)? The brass instruments (bottom, left)? The air (bottom, right)?*

What happens when a lump of sugar is dropped into a glass of lemonade? What takes place when carbon dioxide gas is bubbled through water? And where do mothballs go when they disappear? The answer to these questions is the same: The sugar, gaseous carbon dioxide, and mothballs all dissolve in the substances in which they are mixed.

Careful examination of each of these mixtures—even under a microscope—will not reveal molecules of sugar in lemonade, carbon dioxide in water, or naphthalene in the air. But the sweet taste of lemonade tells you the sugar is there. The "fizziness" of soda water indicates the presence of carbon dioxide. And the smell of mothballs reveals the presence of naphthalene. In each of these mixtures, the molecules of one substance have become evenly distributed among the molecules of the other substance. The mixtures are homogeneous throughout. Each mixture is a **solution.**

A solution is a homogeneous mixture in which one substance is dissolved in another substance. Different parts of a solution are identical. The molecules making up a solution are too small to be seen and do not settle when the solution is allowed to stand. A solution, then, is a "well-mixed" mixture.

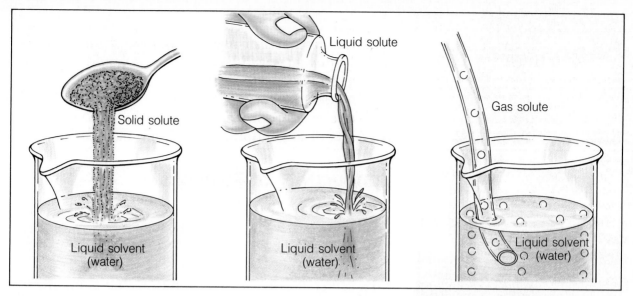

Solid solute

Liquid solute

Gas solute

Liquid solvent (water)

Liquid solvent (water)

Liquid solvent (water)

Properties of Solutions

Let's go back to the glass of sweetened lemonade to discover several important properties of a solution. **A solution consists of two parts: One part is the substance being dissolved, and the other part is the substance doing the dissolving.**

In a solution, the substance that is dissolved is called the **solute** (SAHL-yoot). The substance that does the dissolving is called the **solvent** (SAHL-vuhnt). The solvent is often called the dissolving medium. In the sweetened lemonade, the solute is the sugar and the solvent is the lemonade. Even without the sugar, the lemonade is a solution. It is made of water and lemon juice.

The most common solutions are those in which the solvent is a liquid. The solute can be a solid, liquid, or gas. The most common solvent is water. Solutions in which the solvent is water are called **aqueous** (A-kwee-uhs) **solutions.**

When alcohol is the solvent in a solution, the solution is called a **tincture** (TIHNK-chuhr). Perhaps you are familiar with tincture of iodine, an antiseptic used to treat minor cuts and scratches. What is the solute in this solution?

The particles in a solution are individual atoms, ions, or molecules. Because the particles are so small, they do not scatter light that passes through the solution. A liquid solution appears clear.

Most solutions cannot easily be separated by simple physical means such as filtering. However, a physical change such as evaporation or boiling can

Figure 9–2 *A solution consists of a solute and a solvent. The most common solutions are those in which the solvent is a liquid. Here you see the three types of solutions that can be formed from a liquid solvent and a solid, a liquid, and a gas solute. What is the most common liquid solvent?*

207

Figure 9–3 *The particles in a solution are too small to scatter light, so a solution appears clear (top). The particles are also too small to be separated by filtering. But if the solvent evaporates, deposits of solute are left behind (bottom).*

separate the parts of many solutions. If salt water is boiled, the water will change from a liquid to a gas, leaving behind particles of salt.

Another property of a solution is that solute molecules are evenly spread among solvent molecules. All parts of a solution are uniform, or identical.

Conductivity of Solutions

An important property of a solution is whether or not it can conduct an electric current. An electric current is a flow of electrons. In order for electrons to flow through a solution, ions must be present. Ions are charged atoms. A solution that contains ions is a good conductor of electricity. A solution that does not contain ions is a nonconductor.

Pure water is a poor conductor of electric current because it does not contain ions. However, if a solute such as potassium chloride (KCl) is added to the water, the resulting aqueous solution is a good conductor. The ions making up potassium chloride separate from the compound during the solution process. The separation of ions from a compound during solution is called **dissociation.** The potassium chloride dissociates in water. Potassium ions (K^+) and chloride ions (Cl^-) are free to move through the solution and conduct an electric current. Ionic compounds dissociate in solution, so they form solutions that are good conductors of electricity.

Substances that form aqueous solutions that conduct an electric current are called **electrolytes** (ih-LEHK-truh-lights). Sodium chloride and silver nitrate are examples of electrolytes. Most electrolytes are ionic compounds.

Figure 9–4 *A solution of sugar water is a nonelectrolyte (left). A solution of potassium chloride is an electrolyte (right). What type of a compound is sugar? Potassium chloride?*

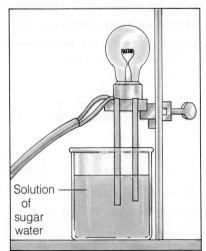

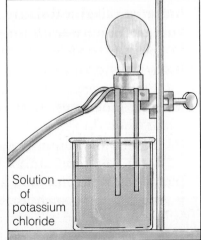

Solution of sugar water

Solution of potassium chloride

Substances whose aqueous solutions do not conduct an electric current are called **nonelectrolytes.** A solution of sugar and water does not conduct an electric current. Sugar is a nonelectrolyte, as are alcohol and benzene.

Many covalent compounds are nonelectrolytes because they do not form ions in solution. However, there are some covalent compounds that will react with certain solvents to form ions. The formation of ions from solute molecules by the action of a solvent is called **ionization** (igh-uhn-ih-ZAY-shuhn). Hydrogen chloride is a covalent compound that ionizes in water. Pure hydrogen chloride liquid is a nonelectrolyte. However, an aqueous solution of hydrogen chloride is an electrolyte. The effect of water on the hydrogen chloride molecule causes it to ionize.

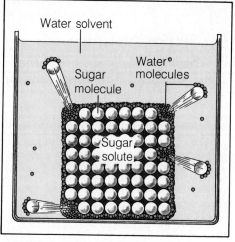

Figure 9–5 *The solution process first involves the separation of solute particles from the surface of the solid solute. Then the solute molecules enter the solution. Finally, the solute molecules are attracted to the solvent molecules.*

A Model of the Solution Process

Although the exact way in which solutes dissolve is not completely understood, scientists have developed a model to describe a probable solution process. This model assumes that three different steps take place in the dissolving of a solid in a liquid.

In the first step, solute particles are separated from the surface of the solid solute. The attraction between solute and solvent molecules is responsible for this dissolving step. This step takes up energy. It is endothermic.

In the second step, solvent molecules are moved apart to allow solute molecules to enter the liquid surrounding the solid solute. This step, too, requires energy. It is endothermic.

In the third step, solute molecules are attracted to solvent molecules. This step gives up energy. It is exothermic. These three steps occur continuously as each surface layer of solute molecules is dissolved, leaving the next layer exposed to the solvent. Finally, all the solute molecules are distributed evenly throughout the solvent.

SECTION REVIEW

1. What is a solution? What are its two parts?
2. What is an aqueous solution? A tincture?
3. Describe three properties of a solution.
4. Compare and contrast dissociation and ionization.

To define solution properties of solubility and concentration

9–2 Making Solutions

Solutions abound in nature. The oceans, the atmosphere, even the earth's interior are solutions. Each solution has a different solute and solvent.

Types of Solutions

Matter can exist as a solid, liquid, or gas. From these three phases of matter, nine different types of solutions can be made. Figure 9–6 shows these types of solutions.

The most common solutions are liquid solutions. In a liquid solution, the solvent is a liquid. The solute can be a solid, liquid, or gas. Two liquids that dissolve in each other are said to be **miscible** (MIHS-uh-buhl). Water and alcohol are miscible. Do you think oil and water are miscible?

Solutions of solids dissolved in solids are called alloys. Most alloys are made of metals. Refer to Figure 6–2 on page 133 for a review of alloys.

Rate of Solution

Suppose you wanted to dissolve some sugar in a glass of water—and you wanted to do it as quickly as possible. What might you do? If your answer included stirring the solution, using granulated sugar, or heating the water, you are on the right track.

Figure 9–6 *Nine different types of solutions can be made from the three phases of matter. What are solutions of solids dissolved in solids called?*

TYPES OF SOLUTIONS

Solute	Solvent	Example
Gas	Gas	Air (oxygen in nitrogen)
Gas	Liquid	Soda water (carbon dioxide in water)
Gas	Solid	Charcoal gas mask (poisonous gases on carbon)
Liquid	Gas	Humid air (water in air)
Liquid	Liquid	Antifreeze (ethylene glycol in water)
Liquid	Solid	Dental filling (mercury in silver)
Solid	Gas	Soot in air (carbon in air)
Solid	Liquid	Ocean water (salt in water)
Solid	Solid	Gold jewelry (copper in gold)

STIRRING THE SOLUTION Normally, the movement of solute molecules away from the solid solute and throughout the solvent occurs rather slowly. Stirring or shaking the solution helps move solute particles away from the solid solute faster. This brings more molecules of the solute in contact with the solvent sooner. So the solute dissolves at a faster rate.

POWDERING THE SOLID SOLUTE Solution action occurs only at the surface of the solid solute. So if the surface area of the solute is increased, the rate of solution is increased. More solute molecules are in contact with the solvent when the solid solute is ground into a fine powder. Finely powdered solids dissolve much faster than large lumps or crystals of the same substance.

HEATING THE SOLUTION If heat is applied to a solution, the molecules move faster and farther apart. As a result, the dissolving action is speeded up.

Solubility

The solubility (sahl-yoo-BIHL-uh-tee) **of a solute is a measure of how much of that solute can be dissolved in a given amount of solvent under certain conditions.** You know that table salt and sugar dissolve readily in water. These compounds are described as being very **soluble.** They have a high degree of **solubility** in water. However, only a small amount of table salt dissolves in alcohol. So the solubility of salt in alcohol is rather low. As you can see from this example, the solubility of a solute depends on the nature of the solute and the solvent.

Solubility is usually described in terms of the mass of the solute that can be dissolved in a definite amount of solvent at a specific temperature. For example, a maximum of 36 grams of table salt, or NaCl, can be dissolved in 100 grams of water at 20°C. So the solubility of NaCl at 20°C is 36 grams per 100 grams of water.

The two main factors that affect the solubility of a solute are temperature and pressure. Generally, an increase in the temperature of a solution increases the solubility of a *solid in a liquid.* The solubility of most solids is increased by raising the temperature of the solution.

Sharpen Your Skills

Solubility of a Gas in a Liquid

1. Remove the cap from a bottle of soda.

2. Immediately fit the opening of a balloon over the top of the bottle. Shake the bottle several times. Note any changes in the balloon.

3. Heat the bottle of soda very gently by placing it in a pan of hot water. Note any further changes in the balloon.

What two conditions of solubility are being tested here? What general statement about the solubility of a gas in a liquid can you now make?

Figure 9-7 *This graph shows the solubility curves of several different solutes. Which solute shows the least change in solubility with an increase in temperature?*

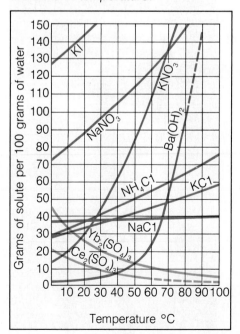

Figure 9–8 *The solubility of a gas solute in a liquid solvent depends on both the pressure and the temperature. When the cap is removed from the bottle, the solubility of the gas decreases. If the bottle is cold, the decrease in solubility is very small. If the bottle is warm, the decrease is obvious.*

Raising the temperature of a gas-in-liquid solution decreases the solubility of the gaseous solute. Thus, the solubility of a gas decreases as the temperature of the solution increases. This is true for all gases. Perhaps you have observed this fact without actually realizing it. Have you ever let a glass of soda get warm? If so, what did you notice? The soda goes flat, or loses its fizz. Soda is given its fizz by dissolving carbon dioxide gas in soda water. As the temperature of the solution increases, the solubility of the carbon dioxide gas decreases. The gas comes out of solution, leaving the soda flat. Why do you think boiled water tastes flat?

For solid and liquid solutes, increases and decreases in pressure have practically no effect on solubility. For gases dissolved in liquids, an increase in pressure increases solubility and a decrease in pressure decreases solubility. A bottle of soda fizzes when the cap is removed because molecules of carbon dioxide gas escape from solution as the pressure is decreased. The solubility of the carbon dioxide gas has been decreased by a decrease in pressure. The escape of a gas from a liquid solution is called **effervescence** (ehf-er-VEHS-uhns).

Figure 9–9 *The rapid escape of gas from a liquid solution is called effervescence. What factors increase effervescence?*

Concentration of Solutions

The concentration of a solution refers to the amount of solute dissolved in a certain amount of solvent. A solution in which a lot of solute is dissolved in a solvent is called a **concentrated solution.** A solution in which there is little solute dissolved in a solvent is called a **dilute solution.** The terms concentrated and dilute are not very precise, however. They do not indicate exactly how much solute and solvent are present.

Using the concept of solubility, the **concentration** of a solution can be expressed in another way. A solution can be described as saturated, unsaturated, or supersaturated. In order to understand these descriptions, remember that solubility measures the *maximum* amount of solute that can be dissolved in a given amount of solvent.

SATURATED SOLUTION A **saturated solution** is a solution that contains all the solute it can possibly hold at a given temperature. In a saturated solution, no more solute can be dissolved at that temperature. If more solute is added to a saturated solution, it will settle undissolved to the bottom of the solution.

In describing a saturated solution, the temperature must always be given. This is because a saturated solution at one temperature will contain a different amount of solute than will a saturated

Figure 9–10 *Many fruit juices are solutions in which a solute of fruit concentrate is dissolved in the solvent water. The concentration of such solutions is often expressed as a percent.*

CAREER   *Chemical Technician*

The bicycle riders jostle for good positions as they pedal toward the last sharp turn of the race. As the pack leans into the curve, a bicycle flies out from under a rider. The fallen rider scrambles out of the way.

At the first aid station it takes only minutes to apply adhesive bandages on the scrapes. But these adhesive bandages took a **chemical technician** months to test in the laboratory.

When a chemist is developing a new product such as an adhesive, a chemical technician helps test experimental formulas for that product. The chemical technician carefully follows a chemist's instructions for setting up laboratory equipment, mixing chemicals, and measuring reactions in experiments.

A chemical technician often uses computers and other instruments to collect data. Chemical technicians work in many fields, including food processing, pharmaceuticals, materials and metals industries, and electronics.

A chemical technician should have a strong interest in science and math, be able to follow instructions, and pay close attention to details. If you would like to learn more about becoming a chemical technician, write to the American Chemical Society, 1155 16th Street NW, Washington, DC 20036.

Figure 9–11 *A saturated solution contains all the solute it can possibly hold at a given temperature. Any additional solute will not dissolve but will fall to the bottom of the solution. What could be done to this solution to make the undissolved solute dissolve?*

solution of the same solute at another temperature. For example, according to Figure 9–7 on page 211, how many grams of sodium nitrate ($NaNO_3$) are there in a saturated solution at 10°C? How many in a saturated solution at 45°C?

UNSATURATED SOLUTION An **unsaturated solution** is a solution that contains less solute than it can possibly hold at a given temperature. In an unsaturated solution, more solute can be dissolved. A solution of sodium nitrate that contains 80 grams of solute at 45°C is unsaturated. How many grams would be needed to make it a saturated solution at 45°C?

SUPERSATURATED SOLUTION Under special conditions, a solution can be made to hold more solute than is normal for that temperature. Such a solution is called a **supersaturated solution.** A supersaturated solution is unstable. If a single crystal of solute is added to a supersaturated solution, the excess solute comes out of solution and settles to the bottom. Only enough solute to make the solution saturated remains dissolved.

A supersaturated solution is prepared by allowing a saturated solution at high temperature to cool gradually and without disturbance. Although the solubility decreases with a decrease in temperature, the excess solute remains in solution. Relatively few solutes will form supersaturated solutions.

Figure 9–12 *Crystals of sugar are growing on a string placed in a supersaturated solution of sugar and water (left). Adding a small crystal of solute to a supersaturated solution—a process called seeding—starts the crystallizing action instantly. The formation of this stalactite (right), which resembles a soda straw, is also the result of solute crystallization from a supersaturated solution.*

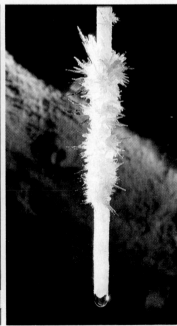

SECTION REVIEW

1. What are three ways of increasing the rate of solution of a solid in a liquid?
2. What is solubility? What two factors affect the solubility of a solute?
3. Compare a saturated, unsaturated, and supersaturated solution.
4. How many grams of KNO_3 are needed to make a saturated solution at 50°C? How many grams of KNO_3 will come out of solution if the temperature drops to 20°C?

9–3 Water—The Universal Solvent

Section Objective

To relate the polarity of a water molecule to its use as a solvent

Water is the most common substance on the earth. About 70 percent of the earth's surface is covered by water, and about 65 percent of your body mass is water. Water plays an important role in dissolving a great variety of substances.

Because thousands of substances are soluble in water, water is sometimes called the universal solvent. You should remember, however, that there are certain substances that will not dissolve in water. These substances are described as **insoluble.** For example, oil and grease are insoluble in water. In order to understand why water is close to being a universal solvent, you need to know about the nature of a water molecule.

Figure 9–13 *This enormous sinkhole in Winter Park, Florida (left), was caused by the collapse of an underground cavern. The cavern originally formed by the dissolving action of water on limestone rock. The polarity of water molecules (right) explains why water is able to dissolve thousands of substances, including polar and ionic solutes. Which end of a water molecule is negative? Positive?*

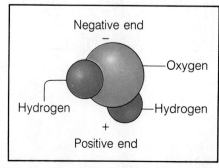

Structure of a Water Molecule

A water molecule is the smallest particle of water that has all the properties of water. It is formed when two hydrogen atoms bond covalently with one atom of oxygen. You may remember that a covalent bond is one in which electrons are shared.

The sharing of electrons in a water molecule is not equal, however. The oxygen atom attracts the shared electrons more strongly than the hydrogen atoms do. So the shared electrons are slightly closer to the oxygen atom than to the hydrogen atoms. The result of this unequal sharing is that the oxygen end of the water molecule has a slight negative charge and the hydrogen end has a slight positive charge. The water molecule has oppositely charged ends. These charged ends give the water molecule the property of **polarity** (poh-LAR-uh-tee).

Polar and Nonpolar Molecules

Water is a **polar molecule.** One end of a polar molecule has a negative charge and the other end has a positive charge. **The charged ends of a polar solvent molecule such as water can separate the charged ends of a polar solute molecule.** This happens when the positive end of the solvent molecule

Figure 9–14 *Water can dissolve both polar solutes (top) and ionic solutes (bottom). What is the name given to each solution process?*

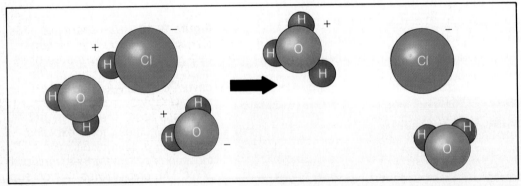

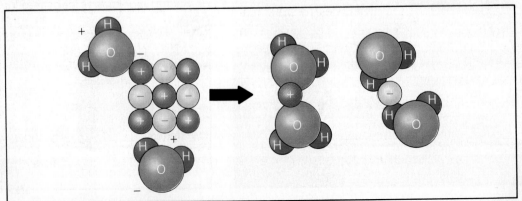

approaches the negative end of the solute molecule. They attract. So a force of attraction is set up between the solvent and solute molecules. This force of attraction separates the molecules of the polar solute, and the solute dissolves. See Figure 9–14.

In addition to dissolving polar solutes, water also dissolves ionic solutes, or substances made of ions. The positive end of the water molecule attracts the negative ion of the ionic solute. Likewise, the negative end of the water molecule attracts the positive ion of the solute. When the water is able to pull the solute ions out of their positions in the solute, dissolving takes place. Each ion is then surrounded by water molecules and spread evenly throughout the solution. See Figure 9–14.

Among the substances that water cannot dissolve are grease, oil, fat, and benzene. These compounds are made of nonpolar molecules, or molecules that do not have charged ends. The nonpolar molecules have no attraction for the polar water molecules. Therefore, no force is exerted. The solute molecules are not separated. Nonpolar solutes, however, dissolve readily in nonpolar solvents. *A general rule for solutions is: Like dissolves like.*

Water Quality

The taste, odor, and appearance of water determine its quality. These properties vary from area to area. The differences depend on the amount and type of material dissolved in the water.

The water you use for all sorts of purposes may come from either a groundwater or a surface source. This water may be "hard" or "soft." The hardness or softness of water depends on the source of the water and the types of rocks and soil the water comes in contact with. **Hard water** contains large amounts of dissolved metal ions, especially calcium and magnesium. Soap does not lather easily in hard water. Also, hard water causes scaly deposits to build up in hot water heaters and plumbing systems. **Soft water** does not contain these metal ions. It does not present problems with lathering soap or depositing metal ions.

Some water is softened naturally as it passes through and reacts with rock formations containing

Figure 9–15 *Hard water causes scaly deposits to build up in hot water heaters and plumbing systems. This scanning electron micrograph shows crystals of calcium salts deposited when hard water evaporates or boils away. What other metal ion dissolved in water causes it to be hard?*

Figure 9–16 *The dumping of industrial wastes from a paper mill in Ontario, Canada, is one example of water pollution. What other substances carelessly dumped into water cause pollution?*

Figure 9–17 *A solute dissolved in a liquid solvent lowers the freezing point of the solvent. Salt spread on an icy surface lowers the freezing point of the ice and causes it to melt (right). Rock salt is used in an ice cream maker to lower the freezing point of the ingredients to allow the ice cream to form at below 0°C (left). What happens to the boiling point of a solvent when a solute is added?*

certain minerals. These minerals remove the calcium and magnesium. Many people in areas with hard water add water softeners to their water to remove the minerals that make it hard.

Water is necessary to all life on the earth. So it is important to maintain the quality of water. Yet many of the earth's sources of fresh water are becoming polluted. Normally, water is naturally filtered through soil and sand, which helps to remove impurities. But carelessness in dumping sewage, silt, industrial wastes, and pesticides into water has caused serious problems. Water is becoming more and more polluted.

Special Properties of Solutions

Why is salt spread on roads and walkways that are icy? Why is salt added to cooking water? Why is a substance known as ethylene glycol added to the cooling systems of cars? The answers to the questions have to do with two special properties of solutions.

Experiments show that when a solute is dissolved in a liquid solvent, the freezing point of the solvent is lowered. The lowering of the freezing point is called **freezing point depression.** The addition of solute molecules interferes with the phase change of solvent molecules. So the solution can exist in the liquid phase at a lower temperature than can the pure solvent. For example, ethylene glycol, commonly known as antifreeze, is added to cooling systems to lower the freezing point of water.

The addition of a solute to a pure liquid solvent also raises the boiling point of the solvent. This increase is called **boiling point elevation.** In this case, the addition of solute molecules interferes with the rapid evaporation, or boiling, of the solvent molecules. So the solution can exist in the liquid phase at a higher temperature than can the pure solvent. Since more energy is needed to make the solvent molecules evaporate, the boiling point increases. When salt is added to cooking water, the water will boil at a higher temperature. Although it may take a longer time to heat the water to boiling, it will take a shorter time to cook the food in that boiling water.

SECTION REVIEW

1. What is polarity? Why is water a polar molecule?
2. What is the general rule for solutions?
3. What is hard water? Soft water?
4. How does a solute affect the freezing point and boiling point of a pure solvent?
5. Of what value is antifreeze to a car's cooling system during extremely hot weather?

9–4 Suspensions and Colloids

Section Objective

To compare suspensions, colloids, and solutions

You learned that solutions are clear, homogeneous mixtures of solute and solvent. The particles in a solution—individual atoms, ions, or molecules—are too small to be seen and do not settle out. Not all solutes dissolved in solvents form true solutions, however. Two other types of mixtures can be formed when a solute dissolves in a solvent. **The physical properties of particle size and separation of solute and solvent particles determine whether a mixture is a suspension or a colloid.**

Suspensions

A **suspension** is a heterogeneous mixture in which the solute particles are larger than atoms, ions, or molecules. The particles are large enough, in fact, to be seen with or without a microscope.

219

Figure 9–18 *The soil and water mixture is a suspension. How can this suspension be separated?*

Figure 9–19 *Fog is a type of colloid in which liquid particles are mixed in a gas (left). Whipped cream is also a colloid (center). What is the solute in whipped cream? The solvent? The constant bombardment of solute particles in a colloid enables a colloid to scatter light, so a beam of light passing through a colloid becomes visible (right).*

The solute particles in a suspension are temporarily suspended, or hanging, in the solvent. The length of time during which they remain this way varies. But eventually, the particles will settle out.

If the solute particles in a suspension are very fine, they will remain suspended for a long time. They can be separated out, however, by filtering the suspension. Can particles of a true solution be separated this way?

Colloids

A **colloid** (KAHL-oid) is a homogeneous mixture that is not a true solution. In a colloid, the size of the solute particles is larger than that in a solution but smaller than that in a suspension. The particles are larger than atoms, ions, or molecules but too small to be seen even with a microscope.

The solute particles in a colloid are kept permanently suspended. They are continuously bombarded by solvent molecules. This bombardment accounts for several properties of a colloid.

A colloid does not separate upon standing, as a suspension does. Because the particles are constantly bombarded, they do not have a chance to settle out. The constant bombardment of solute particles enables a colloid to scatter light. So if a beam of light is passed through a colloid, the beam becomes visible. See Figure 9–19. The white cloudy appearance of milk is due to the scattering of light in this example of a colloid. If you have ever seen a searchlight

TYPES OF COLLOIDS	
Name	**Example**
Fog (liquid in gas)	Clouds
Smoke (solid in gas)	Smoke
Foam (gas in liquid)	Whipped cream
Emulsion (liquid in liquid)	Mayonnaise
Sol (solid in liquid)	Paint
Gel (liquid in solid)	Butter

sweep through the air at night, you have observed this property of colloids.

The bombardment of solute particles in a colloid can be observed under a microscope. You would not see the individual solute particles, but you would see a constant, random motion of the particles. The constant movement of colloidal particles is called **Brownian motion.**

SECTION REVIEW

1. What is a suspension? A colloid?
2. What two physical properties determine whether a mixture is a suspension or a colloid?
3. Describe three types of colloids.
4. How does a solution compare with a suspension and a colloid?

9-5 Acids

If you look in your medicine cabinet and refrigerator and on your kitchen shelves, you will find examples of a group of compounds known as **acids.** Acids are found in aspirin, vitamin C, and eyewash. Fruits such as oranges, grapes, lemons, grapefruits, and apples contain acids. Milk and tea contain acids, as do pickles, vinegar, and carbonated drinks.

Acids play an important role in the life processes that take place in your body. You could not digest food adequately if it were not for a certain acid in your stomach. Many industrial processes use acids. The manufacture of dyes, synthetic fibers, fertilizers, and explosives involves the use of acids.

Properties of Acids

As a class of compounds, all acids have certain physical and chemical properties when dissolved in water. One of the physical properties all acids share is sour taste. Lemons taste sour because they

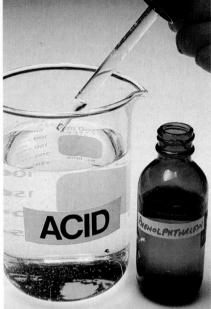

Figure 9–21 *Blue litmus paper turns red in an acid solution (top). Phenolphthalein, another indicator, is colorless in an acid solution (bottom).*

Sharpen Your Skills

Naming Acids

Using books and other reference materials in the library, answer these questions:

1. What is the difference between a binary acid and a ternary acid?

2. What prefix and what suffix are used with the names of all binary acids?

3. In ternary acids, what do the prefixes *hypo-* and *per-* mean? What do the suffixes *-ic* and *-ous* mean?

contain citric acid. Vinegar contains acetic acid. However, you should *never* use taste to identify a chemical substance. You should use other, safer properties to identify acids.

Acids affect the color of **indicators.** Indicators are compounds that show a definite color change when mixed with an acid. Litmus paper, a common indicator, changes from blue to red in an acid solution. Another indicator, phenolphthalein (fee-nohl-THAL-een), is colorless in an acid solution.

Acids react with active metals to produce hydrogen gas and a metal compound. This reaction wears away, or corrodes, the metal and produces a residue. For example, sulfuric acid in a car battery often corrodes the terminals and leaves a residue.

Another important property of acids can be identified by looking at the list of common acids in Figure 9–22. What do all these acids have in common? Acids contain hydrogen. When dissolved in water, acids ionize to produce positive hydrogen ions (H^+). A hydrogen ion is a proton. So acids are often defined as proton donors.

The hydrogen ion, or proton, produced by an acid is quickly surrounded by a water molecule. The attraction between the hydrogen ion (H^+) and the water molecule (H_2O) results in the formation of a **hydronium ion, H_3O^+.**

The definition of an acid as a proton donor helps explain why all hydrogen-containing compounds are *not* acids. Table sugar contains 22 hydrogen atoms, but it is not an acid. When dissolved in water, table sugar does not produce H^+ ions. Table sugar is not a proton donor. So it does not turn litmus paper red or phenolphthalein colorless.

Common Acids

The three most common acids in industry and the laboratory are sulfuric acid (H_2SO_4), nitric acid (HNO_3), and hydrochloric acid (HCl). These three acids are strong acids. That means they ionize to a high degree in water and produce hydrogen ions. The presence of hydrogen ions makes strong acids good electrolytes.

Acetic acid ($HC_2H_3O_2$), carbonic acid (H_2CO_3), and boric acid (H_3BO_3) are weak acids. They do not ionize to a high degree in water, so they produce

COMMON ACIDS

Name	Formula	Uses
Strong Hydrochloric	HCl	Pickling steel Cleaning bricks and metals Digesting food
Sulfuric	H_2SO_4	Manufacturing paints, plastics, fertilizers Dehydrating agent
Nitric	HNO_3	Removing tarnish Making explosives (TNT) Making fertilizers
Weak Carbonic	H_2CO_3	Carbonating beverages
Boric	H_3BO_3	Washing eyes
Phosphoric	H_3PO_4	Making fertilizers and detergents
Acetic	$HC_2H_3O_2$	Making cellulose acetate used in fibers and films
Citric	$H_3C_6H_5O_7$	Making soft drinks

Figure 9–22 *The name, formula, and uses of some common acids are given in this table. What ion do all these acids contain?*

few hydrogen ions. Weak acids are poor electrolytes. Figure 9–22 lists the name, formula, and uses of some common acids. Remember to handle any acid—weak or strong—with care.

SECTION REVIEW

1. What are three important properties of acids?
2. Why are acids called proton donors?
3. How could you *safely* determine whether an unknown solution is an acid?

9–6 Bases

Section Objective

To identify bases

Another class of compounds that are probably quite familiar to you are **bases.** Bases are found in household products such as lye, milk of magnesia, deodorants, ammonia, and soap.

Figure 9–23 *Red litmus paper turns blue in a basic solution (top). Phenolphthalein turns bright pink (bottom).*

Properties of Bases

When dissolved in water, all bases share certain physical and chemical properties. Bases usually taste bitter and are slippery to the touch. However, bases can be poisonous and corrosive. So you should *never* use taste and touch to identify bases.

Bases turn litmus paper from red to blue and phenolphthalein to bright pink. Bases emulsify, or dissolve, fats and oils. They do this by reacting with the fat or oil to form a soap. The base ammonium hydroxide is used as a household cleaner because it "cuts" grease. The strong base sodium hydroxide, or lye, is used to clean clogged drains.

All bases contain the **hydroxide ion, OH⁻.** When dissolved in water, bases produce this ion. Because the hydroxide ion (OH^-) can combine with a hydrogen ion (H^+) and form water, a base is often defined as a proton acceptor.

Common Bases

Strong bases dissolve readily in water to produce large numbers of ions. So strong bases are good electrolytes. Examples of strong bases include

Figure 9–24 *The name, formula, and uses of some common bases are given in this table. What ion do all these bases contain?*

COMMON BASES		
Name	**Formula**	**Uses**
Strong Sodium hydroxide	NaOH	Making soap Drain cleaner
Potassium hydroxide	KOH	Making soft soap Battery electrolyte
Calcium hydroxide	$Ca(OH)_2$	Leather production Making plaster
Magnesium hydroxide	$Mg(OH)_2$	Laxative Antacid
Weak Ammonium hydroxide	NH_4OH	Household cleaner
Aluminum hydroxide	$Al(OH)_3$	Antacid Deodorant

potassium hydroxide (KOH), sodium hydroxide (NaOH), and calcium hydroxide (Ca(OH)$_2$).

Weak bases do not produce large numbers of ions when dissolved in water. So weak bases are poor electrolytes. Ammonium hydroxide (NH$_4$OH) and aluminum hydroxide (Al(OH)$_3$) are weak bases. See Figure 9–24.

SECTION REVIEW

1. What are three important properties of bases?
2. Why are bases called proton acceptors?
3. If an electric conductivity setup were placed in the following solutions, would the light be bright or dim? NH$_4$OH, KOH, NaOH, Al(OH)$_3$

9–7 Acids and Bases in Solution: Salts

Solutions can be acidic, basic, or neutral. To measure the acidity of a solution, the **pH** scale is used. The pH of a solution is a measure of the hydronium ion (H$_3$O$^+$) concentration. Remember that the hydronium ion is formed by the attraction between a hydrogen ion (H$^+$) from an acid and a water molecule (H$_2$O). So the pH of a solution indicates how acidic the solution is.

The pH scale is a series of numbers from 0 to 14. The middle of the scale, 7, is the neutral point.

Figure 9–25 *On the pH scale, 7 is neutral, acids are between 0 and 7, bases between 7 and 14. Are you surprised to learn how many of the substances you use every day contain acids and bases? Which fruit is most acidic? What cleaner is most basic?*

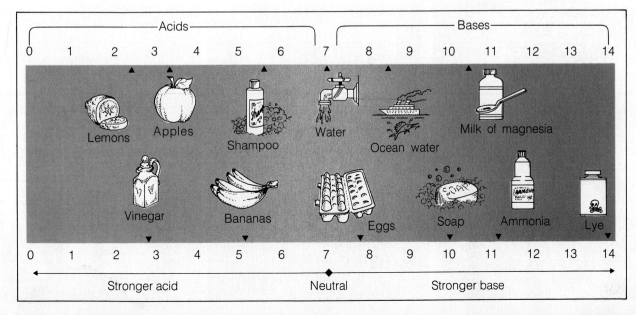

A Homemade Indicator

1. Shred two leaves of red cabbage and boil them in some water until the liquid gets very dark. **CAUTION:** *Wear safety goggles and use extreme care when working with heated liquids.*

2. When the liquid and shreds have cooled, squeeze all the purple juice you can from the shreds. Pour the liquid into a container.

3. Into 5 separate containers, pour about 3 to 4 mL of each of the following substances: shampoo, grapefruit juice, clear soft drink, milk, ammonia cleaner.

4. Add about 2 mL of the cabbage liquid. Stir and observe any color changes.

The cabbage liquid will turn bright red in most acids and blue-purple in most bases. Identify each substance.

A neutral solution has a pH of 7. It is neither an acid nor a base. Water is a neutral liquid.

A solution with a pH below 7 is an acid. Strong acids have *low* pH numbers. Would hydrochloric acid have a pH closer to 2 or to 6?

A solution with a pH above 7 is a base. Strong bases have *high* pH numbers. What would be the pH of NaOH?

Determining Solution pH

The pH of a solution can be determined by using an indicator. You already know about two common indicators—litmus paper and phenolphthalein. Other indicators include pH paper, methyl orange, and bromthymol blue. Each indicator shows a specific color change as the pH of a solution changes.

Common household materials can be used as indicators. Red cabbage juice covers the entire pH range. Grape juice is bright pink in the presence of an acid and bright yellow in the presence of a base. Even tea can serve as an indicator. Have you ever noticed how the color of tea changes when you add lemon juice? For very accurate pH measurements, a pH meter is used.

Formation of Salts

When acids react chemically with bases, they form a class of compounds called salts. A salt is a

Figure 9–26 *Nature has its own indicators! Hydrangeas have pink flowers in basic soil (left) and blue flowers in acidic soil (center). A common indicator used in the laboratory is pH paper (right).*

compound formed from the positive ion of a base and the negative ion of an acid. It is a neutral substance. A salt is usually made of a metal and a nonmetal. For example, NaCl and KBr are salts. What are the names of these salts? Sometimes a salt is made of one or more polyatomic ions. NH_4Cl, $CaSO_4$, and NH_4NO_3 are such salts. Can you name these salts?

The reaction of an acid with a base to produce a salt and water is called **neutralization** (noo-truhl-uh-ZAY-shuhn). In neutralization, the properties of the acid and the base are lost as two neutral substances—water and a salt—are formed.

The reaction of HCl with NaOH is a neutralization reaction. The positive hydrogen ion from the acid combines with the negative hydroxide ion from the base. This produces water. The remaining ion of the acid combines with the remaining ion of the base to form a salt.

$$H^+Cl^- + Na^+OH^- \longrightarrow H_2O + NaCl$$

Many of the salts formed by a neutralization reaction are insoluble in water. They crystallize out of solution and remain in the solid phase. An insoluble substance that crystallizes out of solution is called a **precipitate** (prih-SIHP-uh-tayt). The process by which a precipitate forms is called **precipitation.** Examples of precipitates include magnesium carbonate, silver chloride, and aluminum phosphate. Snow, rain, sleet, and hail are considered forms of precipitation because they fall out of solution. Out of what solution do they precipitate?

A neutralization reaction is a double replacement reaction. And a very important one, too. For a dangerous acid can be combined with a dangerous base to form a harmless salt and neutral water.

Figure 9–27 *To control dangerous acid spills, these firefighters spray a blanket of base over the acid. The result is a neutral salt and water. What is this reaction called?*

SECTION REVIEW

1. What is pH? Describe the pH scale.
2. What is the pH of an acid? A base? A neutral solution?
3. How can the pH of a solution be determined?
4. What is neutralization? What are the products of a neutralization reaction?
5. Use an equation to show the neutralization reaction between H_2SO_4 and NaOH.

Acids, Bases, and Salts

Problem

What are some properties of acids and bases? What happens when acids react with bases?

Materials *(per group)*

safety goggles   stirring rod
6 medium-sized   medicine dropper
  test tubes   evaporating dish
test tube rack   beaker
red and blue litmus paper
phenolphthalein
solutions of H_2SO_4, HCl, HNO_3
solutions of KOH, NaOH, $Ca(OH)_2$

Procedure

A. Acids

1. Put your safety goggles on. Over a sink, pour about 5 mL of each acid into separate test tubes. **CAUTION:** *Handle acids with extreme care. They can burn the skin.* Place the test tubes in the rack. Test the effect of each acid on litmus paper by dipping a stirring rod into the acid and then touching the rod to the litmus paper. Test each acid with both red and blue litmus paper. *Be sure to clean the rod between uses.* Record your observations.
2. Add 1 drop of phenolphthalein to each test tube. Record your observations.

B. Bases

1. Over a sink, pour about 5 mL of each base into separate test tubes. **CAUTION:** *Handle bases with extreme care.* Place the test tubes in the rack. Test the contents of each tube with red and blue litmus paper. Record your observations.
2. Add 1 drop of phenolphthalein to each test tube. Record your observations.
3. Place 5 mL of sodium hydroxide solution in a small beaker and add 2 drops of phenolphthalein. Record the color of the solution.

4. While slowly stirring, carefully add a few drops of hydrochloric acid until the mixture changes color. Record the color change. This point is known as the indicator endpoint. Test with blue and red litmus paper. Record your observations.
5. Carefully pour some of the mixture into a porcelain evaporating dish. Let the mixture evaporate until it is dry. How would you describe its appearance?

Observations

1. What color do acids turn litmus paper? Phenolphthalein?
2. What color do bases turn litmus paper? Phenolphthalein?
3. What happens to the color of the sodium hydroxide-phenolphthalein solution when hydrochloric acid is added?
4. Does the substance formed by the reaction of sodium hydroxide with hydrochloric acid affect litmus paper?
5. Describe the appearance of the substance that remains after evaporation. DO NOT TASTE IT. But how do you think this substance would taste?

Conclusions

1. What are some properties of acids? Of bases?
2. What type of substance is formed when an acid reacts with a base? What is the name of this reaction? What is the other product of this reaction?
3. Why does this substance have no effect on litmus paper?
4. What is meant by an indicator's endpoint?
5. Write a balanced equation for the reaction between sodium hydroxide and hydrochloric acid.

CHAPTER REVIEW

SUMMARY

9–1 Nature of Solutions

❏ A solution is a homogeneous mixture in which a solute is dissolved in a solvent.

❏ A solution in which the solvent is water is an aqueous solution. A solution in which the solvent is alcohol is a tincture.

❏ An aqueous solution that conducts an electric current is called an electrolyte. A nonelectrolyte does not conduct an electric current.

9–2 Making Solutions

❏ Two liquids that dissolve in each other are said to be miscible.

❏ The rate of solution of a solid in a liquid can be increased by stirring the solution, powdering the solvent, and heating the solution.

❏ The solubility of a solute depends on the conditions of temperature and pressure.

❏ Depending upon concentration, a solution can be saturated, unsaturated, or supersaturated.

9–3 Water—The Universal Solvent

❏ The polarity of water enables it to dissolve polar solutes and ionic solutes.

❏ A rule for solutions is like dissolves like.

9–4 Suspensions and Colloids

❏ The solute particles in a suspension are large enough to be seen and to settle out upon standing.

❏ A colloid is a homogeneous mixture whose particle size is intermediate between a suspension and a solution.

9–5 Acids

❏ Acids taste sour, turn blue litmus paper red, and ionize in water to form hydrogen ions (H^+).

9–6 Bases

❏ Bases feel slippery, taste bitter, turn red litmus paper blue, and produce hydroxide ions (OH^-) in solution.

9–7 Acids and Bases in Solution: Salts

❏ The pH of a solution is a measure of the hydronium ion concentration.

❏ A neutral substance has a pH of 7. Acids have pH numbers lower than 7. Bases have pH numbers higher than 7.

❏ When an acid chemically combines with a base, the reaction is called neutralization. The products of neutralization are a salt and water.

VOCABULARY

Define each term in a complete sentence.

acid	concentration	indicator	precipitate	solvent
aqueous solution	dilute solution	insoluble	precipitation	supersaturated solution
base	dissociation	ionization	salt	suspension
boiling point elevation	effervescence	miscible	saturated solution	tincture
Brownian motion	electrolyte	neutralization	soft water	unsaturated solution
colloid	freezing point depression	nonelectrolyte	solubility	
concentrated solution	hard water	pH	soluble	
	hydronium ion	polar molecule	solute	
	hydroxide ion	polarity	solution	

CONTENT REVIEW: MULTIPLE CHOICE

On a separate sheet of paper, write the letter of the answer that best completes each statement.

1. A solution that conducts an electric current is called a(an)
a. nonelectrolyte.   b. tincture.   c. electrolyte.   d. colloid.

2. Which process will not increase the rate of solution of a solid in a liquid?
a. powdering the solution   b. cooling the solution
c. heating the solution   d. stirring the solution

3. A solution that contains all the solute it can hold at a given temperature is
a. saturated.   b. unsaturated.   c. supersaturated.   d. dissociated.

4. If the solute particles are large enough to be seen and to be filtered, the mixture is a (an)
a. colloid.   b. true solution.   c. electrolyte.   d. suspension.

5. Which is *not* a property of a colloid?
a. particles smaller than a suspension   b. shows Brownian motion
c. separates upon standing   d. scatters light

6. Which of the following acids is *not* a strong acid?
a. HCl   b. H_2CO_3 c. H_2SO_4 d. HNO_3

7. Bases contain which ion?
a. OH^- b. H_3O^+ c. H^+ d. NH_4^+

8. The pH of a strong base would be closest to
a. 7.   b. 2.   c. 9.   d. 14.

9. When an acid combines chemically with a base, the products are
a. a salt and hydrogen.   b. water and carbon dioxide.
c. a salt and water.   d. a metal and a nonmetal.

10. The pH of the products formed by a neutralization reaction is
a. 1.   b. 7.   c. 14.   d. 0.

CONTENT REVIEW: COMPLETION

On a separate sheet of paper, write the word or words that best complete each statement.

1. In a solution, the substance being dissolved is called the _____.

2. Solubility is affected by _____ and _____.

3. Because a water molecule has a positive end and a negative end, it is a (an) _____ molecule.

4. The constant movement of colloidal particles as they are bombarded by solvent molecules is called _____.

5. A compound that shows a definite color change when mixed with an acid is called a (an) _____.

6. The attraction between a hydrogen ion and a water molecule results in the formation of the _____ ion.

7. Bases have a (an) _____ taste.

8. As the pH number of an acid decreases, the strength of the acid _____.

9. The chemical reaction in which an acid combines with a base is called _____.

10. The products of the reaction between HCl and KOH are _____ and _____.

CONTENT REVIEW: TRUE OR FALSE

Determine whether each statement is true or false. Then on a separate sheet of paper, write "true" if it is true. If it is false, change the underlined word or words to make the statement true.

1. A solution is a <u>heterogeneous</u> mixture.
2. Two liquids that dissolve in each other are said to be <u>miscible</u>.
3. The escape of a gas from a liquid solution is called <u>ionization</u>.
4. For solutions, like dissolves <u>unlike</u>.
5. Soap does not lather easily in <u>soft</u> water.
6. Acids are often defined as <u>proton donors</u>.
7. Strong acids are <u>poor</u> electrolytes.
8. All bases contain the <u>hydroxide</u> ion.
9. A neutral solution has a pH of <u>0</u>.
10. An acid reacts with a base in <u>neutralization</u>.

CONCEPT REVIEW: SKILL BUILDING

Use the skills you have developed in the chapter to complete each activity.

1. **Classifying compounds** Identify each of the following compounds as an acid, base, or salt: a. $CaCO_3$ b. HI c. CsOH d. H_3PO_4 e. $MgSO_4$ f. $Ga(OH)_3$

2. **Applying concepts** The caps are removed from a warm bottle and a cold bottle of carbonated beverage. The soda in the cold bottle effervesces slightly. The soda in the warm bottle effervesces rapidly.
   a. What two conditions affecting solubility are present here?
   b. Which condition is the variable?
   c. Give an explanation for what happens.

3. **Designing an experiment** Describe an experiment to determine if a solution is saturated or unsaturated.

4. **Interpreting graphs** Using the solubility curves in Figure 9–7, determine the
   a. solubility of KNO_3 at 40°C.
   b. number of grams of $NaNO_3$ needed to make a saturated solution at 10°C.
   c. number of grams of NH_4Cl that settle out when a solution is cooled from 90°C to 70°C.
   d. salt that is most soluble at 20°C.
   e. salt that is least soluble at 20°C.

5. **Identifying patterns** A crystal of solute is added to a saturated, unsaturated, and supersaturated solution. Describe what happens in each case.

6. **Making generalizations** Explain the following observations:
   a. Crystals of ionic sodium chloride will not conduct an electric current unless they are dissolved in water.
   b. Water is both an acid and a base.
   c. A given solution that turns red litmus paper blue will neutralize an acid.
   d. Antacids, such as milk of magnesia, are used to reduce excess stomach acid.

7. **Making inferences** Explain why it would be impossible for you to bring a sample of a true universal solvent to class—if indeed such a solvent existed.

CONCEPT REVIEW: ESSAY

Discuss each of the following in a brief paragraph.

1. Describe three ways in which the rate of solution of a solid in a liquid can be increased. Use a specific example.
2. Explain how a saturated solution of one solute can be concentrated and a saturated solution of a different solute can be dilute.
3. Compare the composition and effects of hard water and soft water.

Carbon Chemistry 10

CHAPTER SECTIONS

10–1 Carbon and Its Compounds

10–2 Hydrocarbons

10–3 Substituted Hydrocarbons

10–4 Chemistry for Life

CHAPTER OBJECTIVES

After completing this chapter, you will be able to

10–1 Describe the nature and properties of organic compounds.

10–1 Draw structural formulas for several simple organic compounds.

10–1 Relate the formation of isomers to the large number of organic compounds.

10–2 Distinguish between saturated and unsaturated hydrocarbons.

10–2 Identify three series of hydrocarbons.

10–3 Classify several groups of substituted hydrocarbons.

10–4 Describe the composition and uses of three types of organic compounds in the chemistry of the human body.

Banana, strawberry, pineapple, peach—what's your special flavor? How would you order your favorite ice cream sundae? Certainly not by asking for a scoop of methyl butylacetate! Yet that is exactly what you are eating when you enjoy a banana ice cream sundae.

Methyl butylacetate is the banana-flavored compound that makes banana ice cream different from strawberry or vanilla ice cream. It is one of a special group of compounds that gives flavors to food. In some cases, these compounds naturally occur in a food. So the flavoring is natural. Pineapples have their characteristic natural flavor because of the presence of ethyl butyrate. In other cases, the compounds are added to foods as artificial flavoring.

Methyl butylacetate, ethyl butyrate, and other substances similar to these belong to a much larger group of compounds known as organic compounds. The sugar and cream in the ice cream also contain organic compounds. Organic compounds are even present in the containers in which ice cream is packaged.

Perhaps you can tell already that organic compounds are important substances with a variety of uses. But what are organic compounds? In this chapter, you will learn the answer to that question. You will also learn the useful, surprising, and sometimes delicious applications of these compounds in your daily life. So just sit back and think about a nice big ethyl cinnemate sundae topped with isoamyl salicylate. . . .

These ice cream sodas and sundaes are delicious examples of the many uses of organic compounds.

10-1 Carbon and Its Compounds

To describe the nature of organic compounds

What do sugar, plastic, paper, and gasoline have in common? All of these substances contain the element carbon. Carbon is present in more than 2 million known compounds, and this number is rapidly increasing. Approximately 100,000 new carbon compounds are being isolated or synthesized every year! In fact, more than 90 percent of all known compounds contain carbon!

Most compounds that contain carbon are known as organic compounds. The word *organic* means "coming from life." Because carbon-containing compounds are present in all living things, scientists once believed that **organic compounds** could be produced only by living organisms. Living things were thought to have a mysterious "vital force" that was responsible for creating carbon compounds. It was believed that the force could not be duplicated in the laboratory.

In 1828, the German chemist Friedrich Wöhler produced an organic compound called urea from two inorganic substances. Urea is a waste product produced by the human body. It was not long

Figure 10-1 *The element carbon is present in more than 2 million known compounds. Here you see two different forms of the pure element—diamond (left) and graphite (right). What branch of chemistry deals with carbon compounds?*

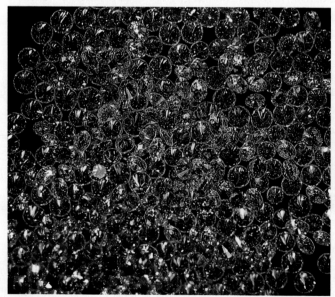

Figure 10–2 *Because of the way carbon atoms combine with other carbon atoms as well as with atoms of different elements, a great variety of organic compounds exists. These include synthetic rubber for automobile tires (top left), candlewax (top right), nylon (right), and aspirin (bottom). What types of bonds can carbon atoms form with other carbon atoms?*

before chemists accepted the idea that organic compounds could be prepared from materials that were never part of a living organism. What is common to all organic compounds is not that they originated in living things but that they all contain the element carbon. Today, the majority of organic compounds are synthesized in laboratories.

The branch of chemistry that deals with the study of carbon compounds is called **organic chemistry.** You should note, however, that there are some carbon compounds that are *not* considered organic compounds. The carbonates of metals, such as calcium carbonate and magnesium carbonate, are considered inorganic compounds. So are the oxides of carbon, such as carbon dioxide and carbon monoxide.

The Bonding of Carbon

Carbon's ability to combine with itself and with other elements explains why such a large number of carbon compounds exist. Carbon atoms form covalent bonds with other carbon atoms. The simplest bond involves 2 carbon atoms. The most complex involves thousands of carbon atoms. The carbon atoms can form long straight chains, branched chains, single rings, or rings joined together.

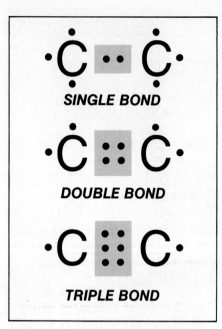

SINGLE BOND

DOUBLE BOND

TRIPLE BOND

Figure 10–3 *In a single bond, one pair of electrons is shared. In a double bond, two pairs of electrons are shared. How many pairs of electrons are shared in a triple bond?*

Figure 10–4 *Nonpolar organic compounds do not dissolve in polar solvents. So oil—a mixture of organic compounds—floats on water, creating this oil slick.*

The bonds between carbon atoms can be single covalent bonds, double covalent bonds, or triple covalent bonds. In a single bond, one pair of electrons is shared between 2 carbon atoms. In a double bond, two pairs of electrons are shared between 2 carbon atoms. How many pairs of electrons are shared in a triple bond?

Carbon atoms also bond with many other elements. These other elements include oxygen, hydrogen, members of the nitrogen family, and the halogens. The simplest organic compounds contain just carbon and hydrogen. Because there are so many compounds of carbon and hydrogen, they form a class of organic compounds all their own. You will read about this class of compounds in the next section.

A great variety of organic compounds exist because the same atoms that bond together to form one compound may be arranged in several other ways in several other compounds. Each different arrangement of atoms represents a separate organic compound.

Properties of Organic Compounds

As you just learned, carbon compounds contain covalent bonds. These covalent bonds form molecules that are typically nonpolar, or without positive and negative ends. These two bonding characteristics determine some of the physical and chemical properties of organic compounds.

Organic compounds usually exist as gases, liquids, or low-melting solids. Organic liquids generally have strong odors and low boiling points. Another property of organic liquids is that they do not conduct an electric current. What is the name for a substance whose solution does not conduct electricity?

Most organic solids have low melting points. Some even melt at temperatures slightly above room temperature. Organic compounds whose molecules are nonpolar will not dissolve in polar solvents, such as water. Oil, which is a mixture of organic compounds, floats on water because the two liquids are insoluble. In what type of solvents will most organic substances readily dissolve?

Structural Formulas

A molecular formula for a compound indicates what elements make up that compound and how many atoms of each element are present in a molecule. For example, the molecular formula for the organic compound ethane is C_2H_6. In every molecule of ethane, there are 2 carbon atoms and 6 hydrogen atoms.

What a molecular formula does not indicate about a molecule of a compound is how the different atoms are arranged. To do this, a **structural formula** is used. A structural formula shows the kind, number, and arrangement of atoms in a molecule. You can think of a structural formula as being a model of a molecule.

Figure 10–5 shows the structural formula for ethane and two other organic compounds—methane and propane. Note that in a structural formula, a dash (—) is used to represent the pair of shared electrons forming a covalent bond. In writing structural formulas, it is important that you remember the electron arrangement in a carbon atom.

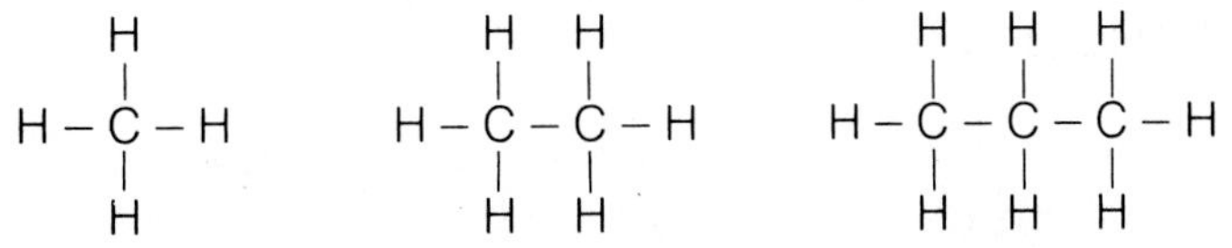

Sharpen Your Skills

Isomers

For this activity you will need a stack of blank index cards, a felt-tipped marker, and a package of straws or pipe cleaners.

1. Take half of the index cards and label one side of each card with the letter C.

2. Take the rest of the index cards and label each card with the letter H.

3. Using the straws or pipe cleaners to represent bonds, see how many isomers you can make for the formula C_6H_{14}. Remember that each carbon atom must be bonded to four other atoms.

$$
\begin{array}{ccc}
\text{H} & \text{H}\quad\text{H} & \text{H}\quad\text{H}\quad\text{H} \\
| & |\quad\ | & |\quad\ |\quad\ | \\
\text{H}-\text{C}-\text{H} & \text{H}-\text{C}-\text{C}-\text{H} & \text{H}-\text{C}-\text{C}-\text{C}-\text{H} \\
| & |\quad\ | & |\quad\ |\quad\ | \\
\text{H} & \text{H}\quad\text{H} & \text{H}\quad\text{H}\quad\text{H}
\end{array}
$$

METHANE
CH_4

ETHANE
C_2H_6

PROPANE
C_3H_8

Figure 10–5 *The first three members of the alkane series are methane, ethane, and propane. Note that each carbon atom is surrounded by four dashes, corresponding to four pairs of shared electrons.*

Carbon has 4 valence electrons, or 4 electrons in its outermost energy level. Each of these 4 electrons will form a covalent bond with an electron of another atom to produce a stable outermost level containing 8 electrons. Therefore, when structural formulas are written, there can be no dangling bonds—no dangling dashes!

Isomers

Structural formulas are very useful in organic chemistry. Knowing the arrangement of atoms in a molecule is important because several different organic compounds may have the same molecular

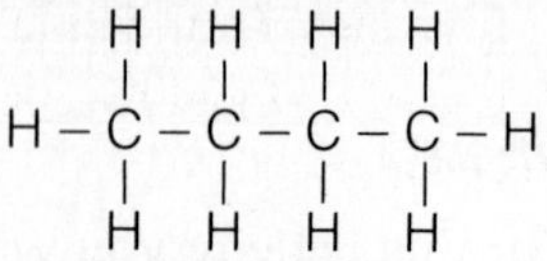

BUTANE
C_4H_{10}

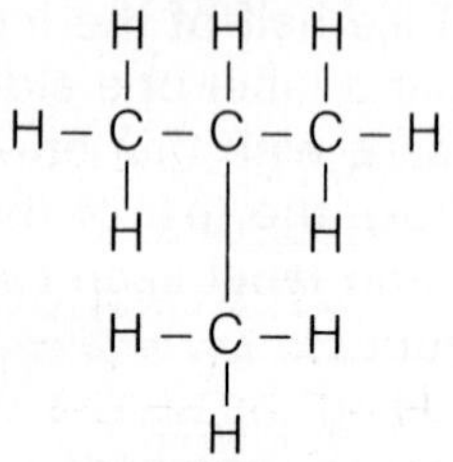

ISOBUTANE
C_4H_{10}

Figure 10-6 *Butane has two isomers—normal butane and isobutane. Which isomer is a branched chain?*

formula. The structural formula helps to tell the compounds apart.

Compounds that have the same molecular formula but different structures are called **isomers.** Figure 10–6 shows two isomers of butane, C_4H_{10}. Notice that one isomer is a straight chain and the other isomer is a branched chain. In a branched chain, all the carbon atoms are not in a straight line. This difference in structure will account for any difference in the physical and chemical properties of these two compounds.

Figure 10–7 shows three isomers of pentane, C_5H_{12}. This time there is one straight chain and two branched chains. To see the difference between the two branched chains, count the number of carbon atoms in the straight-chain portion of each molecule. How many are there in each branched isomer?

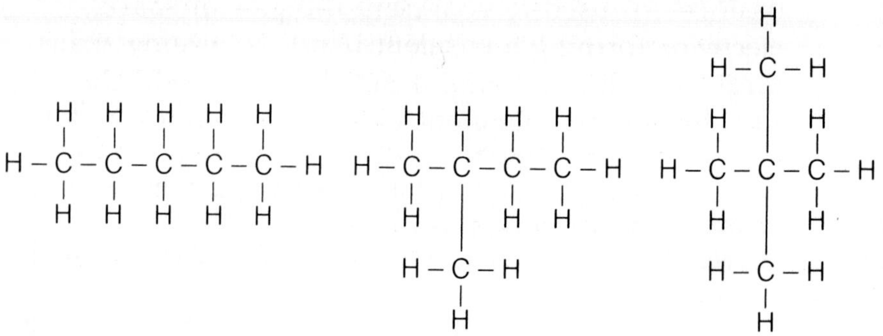

Figure 10-7 *As the number of carbon atoms increases, the number of isomers increases. How many carbon atoms are in the straight-chain portion of each pentane isomer?*

What do you think happens to the number of possible isomers as the number of carbon atoms in a molecule increases? The compound whose formula is $C_{15}H_{32}$ could have more than 400 isomers!

SECTION REVIEW

1. What are organic compounds?
2. What four factors account for the abundance of carbon compounds?
3. What are three general properties of organic compounds?
4. Could two compounds have the same structural formula but different molecular formulas?

10-2 Hydrocarbons

To classify various types of hydrocarbons

Have you ever noticed a sign at a service station advertising "high octane" gasoline? Octane is a member of a large group of organic compounds known as **hydrocarbons.** A hydrocarbon is an organic compound that contains only hydrogen and carbon.

There are thousands of different hydrocarbons. Many fuels contain hydrocarbons. Natural gas and petroleum are the most abundant sources of hydrocarbons. Natural gas is mostly the hydrocarbon methane. Petroleum is a more complex mixture of hydrocarbons. The hydrocarbons in petroleum range from 1-carbon molecules to more than 50-carbon molecules. Hydrocarbons are excellent fuels because they burn in the presence of oxygen to produce heat and light.

Hydrocarbons can be classified as saturated or unsaturated depending upon the type of bonds between carbon atoms. In **saturated hydrocarbons,** all the bonds between carbon atoms are single covalent bonds. In **unsaturated hydrocarbons,** one or more of the bonds between carbon atoms is a double covalent or triple covalent bond.

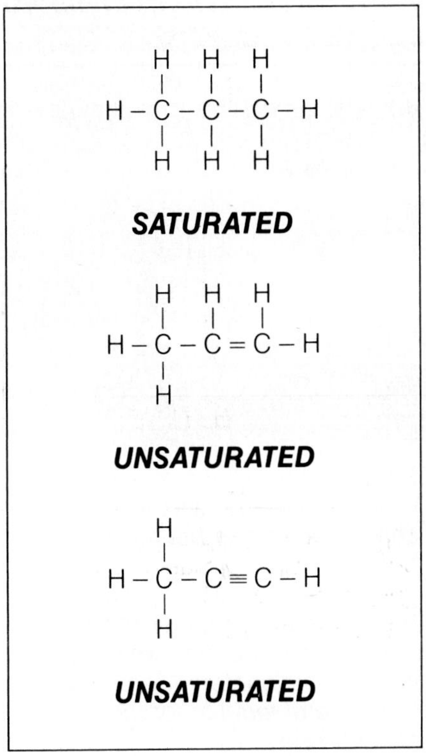

Alkanes

The **alkanes** are straight-chain or branched-chain hydrocarbons in which all the bonds between carbon atoms are single covalent bonds. Alkanes are saturated hydrocarbons. All the hydrocarbons that are alkanes belong to the alkane series. The simplest member of the alkane series is methane, CH_4. Methane consists of 1 carbon atom surrounded by 4 hydrogen atoms. Why are there 4 hydrogen atoms?

The next simplest alkane is ethane, C_2H_6. How does the formula for ethane differ from the formula for methane? After ethane, the next member of the alkane series is propane, C_3H_8. Can you begin to see a pattern to the formulas for each successive alkane? Ethane has one more carbon atom and two more hydrogen atoms than methane. Propane has one more carbon atom and two more hydrogen atoms than ethane. Each member of the alkane series is formed by adding 1 carbon atom and 2 hydrogen atoms to the previous compound.

Figure 10-8 *Hydrocarbons can be classified as saturated or unsaturated on the basis of the type of bonds between carbon atoms. Saturated hydrocarbons contain single covalent bonds. What type of bonds do unsaturated hydrocarbons contain?*

239

Figure 10-9 *Common alkanes include methane, which is also called marsh gas because it is present in swamps and marshes (left); propane, which is burned to provide heat for hot air balloons (center); and butane, which is the fuel in most lighters (right). What is the general formula for the alkanes?*

The pattern that exists for the alkanes can be used to determine the formula for any member of the series. Each alkane differs from the preceding member of the series by the group CH_2. So a general formula for the alkanes can be written. That general formula is C_nH_{2n+2}. The letter n is the number of carbon atoms in the alkane. What would be the formula for a 15-carbon hydrocarbon? For a 30-carbon compound?

Naming Hydrocarbons

Figure 10–10 shows the first ten members of the alkane series. Look at the names of the compounds. How is each name the same? How is each different?

Often in organic chemistry, the names of the compounds in the same series will have the same ending, or suffix. Thus, the members of the alkane series all end with the suffix *-ane*, the same ending as in the series name. The first part of each name, or the prefix, indicates the number of carbon atoms present in the compound. The prefix *meth-* indicates 1 carbon atom. The prefix *eth-*, 2 carbon atoms, and the prefix *prop-*, 3. According to Figure 10–10, how many carbon atoms are indicated by the prefix *but-?* How many carbon atoms are in octane? As you study other hydrocarbon series, you will see that

ALKANE SERIES

Name	Formula	Name	Formula
Methane	CH_4	Hexane	C_6H_{14}
Ethane	C_2H_6	Heptane	C_7H_{16}
Propane	C_3H_8	Octane	C_8H_{18}
Butane	C_4H_{10}	Nonane	C_9H_{20}
Pentane	C_5H_{12}	Decane	$C_{10}H_{22}$

Figure 10-10 *This table shows the names and formulas for the first ten members of the alkane series. What does the prefix dec- mean?*

these prefixes are used again and again. It is important that you become familiar with the prefixes that mean 1 to 10 carbon atoms.

Alkenes

Hydrocarbons in which at least one pair of carbon atoms is joined by a double covalent bond are called **alkenes.** Alkenes are unsaturated hydrocarbons. The first member of the alkene series is ethene, C_2H_4. The next member of the alkene series is propene, C_3H_6.

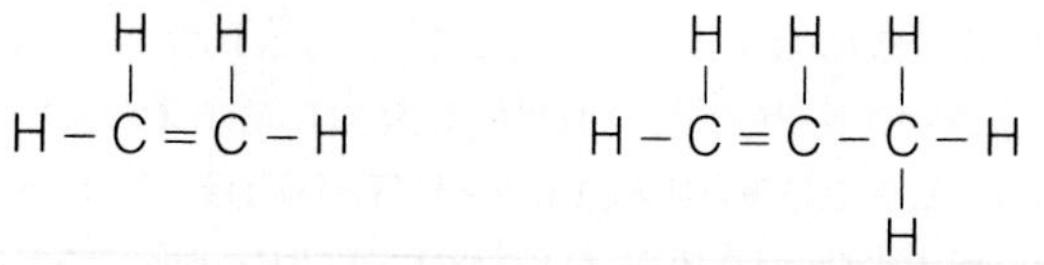

ETHENE
C_2H_4

PROPENE
C_3H_6

Figure 10-11 *The first two members of the alkene series are ethene and propene. What kind of bonds do the alkenes have?*

Figure 10–12 on page 242 shows the first seven members of the alkene series. What do you notice about the name of each compound?

ALKENE SERIES

Name	Formula
Ethene	C_2H_4
Propene	C_3H_6
Butene	C_4H_8
Pentene	C_5H_{10}
Hexene	C_6H_{12}
Heptene	C_7H_{14}
Octene	C_8H_{16}

Figure 10-12 *This table shows the names and formulas for the first seven members of the alkene series. What would a 9-carbon alkene be called?*

Figure 10-14 *This table shows the names and formulas for the first five members of the alkyne series. What is the general formula for the alkynes?*

ALKYNE SERIES

Name	Formula
Ethyne	C_2H_2
Propyne	C_3H_4
Butyne	C_4H_6
Pentyne	C_5H_8
Hexyne	C_6H_{10}

As you look at the formulas for the alkenes, you will again see a pattern in the number of carbon and hydrogen atoms added to each successive compound. The pattern is the addition of 1 carbon atom and 2 hydrogen atoms. The general formula for the alkenes is C_nH_{2n}. The letter n is the number of carbon atoms in the compound. What is the formula for an alkene with 12 carbons? With 20 carbons?

In general, alkenes are more reactive than alkanes because a double bond is more easily broken than a single bond. So alkenes can react chemically by adding other atoms directly to their molecules.

Alkynes

Hydrocarbons in which at least one pair of carbon atoms is joined by a triple covalent bond are called **alkynes.** Alkynes are unsaturated hydrocarbons. The simplest alkyne is ethyne, C_2H_2, which is commonly known as acetylene. Perhaps you have heard of acetylene torches that are used in welding.

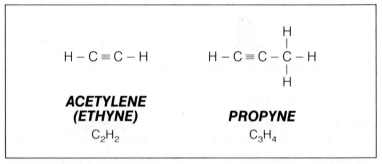

Figure 10-13 *The simplest alkynes are ethyne and propyne. What is the common name for ethyne?*

The first five members of the alkyne series are listed in Figure 10–14. Here again, each successive member of the alkyne series differs by the addition of 1 carbon atom and 2 hydrogen atoms. The general formula for the alkynes is C_nH_{2n-2}.

The alkynes are even more reactive than the alkenes. Very little energy is needed to break a triple bond. Like the alkenes, alkynes can react chemically by adding other atoms directly to their molecules. If a triple bond is broken to form a double bond, what kind of hydrocarbon will result? If the triple bond is broken to form a single bond, what kind of hydrocarbon will result?

Cycloalkanes and Aromatic Hydrocarbons

All the hydrocarbons you have just learned about—the alkanes, alkenes, and alkynes—are either straight-chain or branched-chain molecules. But this is not the only structure a hydrocarbon can have. Some hydrocarbons are in the shape of rings. They are often called cyclic hydrocarbons. The two main groups of cyclic hydrocarbons are the **cycloalkanes** and the **aromatic hydrocarbons.**

Cycloalkanes are saturated hydrocarbon rings. This means that they contain only single covalent bonds between carbon atoms. The simplest cycloalkane contains 3 carbon atoms. Cycloalkanes are named simply by adding the prefix *cyclo-* to the appropriate alkane name. So the simplest cycloalkane is called cyclopropane. The saturated 6-carbon cycloalkane is called cyclohexane. See Figure 10–15. What do you think the saturated 7-carbon cycloalkane is called?

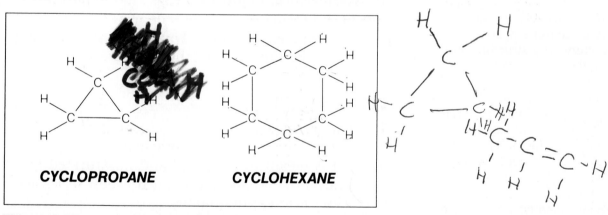

CYCLOPROPANE   **CYCLOHEXANE**

Figure 10-15 *Cycloalkanes are saturated hydrocarbon rings. What would the 5-carbon cycloalkane be called?*

Aromatic hydrocarbons are probably the best-known class of hydrocarbons. The name of this class comes from the fact that aromatic hydrocarbons share a common physical property. These compounds have strong and often pleasant odors.

The basic structure of an aromatic hydrocarbon is a ring of 6 carbon atoms joined by alternating single and double covalent bonds. This means that within the 6-carbon ring, there are 3 carbon-to-carbon single bonds and 3 carbon-to-carbon double bonds. The simplest aromatic hydrocarbon is called

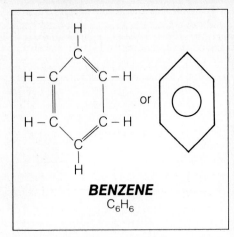

Figure 10-16 *Benzene is an aromatic hydrocarbon with a ring structure containing 6 carbon atoms joined by alternating single and double covalent bonds (left). Benzene is used in the manufacture of explosives (right).*

benzene, C_6H_6. Figure 10–16 shows the structural formula for benzene. Chemists often abbreviate this formula by drawing a hexagon with a circle in the center. Benzene is an excellent solvent for fats, oil, and rubber. It is used in the manufacture of many chemicals—including dyes, drugs, and explosives—and in the formation of synthetic materials. However, benzene is poisonous. For this reason, benzene should not be used in the school laboratory.

SECTION REVIEW

1. What are hydrocarbons?
2. Name three series of hydrocarbons.
3. What is meant by saturated and unsaturated hydrocarbons? Classify each hydrocarbon series according to these definitions.
4. What are the two groups of cyclic hydrocarbons?
5. Why is there no compound named cycloethane?

10–8 Substituted Hydrocarbons

Hydrocarbons are but one of several groups of organic compounds. Hydrocarbons contain only carbon and hydrogen atoms. But as you learned, carbon atoms form bonds with many other elements. So there are many different groups of organic

Figure 10-17 *Methanol, an organic alcohol (right), is used as a solvent in paints (left).*

compounds. **The important groups of organic compounds include alcohols, organic acids, esters, and halogen derivatives.**

Compounds such as alcohols, organic acids, esters, and halogen derivatives are called **substituted hydrocarbons.** A substituted hydrocarbon is formed when one or more hydrogen atoms in a hydrocarbon chain or ring is replaced by a different atom or group of atoms.

Alcohols

Alcohols are substituted hydrocarbons in which one or more hydrogen atoms have been replaced by an –OH group, or **hydroxyl group.** The simplest alcohol is methanol, CH_3OH. You can see from Figure 10–17 that methanol is formed when 1 hydrogen atom in methane is replaced by the –OH group. Methanol is used to make plastics and synthetic fibers. It is also used in automobile gas tank de-icers to prevent water that has condensed in the tank from freezing. Another important use of methanol is as a solvent. Methanol, however, is very poisonous, even when used externally.

As you can tell from the name methanol, alcohols are named by adding the suffix *-ol* to the name of the corresponding hydrocarbon. When an –OH group is substituted for 1 hydrogen atom in ethane, the resulting alcohol is ethanol, C_2H_5OH. Ethanol is produced naturally by the action of yeast or bacteria on the sugar stored in grains such as corn, wheat, and barley.

Figure 10-18 *The structural formula for ethylene glycol shows how two hydrogen atoms have been replaced by two –OH groups. Phenol is an alcohol derivative of benzene. What is a common use for each of these alcohols?*

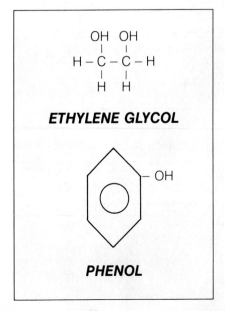

OH OH
| |
H – C – C – H
| |
H   H

ETHYLENE GLYCOL

PHENOL

Ethanol is a good solvent for many organic compounds that do not dissolve in water. Ethanol is used in medicines. It is also the alcohol used in alcoholic beverages. In order to make ethanol available for industrial and medicinal uses only, it must be made unfit for beverage purposes. So poisonous compounds such as methanol are added to ethanol. The resulting mixture is called **denatured alcohol.**

Some alcohols have more than one –OH group. When 2 hydrogen atoms in ethane are replaced by two –OH groups, the resulting alcohol is commonly called ethylene glycol, $C_2H_4(OH)_2$. Ethylene glycol is used as a "permanent" antifreeze in automobile radiators.

When 3 hydrogen atoms in propane are replaced by three –OH groups, the resulting alcohol is called glycerol, or glycerin, $C_3H_5(OH)_3$. Glycerol, a slow-flowing liquid with a sweet taste, is used in making cellophane, soap, cosmetics, and drugs.

An alcohol can be in the form of a ring as well as a chain. When 1 hydrogen atom in a benzene ring is replaced by an –OH group, the resulting alcohol is called phenol. Phenol is used in the preparation of plastics and as a disinfectant.

Organic Acids

Organic acids are substituted hydrocarbons that contain the –COOH group, or **carboxyl group.** Figure 10–19 shows the structural formula for two common organic acids. Notice that one of the carbon–oxygen bonds in the carboxyl group is a double bond.

Organic acids are named by adding the suffix *-oic* to the name of the corresponding hydrocarbon. Most organic acids, however, have common names that are used more frequently. The simplest organic acid is methanoic acid, HCOOH. Methanoic acid is commonly called formic acid. Formic acid is found in nature in the stinging nettle plant and in certain ants. Formic acid, produced by the ant, causes the ant bite to hurt. 540 -

The acid derived from ethane is commonly called acetic acid. Acetic acid is the acid in vinegar. Vinegar contains between 4 and 6 percent acetic acid. Citric acid, which is found in citrus fruits, is a

Figure 10-19 *Formic acid, also known as methanoic acid, is the simplest organic acid. It is the acid produced by ants and is responsible for the pain caused by an ant bite. Acetic acid, the acid in vinegar, is also known as ethanoic acid. What group is characteristic of organic acids?*

FORMIC ACID

ACETIC ACID

more complicated organic acid originally derived from the hydrocarbon propane.

Esters

If an alcohol and an organic acid are chemically combined, the resulting compound is called an **ester.** The reaction that produces an ester is called **esterification.** Esters are noted for their pleasant aromas and flavors. The substances mentioned earlier that give flavor to ice cream are esters.

Many esters occur naturally. Fruits such as strawberries, bananas, and pineapples get their sweet smell from esters. Esters can also be produced in the laboratory. Synthetic esters are used as perfume additives and artificial flavorings.

Halogen Derivatives

Hydrocarbons can undergo substitution reactions in which one or more hydrogen atoms are replaced by an atom or atoms of fluorine, chlorine, bromine, or iodine. The family name for these elements is halogens. So substituted hydrocarbons that contain halogens are called **halogen derivatives.**

A variety of useful substances result from adding halogens to hydrocarbons. The compound methyl chloride, CH_3Cl, is used as a refrigerant.

Figure 10-20 *Substituted hydrocarbons known as halogen derivatives have a wide variety of uses. The rain gear these people are wearing (left) is made of polyvinyl chloride. Teflon—which is a polymer of tetrafluoroethane, $C_2H_2F_4$—is used to make tape, wire insulation, fountain pens, and a nonstick coating for cooking utensils (right).*

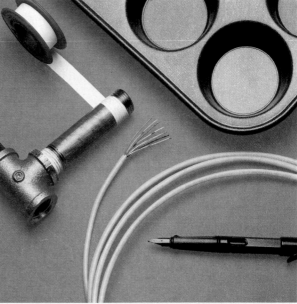

HELP WANTED: PERFUMER to help develop new fragrances for a cosmetics and household-products manufacturer. High school diploma required. On-the-job training provided.

Think about the fragrances that greet your sense of smell every day. Think hard because you may not be fully aware of the many odors around you. For example, try to remember the fragrance of the soap or cosmetics you used today. Or the scents of foods and drinks. Imagine the smell of orange juice or chocolate syrup. Think about the smell of a new car, wallet, or pair of shoes. Almost everything you buy or use has a distinct scent.

Some scents occur naturally in products, but other odors are purposely added. A person who develops scents is called a **perfumer**. Perfumers combine ingredients to make specific fragrances. Some of these ingredients—such as lemon oil—are found in nature, while others are synthetic, or artificial, ingredients.

Many of the more than 3000 ingredients used by perfumers are organic compounds. So an interest in chemistry is useful to a perfumer. Many fragrances are created by combining different ingredients until a combination with the desired fragrance is found. A perfumer may spend up to two years creating and testing one new fragrance. Read some product labels to discover items that contain fragrances created by perfumers.

If you would like information about a career as a perfumer, write to the Fragrance Foundation, 142 East 30th Street, New York, NY 10016.

Tetrachloroethane, $C_2H_2Cl_4$, which consists of 4 chlorine atoms substituted in an ethane molecule, is used in dry cleaning.

When 2 hydrogen atoms in a methane molecule are replaced by chlorine atoms, and the other 2 hydrogen atoms are replaced by fluorine atoms, a compound commonly known as Freon, CCl_2F_2, is formed. The actual name of this halogen derivative is dichlorodifluoromethane. Freon is the coolant used in many refrigerators and air conditioners.

SECTION REVIEW

1. What is a substituted hydrocarbon?
2. What is an alcohol?
3. What is an organic acid?
4. Methanol is used in car de-icers. What does this tell you about the freezing point of methanol?

10–4 Chemistry for Life

Section Objective

To describe the role of organic compounds in the chemistry of the human body

Have you ever thought of yourself as a chemical factory? The human body is one of the most amazing chemical factories ever created. It can produce chemicals from raw materials, start complex chemical reactions, repair and reproduce some of its own parts, and even correct its own mistakes.

What is the fuel that keeps your human chemical factory going? Nutrients contained in the foods you eat maintain the proper functioning of all the systems of the body. **The three main types of nutrients—carbohydrates, fats and oils, and proteins—are organic compounds.**

Carbohydrates

Carbohydrates are organic molecules of carbon, hydrogen, and oxygen in which there are two atoms of hydrogen for every atom of oxygen. Carbohydrates are classified as **sugars** or **starches.** The simplest carbohydrate is the sugar glucose, $C_6H_{12}O_6$.

Glucose has an isomer called fructose. Fructose is found in some fruits and in honey. When a glucose

Sharpen Your Skills

Food Additives

1. Collect the labels or wrappers from several common foods, such as bread, cereal, milk, and candy.

2. Carefully read the labels and make a list of all the additives—chemical substances that have been added to these foods.

3. Find out if each additive is organic or inorganic and the purpose of the additive.

4. Express your opinion about the benefits and/or risks of using additives in foods.

Figure 10-21 *The human body is a chemical factory that does an amazing variety of jobs. But to keep it working properly, the right nutrients must be supplied. What are these nutrients?*

Figure 10-22 *Carbohydrates are organic molecules of carbon, hydrogen, and oxygen. They are the body's main source of energy. The foods shown here (top) are rich in carbohydrates. Fats and oils are complex esters often called lipids. They too are sources of energy. The foods shown here (bottom) are rich in fats and oils.*

molecule is joined to a fructose molecule, the more complex sugar sucrose, $C_{12}H_{22}O_{11}$, is formed. Sucrose is common table sugar, which is also known as cane sugar.

Starches are another kind of carbohydrate. Starches are made of long chains of sugar molecules hooked together. Starch molecules are **polymers** (PAHL-ih-merz) of many simple sugars. A polymer is a giant molecule made up of smaller molecules joined together. The smaller molecules that form a polymer are called **monomers** (MAHN-uh-merz). Starch is found in foods such as bread, cereal, potatoes, pasta, and rice.

Carbohydrates are the body's main source of energy. When you eat starches and complex sugars, your body first breaks them down into simple sugars during the process of digestion. Then the simple sugars are combined with oxygen according to the following reaction:

$$C_6H_{12}O_6 + 6O_2 \longrightarrow 6CO_2 + 6H_2O + energy$$

Fats and Oils

Like carbohydrates, **fats** and **oils** contain carbon, hydrogen, and oxygen. These molecules are large, complex esters. Fats and oils are formed from the reaction between the alcohol glycerol and organic acids called fatty acids. Fats and oils store twice as much energy as carbohydrates.

As a class of organic compounds, fats and oils are sometimes called **lipids** (LIHP-ihdz). Fats are solid at room temperature, while oils are liquid. Lipids include cooking oils, butter, and the fat in meat. Although fats and oils are high-energy nutrients, too much of these substances can be a health hazard. Unused fats are stored by the body. This increases body weight. In addition, scientific evidence indicates that eating too much saturated fat—animal fat—may contribute to heart disease.

Proteins

Proteins are used to build and repair body parts. Every living part of your body contains proteins.

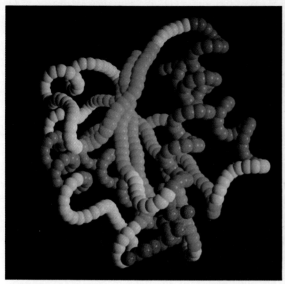

Figure 10-23 *Proteins are made of amino acids, which contain carbon, hydrogen, oxygen, and nitrogen. Most protein chains are hundreds of amino acids long. The molecular model shows the arrangement of atoms in a typical protein molecule (left). Proteins are found in foods such as meat, chicken, milk, eggs, and cheese (right).*

Blood, muscles, brain tissue, skin, and hair all contain proteins.

The raw materials used to make proteins are a special group of organic acids called **amino acids.** All amino acids contain carbon, hydrogen, oxygen, and nitrogen. Some amino acids also contain sulfur and phosphorus. There are 22 different amino acids found in nature.

Your body builds proteins by linking amino acids together. Most protein chains are hundreds of amino acid units long. Some amino acids are produced by the body itself. Others must be obtained from foods. These amino acids are called essential amino acids. Meat, fish, dairy products, and soybeans are sources of essential amino acids.

SECTION REVIEW

1. What are the three main types of organic compounds found in the human body?
2. What is a polymer? A monomer?
3. How are fats and oils formed?
4. Write a balanced equation for the reaction that produces energy from simple sugars. What waste products are given off by the body as a result of this reaction?

Preparing and Identifying Esters

ethyl al a methyl al.

Problem

How are esters prepared? What physical property is used to identify esters?

Materials *(per group)*

safety goggles   3 beakers
3 test tubes   3 glass plates
test tube holder   medicine dropper
test tube rack
hot plate and water bath *(Do not use a burner for this experiment.)*
5 mL concentrated sulfuric acid
5 mL methanol
10 mL ethanol
5 mL butyric acid
5 mL glacial acetic acid
1 g salicylic acid
150 mL cold distilled water

Procedure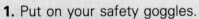

1. Put on your safety goggles.
2. Pour about 3 mL of ethanol into a test tube. Carefully note the odor of the liquid. Add 3 mL butyric acid. Again, carefully note the odor of the liquid.
3. Over a sink, carefully add about 10 drops of sulfuric acid to the mixture in the test tube. **CAUTION:** *Sulfuric acid can burn the skin.*
4. Warm the mixture in a water bath for 5 to 6 minutes. **CAUTION:** *Do not point the test tube toward yourself or any of your classmates.*
5. Pour the contents of the test tube into a beaker containing 50 mL of cold distilled water. Cover the beaker with a glass plate and let stand for 1 to 2 minutes. Note the odor.
6. Repeat steps 2 to 5 using acetic acid instead of butyric acid. Carefully note the odors.

7. Repeat steps 2 to 5 using methanol and about 1 g of salicylic acid. Carefully note the odors.

Observations

1. What is the odor of ethanol? Of butyric acid?
2. Does the product of the reaction between ethanol and butyric acid smell the same as ethanol? As butyric acid? Describe the odor.
3. Describe the odor of the product formed by the reaction between ethanol and acetic acid.
4. Describe the odor of the product formed by the reaction between methanol and salicylic acid.

Conclusions

1. What is the name of the reaction between an alcohol and an organic acid? What product is formed?
2. Give a general description of the odor of an ester.
3. Does an ester have the same odor as the reactants that form it?
4. You produced three esters in this experiment. These esters are ethyl acetate, methyl salicylate, and ethyl butyrate. Identify the alcohol and organic acid from which each ester is formed and describe the odor of each ester.
5. Why is methyl salicylate called oil of wintergreen?

CHAPTER REVIEW

SUMMARY

10-1 Carbon and Its Compounds

❏ Most compounds that contain carbon are called organic compounds

❏ A structural formula shows the kind, number, and arrangement of atoms in a molecule.

❏ Compounds that have the same molecular formula but different structural formulas are called isomers.

10-2 Hydrocarbons

❏ Compounds that contain only hydrogen and carbon are called hydrocarbons.

❏ Saturated hydrocarbons contain only single bonds; unsaturated hydrocarbons contain at least one double or triple bond.

❏ The alkanes are saturated hydrocarbons.

❏ The alkenes are unsaturated hydrocarbons containing at least one double covalent bond.

❏ The alkynes are unsaturated hydrocarbons containing at least one triple covalent bond.

❏ Cycloalkanes are saturated cyclic hydrocarbons, or hydrocarbons with a ring structure.

❏ Aromatic hydrocarbons have a ring structure in which 6 carbon atoms are joined by alternating single and double covalent bonds.

10-3 Substituted Hydrocarbons

❏ A substituted hydrocarbon is formed when one or more hydrogen atoms is replaced by a different atom or group of atoms.

❏ Important substituted hydrocarbons include alcohols, organic acids, esters, and halogen derivatives.

❏ When an alcohol and an organic acid react chemically, an ester is formed. The reaction is called esterification.

10-4 Chemistry for Life

❏ The principal organic compounds in the human body are carbohydrates, fats and oils, and proteins. These compounds are often called nutrients.

❏ Carbohydrates are compounds of carbon, hydrogen, and oxygen. The ratio of hydrogen atoms to oxygen atoms in a carbohydrate is two to one.

❏ Fats and oils are esters formed from the alcohol glycerol and fatty acids.

❏ Proteins are formed from amino acids, which contain carbon, hydrogen, oxygen, and nitrogen. Some amino acids also contain sulfur and phosphorus.

VOCABULARY

Define each term in a complete sentence.

alcohol	denatured alcohol	monomer	starch
alkane		oil	structural formula
alkene	ester	organic acid	
alkyne	esterification	organic chemistry	substituted hydrocarbon
amino acid	fat		
aromatic hydrocarbon	halogen derivative	organic compound	sugar
carbohydrate	hydrocarbon	polymer	unsaturated hydrocarbon
carboxyl group	hydroxyl group	protein	
cycloalkane	isomer	saturated hydrocarbon	
	lipid		

CONTENT REVIEW: MULTIPLE CHOICE

On a separate sheet of paper, write the letter of the answer that best completes each statement.

1. Organic compounds always contain
   a. carbon.   b. oxygen.   c. halogens.   d. carboxyl groups.
2. The type of bonding found in organic compounds is
   a. metallic.   b. ionic.   c. covalent.   d. coordinate.
3. Which of the following is *not* a property of organic compounds?
   a. nonpolar molecules   b. high melting points
   c. nonelectrolytes   d. generally have strong odors
4. A compound that contains only carbon and hydrogen is called a (an)
   a. isomer.   b. hydrocarbon.   c. carbohydrate.   d. alcohol.
5. The molecular formula for methane is
   a. CH_4.   b. C_4H_4.   c. C_4H.   d. C_2H_6.
6. The simplest aromatic hydrocarbon is
   a. cyclohexane.   b. methane.   c. benzene.   d. phenol.
7. The $-OH$ group is characteristic of a (an)
   a. organic acid.   b. aromatic compound.   c. ester.   d. alcohol.
8. Compounds that often give flavor and aroma to foods are
   a. alcohols.   b. esters.   c. organic acids.   d. aromatic compounds.
9. The human body's main source of energy is
   a. carbohydrates.   b. proteins.   c. fats.   d. amino acids.
10. As a class of organic compounds, fats and oils are called
   a. cycloalkanes.   b. lipids.   c. amino acids.   d. hydrocarbons.

CONTENT REVIEW: COMPLETION

On a separate sheet of paper, write the word or words that best complete each statement.

1. The word organic means _____.
2. When two pairs of electrons are shared between atoms, a (an) _____ bond is formed.
3. Compounds that have the same molecular formulas but different structural formulas are called _____.
4. Pentene is a member of the _____ series.
5. To name a saturated ring, the prefix _____ is added to the hydrocarbon name.
6. A hydrocarbon in which one or more hydrogen atoms has been replaced by a different atom or group of atoms is called a (an) _____.
7. The presence of a hydroxyl group, $-OH$, is characteristic of a (an) _____.
8. A compound formed from an alcohol and an organic acid is called a (an) _____.
9. Compounds that contain carbon, hydrogen, and oxygen, in which the ratio of hydrogen atoms to oxygen atoms is two to one, are called _____.
10. Giant molecules that are made of smaller molecules joined together are called _____.

CONTENT REVIEW: TRUE OR FALSE

Determine whether each statement is true or false. Then on a separate sheet of paper, write "true" if it is true. If it is false, change the underlined word or words to make the statement true.

1. Organic compounds contain <u>nitrogen</u>.
2. The <u>molecular</u> formula for a compound tells the kind, number, and arrangement of atoms.
3. Hydrocarbons that contain only single bonds are said to be <u>unsaturated</u>.
4. Ethane is a member of the <u>alkane</u> series.
5. The 4-carbon alkane is called <u>butane</u>.
6. A hydrocarbon containing a double bond is <u>less</u> reactive than a hydrocarbon containing a single bond.
7. Unsaturated hydrocarbons containing a triple covalent bond are called <u>alkenes</u>.
8. An organic acid is characterized by the group <u>–COOH</u>.
9. Large starch polymers are made of smaller units called <u>monomers</u> linked together.
10. <u>Fats</u> are formed from amino acids.

CONCEPT REVIEW: SKILL BUILDING

Use the skills you have developed in the chapter to complete each activity.

1. **Classifying hydrocarbons** Classify each of the following hydrocarbons as an alkane, alkene, alkyne, or aromatic compound.
   a. C_4H_{10} b. C_3H_4 c. C_2H_4
   d. C_6H_6 e. $C_{13}H_{26}$ f. $C_{42}H_{82}$

2. **Identifying patterns** Using the general formulas for the alkanes, alkenes, and alkynes, show why the number of hydrogen atoms in each series decreases by two.

3. **Making diagrams** Draw structural formulas for the following compounds.
   a. hexane   c. butene
   b. cyclopentane   d. propyne

4. **Classifying substituted hydrocarbons** Classify each of the following compounds as a (an) ester, alcohol, organic acid, or halogen derivative.
   a. $C_2H_5COOC_3H_7$ c. C_6H_5OH
   b. C_4H_9Cl d. C_2H_5COOH

5. **Applying definitions** Draw the structural formulas for the isomers of hexane.

6. **Making comparisons** Choose a number of carbon atoms from three to eight. Using the number you have chosen, draw the structural formulas for each of the following: the alkane, alkene, alkyne, cycloalkane, alcohol, and organic acid corresponding to that number of carbon atoms.

7. **Drawing a conclusion** Explain why the alkene series and the alkyne series begin with a 2-carbon hydrocarbon rather than a 1-carbon hydrocarbon, as the alkane series does. Use structural formulas to support your explanation.

CONCEPT REVIEW: ESSAY

Discuss each of the following in a brief paragraph.

1. Discuss four reasons why carbon compounds are so abundant.
2. Explain the importance of structural formulas in organic chemistry.
3. In Chapter 9 you learned that compounds called bases contain the hydroxide ion, OH^-. Alcohols also contain the –OH group. Why are alcohols not bases?
4. If your body contains proteins, why is it necessary to eat a balanced diet in which protein is an important nutrient?

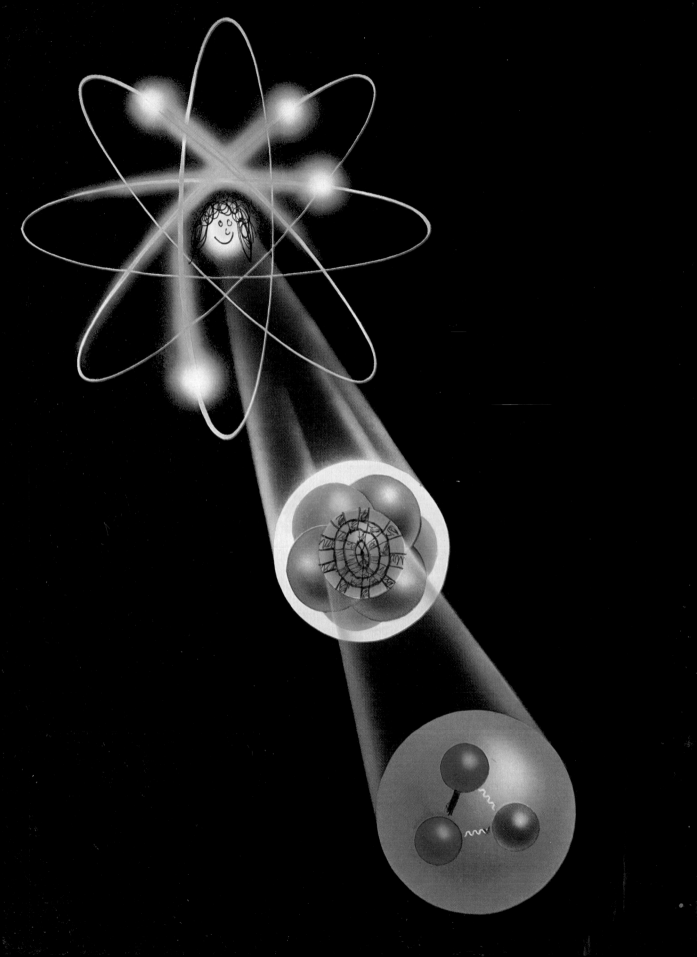

Nuclear Chemistry 11

CHAPTER SECTIONS

11–1 Radioactive Elements

11–2 Transmutation of Elements

11–3 Harnessing the Nucleus

11–4 Detecting and Measuring Radioactivity

11–5 Uses of Radioactivity

CHAPTER OBJECTIVES

After completing this chapter, you will be able to

11–1 Define radioactivity.

11–1 Identify the steps leading up to the discovery of radioactivity.

11–2 Compare natural and artificial transmutation.

11–2 Describe the process and products of radioactive decay.

11–3 Describe nuclear fission and nuclear fusion.

11–4 Identify instruments that can detect and measure radioactivity.

11–5 Discuss ways in which radioactive substances can be used.

In the rich prairie lands near Waxahachie, Texas, construction will soon begin on a project that will take many years and billions of dollars to complete. Yet even when construction begins, to the eye it would not appear as if much is going on at all. Why? This project is being built almost 46 meters beneath the soil.

The project being considered for Waxahachie is the world's largest Superconducting Supercollider (S.S.C.). The supercollider will be housed in a circular tunnel some 85 kilometers in length! The S.S.C. has been called the world's most ambitious high-tech project. It's goal, when completed, is to reveal information about the basic building blocks of matter. And, at the same time, it will reveal secrets about how the Universe formed.

Within the circular tunnel protons will be sent shooting around and around, gaining speed with each pass. Some 9000 superconducting magnets will be used to keep the protons on track and to help boost their speed with each trip through the tunnel. Then, at a certain point, the protons will be split into two beams, each traveling at about the speed of light. Finally, they will be diverted so that individual protons traveling at nearly light speed will collide head on.

The energy produced during the collision will cause the creation of particles that exist only at high energies. Scientists believe that similar particles were formed during the creation of the Universe when energy levels were at least as high as those created in the Supercollider. Thus, scientists believe they will learn more about the creation of the Universe through a tunnel built under the Texas prairie.

An atom consists of one or more electrons whirling about the nucleus, which is made up of protons (red) and neutrons (blue). Each proton and neutron is made up of three quarks, bound together by the strong nuclear force.

11–1 Radioactive Elements

Have you ever looked for something and in the process discovered something quite different? One of the greatest scientific discoveries was made in this way. In 1896, the French scientist Henri Becquerel (ahn-REE bek-REL) was experimenting to see if a uranium compound gave off X-rays. Becquerel's experiments indeed provided evidence of X-rays. But they also showed something else rather exciting. Quite by accident, Becquerel discovered that the uranium compound gave off rays that had never been detected before. Little did Becquerel know then that these mysterious rays would open up a whole new world of modern science.

An Illuminating Discovery

At the time of Becquerel's work, scientists knew that certain substances glowed when exposed to sunlight. Such substances are said to be fluorescent. Becquerel wondered if in addition to glowing, fluorescent substances gave off X-rays.

To test his hypothesis, Becquerel wrapped some photographic film in lightproof paper. He placed a piece of fluorescent uranium salt on top of the film and left both out in the sun. Becquerel reasoned that if X-rays were produced by the fluorescent uranium salt, the X-rays would pass through the lightproof paper and produce an image on the film.

Figure 11–1 *Yellowcake, shown here being processed, is 65 percent pure uranium (left). A fragment of uranium was used by Becquerel in his famous experiments. The image that showed up on the photographic film (right) convinced Becquerel that an invisible "something" had been given off by the uranium. What is this "something" called?*

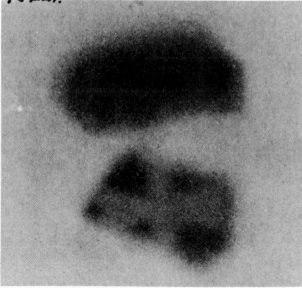

When Becquerel developed the film, he was delighted to see an image. The image was evidence that fluorescent substances give off X-rays when exposed to sunlight. Becquerel did not test his hypothesis with just one experiment. He prepared another sample of uranium salt and left it in his desk for use the next day. Much to his disappointment, the next two days were cloudy. Impatient to get on with his work, Becquerel decided to develop the film anyway. What he saw on the film amazed him. Once again there was an image of the sample. In fact, the image on the film was just as strong and clear as the image that had been formed when the sample was exposed to sunlight.

Becquerel realized that an invisible "something" given off by the salt had gone through the light-proof paper and produced an image. In time, this invisible "something" was named **radiation.** Becquerel tested many more uranium compounds and concluded that the source of radiation was the element uranium. An element that gives off radiation is said to be **radioactive.**

Marie Curie, a Polish scientist working in France at the time of Becquerel's discovery, became very interested in Becquerel's work. She suspected that a uranium ore known as pitchblende contained other radioactive elements. She and her husband, French scientist Pierre Curie, began searching for these elements.

In 1898, the Curies discovered a new radioactive element in pitchblende. They named the element polonium in honor of Marie Curie's native Poland. Later that year, they discovered another radioactive element. They named this element radium, which means "shining element." Both polonium and radium are more radioactive than uranium. Since the Curies' discovery of polonium and radium, many other radioactive elements have been identified.

Radiation from Nuclei

Today, scientists know that it is **radioactivity** that Becquerel and the Curies had observed. **Radioactivity is the release of energy and matter that results from changes in the nucleus of an atom.**

Figure 11–2 *Marie Curie (bottom) and her husband, Pierre, were responsible for the discovery of the radioactive elements radium and polonium. Since that time, many other radioactive elements have been identified. Rectangular blocks containing radioactive cesium were the only source of illumination for this time-exposure photograph (top). The photograph was taken through a heavy glass window 1 meter thick.*

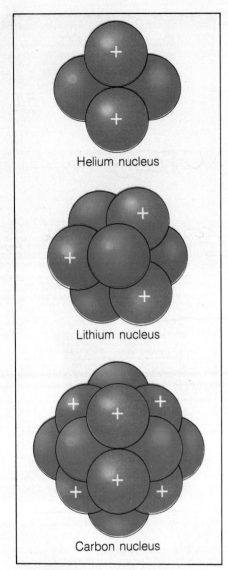

Helium nucleus

Lithium nucleus

Carbon nucleus

Figure 11–3 *The nucleus of an atom contains positively charged protons and neutral neutrons. A helium nucleus contains 2 protons and 2 neutrons. How many protons and neutrons does a lithium nucleus contain? A carbon nucleus?*

Figure 11–4 *Many elements have radioactive isotopes. An isotope is an atom of an element that has the same number of protons but a different number of neutrons. The number at the upper left of the symbol is the mass number. The number at the lower left is the atomic number.*

Not all elements are radioactive. To understand why some elements are radioactive and others are not, you must understand the structure of the atom—especially the nucleus. For it is the interaction of particles and energy in the nucleus that gives rise to radioactivity.

You will recall that the nucleus of an atom contains protons and neutrons. Protons are positively charged particles. Neutrons are neutral particles. They have no charge. Protons and neutrons are held together in the nucleus by the strong force. The energy associated with the strong force is called **binding energy.** In some atoms, the binding energy is great enough to hold the nucleus together permanently. The nuclei of such atoms are said to be stable. In other atoms, the binding energy is not as great. The nucleus is not held together permanently. The nuclei of these atoms are said to be unstable. Atoms with unstable nuclei are radioactive.

Scientists believe that unstable nuclei are caused by an imbalance in the number of protons and neutrons. In a stable nucleus, the number of protons is about equal to the number of neutrons. In an unstable nucleus, however, there are either more neutrons than protons or more protons than neutrons.

Elements with atomic numbers greater than 83 are radioactive. This means that *all* isotopes of these

NONRADIOACTIVE AND RADIOACTIVE ISOTOPES OF SOME COMMON ELEMENTS

Element	Nonradioactive Isotope	Radioactive Isotope
Hydrogen	^1_1H	^3_1H
Helium	^4_2He	^6_2He
Oxygen	$^{16}_8O$	$^{14}_8O$
Potassium	$^{39}_{19}K$	$^{40}_{19}K$
Nitrogen	$^{14}_7N$	$^{16}_7N$
Lithium	^7_3Li	^8_3Li
Carbon	$^{12}_6C$	$^{14}_6C$

RADIOACTIVE ELEMENTS

Element	Symbol	Atomic Number	Atomic Mass Number	Element	Symbol	Atomic Number	Atomic Mass Number
technetium	Tc	43	99	curium	Cm	96	247
promethium	Pm	61	145	berkelium	Bk	97	247
polonium	Po	84	209	californium	Cf	98	251
astatine	At	85	210	einsteinium	Es	99	254
radon	Rn	86	222	fermium	Fm	100	253
francium	Fr	87	223	mendelevium	Md	101	256
radium	Ra	88	226	nobelium	No	102	253
actinium	Ac	89	227	lawrencium	Lr	103	257
thorium	Th	90	232	unnilquadium	Unq	104	261
protactinium	Pa	91	231	unnilpentium	Unp	105	260
uranium	U	92	238	unnilhexium	Unh	106	263
neptunium	Np	93	237	unnilseptium	Uns	107	262
plutonium	Pu	94	244	unniloctium	Uno	108	265
americium	Am	95	243	unnilennium	Une	109	266

elements are radioactive. You will recall that isotopes are atoms of an element that have the same number of protons but different numbers of neutrons.

Many elements with atomic numbers less than 84 have at least one radioactive isotope. For example, carbon has two common isotopes—carbon-12 and carbon-14. Carbon-12, which you are familiar with as coal, graphite, and diamond, is not radioactive. Carbon-14, used in dating fossils, is radioactive. Figure 11–4 shows the radioactive and nonradioactive isotopes of some common elements. What do you notice about the numbers of protons and neutrons in the nonradioactive isotopes? In the radioactive isotopes?

Figure 11–5 *The elements listed in this table are radioactive. All elements with atomic numbers greater than 83 are radioactive. What two elements with atomic numbers less than 84 are radioactive?*

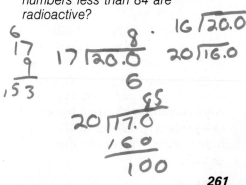

261

SECTION REVIEW

1. Why were Becquerel's experiments important?
2. How did the Curies use Becquerel's discovery?
3. What is radioactivity?
4. How does the nucleus of a radioactive atom differ from the nucleus of a nonradioactive atom?
5. The nucleus of a certain atom contains 15 protons and 18 neutrons. Do you think this atom is radioactive? Explain your answer.

11–2 Transmutation of Elements

Section Objective

To describe the transmutation of elements

Transmutation is the process by which the nucleus of an atom changes so that a new element is formed. **Transmutation, the change of one element into another as a result of nuclear changes, can occur naturally or by artificial means.**

Radioactive Decay

As you read before, an unstable nucleus is radioactive. The nucleus undergoes changes that release energy and matter. As a result of the nuclear changes, a new element is formed. Natural transmutation has taken place. This form of natural transmutation is called **radioactive decay.** Radioactive decay is the spontaneous breakdown of an unstable atomic nucleus. Elements whose atoms undergo radioactive decay are called radioactive elements.

As radioactive elements decay, they change into other elements. These elements may in turn decay, forming still other elements. The spontaneous breakdown continues until a stable, nonradioactive nucleus is formed. The series of steps by which a radioactive nucleus decays into a nonradioactive nucleus is called a **decay series.** Figure 11–6 shows the decay series for uranium. What stable nucleus results from this decay series?

Radioactive decay releases both particles and energy that together are known as **nuclear radiation.** The nature of the decay determines the type of radiation. There are three types of radioactive decay.

Sharpen Your Skills

What Is a Quark?

Scientists have proposed that all nuclear subatomic particles are made up of basic particles called quarks. Using books and other reference materials in the library, look up the word quark. Find out what quarks are and how they were discovered. Describe some different types of quarks and what they do. Find out what recent discoveries have been made involving quarks. Report your findings to the class.

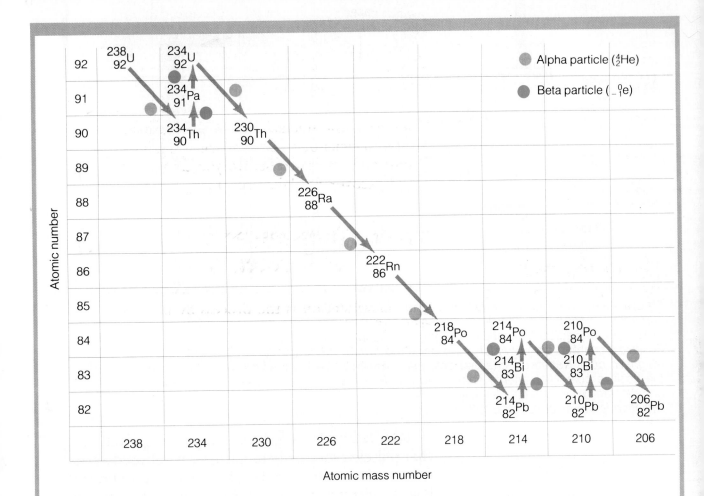

Figure 11–6 *The decay series for uranium-238 is shown in this graph. Radioactive uranium forms nonradioactive lead as a result of the decay series. What happens to the atomic mass number during a decay series? The atomic number?*

ALPHA DECAY In **alpha decay,** the nucleus of a radioactive atom releases 2 protons and 2 neutrons. These 4 particles are released together and are known as an alpha particle. An alpha particle is actually the nucleus of a helium atom—2 protons and 2 neutrons.

When an atom gives off an alpha particle, it loses 2 protons. The result is a new atom with an atomic number *two less* than the original. Remember, the atomic number of an atom is the number of protons in its nucleus. An example of an element that undergoes alpha decay is uranium-238. This isotope of uranium has 92 protons and 146 neutrons. By losing an alpha particle, it changes into an atom of thorium, which has 90 protons and 144 neutrons. What do you think happens to the mass number of an atom that undergoes alpha decay?

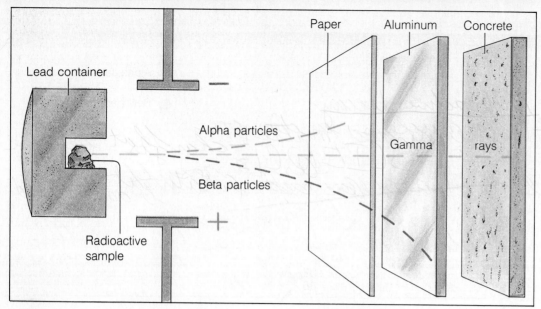

Figure 11–7 *The radiation released during radioactive decay can be separated according to charge and penetrating power. The radiation given off by a radioactive sample is passed through a magnetic field. Positively charged alpha particles are deflected toward the negative magnetic pole. Negatively charged beta particles are deflected toward the positive pole. High-energy gamma rays, which have no charge, are undeflected. Which particle is deflected the most? Which type of radiation is the most penetrating?*

Figure 11–8 *Alpha and beta decay release particles as well as energy. An alpha particle is a helium nucleus. A beta particle is an electron. Where does a beta particle come from?*

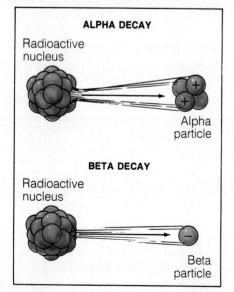

BETA DECAY During **beta decay,** a negatively charged electron, or beta particle, is released from the nucleus of an atom. Perhaps you are wondering how an electron can be in the nucleus. The answer is that a neutron is thought to be made up of a proton and an electron.

During beta decay, the neutron breaks up. The proton stays in the nucleus, but the electron is released as a beta particle. So beta decay produces a new atom with the same mass number as the original atom but with an atomic number *one higher* than the original atom. The atomic number is one higher because there is now an additional proton.

An example of an element that undergoes beta decay is carbon-14. An atom of carbon-14 has 6 protons and 8 neutrons. During beta decay it changes into an atom of nitrogen-14. An atom of nitrogen-14 has 7 protons and 7 neutrons.

GAMMA DECAY Alpha and beta decay are almost always accompanied by **gamma decay.** Gamma decay is the release of energy in the form of gamma rays. Gamma rays are electromagnetic waves of very high frequency and energy.

Artificial Transmutation

One instrument in which artificial transmutation takes place is called a **particle accelerator.** By using a particle accelerator, scientists are able to bombard atomic nuclei with high-speed protons or neutrons. As the atomic nuclei are forced to absorb additional protons or neutrons, new elements are produced.

All of the elements with atomic numbers greater than 92, the atomic number of uranium, were produced by artificial transmutation. These elements are called **synthetic** or **transuranium elements.** All of the synthetic elements are radioactive.

Radioactive isotopes of natural elements can be made by using a similar technique. For example, by shooting neutrons at the nucleus of an iodine atom, scientists have been able to make I-131, a radioactive isotope of iodine. A particle accelerator can also be used to create an element from several other elements. For example, scientists can now change mercury and lead into gold.

Describing Nuclear Reactions

Nuclear reactions can be described by equations in much the same way chemical reactions can. However, the nature of the reactions is very different. The main difference between a chemical reaction and a nuclear reaction is that a chemical reaction involves an atom's electrons and a nuclear reaction involves its nucleus.

Figure 11–9 *Artificial transmutation of elements is done in a particle accelerator such as the one at Fermilab in Illinois. This aerial view (left) shows the outline of the underground tunnel, which is more than 6.3 kilometers long. Protons traveling through long tubes (right) will reach a final speed greater than 99.999 percent of the speed of light!*

Sharpen Your Skills

Writing Nuclear Equations

1. Write an equation to describe the alpha decay of a radium-226 nucleus to form a radon nucleus.

2. Write an equation to describe the alpha decay of a radon nucleus to form a polonium-218 nucleus.

3. Write an equation to describe the beta decay of a lead-214 nucleus to form a bismuth-214 nucleus.

TYPES OF NUCLEAR RADIATION

Type	Atomic Mass	Atomic Number
Alpha $^{4}_{2}$He or α	4	2
Beta $^{0}_{-1}$e or β	0	−1
Gamma γ	0	none

Figure 11–10 *The three types of nuclear radiation are summarized in this table. How does the mass of an alpha particle relate to its speed?*

In order to write an equation for a nuclear reaction, you must first learn certain rules. Each atom of an element in the reaction is represented by the chemical symbol for that element. Two small numbers are written to the left of the symbol. The number at the upper left is the mass number of the element. The number at the lower left is the atomic number of the element. The symbol for uranium-238 would be $^{238}_{92}$U, since uranium-238 has a mass number of 238 and an atomic number of 92. How would protactinium be represented in a nuclear equation? Radium?

Symbols are also used to represent alpha particles, beta particles, and neutrons. The symbol for an alpha particle is the helium nucleus, $^{4}_{2}$He. An alpha particle has a mass number of 4 and an atomic number of 2. The symbol for a beta particle, or electron, is $^{0}_{-1}$e. A beta particle has a mass number almost equal to 0 and an atomic number considered −1. The symbol for a neutron is $^{1}_{0}$n. What is the mass number and atomic number of a neutron?

Now let's see how some of these symbols are used in a nuclear equation. Uranium-238 undergoes alpha decay to produce thorium and gamma rays.

$$^{238}_{92}\text{U} \longrightarrow ^{234}_{90}\text{Th} + ^{4}_{2}\text{He} + \textbf{gamma rays}$$

Notice that when the mass numbers on each side of the equation are added together, they equal each other. The same thing is true of the atomic numbers. You can check to see if you have written a correct nuclear equation by using this rule.

Radioactive Half-Life

The decay of radioactive elements occurs at a fixed rate. The fixed rate of decay of a radioactive element is called the **half-life.** The half-life is the amount of time it takes for half the atoms in a given sample of the element to decay.

Figure 11–11 *The half-life of a radioactive element is the amount of time it takes for half the atoms in a given sample of the element to decay. After the first half-life, half the atoms in the sample are the radioactive element and half are the decay element. What remains of the sample after the second half-life? After the third?*

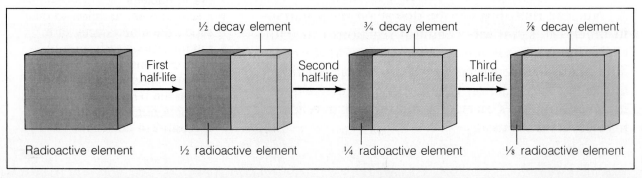

½ decay element   ¾ decay element   ⅞ decay element

First half-life   Second half-life   Third half-life

Radioactive element   ½ radioactive element   ¼ radioactive element   ⅛ radioactive element

HALF-LIVES OF SOME RADIOACTIVE ELEMENTS

Element	Half-Life	Element	Half-Life
Bismuth-212	60.5 minutes	Polonium-215	0.0018 second
Carbon-14	5730 years	Polonium-216	0.16 second
Chlorine-36	400,000 years	Radium-226	1600 years
Cobalt-60	5.26 years	Sodium-24	15 hours
Iodine-131	8.07 days	Uranium-235	710 million years
Phosphorus-32	14.3 days	Uranium-238	4.5 billion years

The half-life of carbon-14 is 5568 years. In 5568 years, half the atoms in a given sample of carbon-14 will have decayed to another element, nitrogen-14. In another 5568 years, half the remaining carbon-14 will have decayed. At this time, one-fourth, or one-half of one-half, of the original sample will be left. One-fourth of the original sample will be carbon-14 and three-fourths will be nitrogen-14.

Suppose you had 20 grams of pure barium-139. Its half-life is 86 minutes. So after 86 minutes, half the atoms in the sample would have decayed into another element, lanthanum-139. You would have 10 grams of barium-139 and 10 grams of lanthanum-139. After another 86 minutes, half the atoms in the 10 grams of barium-139 would have decayed into lanthanum-139. You would have 5 grams of barium-139 and 15 grams of lanthanum-139. What will you have after the next half-life?

The half-lives of certain radioactive isotopes are very useful in determining the ages of rocks and fossils. Scientists can use the half-life of carbon-14 to determine the approximate age of organisms and objects less than 50,000 years old. This technique is called carbon-14 dating. Other radioactive elements, such as uranium-238, can be used to date objects many millions of years old.

Half-lives vary greatly from element to element. Some half-lives are only seconds while others are billions of years. For example, the half-life of rhodium-106 is 30 seconds. The half-life of uranium-238 is 4.5 billion years!

Figure 11–12 *The half-lives of radioactive elements vary greatly. How long would it take a 10-gram sample of chlorine-36 to be reduced to 5 grams? How long would it take a 20-gram sample of sodium-24 to be reduced to 5 grams?*

Sharpen Your Skills

A Model of Half-Life

For this activity you will need about 100 small objects of the same size, such as jellybeans, marbles, buttons, or pennies; a piece of posterboard; and tape or glue.

1. Illustrate half-life by letting each small object represent one atom. Choose the starting number carefully.

2. Display the "atoms" on the posterboard to show how the number of atoms is reduced in each half-life.

3. Decide on a half-life for your sample. Label each group of atoms with the time it has taken to reach that number, how many "atoms" remain, and which half-life is represented.

SECTION REVIEW

1. What is transmutation? What are the two types of transmutation?
2. What happens during radioactive decay? What are the three types of radioactive decay?
3. What is half-life?
4. The half-life of radium-222 is 38 seconds. How many grams of a 12-gram sample are left after 76 seconds? After 114 seconds? How many half-lives have occurred when 0.75 grams remain?

11–3 Harnessing the Nucleus

Sharpen Your Skills

Cold Fusion

On March 23, 1989, B. Stanley Pons of the University of Utah and his colleague Martin Fleischmann of the University of Southhampton in England announced to the world that they had found a way to achieve fusion in a bottle. Because most scientists believe that fusion can be achieved only at extremely high temperatures similar to those on the sun, the discovery was quickly dubbed "cold fusion."

Your task, using library resources, is to determine whether or not Pons and Fleischmann followed the scientific method while doing their experiments. As you know, data from an experiment that does not follow the scientific method is usually not considered valid. Were the data from the cold fusion experiment accepted by the scientific community? Or did scientists reject cold fusion based on faulty data?

Radioactive decay is one way in which energy is released from the nucleus of an atom. The amount of energy released during radioactive decay is quite small, however. For many years, scientists have known that the binding energy of a nucleus is enormous. After all, a huge quantity of energy is required to hold the protons together. If somehow the nucleus could be split apart, some of the nuclear energy would be released.

Nuclear Fission

In 1938, Italian physicist Enrico Fermi and a team of other scientists made an extremely important discovery. They found that when the nucleus of an atom of uranium-235 is struck by a neutron, it splits into two nuclei of roughly equal mass. This reaction, the first of its kind ever to be produced, is an example of **nuclear fission** (FIHSH-uhn). With the discovery of nuclear fission, Fermi made a tremendous contribution to the field of nuclear chemistry.

Nuclear fission is the splitting of an atomic nucleus into two smaller nuclei of approximately equal mass. Fission does not occur spontaneously. Elements with atomic numbers greater than 90 can be made to undergo fission. As a result of fission, a radioactive element forms a stable element.

In one typical fission reaction, a uranium-235 nucleus is bombarded by a neutron, or nuclear "bullet." The products of the reaction are a barium-141 nucleus and a krypton-92 nucleus. Three neutrons

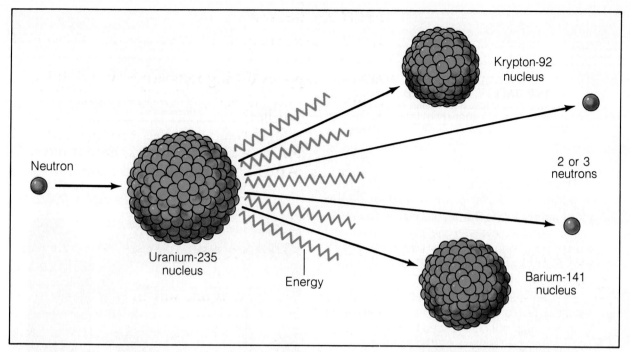

Figure 11–13 *In this diagram of a chain reaction, a uranium-235 nucleus is bombarded with a neutron. The nucleus breaks up, producing a nucleus of krypton-92 and one of barium-141. Large amounts of energy as well as two additional neutrons are released. Each neutron is capable of splitting another uranium-235 nucleus. What nuclear reaction is involved in a chain reaction?*

are also released—the original "bullet" neutron and two neutrons from the uranium nucleus.

$$^{235}_{92}\text{U} + ^{1}_{0}\text{n} \longrightarrow ^{92}_{36}\text{Kr} + ^{141}_{56}\text{Ba} + 3^{1}_{0}\text{n} + \textbf{energy}$$

The amount of energy released when a single uranium-235 nucleus splits is not very great. But the neutrons released in the first fission reaction become nuclear "bullets" capable of splitting other uranium-235 nuclei. Each uranium nucleus that is split releases three neutrons. These neutrons may then split even more uranium nuclei. The continuous series of fission reactions is called a **nuclear chain reaction.** In a nuclear chain reaction, billions of fission reactions may take place each second!

When many atomic nuclei are split in a chain reaction, huge quantities of energy are released. This energy is produced as a result of the conversion of a small amount of mass into a huge amount of energy. The total mass of the barium, krypton, and two neutrons is slightly less than the total mass of the original uranium plus the initial neutron. The missing mass has been converted into energy. An uncontrolled chain reaction produces a nuclear explosion. In Chapter 25 you will learn how scientists control fission reactions in order to produce energy for human energy needs.

HELP WANTED: NUCLEAR POWER PLANT SAFETY INSPECTOR College degree in occupational health or biology preferred, but experience in safety inspection field acceptable. Must pass written exam after training.

The news spreads quickly among workers at the nuclear power plant: A **nuclear power plant safety inspector** is making the rounds to check radiation levels in the plant. The federal government requires frequent inspections as a safeguard to employees' health and the health of the community.

A safety inspector at a nuclear site monitors radiation levels inside and outside the plant. Workers must not be exposed to levels of radiation determined unsafe by the federal government. Sometimes samples of air, water, soil, or other materials are collected by the inspector and sent to laboratories for analysis.

A safety inspector often uses portable X-ray equipment to examine walls, pipes, and wiring in a nuclear power plant for cracks or weak spots. If a regulation is being violated, the nu-clear safety inspector writes a report to the federal Nuclear Regulatory Commission and to the company that runs the nuclear power plant. Later, the safety inspector may return to a site to be sure the problem has been corrected.

If you would like to learn more about a career as a nuclear power plant safety inspector, contact the American Society of Safety Engineers, 1800 East Oakton Street, Des Plaines, IL 60018.

Nuclear Fusion

There is another kind of nuclear reaction that certain radioactive elements can undergo. Like fission, this kind of nuclear reaction produces a great deal of energy. Unlike fission, which involves the splitting of a high-mass nucleus, this reaction involves the joining of two low-mass nuclei. The reaction is called **nuclear fusion.** The word fusion means joining together. **Nuclear fusion is the joining of two atomic nuclei of smaller masses to form a single nucleus of larger mass.**

Nuclear fusion is a thermonuclear reaction. Thermo means heat. For nuclear fusion to take place, temperatures well over a million degrees Celsius must be reached. At such temperatures, the phase of matter known as plasma is formed. Plasma consists of positively charged ions, which are the nuclei of original atoms, and free electrons.

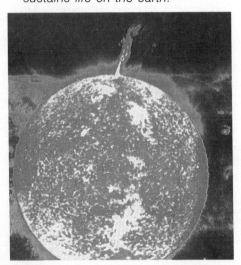

Figure 11–14 *You can get an idea of just how much energy is produced by nuclear fusion by considering that only a tiny fraction of the sun's total energy is what sustains life on the earth.*

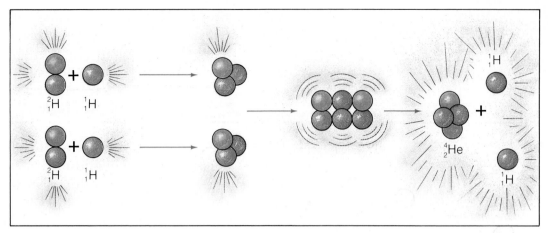

The temperature conditions required for nuclear fusion exist in the sun and other stars. In fact, it is nuclear fusion that produces the sun's energy and the energy of other stars. In the sun's core, temperatures of about 20 million degrees Celsius keep fusion going continuously. In a series of steps, hydrogen nuclei are fused into a helium-4 nucleus. See Figure 11–15.

Nuclear fusion produces a tremendous amount of energy. The energy comes from matter that is converted into energy during the reaction. In fact, the products formed by fusion have a mass that is about one percent less than the mass of the reactants. Although one percent loss of mass may seem a small amount to you, its conversion produces an enormous quantity of energy. Nuclear fusion,

Figure 11–15 *In the process of nuclear fusion that takes place in the sun, hydrogen nuclei fuse to produce helium and tremendous amounts of energy. What other products are formed by this fusion reaction?*

Figure 11–16 *These laser technicians at Lawrence Livermore Laboratory are adjusting the target chamber of Nova, the device in which experimental fusion reactions are being conducted (left). Ten powerful laser beams converge simultaneously onto a small fuel pellet such as the one shown here (right). What element makes up this double-shell target?*

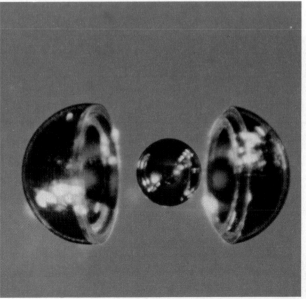

however, is more difficult to control than nuclear fission. Scientists are continuing their search for ways to control this powerful reaction and tap a tremendous energy resource.

SECTION REVIEW

1. What is nuclear fission? Nuclear fusion?
2. How is the sun's energy produced?
3. Where does the energy produced in both fission and fusion reactions come from?
4. Compare the energy produced by fission and fusion reactions with the energy produced by radioactive decay.

11-4 Detecting and Measuring Radioactivity

Figure 11–17 *Because radioactive substances will cause an electroscope to discharge, an electroscope can be used to detect radiation. What do radioactive substances do to molecules of air?*

Radioactivity cannot be seen or felt. Becquerel discovered radioactivity because it left marks on photographic film. Although film is still used today to detect radioactivity, scientists have more specialized instruments for this purpose. **The instruments scientists use to detect and measure radioactivity include the electroscope, Geiger counter, cloud chamber, and bubble chamber.**

Electroscope

An **electroscope** is a simple device that consists of a metal rod with two thin metal leaves at one end. If an electroscope is given a negative charge, the metal leaves separate. In this condition, the electroscope can be used to detect radioactivity.

Radioactive substances remove electrons from molecules of air. As a result, the molecules of air become positively charged ions. When a radioactive substance is brought near a negatively charged electroscope, the air molecules that have become positively charged attract the negative charge on the leaves of the electroscope. The leaves discharge, or lose their charge, and collapse. You will learn more about the electroscope when you study electricity in Chapter 19.

Geiger Counter

In 1928, Hans Geiger designed an instrument that detects and measures radioactivity. Named the **Geiger counter** in honor of its inventor, this instrument produces an electric current in the presence of a radioactive substance.

A Geiger counter consists of a tube filled with a gas such as argon or helium at reduced pressure. When radiation enters the tube through a thin window at one end, it removes electrons from the atoms of the gas. The gas atoms become positively charged ions. The electrons move through the positively charged ions to a wire in the tube, setting up an electric current. The current, which is amplified and fed into a recording or counting device, produces a flashing light and a clicking sound. The number of flashes and clicks per unit of time indicates the strength of the radiation. A counter attached to the wire is able to measure the amount of radioactivity by measuring the amount of current.

Cloud Chamber

A **cloud chamber** contains evaporated alcohol. Dry ice surrounding the chamber causes the alcohol vapor to condense. When a radioactive substance is put inside the chamber, droplets of alcohol condense around the radioactive particles. This process is similar to what happens in "cloud seeding" when rain droplets condense around particles that have been injected into the clouds. The droplets formed around the particles of radiation in a cloud chamber leave a trail that shows up along the chamber lining. An alpha particle leaves a short, fat trail while a beta particle's trail is long and thin.

Bubble Chamber

The **bubble chamber** is similar in some ways to the cloud chamber, although its construction is more complex. A bubble chamber contains a superheated liquid. A superheated liquid is hot enough to boil, but does not. Instead it remains in the liquid phase. The superheated liquid often contained in a bubble chamber is hydrogen.

Figure 11–18 *A Geiger counter detects and measures radioactivity (top). A spiderwort plant is nature's radiation detector (bottom). The stamens of the spiderwort flower are usually blue or blue-purple. In the presence of radiation, however, the stamens turn pink.*

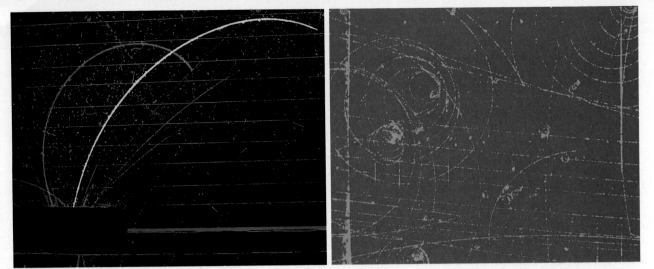

Figure 11–19 *This cloud chamber photograph (left) shows the difference between a proton (red) and an alpha particle (yellow). Which particle curves more in the chamber's magnetic field? When protons collide, a variety of other subatomic particles are produced. The tracks of these particles are shown in this bubble chamber photograph (right). By studying the tracks, scientists can learn more about the nature of subatomic particles and matter.*

When radioactive particles pass through the chamber, they cause the hydrogen to boil. The boiling liquid leaves a trail of bubbles, which is used to track the radioactive particle.

SECTION REVIEW

1. Name four instruments that are used to detect radioactivity.
2. What instrument can both detect and measure radioactivity?
3. Compare a bubble chamber and a cloud chamber.

11–5 Uses of Radioactivity

Radioactive substances have many practical uses. Among the most useful radioactive substances are **radioisotopes.** Radioisotopes are artificially produced radioactive isotopes of common elements. **Radioisotopes are used to study living organisms, to diagnose and treat disease, to sterilize foods, and to monitor industrial processes.**

Radioisotopes are frequently used as **tracers.** A tracer is a radioactive element whose pathway through the steps of a chemical reaction can be followed. An example of a tracer is phosphorus-32.

The nonradioactive element phosphorus is used in small amounts by both plants and animals. If phosphorus-32 is given to an organism, the organism will use the radioactive phosphorus just as it does the nonradioactive phosphorus. However, the path of the radioactive element can be traced with a Geiger counter. In this way, scientists learn a great deal about how plants and animals use phosphorus.

Tracers are extremely valuable in diagnosing diseases. Radioactive iodine, iodine-131, can be used to study the function of the thyroid gland, which absorbs iodine. Sodium-24 can be used to detect diseases of the circulatory system. Iron-59 can be used to study blood circulation.

Tracers are also valuable in industry. Leaks in pipes can be detected if some of the material flowing through the pipes is tagged with the radioisotope iodine-131.

Radioisotopes are used to treat certain diseases. When administered carefully and in the proper amounts, radiation can kill cancer cells without damaging healthy tissue. The radioisotope cobalt-60 is used extensively in cancer radiation treatments. Carbon-14 has been used to treat brain tumors.

Radioisotopes can also be used to kill bacteria that cause food to spoil. Radiation was used to preserve the food that the astronauts ate while on the moon and in orbit.

One of the difficulties in using radioactive materials is that these substances must be handled with great care. Large amounts of radiation can damage or kill living things. Marie Curie's death in 1934 was caused by too much exposure to radiation.

Today, people who work with radioactive materials take extreme precautions. They wear radiation-sensitive badges that serve as a warning of unsafe levels of radiation. Specially designed protective clothing is worn to block radiation. Scientists continue to search for greater understanding and control of radiation so that its benefits can be enjoyed without the threat of danger.

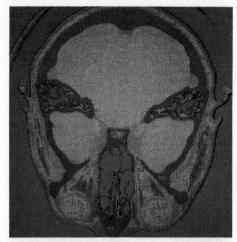

Figure 11–20 *Radioisotopes can be used as tracer elements to produce images such as this one of the brain (top). Any radioactive substance must be handled with extreme caution, as this technician is doing (bottom).*

SECTION REVIEW

1. What is a radioisotope? What are its uses?
2. What is a tracer?
3. How are radioisotopes useful in treating cancer?
4. A person has a disease in which too much sodium is retained by the body. How might a tracer help to diagnose the cause of this problem?

275

The Half-Life of a Sugar Cube

Problem

How can the half-life of a large sample of sugar cubes be determined?

> **Materials** *(per group)*
>
> 250 sugar cubes   large bowl
> food coloring   medicine dropper

Procedure

1. Place a small drop of food coloring on one side of each sugar cube.
2. Put all the sugar cubes in a bowl. Then spill them on the table. Move any cubes that are on top of other cubes. Be gentle with the cubes, since they are easily broken.
3. Remove all the sugar cubes that have the colored side facing up. If you have room on the table, arrange the sugar cubes you removed in a vertical column. Put the rest of the cubes back in the bowl.
4. Repeat step 3 several more times until five or fewer sugar cubes remain.
5. On a chart similar to the one shown, record the number of tosses (times you spilled the sugar cubes), the number of sugar cubes removed each time, and the number of sugar cubes remaining. For example, suppose after the first toss you removed 40 sugar cubes. The number of tosses would be 1, the number of cubes removed would be 40, and the number of cubes remaining would be 210 (250 − 40).

Observations

1. Make a full-page graph of tosses versus cubes remaining. Place the number of tosses on the X (horizontal) axis and the number of cubes remaining on the Y (vertical) axis. Start at zero tosses with all 250 cubes remaining.

2. Determine the half-life of the decaying sugar cubes in the following way. Find the point on the graph that corresponds to one-half of the original sugar cubes (125). Move vertically down from this point until you reach the horizontal axis. Your answer will be the number of tosses.

Conclusions

1. What is the shape of your graph?
2. How many tosses are required to remove one-half of the sugar cubes?
3. How many tosses are required to remove one-fourth of the sugar cubes?
4. Assuming tosses are equal to years, what is the half-life of the sugar cubes?
5. Using your answer to question 4, how many sugar cubes should remain after 8 years? After 12 years? Do these numbers agree with your observations?
6. What factor(s) could account for differences in your observed results and those you calculated?
7. Would the determined half-life be different if you had used a larger number of sugar cubes?

Tosses	Sugar Cubes Removed	Sugar Cubes Remaining
0	0	250
1	40	210
2		
3		
4		
5		
6		

CHAPTER REVIEW

SUMMARY

11–1 Radioactive Elements

❑ Radioactivity was discovered accidentally by Henri Becquerel in 1896, when he observed something unusual being given off by a uranium compound.

❑ An element that gives off radiation is said to be radioactive.

❑ Radioactivity is the release of energy and matter that results from changes in the nucleus of an atom.

❑ If the binding energy—the force that holds the nucleus together—is not strong, an atom is said to be unstable. Atoms with unstable nuclei are radioactive.

11–2 Transmutation of Elements

❑ Transmutation, the process by which one element changes into another as a result of nuclear changes, can occur naturally or by artificial means.

❑ Radioactive decay is the spontaneous breakdown of an unstable atomic nucleus.

❑ The three types of radioactive decay are alpha decay, beta decay, and gamma decay.

❑ Artificial transmutation can be made to take place by bombarding atomic nuclei with high-speed subatomic particles, such as protons or neutrons, in a particle accelerator.

❑ Equations describe nuclear reactions.

❑ The decay of a radioactive element occurs at a fixed rate called the half-life.

11–3 Harnessing the Nucleus

❑ Great amounts of energy are released during fission and fusion reactions.

❑ Fission is the splitting of an atomic nucleus to form two smaller nuclei of roughly the same mass.

❑ Fusion is the joining together of two atomic nuclei to form a single nucleus of larger mass.

11–4 Detecting and Measuring Radioactivity

❑ Four devices that can detect radioactivity are the electroscope, Geiger counter, cloud chamber, and bubble chamber. The Geiger counter can also measure radioactivity.

11–5 Uses of Radioactivity

❑ Artificially produced radioactive isotopes of common elements are called radioisotopes. They can be used to diagnose and treat diseases, study plant and animal metabolism, and solve industrial problems.

❑ Radioactive isotopes whose path can be followed through the steps of a chemical reaction are called tracers.

❑ Radioactive substances must be handled carefully since large amounts of radiation can be harmful to living things.

VOCABULARY

Define each term in a complete sentence.

alpha decay	gamma decay	nuclear radiation	radioisotope
beta decay	Geiger counter	particle accelerator	synthetic element
binding energy	half-life	radioactive	tracer
bubble chamber	nuclear chain reaction	radioactive decay	transmutation
cloud chamber	nuclear fission	radioactivity	transuranium element
decay series	nuclear fusion	radiation	
electroscope			

CONTENT REVIEW: MULTIPLE CHOICE

On a separate sheet of paper, write the letter of the answer that best completes each statement.

1. In a stable nucleus, the number of neutrons is
   a. about half the number of protons.   b. about twice the number of protons.
   c. three less than the number of protons.   d. about equal to the number of protons.

2. The process that changes one element into another is called
   a. alchemy.   b. transmutation.   c. fluorescence.   d. synthesis.

3. An atom that results from alpha decay has an atomic number that is
   a. two less than the original atom.   b. one less than the original atom.
   c. the same as the original atom.   d. two more than the original atom.

4. During beta decay, which of the following is (are) released from the nucleus?
   a. an electron and a proton   b. an electron and a neutron
   c. a neutron   d. an electron

5. The radioactive isotope that enables scientists to date ancient remains is
   a. iodine-131.   b. phosphorus-32.   c. carbon-14.   d. cobalt-60.

6. An atomic nucleus splits into two smaller nuclei of roughly equal mass in
   a. fusion.   b. alpha decay.   c. fission.   d. transmutation.

7. A device in which radioactive materials leave a trail of liquid droplets is a (an)
   a. bubble chamber.   b. cloud chamber.   c. decay chamber.   d. electroscope.

8. A Geiger counter detects radioactivity when the radioactive substance
   a. leaves a trail of bubbles.   b. causes air molecules to become ionized.
   c. causes liquid gas to boil.   d. produces an electric current.

9. An artificially produced radioactive isotope of an element is called a (an)
   a. synthetic isotope.   b. transmutation.   c. radioisotope.   d. gamma isotope.

10. The radioactive isotope often used to treat cancer is
   a. iodine-131.   b. iron-59.   c. sodium-24.   d. cobalt-60.

CONTENT REVIEW: COMPLETION

On a separate sheet of paper, write the word or words that best complete each statement.

1. The scientist who discovered radiation was _____.

2. The release of energy and matter that results from changes in the nucleus of an atom is called _____.

3. In the nucleus of an atom, the energy associated with the strong force is called the _____.

4. All of the elements above atomic number _____ are radioactive.

5. Two protons and two neutrons are released from the nucleus of an atom during _____.

6. Scientists are able to bombard atomic nuclei with high speed particles in an instrument called a (an) _____.

7. The fixed rate at which a radioactive element decays is the _____.

8. A constant series of fission reactions is called a (an) _____.

9. A device that detects radioactivity by reacting to ionized air molecules is the _____.

10. A radioactive element whose path can be followed through the steps of a chemical reaction is called a (an) _____.

CONTENT REVIEW: TRUE OR FALSE

Determine whether each statement is true or false. Then, on a separate sheet of paper, write "true" if it is true. If it is false, change the underlined word or words to make the statement true.

1. One of the radioactive elements discovered by the Curies was <u>uranium</u>.
2. Radioactive atomic nuclei are <u>stable</u>.
3. <u>Gamma rays</u> are electromagnetic waves of very high frequency and energy.
4. All synthetic elements <u>are</u> radioactive.
5. <u>Carbon-14 dating</u> determines the age of ancient objects and organisms.
6. Two atomic nuclei join to form a single nucleus of greater mass during <u>fission</u>.
7. Radioactivity <u>can</u> be seen.
8. Gas molecules are ionized by a radioactive substance in a <u>bubble chamber</u>.
9. <u>Iodine-131</u> can be used to study the function of the thyroid gland.
10. <u>Radioisotopes</u> are used to kill bacteria.

CONCEPT REVIEW: SKILL BUILDING

Use the skills you have developed in the chapter to complete each activity.

1. **Making graphs** Sodium-24 has a half-life of 15 hours. Make a graph to show what happens to a 100-gram sample of sodium-24 over a 5-day period. Hint: Plot the time along the horizontal axis and the mass along the vertical axis.
2. **Making calculations** The half-life of cobalt-60 is 5.26 years. How many grams of a 20-gram sample of cobalt-60 remain after 10.52 years? After 15.78 years?
3. **Applying concepts** An atom of lead-210 undergoes the following decay reaction:

   $$^{210}_{82}Pb \longrightarrow X + ^{0}_{-1}e$$

   What is element X? What is its mass number? Its atomic number?
4. **Analyzing data** A skeleton of an ancient fish is found to contain one-eighth the amount of carbon-14 that it contained when it was alive. How old is the skeleton?
5. **Making calculations** After 3200 years, 0.5 gram of a 2-gram sample of a radioactive element remains. What is its half-life?
6. **Applying concepts** Complete the nuclear equations. How are they related?
   a. $^{235}_{92}U + ^{1}_{0}n \longrightarrow ^{90}_{37}Rb + ^{144}_{55}Cs + ?^{1}_{0}n$
   b. $^{235}_{92}U + ^{1}_{0}n \longrightarrow ? + ^{146}_{57}La + 3^{1}_{0}n$
   c. $^{235}_{92}U + ^{1}_{0}n \longrightarrow ^{160}_{62}Sm + ^{72}_{30}Zn + ?^{1}_{0}n$
7. **Designing an experiment** In the reaction known as photosynthesis, during which green plants make food, carbon dioxide (CO_2) combines with water (H_2O) to form sugar ($C_6H_{12}O_6$) and oxygen (O_2). For a long time, scientists wondered from which compound—carbon dioxide or water—the oxygen came. Using your knowledge of radioisotopes, describe an experiment by which the origin of oxygen could be determined.

CONCEPT REVIEW: ESSAY

Discuss each of the following in a brief paragraph.

1. Describe how Becquerel's work illustrates the scientific method.
2. Describe how a Geiger counter works. How is it different from a bubble chamber, cloud chamber, and electroscope?
3. Describe the three types of radioactive decay. What is the penetrating power of each type?
4. Explain why the amount of helium in the sun is increasing.

Adventures in Science

SHIRLEY ANN JACKSON:
HELPING OTHERS THROUGH SCIENCE

Imagine what it would be like to catch a glimpse of the universe as it was forming—to look back in time nearly 20 billion years! Of course, no one can really see the beginning of time. But physicists such as Shirley Ann Jackson believe that learning about the universe as it was in the past will help us understand the universe as it is now and as it will be in the future.

By unraveling some of the mysteries of the universe, Dr. Jackson hopes to fulfill a basic ambition: to enrich the lives of others and make the world a better place in which to live. This contribution, Dr. Jackson believes, can be achieved through science.

Jackson was born and raised in Washington, D.C. After graduating from high school as valedictorian, she attended the Massachusetts Institute of Technology, M.I.T. There, her role as a leader in physics began to take root. Jackson became the first American black woman to receive a doctorate degree from M.I.T. She also achieved the distinction of being the first American black woman to receive a Ph.D. in physics in the United States.

After graduate school, Jackson began work as a research associate in high-energy physics at the Fermi National Accelerator Laboratory in Batavia, Illinois. This branch of physics studies the characteristics of subatomic particles—such as protons and electrons—as they interact at high energies.

Using devices at Fermilab called particle accelerators, physicists accelerate subatomic particles to speeds that approach the speed of light. The particles collide and produce new subatomic particles. By analyzing these subatomic particles, physicists are able to learn more about the structure of atoms and the nature of matter.

The experiments in which Jackson participated at Fermilab helped to prove the existence of certain subatomic particles whose identity had only been theorized. This information is important in understanding the nuclear reactions that are taking place at the center of the sun and other stars.

Jackson's research is not limited to the world of subatomic particles alone. Her work also includes the study of semiconductors—materials that conduct electricity better than insulators but not as well as metal conductors. Semiconductors have made possible the development of transistor radios, televisions, and computers.

Jackson's current work in physics at Bell Laboratories in Murray Hill, New Jersey, has brought her from the beginnings of the universe to the future of communication. This talented physicist is presently doing research in the area of optoelectronic materials. This branch of electronics—which deals with solid-state devices that produce, regulate, transmit, and detect electromagnetic radiation—is changing the way telephones, computers, radios, and televisions are made and used.

Shirley Ann Jackson, in her office at Bell Laboratories, is presently doing research in the field of optoelectronic materials used in communication devices.

Looking back on her past, Jackson feels fortunate to have been given so many opportunities at such a young age. And she is optimistic about the future. "Research is exciting," she says. Motivated by her research, Shirley Ann Jackson is happy to be performing a service to the public in the way she knows best—as a dedicated and determined scientist.

◀ This particle-accelerator generator at Fermilab is familiar equipment to Shirley Ann Jackson.

Issues in Science

FUSION ENERGY: FUTURE FUEL OR FOLLY?

By the time you finish reading this sentence, more than 2 million tons of hydrogen will have exploded in the center of the sun. The energy released by the explosions provides the earth with light and heat necessary to sustain life.

The sun and other stars produce energy as a result of a process called *fusion*. The explosions in the sun are fusion reactions. Fusion is the combining of atomic nuclei of small mass to form an atomic nucleus of larger mass. In the sun, two isotopes of hydrogen—deuterium and tritium—fuse to form helium. The fusion reaction releases tremendous amounts of energy.

In the sun, fusion occurs spontaneously and uncontrollably. On the earth, this same fusion reaction produces the uncontrolled explosion associated with the hydrogen bomb. But what if fusion could be controlled? Could the energy released by the reaction help to meet the energy needs of people all over the world in a safe, efficient, and inexpensive manner?

Some scientists believe fusion power could solve the worldwide problem of shrinking energy supplies. The fuel for fusion is deuterium. Because the oceans are rich in deuterium, fuel for this process is almost limitless. A liter of ocean water contains the energy potential of 300 liters of gasoline. Fusing just 1 kilogram of deuterium could pro-duce as much energy as burning 2000 tons of fuel oil.

If the nucleus of a deuterium atom closely approaches the nucleus of a tritium atom, the two nuclei will fuse and release energy. But deuterium and tritium have a natural, and very powerful, tendency to repel each other. It takes enormous quantities of energy to force them close enough to fuse.

The energy needed for fusion can come from heat. But the heat must be great enough to produce temperature conditions similar to those at the center of the sun. In fact, for fusion to occur deuterium and tritium nuclei must be squeezed together until they heat up to nearly 100 million degrees Celsius. So for a long time, physicists faced the problems of producing such extreme temperatures and confining the hot wisps of matter known as plasma that were produced.

In the early 1950s, Russian scientists proposed the use of magnetic fields to squeeze the hydrogen atoms together to produce the intense temperatures required for fusion. In addition, the magnetic fields could hold the plasma—something no ordinary container could do.

For the next thirty years, however, progress in fusion was slow. Then in 1983, scientists at the Princeton Plasma Physics Laboratory produced the sizzling temperatures needed for a fusion reaction in their doughnut-shaped *Tokamak Fusion Test Reactor*. But this first successful test lasted only one-tenth of a second. To those scientists who support further development of nuclear fusion, even this brief test was a milestone. To those scientists who doubt the potential of fusion, this brief test was an argument against nuclear fusion.

Critics of fusion also argue that the amount of energy needed to produce the magnetic fields is much greater than the amount of energy produced by the fusion reaction.

Another argument used by critics is that not enough useful energy is produced by fusion. In recent experiments, even though temperatures of 70 million degrees were reached, the amount of heat produced could not boil a cup of water!

Another problem associated with fusion power is radioactivity. The waste products of fusion are radioactive and must be disposed of carefully. Ensuring that radiation is not released into the environment must be a primary concern of any fusion proposal.

The fusion reaction itself causes the reactor's walls to become radioactive. The walls would have to be replaced about every five years. This would be an expensive and hazardous task, and would add to the waste-disposal problem.

Fusion energy will be a costly, complex technology to develop and commercialize. Once built, however, fuel for the plants would be almost unlimited and the energy produced almost infinite. Do you think that exploring fusion power is worth the necessary time, effort, and money? Is fusion power the answer to future energy problems? Or is it just an expensive experiment?

In the laboratory, researchers are experimenting with lasers to create temperatures high enough to bring about fusion reactions between hydrogen atoms.

UNIT FOUR

Motion, Forces, and Energy

On August 23, 1977, the *Gossamer Condor,* a strange aircraft made of Styrofoam and cardboard, flew 2.2 kilometers powered by the force of human legs!

In response to an unusual challenge, Paul MacCready designed a plane that was the first to complete a human-powered flight over a short figure-eight course. MacCready knew that if he made the plane's wings as large as possible but kept its mass as small as possible, the power needed to fly the plane could be reduced. The *Gossamer Condor* had a mass of only 32 kilograms, but it had a wingspan as wide as a commercial airliner. Using only the force of his muscles, the pilot, Brian Allen, pedaled the plane around the course.

Muscle power is only one of the forces Paul MacCready understands. By reading the chapters in this unit, you too will gain an understanding of forces, motion, and energy.

CHAPTERS

12 Motion

13 Forces

14 Forces in Fluids

15 Work, Power, and Simple Machines

16 Energy

Brian Allen crossed the English Channel by using the power of his muscles. This delicate looking plane, the Gossamer Albatross, *flies by pedal power— the same kind of power that moves a bicycle.*

Motion

12

CHAPTER SECTIONS

12–1 Frames of Reference

12–2 Speed and Velocity

12–3 Acceleration

12–4 Momentum

CHAPTER OBJECTIVES

After completing this chapter, you will be able to

12–1 Describe a frame of reference.

12–2 Calculate speed.

12–2 Distinguish between speed and velocity

12–3 Define and calculate acceleration and deceleration.

12–4 Describe momentum.

The eyes of the crowd are fixed on the sleek, dazzling skier as he sweeps down the ski jump track at 100 kilometers per hour. Reaching the bottom of the track, he leaps into the air. The icy wind lashes at his face. Even with goggles on, he is blinded by the glare of the snow on the mountainside below—far below.

Then, in an attempt to defy gravity, he leans forward. His body and skis take the form of an airplane wing as he rides the wind farther. Finally, his skis make contact with the snow-covered landing area. The snow flies up in his face in two streams. The sound of the cheering crowd mingles with the sound of the wind. His ride is over.

The scene is the Winter Olympics. And the ski jumper has just flown 117 meters through the air to set a new record for distance. He owes his gold medal not only to courage and years of training but also to an understanding of motion.

In this sense, ski jumping is not merely a sport. It is also a science. Learning about the science of motion may not earn you an Olympic medal, but it can be a leap into adventure and discovery.

Although this ski jumper seems to be floating in midair, his body is really in motion. You would quickly observe this fact if you were watching the ski jump from the ground below.

12–1 Frames of Reference

Sharpen Your Skills

Frames of Reference

1. Mount a camera on a tripod or firm base.
2. Aim the camera at Polaris, the North Star.
3. Take a 15–20-minute time exposure of the stars.
4. Describe the motion you see in the photograph.

Is the motion a result of the movement of the earth or of the stars?

Is the photo in Figure 12–1 a picture of the sun setting or the earth rising? Actually, both answers could be considered correct! If you said the sun setting, you assumed the sun was moving relative to the earth. If you said the earth rising, you assumed the earth was moving relative to the sun. **The object or point from which movement is determined is called a frame of reference.** For the sunset, the **frame of reference** is the earth. It is the earth that appears to stay in place while the sun moves. What is the frame of reference for an earthrise?

Suppose you are watching a car moving past you at a moderate speed. A train, moving at a greater speed, passes the car. For both movements, the earth is the frame of reference. Now suppose you are riding in the car. The car is the frame of reference. The train's speed relative to the car is greater. So the train appears to be whizzing past you as you look out the window. If the train is the frame of reference, the speed of the car relative to the train is less. So the car appears to be moving backward!

Figure 12–1 *From your frame of reference, the sun seems to be setting below the horizon in Cottonwood, Idaho. But is the sun really moving below the horizon?*

If movement is constant, it is impossible to determine whether you or another object is moving. Movement can be measured only with reference to something that is assumed to be fixed in place. Astronauts who traveled in space at 30,000 kilometers per hour were asked how it felt to move that fast. They replied that they had no sensation of movement because there was nothing nearby with which to compare their movement. Perhaps you have had a similar experience if you have ever flown in a jet plane. Did you feel that you were moving at about 800 kilometers per hour? You probably did not sense any motion because you had no other frame of reference.

The fact that movement is related to a frame of reference is often used in the movies. Sometimes the actor stays in one place and just the background moves. On the screen it looks as if the actor is moving. This is because your frame of reference is the background. What would appear to move if your frame of reference were the earth?

The most common frame of reference is the earth. But as you can see, there is more than one frame of reference that can be chosen. No single one is more "correct" than any other. But one or another must be used to describe movement.

Figure 12–2 *A frame of reference must be chosen to describe how objects move in relation to one another. How would a person riding in the airplane describe the motion of the car?*

Figure 12–3 *Although they are traveling at more than 30,000 kilometers per hour, astronauts on the Space Shuttle feel no sensation of movement. Why do you think this is so?*

SECTION REVIEW

1. What is a frame of reference?
2. What is the most common frame of reference?
3. Under what conditions might a car moving along-side your car appear to be moving backward?
4. Suppose you are standing on a sidewalk and your friend rides past you on her skateboard. Are you moving relative to the earth? Are you moving relative to your friend?

12–2 Speed and Velocity

Section Objective

To define and calculate speed and velocity

The runners are poised at the starting blocks. One hundred meters down the track, the timers ready their stopwatches. The starting gun sounds. The timers start their watches as the runners leap from their blocks. Seconds later, the winner breaks the tape and the timers check their watches.

The runners got from the starting blocks to the finish line because they moved, or changed their position. **Motion** is a change in position relative to a frame of reference. The motion of the runners was measured relative to the starting blocks. Motion is measured by distance and time. Distance is the length between two places. In the metric system, distance is measured in meters or kilometers. Time is measured in seconds or hours. In the race, the fastest runner ran 100 meters in 12 seconds.

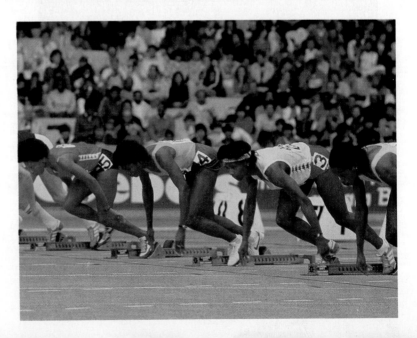

Figure 12–4 *Three seconds after this race began in Cologne, Germany, the lead runner had traveled 20 meters. What was her speed at that point?*

1 km/hr
Baby crawling

80 km/hr
Cyclist

110 km/hr
Cheetah

3600 km/hr
Concorde SST

Figure 12–5 *You can compare the speeds of some common objects on this scale. Where do you think your walking speed would fit?*

Speed

Speed is the distance traveled by a moving object per unit of time. You can calculate the **speed** of a moving object by dividing the distance the object travels by the time it takes to travel that distance.

$$\text{speed} = \frac{\text{distance}}{\text{time}}$$

Since distance is measured in meters or kilometers and time is measured in seconds or hours, the units of speed are meters per second (m/sec) or kilometers per hour (km/hr). What was the speed of the winning runner?

Sample Problem

A car travels 300 kilometers in 6 hours. What is the speed of the car?

Solution

Step 1 Write the formula

$$\text{speed} = \frac{\text{distance}}{\text{time}}$$

Step 2 Substitute given numbers and units

$$\text{speed} = \frac{300 \text{ kilometers}}{6 \text{ hours}}$$

Step 3 Solve for unknown variable

$$\text{speed} = \frac{50 \text{ kilometers}}{\text{hour}} \text{ or 50 kilometers/hour}$$

Practice Problems

1. What is the speed of a jet plane that flies 7200 km in 9 hours?

2. The speed of a cruise ship is 50 km/hr. How far will the ship travel in 14 hours?

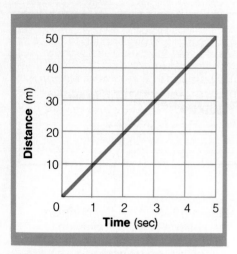

Figure 12–6 50, 40, 30, 20, 10

Distance (m)

0   1   2   3   4   5
Time (sec)

Figure 12–6 *In a distance–time graph, the distance an object travels is plotted as a function of the time it takes the object to go that distance. How do you know that the object whose motion is shown here traveled at a constant speed?*

Figure 12–7 *Study the distance–time graphs for the two lead swimmers in this race. Which graph has the steepest slope? What does that tell you about the speed of the two swimmers?*

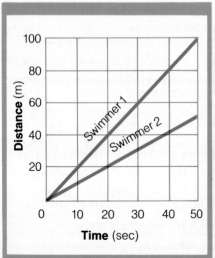

100, 80, 60, 40, 20

Distance (m)

Swimmer 1
Swimmer 2

0   10   20   30   40   50
Time (sec)

CONSTANT SPEED   Figure 12–6 is a distance–time graph of a runner's motion. Distance is plotted on the vertical, or Y, axis. Time is plotted on the horizontal, or X, axis. According to the graph, how many meters did the runner travel after 1 second? You are right if you said 10 meters. The runner's speed was 10 m/sec. After 3 seconds, the runner had run 30 meters. So his speed was 30 m/3 sec = 10 m/sec. The runner's speed did not change. Speed that does not change is called **constant speed.** The speed at any particular instant can be found by dividing distance by time. Notice that a distance–time graph for constant speed is a straight line.

In Figure 12–7, the motions of two swimmers are plotted on a graph. Are the speeds of both swimmers constant? How can you tell? Now use the graph to determine if both swimmers are moving at the same speed. Swimmer 1 swims 100 meters in 50 seconds. So her speed is 100 m/50 sec = 2 m/sec. Swimmer 2 swims 50 meters in 50 seconds. Her speed is 50 m/50 sec = 1 m/sec. Swimmer 1 is the faster swimmer. If you compare the graphs of the two swimmers, you will see that the graph for swimmer 1 has a steeper, or greater, **slope.** The slope of a distance–time graph is directly related to the speed. The steeper the slope, the faster the speed.

AVERAGE SPEED   The speed of a moving object is not always constant. Look at Figure 12–8. The distance–time graph describing this motion is not a straight line. According to the graph, after the first

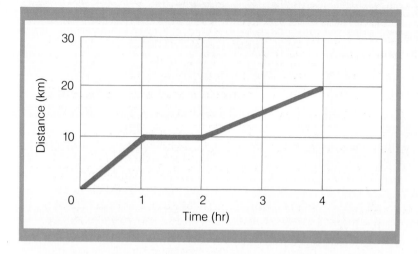

Figure 12–8 *According to this distance–time graph, how far did the object move between the first and second hour? What was the object's average speed after one hour? After two hours?*

hour the speed of the moving object was 10 km/hr. During the second hour, no additional distance was covered. There was no motion. What happened during the next two hours? How did the speed between hours three and four compare to the speed during the first hour? At the end of the fourth hour, the object had gone a distance of 20 km. But as you can see, the object did not move at a constant speed.

Speed that changes is not constant speed. Dividing the total distance by the total time gives the **average speed** and not the actual speed at that instant. What is the average speed of the object in Figure 12–8?

Velocity

"The National Weather Bureau reports that Hurricane Heather is moving east at a speed of twenty kilometers per hour." A weather forecast such as this causes people to worry. But those in the potential path of a hurricane are more concerned about its direction than its speed. They want to know the **velocity** of the hurricane. **Velocity is speed in a given direction.** The speed of the hurricane is 20 km/hr. The velocity is 20 km/hr east, or 20 km/hr E. If the storm suddenly moves north, is the speed the same? Is the velocity the same?

Navigation by land, sea, or air requires precise measurements of velocity. To reach the Hawaiian Islands, a pilot must determine both the direction and speed of the plane. If either measurement is wrong, the plane will not reach its destination.

A blanket of fog covers the airport. Aboard a jumbo jet, the pilot studies the cockpit instruments and listens carefully to orders radioed by an **air traffic controller.** The pilot cannot see the runway. The air traffic controller sees the airplane only as a moving dot on a radar screen.

An air traffic controller has several responsibilities. These include directing arriving airplanes, departing airplanes, and airplanes that are in flight between airport destinations. A controller communicates with a pilot by radio, providing the information necessary to keep the airplane safely on its course.

An air traffic controller informs pilots of weather conditions, ground conditions, and suggested routes. The job of an air traffic controller requires a great deal of concentration, steady nerves, and efficient work habits. In order to become an air traffic controller, an applicant must pass a federal civil service exam as well as physical and psychological exams. A college degree is usually necessary.

If you would like to find out how to become an air traffic controller, write to the U.S. Government Printing Office, Library and Statutory Distribution Service, 5208 Eisenhower Avenue, Alexandria, VA 22304. Enclose a self-addressed mailing label and ask for a copy of the publication *Government Careers # GA-300-128.*

Figure 12–9 *When walking into a heavy wind, this person must increase the amount of energy she expends in order to travel at her normal walking speed. Explain why.*

Suppose you are rowing a boat downstream at 16 km/hr. Would it surprise you to learn that you are actually going faster than 16 km/hr? How is this possible? The river is also moving. Since you are rowing downstream, you are going in the same direction as the river. The two velocities combine.

Velocities that have the same direction combine by addition. If the velocity of the river is 10 km/hr, then you are actually moving at 16 km/hr + 10 km/hr, or 26 km/hr.

Velocities that have opposite directions combine by subtraction. If you are rowing 16 km/hr upstream, then you are actually moving at 16 km/hr − 10 km/hr, or 6 km/hr. What would happen if you were rowing at 8 km/hr upstream in the river?

This idea is very important in launching rockets. Rockets are launched in the same direction as the earth rotates. The speed of the earth's rotation is about 1800 km/hr. Thus, the rocket gets an added boost of 1800 km/hr to its speed. That boost is enough to allow the rocket to escape the earth's gravitational force.

SECTION REVIEW

1. What is motion?
2. What is speed? How is it calculated?
3. What is average speed?
4. What is the relationship between steepness of the slope of a distance–time graph and speed?
5. What is velocity?
6. Draw a distance–time graph for the following motion. Starting from home, Jack walks 100 meters in 50 seconds. He stops to talk to his best friend for 100 seconds. He then turns around and sprints back home in 20 seconds. Is Jack's speed constant? What is Jack's average speed to the nearest tenth of a meter?

12–3 Acceleration

Have you ever ridden in a roller coaster? You are pulled up to the top of the first hill at constant velocity. But as you roll down the other side, your velocity rapidly increases. At the bottom of the hill you make a sharp right turn. Then your velocity rapidly decreases as you climb the second hill. In a roller coaster ride, you experience rapid changes in velocity.

Acceleration (ak-sehl-uh-RAY-shuhn) is the rate of change in velocity. To calculate **acceleration,** divide the change in velocity by the time it takes the velocity to change. The change in velocity is the final velocity minus the original velocity.

$$\text{acceleration} = \frac{\text{final velocity} - \text{original velocity}}{\text{time}}$$

The change in velocity is measured in meters per second (m/sec). The time is usually measured in seconds (sec). So acceleration is measured in m/sec divided by sec, or m/sec/sec.

A decrease in velocity is called **deceleration** (dee-sehl-uh-RAY-shuhn). Because the final velocity is less than the original velocity, deceleration has a negative value. Deceleration is sometimes called negative acceleration. When a roller coaster climbs a hill, it decelerates. Can you think of another example of deceleration?

Figure 12–10 *The original velocity of this roller coaster at the Arizona State Fair is 0 km/hr. The ride takes 20 seconds to complete. What other information do you need to determine its acceleration?*

A roller coaster's velocity at the top of a hill is 10 meters/second. Two seconds later it reaches the bottom of the hill with a velocity of 26 meters/second. What is the acceleration of the roller coaster?

Solution

Step 1 Write the formula

$$acceleration = \frac{final\ velocity - original\ velocity}{time}$$

Step 2 Substitute given numbers and units

$$acceleration = \frac{26\ meters/second - 10\ meters/second}{2\ seconds}$$

$$acceleration = \frac{16\ meters/second}{2\ seconds}$$

Step 3 Solve for unknown variable

$$acceleration = 8\ meters/second/second$$

The roller coaster is increasing its velocity by 8 meters/second for every second it is moving.

Practice Problems

1. A roller coaster has a velocity of 10 m/sec at the top of a hill. Two seconds later it reaches the bottom of the hill with a velocity of 20 m/sec. What is the acceleration of the roller coaster?

2. A roller coaster is moving at 25 m/sec at the bottom of a hill. Three seconds later it reaches the top of the next hill, moving at 10 m/sec. What is the deceleration of the roller coaster?

Graphing Acceleration

The data table in Figure 12–11 is a record of a professional drag-strip race. The driver had traveled a distance of 5 meters after the first second. The distance covered in the next second was 15 meters (20 m − 5 m). By the end of four seconds, the driver had traveled 80 meters. Figure 12–11 also shows a distance–time graph of the racing car's motion. The graph is a curve rather than a straight line. A distance–time graph for acceleration is always a curve. According to the graph, how far did the driver travel in the first five seconds of the race? In the last four seconds?

Time (sec)	Distance (m)
0	0
1	5
2	20
3	45
4	80
5	125
6	180
7	245
8	320
9	405

Figure 12–11 *The data from a professional drag race is shown on the left. A distance–time graph of the racer's motion is shown on the right. What is the acceleration of the race car? What is the shape of a distance–time graph for acceleration?*

Circular Motion

Acceleration is a change in velocity, and velocity expresses direction as well as speed. In circular motion the velocity is continuously changing because the direction is continuously changing. An object in circular motion is accelerating even though its speed may be constant.

The speed of the people riding the loop-the-loop in Figure 12–12 is relatively constant. But their direction is changing. So they are accelerating. They

Figure 12–12 *The gymnast on the high bar (left) and the loop-the-loop ride (right) both exhibit circular motion. The direction of the velocity is constantly changing in circular motion. What is the term for acceleration directed toward the center of a circular path?*

Sharpen Your Skills

Momentum

Place the following objects in the correct order from the lowest to the highest momentum. Assume that all the objects are moving at their maximum velocity.

freight train   mosquito
bullet   battleship
Space Shuttle

are accelerating toward the center. Acceleration that is directed toward the center of a circular path is called **centripetal** (sehn-TRIHP-uh-tuhl) **acceleration.**

SECTION REVIEW

1. What is acceleration?
2. What is the shape of a distance–time graph for accelerated motion?
3. What is centripetal acceleration?
4. The acceleration of a freely falling body is about 10 m/sec/sec. If a ball is dropped from the top of a building, what would its velocity be after 2 seconds? Hint: What is its original velocity?

12–4 Momentum

The 100-kg fullback runs up the middle of the football field. Suddenly he collides with a 75-kg defensive back running toward him. The more massive fullback is thrown back two meters! How can a 75-kg defensive back stop a 100-kg fullback?

The answer is that the defensive back has more **momentum.** All moving objects have momentum. **Momentum is equal to the mass of an object multiplied by its velocity.**

$$\text{momentum} = \text{mass} \times \text{velocity}$$

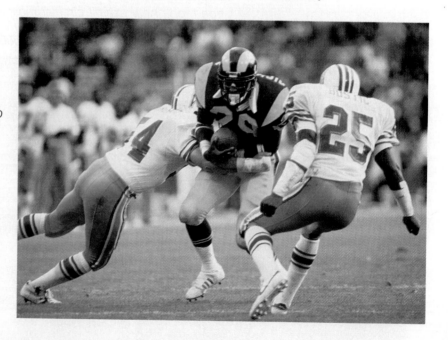

Figure 12–13 *It has been said that football is a game of momentum. What must be true of the smaller player's velocity if his momentum is great enough to stop a larger player?*

Although he has less mass, the defensive back has more momentum because he is moving faster than the fullback. His greater velocity compensates for his smaller mass. If both players had the same velocity, who would have more momentum?

A train has a large momentum because of its mass. A bullet has a large momentum because of its velocity. As you can see, an object's momentum depends on both its mass and its velocity. Why is it harder to stop a car moving at 100 km/hr than the same car moving at 25 km/hr? You are right if you said the car moving at 100 km/hr has more momentum and is harder to stop. This means that a car having greater momentum requires a longer distance in which to stop. The stopping distance of a car is directly related to its momentum.

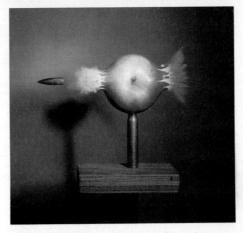

Figure 12–14 *Although this bullet has a very small mass, its high speed gives it a momentum great enough to cut right through the apple.*

Conservation of Momentum

If you have ever played billiards, you know that the momentum of the moving object is transferred to the stationary object when the two objects collide. The total momentum before and after the collision is unchanged. None of the momentum is lost. The **law of conservation of momentum** states that the total momentum of any group of objects remains the same unless outside forces act on the objects. One object may lose momentum. But the momentum lost by this object is gained by another.

The momentum of a baseball bat is transferred to the ball when bat and ball meet. The more momentum the bat has, the more momentum is transferred to the ball. Why do you think a pitcher winds up before throwing the ball? In each of these situations the total momentum is conserved.

Figure 12–15 *Carol Lewis has held the American long-jump record. How does her great speed help her in the long-jump event?*

SECTION REVIEW

1. What is momentum?
2. What is the law of conservation of momentum?
3. Which object has more momentum: a large cruise ship moving at 40 km/hr or a small jet plane moving at 500 km/hr? Explain your answer.
4. Using the formula for calculating momentum, determine the units of measurement.

LABORATORY INVESTIGATION

Measuring Constant Speed

Problem

What is the shape of a distance–time graph of constant speed?

Materials *(per student)*

pencil
graph paper
metric ruler

Procedure

1. The illustration on this page represents a series of flash shots taken of a dry-ice puck sliding across the floor. The time between each flash is 0.1 second. Study the illustration carefully.
2. Copy the sample data table on a piece of graph paper.
3. Position the 0-cm mark of the metric ruler on the front edge of the first puck. This position will represent distance 0.0 cm at time 0.0 second. Record this data in your data table.
4. Without moving the ruler, determine the distance of each puck from the first one.
5. Record each distance to the nearest 0.1 cm in your data table.

Observations

1. Make a distance–time graph using the data in your table. Plot the distance on the vertical, or Y, axis and the time on the horizontal, or X, axis.

Time *(sec)*	Distance *(cm)*
0.0	0.0
0.1	
0.2	
0.3	
0.4	
0.5	
0.6	

Conclusions

1. What is the shape of the graph?
2. Is the speed constant? Explain your answer.
3. Calculate the average speed.

0.0 sec   0.1 sec   0.2 sec   0.3 sec   0.4 sec   0.5 sec   0.6 sec

CHAPTER REVIEW

12–1 Frames of Reference

❑ A frame of reference is an object or point from which motion is determined.

❑ The earth is the most common frame of reference.

12–2 Speed and Velocity

❑ Motion is a change in position relative to a frame of reference.

❑ Speed is the distance traveled by a moving object per unit of time.

❑ Speed that does not change is called constant speed.

❑ The distance–time graph of constant speed is a straight line. The steeper the slope of the line, the greater the speed.

❑ The average speed of a moving object is the total distance divided by the total time.

❑ Velocity is speed in a given direction.

❑ Velocities that have the same direction combine by addition. Velocities that have opposite directions combine by subtraction.

12–3 Acceleration

❑ Acceleration is the rate of change in velocity. It is equal to the change in velocity divided by the time it takes to make the change.

❑ Deceleration, or negative acceleration, is a decrease in velocity.

❑ The distance–time graph for acceleration is a curve.

❑ Acceleration is a change in direction as well as in speed.

❑ Circular motion always involves acceleration because an object's direction is constantly changing. Acceleration directed toward the center of a circular path is called centripetal acceleration.

12–4 Momentum

❑ Momentum is equal to the mass of an object multiplied by its velocity.

❑ The law of conservation of momentum states that the total momentum of any group of objects remains the same if no outside forces act on the objects.

VOCABULARY

Define each term in a complete sentence.

acceleration	deceleration	momentum
average speed	frame of reference	motion
centripetal acceleration	law of conservation of momentum	slope
constant speed		speed
		velocity

CONTENT REVIEW: MULTIPLE CHOICE

On a separate sheet of paper, write the letter of the answer that best completes each statement.

1. The most commonly used frame of reference is the
   a. sun.   b. moon.   c. earth.   d. ocean.
2. A change in position relative to a frame of reference is
   a. motion.   b. acceleration.   c. momentum.   d. direction.

3. The distance traveled by a moving object per unit of time is called
   a. acceleration.   b. speed.   c. momentum.   d. motion.
4. Total distance divided by total time is
   a. constant speed.   b. average speed.   c. acceleration.   d. momentum.
5. Velocity is speed and
   a. motion.   b. distance.   c. mass.   d. direction.
6. A distance–time graph is a straight line for
   a. constant speed.   b. acceleration.   c. momentum.   d. average speed.
7. The rate of change in velocity is called
   a. momentum.   b. speed.   c. acceleration.   d. motion.
8. Acceleration is a change in speed or
   a. direction.   b. distance.   c. time.   d. momentum.
9. A distance–time graph is a curve for
   a. momentum.   b. speed.   c. acceleration.   d. velocity.
10. Momentum is mass times
   a. acceleration. b. velocity.   c. motion.   d. distance.

CONTENT REVIEW: COMPLETION

On a separate sheet of paper, write the word or words that best complete each statement.

1. The most commonly used frame of reference is the _____.

2. Speed is equal to distance divided by _____.

3. The distance–time graph for constant speed is a _____.

4. Velocity is speed and _____.

5. Velocities in the same direction combine by _____.

6. Acceleration is the rate of change in _____.

7. A decrease in velocity, or negative acceleration, is called _____.

8. Acceleration is a change in speed or _____.

9. Momentum is defined as mass times _____.

10. According to the _____, the total momentum of a group of objects remains the same unless outside forces act on the objects.

CONTENT REVIEW: TRUE OR FALSE

Determine whether each statement is true or false. Then on a separate sheet of paper, write "true" if it is true. If it is false, change the underlined word or words to make the statement true.

1. A <u>frame of reference</u> is a point or object from which motion is determined.

2. The <u>sun</u> is the most commonly used frame of reference.

3. The distance–time graph of <u>constant</u> speed is a straight line.

4. <u>Average</u> speed equals the total distance divided by the total time.

5. <u>Speed</u> is the rate of change in velocity.

6. Deceleration is <u>positive</u> acceleration.

7. The distance–time graph for acceleration is a <u>curve</u>.

8. <u>Centripetal</u> acceleration acts toward the center of a circular path.

9. Momentum is mass times <u>acceleration</u>.

10. Momentum is <u>lost</u> during a collision between two objects.

CONCEPT REVIEW: SKILL BUILDING

Use the skills you have developed in the chapter to complete each activity.

1. **Applying concepts** A satellite is in orbit 210 km above the earth. Another satellite orbiting at 200 km above the earth passes it. Describe the motion of the two satellites using the following frames of reference: (a) the earth (b) the higher satellite (c) the lower satellite.

2. **Making and interpreting graphs** A jogger sprints 100 meters in 12 seconds. She stops and does 20 push-ups in 88 seconds. She then jogs 1000 meters in 300 seconds. She walks another 500 meters in 400 seconds. Make a distance–time graph of her motion. What is her average speed?

3. **Interpreting graphs** Fully describe the motion at each labeled portion of the following distance–time graph.

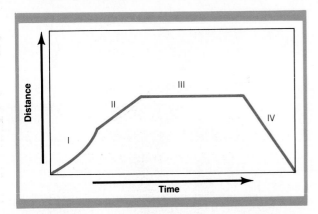

4. **Making calculations** If the acceleration of the car in Figure 12–11 is 10 m/sec/sec, what is its velocity after 5 seconds?

5. **Applying concepts**

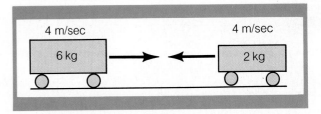

a. What is the momentum of the 6-kg cart? Of the 2-kg cart? What is the total momentum of the system?

b. If the two carts collide and stick together, what will be the direction of their motion?

c. What is the total momentum after the two carts collide? Explain your answer.

d. What is the velocity of the two carts after they collide and stick together?

6. **Relating cause and effect** Use the following information to explain the launch of a rocket: Hot gases that escape from a rocket have a very small mass but a high velocity. As fuel is used up, the mass of the rocket decreases.

7. **Identifying relationships** The jet stream is a belt of strong wind that moves west to east across the United States. Explain how the jet stream affects a plane's travel time from San Francisco to New York? From New York to San Francisco?

CONCEPT REVIEW: ESSAY

Discuss each of the following in a brief paragraph.

1. Suppose that you are sitting in a parked car. Another car passes you at a speed of 50 km/hr. Describe what a passenger in the other car sees.

2. Suppose that you are riding on a Ferris wheel moving at constant speed. Are you being accelerated? Explain your answer.

3. A drag-strip racer reaches a speed of 90 m/sec from a standing start in 9.0 sec. What is her acceleration? What would a distance–time graph of her motion look like?

4. Explain why an ocean liner slowly docking and a bullet rapidly fired both have a large momentum.

Forces

13

CHAPTER SECTIONS

13–1 Nature of Forces

13–2 Balanced and Unbalanced Forces

13–3 Force and Motion

13–4 Gravity

13–5 Weight and Mass

CHAPTER OBJECTIVES

After completing this chapter, you will be able to

13–1 Define force and describe its relationship to motion.

13–1 Compare the three types of friction.

13–2 Distinguish between balanced and unbalanced forces.

13–3 Describe Newton's three laws of motion.

13–3 Apply Newton's laws to everyday examples of motion.

13–4 Relate the force of gravity to free fall, projectile motion, and orbital motion.

13–4 Explain the relationship between gravitational force, mass, and distance.

13–5 Compare weight and mass.

The year was 1665. Throughout London, schools and businesses had closed down. The deadly bubonic plague raged through the city, killing hundreds of people every day. Twenty-two-year-old Isaac Newton, a student and teacher at Trinity College in London, had been forced to return to his mother's farmhouse in Woolsthorpe.

As he was drinking tea in the garden at Woolsthorpe, Newton observed an apple falling from a tree. He began to wonder: Why does the apple fall vertically down to the earth? Why does it not fall sideways, or even up?

During the next year, Isaac Newton proved that the force that pulls an apple to the ground is the same force that helps keep the moon in orbit around the earth. He also was able to show that this force keeps the planets in their orbits around the sun. While Newton was making this discovery, he also was discovering the secrets of light and color, and inventing a branch of mathematics called calculus. Incredibly, Newton accomplished all this in just 18 months!

Isaac Newton is considered the founder of modern physics and "one of the greatest names in the history of human thought." Many students of his time complained that he left nothing new to be discovered! Certainly, this was not the case. You will gain an appreciation for Newton and his contribution to science as you read about his beautifully simple explanation of forces and motion: how forces determine all the motions of the earth, moon, solar system, and the entire universe.

Isaac Newton discovered the force that helps keep the moon in orbit around the earth. This photograph, taken by United States astronauts, shows the earth rising over the moon's horizon.

13–1 Nature of Forces

Do you play baseball or tennis? Have you raked a pile of leaves or shoveled snow off a sidewalk? Have you ever hammered a nail into a piece of wood or moved a large piece of furniture? How about something as simple as riding a bicycle, picking this book up off your desk, or opening a door? In each of these activities, a **force** is involved. You are exerting a force on an object. And although you may not know it, the object is exerting a force on you! What is force? How is it related to motion?

A force is a push or pull. A force may give energy to an object and cause it to start moving, stop moving, or change its motion. The wind pushes against you and the flag on a flagpole. A magnet pulls iron toward it. A jet engine pushes a plane forward. The moon pulls on the oceans, causing the daily tides. A nuclear explosion pushes nearby objects outward with tremendous force. A negatively charged particle and a positively charged particle are attracted to each other. In each of these examples, a force is involved. The force gives energy to an object. The energy can set the object in motion, stop its motion, or change the speed and direction of its motion.

Figure 13–1 *A force is a push or pull that may give rise to motion. What force is pushing these sailboats forward (left)? Where does the force that pushes these motorcycles forward originate (right)?*

Figure 13–2 *Friction is a force that opposes the motion of an object. What type of friction is acting on the sled and speed skaters?*

Friction: A Force Opposing Motion

The early Greek philosopher Aristotle believed that in order to set an object in motion and keep it moving at a constant speed, a constant force had to be applied. If the force were removed, the object would come to rest. In other words, the natural state of an object was to be at rest. For example, a horse had to pull a cart continuously to keep the cart moving. If the horse stopped pulling, the cart came to rest.

Based on many of your everyday experiences, you probably would agree with Aristotle. A ball rolled along the ground comes to rest. A sled glided along the snow eventually ends its ride. And a book pushed along a table soon stops. So it is not surprising that Aristotle's idea of constant force for constant motion lasted for almost 2000 years.

In the seventeenth century, Isaac Newton suggested a different explanation for motion. He proposed that an object in motion should move at constant velocity. No force is necessary to keep it moving in a straight line at a constant speed. If a book sliding across a table comes to rest, there must be a force acting on the book that opposes its motion. Objects do not come to rest on their own!

The force that opposes the motion of an object is called **friction** (FRIHK-shuhn). Friction is the force

307

that brings an object to rest. When objects are in contact with each other, friction acts in a direction opposite to the motion of the moving object. The moving object slows down and finally stops.

Sliding Friction

When two solid surfaces slide over each other, **sliding friction** acts between the surfaces. When you push a chair across the floor, sliding friction opposes your motion.

The amount of sliding friction present depends on two factors: the weight of the object that is moving and the types of surfaces that the object slides across. There is more friction when a stack of cartons is pushed than when just one carton is pushed. But there is less friction opposing the motion if the cartons are pushed across a smooth floor rather than across a carpeted one.

Rolling Friction

When an object rolls over a surface, the friction produced is called **rolling friction.** Rolling friction tends to oppose motion less than sliding friction does. So wheels are often placed under objects to make it easier to move them.

Wheels and ball bearings are used to reduce friction. A train would not be able to move without wheels. And just imagine how much force would be needed if automobiles had to overcome sliding friction instead of rolling friction.

Fluid Friction

All liquids and gases are fluids. Air, water, and oil are fluids. When an object moves through a fluid, **fluid friction** opposes the motion. Air resistance is an example of fluid friction. The fall of a feather is opposed by air resistance. When you dive

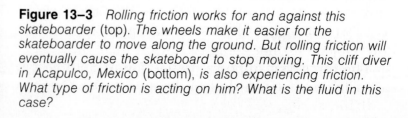

Figure 13–3 *Rolling friction works for and against this skateboarder (top). The wheels make it easier for the skateboarder to move along the ground. But rolling friction will eventually cause the skateboard to stop moving. This cliff diver in Acapulco, Mexico (bottom), is also experiencing friction. What type of friction is acting on him? What is the fluid in this case?*

from a diving board, you encounter air resistance. It is a relatively small amount of air resistance, so your motion is slowed down only a little. But the fluid resistance of the water is great enough to stop your motion before you reach the bottom of the pool.

Fluid friction usually opposes motion less than sliding friction does. Substances called **lubricants** change sliding friction to fluid friction. This reduces the friction and makes motion easier. Oil, grease, and wax are examples of lubricants.

Friction is not always an "unfriendly" force. Friction can be helpful. You often want to increase friction rather than decrease it. Tires have treads to increase the friction of the wheels on the road. Car brakes use friction to stop motion. Why do you suppose increasing friction is desirable?

Without friction you could not walk. The friction between the soles of your shoes and the ground keeps you from slipping and sliding. Why do you think sand is placed on icy streets?

SECTION REVIEW

1. What is force?
2. What is friction? What are the three types of friction?
3. What type of friction is involved in the following situations: a train moving along a track, a bird in flight, skiing, walking?

13–2 Balanced and Unbalanced Forces

Figure 13–5 *This arm-wrestling match appears to be a standoff. What must be true about the force exerted by each participant?*

Suppose you are arm-wrestling with a friend. You and your friend are exerting a maximum force against each other. Yet neither of you can move the other's hand. There is no change in motion. If two forces are being exerted, how can this be?

Forces that are opposite in direction and equal in size are called **balanced forces.** When forces are balanced, there is no change in motion. A book resting on a desk illustrates balanced forces. Gravity pulls the book down and the table pushes it up. The two forces are opposite and equal, so the book does not move.

A force can be represented by an arrow. The length of the arrow indicates the strength of the force. The head of the arrow indicates the direction of the force. The balanced forces exerted in the arm-wrestling contest are shown below. Notice that

the combined force is zero. Combined forces that are balanced always equal zero.

Figure 13–6 *Two forces are acting on the book. The force of gravity pulls the book down. The force of the table pushes the book up. What is true about the two forces?*

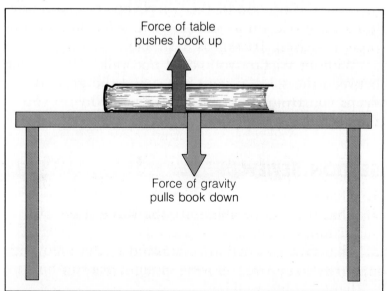

Force of table
pushes book up

Force of gravity
pulls book down

Figure 13–7 *In this tug-of-war, forces combine in opposite directions. The rope will move in the direction of the greater force— if there is one. What other force is involved in this competition? Hint: What effect would rain have on the tug-of-war?*

If you were playing tug of war and the forces were balanced, who would win? The figure below shows the forces. What is the combined force?

A balanced force cannot change the motion of an object. A balanced force keeps an object moving at a constant velocity. For example, a car engine continuously exerts a force against friction in order to move the car at constant velocity. The force of the engine balances the force of friction.

Unbalanced Forces

Forces that are not opposite and equal are called **unbalanced forces.** In unbalanced forces, one force is greater than the other. **While balanced forces cause no change in motion, unbalanced forces always cause a change in motion.**

When two unbalanced forces are exerted in opposite directions, the combined force is the

---

Sharpen Your Skills

Move That Barge

Tugboat A exerts a force of 4000 N on a barge. Tugboat B exerts a force of 8000 N in the same direction. What is the combined force on the barge? Using arrows, draw the individual and combined forces acting on the barge.

HELP WANTED: INDUSTRIAL DE-SIGNER to join a team of planners, engineers, and others working to improve sailboats and other products. Applicants must have a college degree in industrial design plus artistic ability.

A 130-year-long winning streak for the United States ended in 1983 when an Australian sailboat, the *Australia II,* won the America's Cup, a world-famous sailboat competition.

The *Australia II* knifed through the rolling waves of Rhode Island Sound as if the chilly water had somehow become thinner and lost its resistance. The "friction fighter" of the *Australia II* was its unique winged keel. Credit for the new keel goes to the **industrial designer** who created the *Australia II.*

An industrial designer creates the designs for new products. Designing boats, cars, airplanes, bicycles, and other vehicles that will move through air, water, or space involves the designer in the study of forces such as friction, pressure, and gravity. An industrial designer is also concerned with the safety, usefulness, attractiveness, and cost of the finished product.

In addition to engineering skills, an industrial designer must have an aptitude for art and a knowledge of production methods. Many designs, including the keel of *Australia II,* are created with the aid of computers. So knowledge of computers also is useful for industrial designers. If you would like information about a career as an industrial designer, contact: Industrial Designers Society of America, 1142 Walker Road, Suite E, Great Falls, VA 22066.

Figure 13–8 *When two forces are exerted in opposite directions, the combined force is the difference between the two forces (top). What is true of the combined force when two forces are exerted in the same direction (bottom)?*

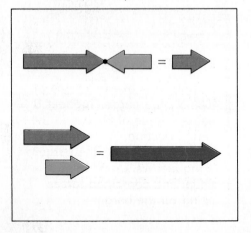

difference between the two forces. See Figure 13–8. If someone wins the arm-wrestling contest, it means there is an unbalanced force. Both arms will move in the direction of the greater force.

When two unbalanced forces are exerted in the same direction, the combined force is the sum of the two forces. See Figure 13–8. If you and your friend were pushing a car, the forces would be in the same direction. The two forces would "add together." The total force exerted by you and your friend would be greater because it would be the sum of the individual forces.

SECTION REVIEW

1. What are balanced forces?
2. What effect does a balanced force have on an object at rest? On an object in constant motion?
3. What are unbalanced forces?

4. What effect does an unbalanced force have on the speed and direction of an object?
5. A gorilla is playing tug of war with three monkeys. The gorilla is winning.
   a. Are the combined forces balanced or unbalanced?
   b. Draw arrows representing each monkey and the gorilla. Assume the gorilla is pulling to the right.
   c. Draw a single arrow that represents the combined forces of the three monkeys and the gorilla.

13–3 Force and Motion

Section Objective

To describe Newton's three laws of motion

During the year 1665 to 1666, Isaac Newton developed his famous three laws of motion. **The three laws of motion explain rest, constant motion, and accelerated motion, as well as how balanced and unbalanced forces act to cause these states of motion.** The importance of Newton's laws has been recognized for hundreds of years. But perhaps the significance of his contribution was best expressed by the Apollo crew as they were hurtling toward the moon. They radioed a message to mission control saying: "We would like to thank the person who made this trip possible . . . Sir Isaac Newton!"

Newton's First Law of Motion

If it were not for friction, an object set in motion would continue to move forever. Newton recognized this fact about objects in motion. He also realized that an object at rest would stay at rest unless it was acted upon by an unbalanced force. Newton called this tendency of objects to remain in motion or stay at rest **inertia** (ihn-ER-shuh).

Inertia is the property of matter that tends to resist any change in motion. The word *inertia* comes from the Latin word *iners*, which means "idle" or "lazy." Why do you think Newton used this word?

The concept of inertia forms the basis for Newton's **first law of motion.** The first law of motion states that an object at rest will remain at rest, and an object in motion will remain in motion at

Sharpen Your Skills

Newton's First Law of Motion

1. Place a playing card on top of an empty glass.
2. Place a coin on the center of the card.
3. Flick the card with your finger.

What happens to the coin? Explain what you observed using Newton's first law of motion.

Figure 13–9 *The inertia of the running back is changed as he is brought to a sudden stop. What outside force acted on the running back to alter his inertia?*

constant velocity unless an unbalanced force acts upon it. Remember that constant velocity means the same speed and the same direction. Only an unbalanced force can affect an object's state of inertia.

Imagine that you are standing in the aisle of a jumbo jet that is moving at a speed of 800 km/hr. All of a sudden you jump straight up in the air. Where will you land? On the same spot from which you jumped? In front of the spot from which you jumped? Behind it?

The answer to where you would land in the jet plane is found in Newton's first law of motion. You would land on the same spot from which you jumped. You are moving at the same speed the jet plane is moving. When you leave the floor, no unbalanced force changes your forward velocity. So you must land on the same spot. The effect is the same as it would be if the jet were at rest on the runway. Where would you land if the plane accelerated while you were jumping in the air?

You feel the effects of inertia every day. When you are riding in a car and it stops suddenly, you keep moving forward. If you did not have a safety belt to stop you, your inertia could send you through the windshield! Perhaps you never thought about it in this way, but safety belts protect passengers from the effects of inertia.

When you are standing in a bus, you experience inertia in two ways. When the bus starts to move forward, what happens to you? You are thrown off balance and fall backward. Your body has inertia. It is at rest and tends to stay at rest, even though the bus is moving. When the moving bus stops, you fall forward. Even though the bus stops, you do not. You are an object in motion.

Because of inertia, a car traveling along a road will tend to move in a straight line. What happens, then, if the road curves? The driver turns the steering wheel. Because of friction between the road and the car's tires, the car will move along the curve. But the people in the car will continue to move in a straight line. As a result, they will bump into the walls of the car. You might want to observe the effects of inertia the next time you are riding in a car. Notice what happens when the car starts, stops, and changes direction.

Figure 13–10 *The baseball player's inertia tends to keep him running in a straight line. Because it is hard for him to make a sharp left turn, he "rounds" the bases instead. What force enables the runner to round third base and head for home?*

Newton's Second Law of Motion

Newton's first law of motion describes motion when a balanced force acts on an object. Newton also described motion when an unbalanced force acts on an object. An unbalanced force accelerates an object in the direction of that force. The larger the force is, the greater the acceleration will be. The mass of an object also determines its acceleration. If the same force is applied to a bowling ball and a tennis ball, which ball will have the greater acceleration? Why?

The relationship between force, mass, and acceleration is stated in Newton's **second law of motion.**

force = mass × acceleration

When mass is in kilograms and acceleration is in meters/second/second, force is in newtons (N). One newton equals the force required to accelerate one kilogram of mass at one meter/second/second.

1 N = 1 kg × 1 m/sec/sec

Newton's second law of motion explains why a small car has better gas mileage than a large car. Suppose the acceleration of both cars is 2 m/sec/sec.

Figure 13–11 *It is easy to make this ball move with great speed after it makes contact with the racket. Although the ball has a small mass, its acceleration off the racket is great. Why?*

Figure 13–12 *One of the reasons these stock cars can accelerate around the curve is the unbalanced force of friction. In what direction does the unbalanced force of friction act?*

The mass of the small car is 750 kg. The mass of the large car is 1000 kg. According to the second law of motion, the force required to accelerate the small car is 750 kg × 2 m/sec/sec, or 1500 N. The force required to accelerate the large car is 1000 kg × 2 m/sec/sec, or 2000 N. More gasoline will have to be burned in the engine of the large car to produce the additional force.

Remember that acceleration is a change in speed *or* direction. If an object is moving in a curved path, its direction is constantly changing. It is constantly accelerating. According to the second law of motion, an unbalanced force must be present when there is a change in speed or direction. Any object moving in a curved path must have an unbalanced force acting on it. The acceleration is always in the direction of the unbalanced force.

Newton's Third Law of Motion

Suppose you are an astronaut making a spacewalk outside the Space Shuttle. In your excitement about your walk, you use up all the gas in your reaction jet. How do you get back to the Shuttle?

In order to save yourself, you need to know Newton's **third law of motion.** The third law of motion states that for every action, there is an equal and opposite reaction. Another way to state the third law is to say that every force must have an equal and opposite force. All forces come in pairs.

Now, back to your problem of being stranded in space. You have no walls or floor to push against.

So you throw your jet pack in the opposite direction of the Shuttle. In throwing the jet pack, you push on it and it pushes on you. The jet pack moves away from the Shuttle. You move toward safety!

Every time you walk you are using the third law of motion. As you walk, your feet push against the ground. The ground pushes against your feet with an equal and opposite force. You move forward and the earth moves in the opposite direction! Since the mass of the earth is so large, its motion is unobservable. If you were suspended a few meters above the ground, could you walk forward?

The reaction engine of a rocket is another application of the third law of motion. Various fuels are burned in the engine, producing hot gases. The hot gases push against the inside tube of the rocket and escape out the bottom of the tube. As the gases move downward, the rocket moves in the opposite direction, or upward.

Newton's three laws of motion can explain all aspects of an object's motion. His first law describes motion when a balanced force acts on an object. His

Figure 13–13 *Which of Newton's three laws of motion explains why the jumper lands in the water, not on the dock?*

Figure 13–14 *How does Newton's third law of motion explain the movement of a water sprinkler and the launch of a rocket?*

Movement of water

Movement of sprinkler arm

Sharpen Your Skills

Reaction Engines

Newton's third law of motion is the basis for the operation of reaction engines. Using books and other reference materials in the library, find out what a reaction engine is. Then find out how the following devices operate as reaction engines:

automatic lawn sprinkler
Hero's engine
jet and rocket motors

second law describes motion when an unbalanced force acts on an object. His third law explains why forces act in pairs.

SECTION REVIEW

1. State Newton's first law of motion.
2. What is inertia?
3. State Newton's second law of motion in terms of force, mass, and acceleration.
4. State Newton's third law of motion in terms of force.
5. You and a friend are pulling on opposite ends of a rope. Both of you are exerting a force of 200 N. What force is being exerted in the middle of the rope? Explain your answer.

Section Objective

To relate gravity to the motion of falling objects

13–4 Gravity

Legend has it that in the late 1500s, the famous Italian scientist Galileo dropped two cannonballs at exactly the same time from the top of the Leaning Tower of Pisa in Italy. One cannonball had ten times the mass of the other cannonball. According to the scientific theories of Galileo's day, the more massive ball should have landed first. But Galileo believed that the cannonballs would land at the same time. And, according to the legend, both cannonballs did land at exactly the same time! Galileo's hypothesis formed the basis of his description of the motion of falling objects.

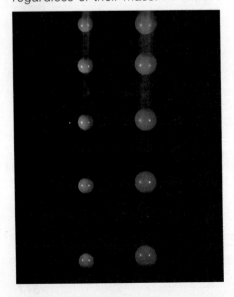

Figure 13–15 *This photograph illustrates that two objects will fall toward the earth at the same rate regardless of their mass.*

Free Fall

All objects accelerate at the same rate, regardless of their masses. **The acceleration of a falling object is due to the force of gravity between the object and the earth.** The attractive force between all objects in the universe is called **gravity.** A pebble, a rock, and a boulder dropped from the same height at the same moment will all hit the ground at exactly the same time. And because of gravity, they will all accelerate at the same rate.

Near the surface of the earth the acceleration due to gravity (g) is 9.8 meters per second per second, or 9.8 m/sec/sec. That means that for every second an object is falling, its velocity is increasing by 9.8 m/sec. Suppose an object is dropped from the top of a mountain. Its starting velocity is 0 m/sec. At the end of the first second of fall, the object has a velocity of 9.8 m/sec. After two seconds, its velocity is 19.6 m/sec. After three seconds, 29.4 m/sec. If it takes five seconds for the object to reach the ground, how fast will it be traveling? Perhaps you can now understand why even a dime can cause damage if it is dropped from a great height!

Do a leaf, a piece of paper, and a feather fall at 9.8 m/sec/sec? You have probably seen these objects fluttering through the air to the ground. Their acceleration is much less than 9.8 m/sec/sec.

As a leaf falls, air resistance opposes its downward motion. So it moves more slowly. Air resistance is a result of the force of friction. Air resistance also opposes the downward motion of a falling rock. But the shape of the leaf causes greater air resistance. If both the leaf and the rock were dropped in a vacuum, they would accelerate at 9.8 m/sec/sec.

Any falling object meets air resistance. You can think of the object as being pushed up by this opposing force of the air. As the object falls, the air resistance gradually becomes equal to the pull of gravity. The forces are then balanced. According to the first law of motion, the object continues to fall at a constant velocity. There is no further

Figure 13–16 *Although gravity pulls both a leaf and a rock toward the earth, the two objects do not accelerate at the same rate. The leaf and rock do not strike the earth at the same time. On the moon, however, they would. Why?*

Figure 13–17 *The skydivers are accelerating toward the earth at the same rate. At some point, air resistance will cause them to reach terminal velocity. They will no longer accelerate but will continue to fall at a constant rate. What effect does opening a parachute have on a skydiver's fall?*

acceleration. When a falling body no longer accelerates, it has reached its **terminal velocity.** Sky divers reach a terminal velocity of about 190 km/hr. When they reach this velocity, they stop accelerating. There is no longer any sensation of falling!

Projectile Motion

If you drop a baseball directly downward, it will accelerate at a rate of 9.8 m/sec/sec. What will be the downward acceleration of a ball that is thrown forward? The downward acceleration of the ball is still 9.8 m/sec/sec! Once you release the ball either directly downward or horizontally, the only force acting on it is gravity. Near the surface of the earth the acceleration due to gravity is 9.8 m/sec/sec.

When any object is thrown in the air, it becomes a **projectile.** A projectile moves forward due to its inertia and accelerates downward due to gravity. The path of a projectile is called **projectile motion.**

Projectile motion is always a curve. In projectile motion, gravity is an unbalanced force that changes the direction of the projectile. Gravity pulls the projectile downward as it moves forward. The combination of the two motions is a curved path. The next time you watch a display of fireworks, observe the trail left behind by the skyrockets. You will see a curved path.

Figure 13–18 *The illustration at the right shows the motion of one ball dropped straight down and two balls thrown forward. The two balls exhibit projectile motion. In what order will the three balls strike the ground? You can also see projectile motion in the trails of the fireworks.*

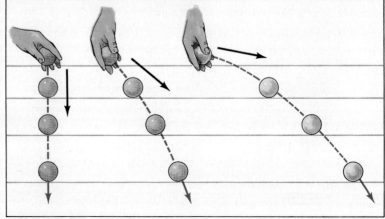

Orbital Motion

An object that orbits another object is in **orbital motion.** Orbital motion is the result of the combination of the object's forward inertia and the downward pull of gravity on the object. In order for a Space Shuttle to orbit the earth, it must be accelerated to a horizontal speed of 8000 m/sec. At this speed, its inertia balances the earth's pull of gravity. Inertia causes the Shuttle to move in a straight line. Gravity pulls the Shuttle toward the earth. The combination of inertia and gravity causes the Shuttle to orbit the earth. What will happen to the Shuttle as it begins to slow down?

Newton's Law of Universal Gravitation

Isaac Newton was the first scientist to prove that the force pulling an apple to the ground was the same force pulling the moon toward the earth. At this time, most scientists believed that the forces on the earth were different from the forces in the rest of the universe. Newton discovered the first universal law of forces. A universal law applies to all objects in the universe.

Newton's **law of universal gravitation** states that all objects in the universe attract each other by the force of gravity. The size of the force depends on two factors: the masses of the objects and the distance between them. The moon is held in orbit around the earth by gravity. The entire solar system is held together by gravity.

There is a force of gravity between you and this book. But the book is not pulled over to you. Why? The force of gravity depends on the masses of the objects. The gravitational force between a book and you is extremely small because your mass and the book's mass are relatively small.

The force of gravity increases as the masses of the objects increase. Gravitational forces only become observable when the masses are as large as those of the planets, moon, and stars.

The force of gravity depends on the distance between the objects. The gravitational force decreases rapidly as the distance between the objects increases. The gravitational force between an apple

Sharpen Your Skills

A Speeding Snowball

A snowball is dropped over a cliff. If its starting velocity is 0 m/sec, how fast will it be traveling after 5 seconds? After 7 seconds? Right before it hits the ground at the end of its 11-second fall?

Figure 13–19 *Newton's law of universal gravitation explains why the apple falls to the ground and why the moon stays in orbit around the earth.*

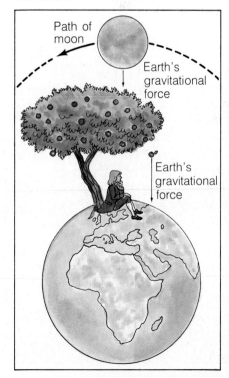

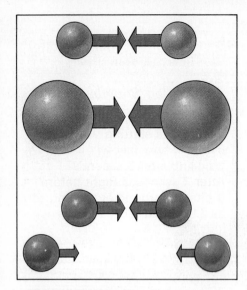

Figure 13–20 *Gravitational force between two objects depends on the masses of the objects and the distance between them. The larger arrows in the top diagram show that as mass increases, gravitational force increases. What do the arrows in the bottom diagram indicate about gravitational force and distance?*

To distinguish between weight and mass

and the earth is 5 N on the surface of the earth. At 380,000 km—the distance to the moon—the gravitational attraction between the apple and the earth is only 0.001 N!

SECTION REVIEW

1. What is the value of the acceleration due to gravity near the surface of the earth?
2. What is terminal velocity?
3. What force acts on a projectile? What kind of path does a projectile follow?
4. What is a universal law? State Newton's law of universal gravitation.
5. What happens to the force of gravity if the mass increases? If the distance increases? Using the symbol g for force of gravity, m for mass, and d for distance, write a proportion that shows the relationship involved in Newton's law of universal gravitation.

13–5 Weight and Mass

Weight is a measure of the force of gravity on an object. Since weight is a force, its unit is the newton (N). This book weighs about 15 N. You probably weigh between 450 and 550 N.

If your weight is 500 N on the earth, would it be the same on the moon? The answer is no. The mass of the moon is much smaller than the mass of the earth. According to Newton's law of universal gravitation, a smaller mass means a smaller gravitational force. So the gravitational force on the moon is less than that on the earth. You would weigh about 80 N on the moon!

Your weight can also change on the earth. As you move farther from the center of the earth, your weight decreases. You would weigh about one newton less on a mountaintop than at sea level.

Your weight varies according to the force of gravity pulling on you. And the force of gravity varies according to location. Is there less of you when you weigh less? The answer, of course, is no. You have the same amount of mass regardless of your location. Your mass is a constant value. It does not

Figure 13–21 *What effect did traveling to the moon have on the mass and weight of John Young, Apollo 16 commander?*

change. Your mass is the same anywhere on the earth, on the moon, and even on Jupiter.

Before Newton's time, mass and weight were thought to be the same property. But they are not. **Weight is a measure of the force of gravity, and mass is an amount of matter.** Weight varies according to the force of gravity, and mass is a constant.

Mass and weight, however, are related. Newton's second law of motion, force = mass × acceleration, can be rewritten in terms of weight:

> **weight = mass × acceleration due to gravity**
> **w = m × g**

Remember that the unit of weight is the newton and the unit of mass is the kilogram.

On the surface of the earth the acceleration due to gravity is 9.8 m/sec/sec. A 10-kg mass would weigh 10 kg × 9.8 m/sec/sec, or 98 N. If your mass is 50 kg, your weight would be 490 N. What would be the weight of a 100-kg mass?

SECTION REVIEW

1. What is weight?
2. Why does an object weigh less on the moon than on the earth?
3. A 600-N astronaut is standing on an asteroid. The gravitational force of the asteroid is one-hundredth that of the earth. What is the astronaut's weight on the asteroid?

Would a Gorilla Fall Faster Than a Banana?

Problem

Does mass affect the rate of free fall?

Materials *(per group)*

wood block, 10 cm × 15 cm × 2.5 cm
Styrofoam pad, 10 cm × 15 cm × 2.5 cm
sheet of notebook paper
triple-beam balance

Procedure

1. Use the triple-beam balance to determine the masses of the block, Styrofoam pad, and paper. Record each mass to the nearest 0.1 gram.
2. Hold the block and foam pad horizontally at arm's length. The largest surface area of each object should be parallel to the ground.
3. Release both block and foam pad at the same time. Observe if they land at the same time or if one hits the ground before the other.
4. Repeat step 3 several times. Record your results.
5. Repeat steps 2 to 4 for the foam pad and the paper.
6. Crumple the paper into a tight ball.

7. Compare the falling rates of the crumpled paper and foam pad. Record your observations.
8. Compare the falling rates of the crumpled paper and the wood block. Record your observations.

Observations

1. Which reaches the ground first, the wood block or the foam pad?
2. Are your results the same in each trial?
3. Which reaches the ground first, the foam pad or the paper?
4. Which reaches the ground first, the foam pad or the crumpled paper? The wood block or the crumpled paper?

Conclusions

1. Galileo stated that two bodies with different masses fall at the same rate. Do your observations verify his hypothesis? Explain your answer.
2. Did crumpling the paper have any effect on its falling rate? Explain your answer.
3. Now answer this question: Would a gorilla fall faster than a banana? Explain your answer.

CHAPTER REVIEW

SUMMARY

13–1 Nature of Forces

❏ Force is a push or pull. A force may give energy to an object, setting the object in motion, stopping it, or changing its direction of motion.

❏ Friction is a force that opposes motion.

❏ The three kinds of friction are sliding, rolling, and fluid friction.

13–2 Balanced and Unbalanced Forces

❏ Balanced forces are opposite in direction and equal in size to each other.

❏ A balanced force does not change motion. A balanced force keeps an object moving at a constant velocity.

❏ Unbalanced forces cause a change in motion.

❏ Forces in the same direction are added to obtain the combined force. Forces in opposite directions are subtracted.

❏ An unbalanced force can start, stop, or change the speed or direction of motion.

13–3 Force and Motion

❏ Inertia is the tendency of matter to resist a change in motion.

❏ Newton's first law of motion states that an object at rest will remain at rest and an object in motion will remain in motion at constant velocity unless acted upon by an unbalanced force.

❏ Newton's second law of motion states that force equals mass times acceleration.

❏ Newton's third law of motion states that every action has an equal and opposite reaction. Thus, forces come in pairs.

13–4 Gravity

❏ The acceleration due to gravity at the surface of the earth is 9.8 m/sec/sec.

❏ Terminal velocity is reached when the pull of gravity equals the air resistance.

❏ The path of a projectile is a curve.

❏ Newton's law of universal gravitation states that all objects in the universe attract each other by a force of gravity.

❏ An increase in mass increases the force of gravity.

❏ An increase in distance decreases the force of gravity.

13–5 Weight and Mass

❏ Weight is a measure of the pull of gravity.

❏ Weight is a force and mass is an amount of matter. Weight varies according to the force of gravity, and mass is a constant.

❏ Weight and mass are related by the equation: $w = m \times g$

VOCABULARY

Define each term in a complete sentence.

balanced force	inertia	projectile motion	terminal velocity
first law of motion	law of universal gravitation	rolling friction	third law of motion
fluid friction	lubricant	second law of motion	unbalanced force
force	orbital motion	sliding friction	
friction	projectile		
gravity			

CONTENT REVIEW: MULTIPLE CHOICE

On a separate sheet of paper, write the letter of the answer that best completes each statement.

1. Force is
   a. a push.   b. a pull.
   c. the ability to change motion.   d. all of the above.
2. A shark swimming in the ocean illustrates which type of friction?
   a. sliding   b. rolling   c. fluid   d. stationary
3. Lubricants are used to change
   a. fluid friction to sliding friction.   b. sliding friction to fluid friction.
   c. sliding friction to rolling friction.   d. rolling friction to sliding friction.
4. The property of matter that resists a change in motion is called
   a. inertia.   b. weight.   c. gravity.   d. friction.
5. According to Newton's second law of motion, force equals mass times
   a. velocity.   b. direction.   c. acceleration.   d. weight.
6. According to Newton's third law of motion, for every force there is
   a. always a change in motion.   b. an equal and opposite force.
   c. an unbalanced force.   d. a combined force.
7. When terminal velocity is reached, the acceleration of an object is
   a. increasing.   b. decreasing.   c. zero.   d. constant.
8. When the forward inertia of a projectile balances the downward pull of gravity, the object is
   a. stationary.   b. in orbital motion.
   c. decelerating.   d. moving at constant velocity.
9. Which force explains the attraction between all objects?
   a. gravitational   b. electric   c. nuclear   d. magnetic
10. Weight equals
   a. mass.   b. acceleration due to gravity.
   c. mass times acceleration due to gravity.   d. mass times distance.

CONTENT REVIEW: COMPLETION

On a separate sheet of paper, write the word or words that best complete each statement.

1. _____ is a push or pull that gives energy to an object.
2. Friction is a force that _____ motion.
3. Substances that change sliding friction to fluid friction are called _____.
4. The types of friction are _____, _____, and _____.
5. Forces that are opposite and equal are _____.
6. _____ is the property of matter that tends to resist any change in motion.

7. A force of one _____ is needed to accelerate a mass of one kilogram one meter/second/second.
8. When a falling body no longer accelerates, it has reached its _____.
9. A projectile moves forward due to its _____ and accelerates downward due to _____.
10. _____ is a measure of the force of gravity on an object.

CONTENT REVIEW: TRUE OR FALSE

Determine whether each statement is true or false. Then on a separate sheet of paper, write "true" if it is true. If it is false, change the underlined word or words to make the statement true.

1. A <u>force</u> can set an object in motion, stop its motion, or change the speed and direction of its motion.
2. Friction is a force that always acts in a direction <u>opposite</u> to the motion of the moving object.
3. Rolling friction tends to oppose motion <u>more</u> than sliding friction does.
4. The combined force of balanced forces is <u>zero</u>.
5. Objects will remain at constant velocity unless acted upon by <u>balanced</u> forces.
6. <u>Inertia</u> is the property of matter that resists any change in motion.
7. Force equals mass times <u>velocity</u>.
8. For every action there is an equal and opposite <u>reaction</u>.
9. The acceleration due to gravity at the surface of the earth is <u>1 m/sec/sec</u>.
10. <u>Mass</u> is a measure of the force of gravity.

CONCEPT REVIEW: SKILL BUILDING

Use the skills you have developed in the chapter to complete each activity.

1. **Applying definitions** Identify each of the following as sliding, rolling, or fluid friction: a. sky diving; b. roller derby; c. water slide; d. stealing second base.
2. **Applying concepts** A snowmobile is pulling a sled across a frozen lake at constant velocity. You are sitting in the sled. You throw a baseball straight up in the air. Assuming there is no wind resistance, where will the ball land if a. the snowmobile continues moving at constant velocity? b. the snowmobile speeds up? c. the snowmobile stops in front of you?
3. **Applying concepts** A plane drops a flare directly over you. Does the flare hit you? Explain your answer. Draw its path.
4. **Identifying relationships** Suppose the acceleration due to gravity on a planet called Zorb is 20 m/sec/sec. What is the weight of a 100-kg Zorbian?
5. **Relating concepts** You are on ice skates facing due north on a frozen pond. You are not moving. You throw your backpack to your friend who is also on ice skates and is facing due south. Your friend catches the backpack. What is the direction of motion for a. you? b. the backpack? c. your friend?
6. **Making calculations** A heavy object is dropped from the top of a building. What is its velocity at the end of 2 seconds? At the end of 5 seconds? Just before it hits the ground after 11 seconds?

CONCEPT REVIEW: ESSAY

Discuss each of the following in a brief paragraph.

1. Distinguish between balanced and unbalanced forces.
2. Explain why a single force cannot exist.
3. What is the relationship between weight and mass?
4. Explain how Newton's three laws describe all aspects of an object's motion.
5. Explain why the path of a projectile is a curve. Use a diagram to illustrate your explanation.
6. Explain why a flat sheet of paper dropped from a height of 2 meters will not accelerate at the same rate as a sheet of paper crumpled into a ball.

Forces in Fluids 14

CHAPTER SECTIONS

14–1 Fluid Pressure

14–2 Buoyancy

14–3 Hydraulics

14–4 Bernoulli's Principle

CHAPTER OBJECTIVES

After completing this chapter, you will be able to

14–1 Describe fluid pressure.

14–1 Relate fluid pressure to altitude and depth.

14–2 Describe Archimedes' principle in terms of buoyancy and density.

14–2 Apply Archimedes' principle to the floating and sinking of objects.

14–3 Explain how hydraulic devices operate.

14–4 Describe Bernoulli's principle.

14–4 Relate Bernoulli's principle to airplane flight.

14–4 Identify the forces involved in flight.

It is December 17, 1903. Wilbur and Orville Wright stand on a deserted beach at Kitty Hawk, North Carolina. Orville climbs into a strange-looking seat made from pieces of wood and canvas. A 12-horsepower gasoline engine is connected to two large propellers by a chain and sprocket. The Wright brothers are about to try something no one has ever succeeded in doing before. They are going to fly this machine!

They have prepared well for their attempt at flight. For the past 25 years they have studied the dynamics of air flight. They have experimented with more than 200 different wing surfaces in their homemade wind tunnel. They have observed and analyzed the flight of buzzards, carefully noting how they turn in the sky without losing balance.

Now they are finally ready. Wilbur rotates a propeller and the engine starts. Orville pulls the throttle wide open. The plane takes to the air. In a flight that lasts just 12 seconds, the plane manages to travel 36 meters. It is a small distance but a significant step in science: Human flight has become a reality!

The first flying machine was designed in the fifteenth century by Leonardo da Vinci. Why did it take so long to fly the first plane? How can a large jumbo jet weighing 3.5 million newtons fly at speeds exceeding 800 kilometers per hour? As you read this chapter, you will learn the answers.

As Wilbur Wright stood watching on the deserted beach at Kitty Hawk, North Carolina, his brother Orville took one of the most important trips in history—a 12-second, 36-meter leap toward the attainment of human flight.

14–1 Fluid Pressure

Although you may not be aware of it, forces that exist naturally in gases and liquids affect you constantly. When you breathe, when you swim, when you drink from a straw, you are experiencing forces. As a matter of fact, you have a force approximately equal to the weight of an automobile pushing down on you right now!

In Chapter 13, you learned that fluids can produce frictional forces. But these are not the only forces caused by fluids. Fluids also push against objects. For example, water pushes against you when you swim. When you drink through a straw, air pushes against the liquid forcing it up. And at this moment, air is pushing against you with a force equal to more than 10,000 newtons!

The "push" that fluids exert on an object is called **pressure**. Perhaps you are familiar with the word pressure as it is used to describe water, air, or even blood. Scientists define pressure in a more precise way than a "push." **Pressure is a force that acts over a certain area.** In other words, pressure is force per unit area.

$$\text{pressure} = \frac{\text{force}}{\text{area}}$$

Figure 14–1 *This wind surfer is enjoying a ride thanks to the natural force of the air. What three types of fluid forces are being exerted on the wind surfer?*

Pressure can be calculated by dividing the force exerted by a fluid by the total area over which the force acts. When force is measured in newtons (N) and area is measured in square centimeters (cm²), pressure is measured in newtons per square centimeter (N/cm²).

All liquids and gases are fluids. All fluids exert pressure. The pressure a fluid exerts is due to the fact that the fluid is made of particles that have weight and motion. The weight of the particles in a fluid causes them to push against objects.

Air, for example, exerts a pressure of 10.13 N/cm² *at sea level.* If standard air pressure is 10.13 N/cm² and your back has an area of approximately 1000 cm², then you have a force of 10,130 N pushing on your back. What keeps this force from crushing you? The fluids inside your body exert pressure, too. The air pressure outside your body is balanced by the pressure inside your body. So you do not feel 10,130 N of force.

At higher altitudes, there are fewer particles of air in a given area. So the air pressure decreases. The air pressure inside your body is now greater than the air pressure outside your body. The air rushes out of your ears and you hear a "pop." In this way, air pressure outside your body is again equal to the pressure inside your body.

Suction is a result of unequal air pressure. When you suck on a straw, you remove most of the air inside the straw. Standard air pressure, which is now greater than the air pressure inside the straw, pushes down on the surface of your drink. This pushes the drink up through the straw.

Figure 14–2 *This can was crushed because of a change in air pressure. Was the air pressure greater inside the can or outside it?*

Figure 14–3 *It would be very difficult for this girl to enjoy her ice cream soda if it were not for unequal air pressure. The air pressure pushing down on the liquid outside the straw is greater than the air pressure inside the straw. The liquid is forced up the straw. What causes the air pressure inside the straw to decrease?*

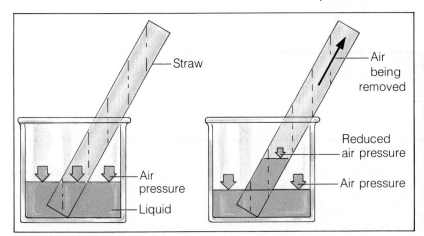

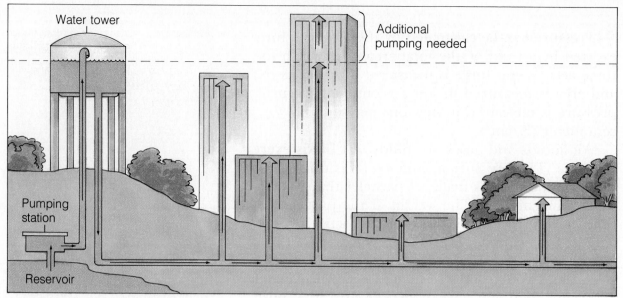

Water tower

Additional pumping needed

Pumping station

Reservoir

Figure 14–4 *One important application of increased fluid pressure with depth is a water tower. Notice that the tower is higher than most of the homes and buildings in the area. The weight of the water in the tower produces tremendous pressure. When the water is released from the tower, the pressure is great enough to drive the water through piping systems. What do you think must be used to pipe water through buildings higher than the tower?*

The operation of a vacuum cleaner is another example of unequal air pressure. A vacuum cleaner does not suck up dirt. A fan inside the cleaner causes the air pressure inside the machine to become less than the pressure of the air outside the machine. The outside air pressure pushes the air and dirt into the vacuum cleaner.

The pressure a liquid exerts also varies with its depth. The deeper the liquid, the greater its pressure becomes. If you have ever swum to the bottom of a pool, you probably are familiar with this fact. The pressure of the water, increasing rapidly with depth, makes your ears ache. In this case, the pressure outside your body is greater than the pressure inside your body. Submarines that have descended too deep in the ocean have on occasion been crushed by the tremendous pressure. Can you explain in terms of the particles in the liquid why the pressure increases with depth?

SECTION REVIEW

1. What is fluid pressure? How is it calculated?

2. What is the relationship between air pressure and altitude? Between liquid pressure and depth?

3. Explain your answers to question 2 in terms of particles of fluid.

4. Explain how a woman weighing 500 N and wearing high-heeled shoes can exert a pressure on the floor equal to about three times the pressure exerted by a 45,000-N elephant.

14–2 Buoyancy

Section Objective

*To describe Archimedes'
principle in terms of
buoyancy and density*

Have you ever wondered how a submarine can sink down in the ocean and then float on the surface again? How can a steel ship weighing about five million newtons float in water? And on a more practical level, what enables you to float in a swimming pool, pond, or lake?

Fluid pressure is exerted in all directions: down, up, and to the sides. The force of a fluid that pushes an object up is called **buoyancy** (BOI-uhn-see). The upward buoyant force of a fluid opposes the downward force of gravity on an object. In other words, buoyancy acts against the weight of an object. Buoyancy makes it seem as if an object weighs less in a fluid.

The buoyant force of a fluid can be greater than, less than, or equal to the weight of an object. The size of the buoyant force determines what will happen to an object placed in a fluid. But how can the size of the buoyant force be determined?

Think for a moment of what happens when you put several ice cubes in a glass of water. The level of the water rises. The ice cubes displace, or move aside, a certain amount of water. The amount of water that is displaced has a definite weight. And the weight of the displaced water is related to the buoyant force.

Figure 14–5 *The ice cube floats in water because the buoyant force on it is equal to the weight of water it displaces (left). The same principle applies to a submarine afloat on the surface of the water (right). What principle is this?*

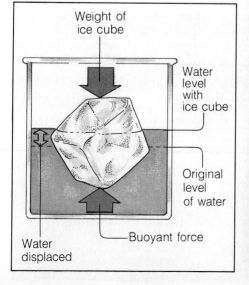

More than 2000 years ago, the Greek scientist Archimedes discovered the exact nature of the relationship between buoyant force and the weight of the fluid displaced. This relationship, sometimes called **Archimedes' principle,** is basic to the study of the behavior of fluids. **Archimedes' principle states that the buoyant force on an object is equal to the weight of the fluid displaced by the object.**

Have you ever noticed that it is easier to lift a friend while you are both in the water? Your friend's weight seems to be much less in the water. Why? The buoyant force of the water on your friend equals the weight of the water your friend displaces. Your friend seems to weigh less because of the buoyant force of the water.

Buoyancy helps to explain why an object sinks or floats in a fluid. An object floats in a fluid because the buoyant force—the upward push—on the object is equal to or greater than the object's weight—the downward push. According to Archimedes' principle, the buoyant force is the same as the weight of the fluid displaced. So an object floats because it displaces a weight of fluid equal to or greater than its own weight.

Now, let's go back to the operation of a submarine. When a submarine is floating on the surface of the water, the weight of the water it displaces is

Figure 14–6 *This bather in the Dead Sea in Israel (left) is taking advantage of the fact that the density of salt water is greater than that of fresh water. The density of ice is slightly less than the density of water. So a portion of this huge iceberg rises above the water's surface (right).*

equal to its own weight. To make the submarine dive, special ballast tanks are flooded with water. Now the weight of the submarine is greater than the weight of the water it displaces. The submarine sinks. To resurface, air compressors force the water out of the ballast tanks. The weight of the submarine is once again less than the weight of the water it displaces. The submarine again floats.

If you place a block of wood in water, it will begin to sink. The block will continue to sink until the weight of the displaced water equals the weight of the block. At this point the block will float. If you place a block of steel in water, it will never float. The weight of the displaced water can never equal the weight of the steel block.

A steel block can never float because it weighs more than the water it displaces. Another way of saying this is that the **density** of steel is greater than the density of water. Density is the mass of a substance divided by its volume.

Archimedes' principle can now be stated in terms of density: An object will float in a fluid if the density of the object is less than the density of the fluid. The density of water is 1.0 g/cm^3. The density of wood is about 0.8 g/cm^3. Wood will float in water. The density of steel is 7.8 g/cm^3. A steel block will not float in water. The density of liquid mercury is 13.5 g/cm^3. Will a steel block float in mercury?

Figure 14–7 *The density of hot air is less than the density of cold air. A hot air balloon rises as the air inside the balloon is heated. The balloon returns to the earth as the air inside it is cooled. Compare the density of the air inside the balloon to the density of the air outside the balloon during an ascent. During a descent.*

A Bathtub Submarine

1. Obtain an empty jar with a metal lid.

2. Carefully punch several holes in the lid of the jar.

3. Insert the short end of a flexible straw in one of the holes.

4. Fill a basin with water.

5. Place the jar in the water while holding the long end of the straw out of the water. Observe what happens to the jar.

6. When the jar is filled with water, blow on the straw. Observe what happens to the jar.

Explain your observations in terms of density and fluid pressure.

If the density of steel is 7.8 g/cm^3, how does a large cruise ship float in water? The answer is that the ship is not solid steel. The ship is built of a shell of steel that is hollow inside. Most of the ship contains air. The total density of the steel ship and air is less than the density of water. How would you describe this situation in terms of the weight of water the ship and air displace?

A ship floats lower in the water when it is fully loaded. And if water leaks into the hull of a ship, the density can eventually become greater than 1 g/cm^3. What do you think will happen to the ship?

Air is also a fluid. So air exerts a buoyant force. You are buoyed up by the air. The density of air, however, is only 0.00118 g/cm^3. Its buoyant force is very small. You cannot actually feel the buoyant force of the air. The density of helium gas is one-tenth the density of air. A balloon filled with helium gas will float in air. The density of carbon dioxide is almost twice the density of air. Will a balloon filled with carbon dioxide float in air?

SECTION REVIEW

1. Define buoyancy.
2. State Archimedes' principle in terms of buoyancy. In terms of density.
3. The density of alcohol is 0.816 g/cm^3. The density of an ice cube is 0.917 g/cm^3. Will an ice cube float in alcohol? Explain your answer.
4. The density of ocean water is 1.02 g/cm^3. Will a boat float higher in ocean water than in fresh water? Explain your answer.

14–3 Hydraulics

At any given depth, the pressure that a fluid exerts is equal in all directions—up, down, and sideways. Look at Figure 14–8. A bottle is filled to the top with water. Water is a fluid. As you just learned, all fluids exert pressure.

What would happen to the fluid pressure if a rubber stopper were pushed down the neck of the bottle? You can see the answer in Figure 14–8. Because the water particles are already packed tightly together, they cannot move any closer than they are. The added pressure of the stopper is transmitted equally in all directions to all parts of the fluid. Why is the water pushed out the top of the bottle?

Hydraulic devices use the principle that pressure is transmitted equally in all directions throughout a liquid. Hydraulic devices produce enormous forces with the application of only a very small force. The brakes on your family car operate on a hydraulic system. A small force is applied to the brake pedal and the hydraulic system stops a car weighing 10,000 N. A tractor operator uses a relatively small force to pull a handle, and a large scoop digs out several thousand newtons of soil.

How do hydraulic devices produce such enormous forces? In hydraulic devices, a force acts on a small area of liquid, producing an enormous pressure in the liquid. This original force is transmitted throughout the liquid. And at the same time, this force is multiplied into a much larger force.

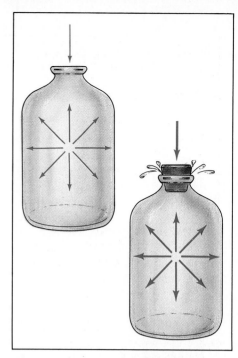

Figure 14–8 *A liquid in a confined space such as a bottle exerts pressure equally in all directions. When a stopper is pushed into the bottle, the added pressure it exerts is also transmitted equally in all directions—including up.*

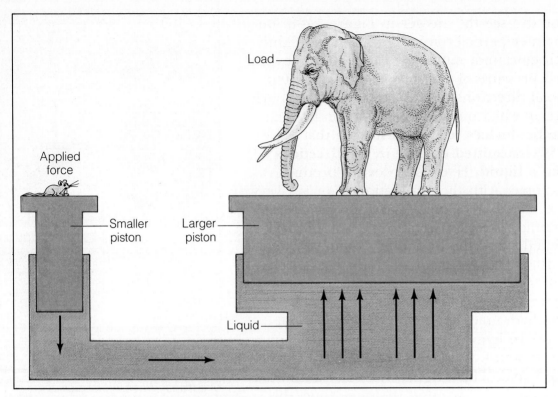

Figure 14–9 *A hydraulic lift operates on the principle that pressure is transmitted equally in all directions in a liquid. The applied force moves the smaller piston down and produces pressure in the liquid. That pressure is then exerted on every square centimeter of the larger piston. Since there are more square centimeters on the larger piston, more force is produced. The larger piston and its load move up. How do you think the distances the pistons move compare?*

Look at Figure 14–9. There are two movable pistons in the same container of liquid. The piston on the left is much smaller than the piston on the right. The mouse on the smaller piston pushes on the liquid with a certain force. The force is transmitted equally throughout the liquid. The pressure of the liquid is increased equally throughout.

The pressure on the two pistons is the same. Remember that pressure is force divided by area. Is the total area of each piston the same? You are right if you answered no. The area of the larger piston is greater than the area of the smaller piston. The larger piston has more square centimeters on which force can be exerted. Since the surface area of the larger piston is larger, the force is larger.

In a hydraulic device, the pressure is the same throughout the liquid. But the surface areas of the two pistons are quite different. The piston with the larger surface area has the larger force.

Suppose the area of the piston on the left is 10 cm^2 and a force of 10 N is applied to it. The pressure that is transmitted equally throughout the liquid is 10 N divided by 10 cm^2, or 1 N/cm^2. The pressure exerted on the right piston is also 1 N/cm^2. If the area of the larger piston is 1000 cm^2, then the force must be 1000 N. The force on the larger piston is 100 times greater than the force on the smaller piston. Now do you know why a light push on the brake pedal stops a 10,000-N car?

You see hydraulic devices all around you. Rescue ladders operate on hydraulic systems. Barber chairs, automobile lifts, tractors, and many amusement-park rides use hydraulic devices.

Figure 14–10 *Hydraulic devices, such as those used in a power shovel (top) and an amusement park ride (bottom), can produce enormous forces with the application of a very small force.*

SECTION REVIEW

1. What is the effect on the pressure of a fluid if an outside pressure is applied?
2. What principle is used in the operation of hydraulic devices?
3. A 10-cm^2 piston exerts a pressure of 10 N/cm^2. What is the pressure on a 1000 cm^2 piston that is in the same liquid?
4. In a hydraulic lift, more force is exerted on the larger piston than is applied to the smaller piston. The larger piston can move a heavier load. Compare the distances the pistons move.

14–4 Bernoulli's Principle

Section Objective

To relate Bernoulli's principle to flight

You have learned that all fluids exert pressure. Liquids and gases are fluids. Air is a gas, so it exerts pressure. The pressure of air is due to the motion of its particles and the downward pull of gravity.

The Wright brothers knew that the secret to flight was the fact that air exerts pressure. They understood a principle of fluid pressure called **Bernoulli's principle,** which was first developed by the Swiss scientist Daniel Bernoulli in the eighteenth century. **Bernoulli's principle states that the pressure in a moving stream of fluid is less than the pressure in the surrounding fluid.** In other words, the faster a fluid moves, the less pressure it

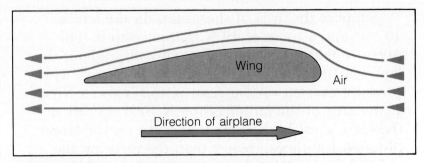

Figure 14–11 *An airplane wing is designed so that the air passing over the wing travels faster than the air passing below. Where air is flowing faster, it exerts less pressure. This is Bernoulli's principle. How does this principle account for the fact that airplanes can fly?*

Sharpen Your Skills

Bernoulli's Principle

1. Place the bottom edge of a sheet of notebook paper between the pages of a book.

2. Hold the book upright. The paper should be hanging loosely down.

3. Blow over the top of the hanging paper. What happens to the paper?

Explain your observation in terms of Bernoulli's principle.

exerts. Try the activity on this page to convince yourself that Bernoulli was right.

An airplane wing is shaped to take advantage of Bernoulli's principle. Look at Figure 14–11. An airplane wing is like a wedge. It is round in the front, thickest in the middle, and narrow at the back. The top of the wing bulges, but the bottom is almost perfectly flat. As a result, the top surface is longer than the bottom surface.

As the wing moves forward, the air that moves over the top of the wing must travel a longer distance than the air that moves under the wing. But the particles of air must reach the back of the wing at the same time. Thus, the air above the wing is moving faster than the air under the wing. According to Bernoulli's principle, the pressure on top of the wing is less than the pressure under the wing. The unbalanced force pushes the wing up.

Figure 14–12 *The combined action of these four forces on an airplane enables it to take off, stay aloft, and land. Which of these four forces is the result of fluid friction?*

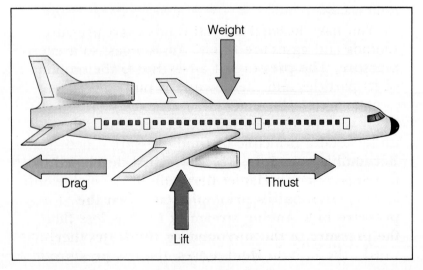

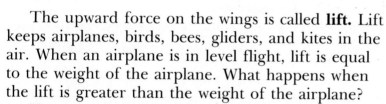

Figure 14–13 *In order to decrease drag, vehicles such as this unusual airplane (right) and this record-setting bicycle (left) have streamlined designs.*

The upward force on the wings is called **lift.** Lift keeps airplanes, birds, bees, gliders, and kites in the air. When an airplane is in level flight, lift is equal to the weight of the airplane. What happens when the lift is greater than the weight of the airplane?

To move through the air, a plane must receive a forward force. This forward force is called **thrust.** The thrust is provided by either a jet engine or a propeller. An airplane also encounters fluid friction as it moves through the air. This force, which is called **drag,** tends to slow an airplane down. Drag can be reduced by making the air pass more smoothly along the airplane's surfaces. So airplanes are designed with pointed noses and thin tails. This streamlined design produces less drag.

SECTION REVIEW

1. Explain Bernoulli's principle.
2. What is lift? Thrust? Drag?
3. How does the shape of an object affect the drag on the object?
4. What lift is required to keep a jumbo jet weighing 3.5 million N in level flight?

A Cartesian Diver

Problem

What is the relationship between the density of an object and its buoyancy in a fluid?

Materials *(per group)*

copper wire
medicine dropper
large clear-plastic bottle with an airtight lid
glass
water

Procedure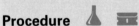

1. Wrap several turns of wire around the middle of the medicine dropper.
2. Fill the glass with water and place the dropper in the glass. The dropper should barely float, with only the very top of it above the surface of the water.
3. If the dropper floats too high, add more turns of wire. If the dropper sinks, remove some turns of wire.

4. Completely fill the large plastic bottle with water.
5. Place the dropper in the bottle of water. The water should overflow.
6. Screw the cap tightly on the bottle. No water or air should leak out when the bottle is squeezed.
7. Squeeze the sides of the bottle. Record your observations. If the dropper does not move, take it out and add more turns of wire.
8. Release the sides of the bottle. Record your observations.

Observations

1. What happens to the dropper when the sides of the bottle are squeezed?
2. What happens to the dropper when the sides of the bottle are released?

Conclusions

1. What happens to the pressure of the water when you squeeze the sides of the bottle?
2. When you squeeze the bottle, some of the water is pushed up into the dropper. Why?
3. Why does the dropper sink when you squeeze the sides of the bottle?
4. Why does the dropper rise when you release the sides of the bottle?
5. How is the density of an object related to its buoyancy in a fluid?

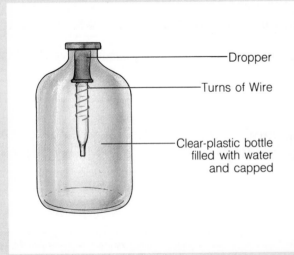

Dropper
Turns of Wire
Clear-plastic bottle filled with water and capped

CHAPTER REVIEW

SUMMARY

14–1 Fluid Pressure

❏ Pressure is a force that acts over a certain area.

❏ Pressure is force divided by area. A unit of pressure is newtons per square centimeter (N/cm^2).

❏ All liquids and gases are fluids. All fluids exert pressure equally in all directions.

❏ The pressure a fluid exerts is due to the fact that the fluid is made of particles that have weight and motion.

❏ Air pressure decreases as altitude increases.

❏ The pressure a liquid exerts increases as the depth of the liquid increases.

14–2 Buoyancy

❏ Buoyancy is the force caused by fluid pressure pushing upward.

❏ The buoyant force on an object is equal to the weight of the fluid displaced by the object. This relationship is Archimedes' principle.

❏ An object floats in a fluid when the buoyant force on the object is equal to or greater than the weight of the object.

❏ Density is mass divided by volume. The density of water is $1.0 \ g/cm^3$.

❏ An object will float if its density is less than the density of the fluid.

14–3 Hydraulics

❏ Pressure applied to a fluid is transmitted equally in all directions throughout the fluid.

❏ Hydraulic devices apply a small force over a small area to produce a large force over a large area.

❏ Hydraulic devices include rescue ladders, barber chairs, automobile lifts, automobile brakes, and tractors.

14–4 Bernoulli's Principle

❏ Bernoulli's principle states that the pressure in a moving stream of fluid is less than the pressure in the surrounding fluid.

❏ An airplane wing is designed to make the air move faster over the top than under the bottom. Thus, the pressure on the top of the wing is less than the pressure under the wing. The wing is pushed up against gravity.

❏ The upward force on the wing is called lift.

❏ The forward force on a plane is called thrust.

❏ Fluid friction produces drag, which opposes thrust.

VOCABULARY

Define each term in a complete sentence.

**Archimedes'
 principle**
**Bernoulli's
 principle**
buoyancy
density

drag
lift
pressure
thrust

CONTENT REVIEW: MULTIPLE CHOICE

On a separate sheet of paper, write the letter of the answer that best completes each statement.

1. Force that acts over a certain area is called
   a. density.   b. pressure.   c. drag.   d. thrust.
2. The pressure of air at sea level is
   a. zero.   b. 1.0 g/cm^3.   c. 10.13 N/cm^2.   d. 1.0 N/cm^2.
3. Pressure in a fluid acts
   a. upward only.   b. downward only.
   c. upward and downward only.   d. in all directions.
4. A submarine surfaces by
   a. increasing its density.   b. taking in more water.
   c. decreasing its density.   d. decreasing its drag.
5. The buoyant force of a fluid is equal to
   a. the weight of the object.
   b. the weight of the fluid displaced by the object.
   c. the pressure of the object.
   d. the volume of the fluid.
6. The relationship between buoyant force and weight of displaced fluid was stated by
   a. Archimedes.   b. Bernoulli.   c. Orville Wright.   d. Aristotle.
7. The brake system in a car is an example of
   a. a hydraulic system.   b. Bernoulli's principle.
   c. Archimedes' principle.   d. density.
8. The flight of a bird is an example of
   a. a hydraulic system.   b. Bernoulli's principle.
   c. Archimedes' principle.   d. density.
9. The upward force on the wing of an airplane is called
   a. antithrust.   b. weight.   c. drag.   d. lift.
10. The force on an airplane that opposes thrust is called
    a. antithrust.   b. weight.   c. drag.   d. lift.

CONTENT REVIEW: COMPLETION

On a separate sheet of paper, write the word or words that best complete each statement.

1. Pressure is force per unit _____.
2. A unit of pressure is _____.
3. The force of a fluid that pushes an object up is called _____.
4. The buoyant force of a fluid opposes the downward force of _____.
5. Buoyant force on an object equals the _____ of displaced fluid.
6. _____ is measured in g/cm^3.
7. _____ devices include auto lifts and barber chairs.
8. Pressure in a moving stream of fluid is _____ than the pressure in the surrounding fluid.
9. The upward force on an airplane wing is called _____.
10. The force that opposes thrust is called _____.

CONTENT REVIEW: TRUE OR FALSE

Determine whether each statement is true or false. Then on a separate sheet of paper, write "true" if it is true. If it is false, change the underlined word or words to make the statement true.

1. A unit of pressure is g/cm³.
2. All fluids exert pressure.
3. Suction is a result of equal air pressure.
4. The upward buoyant force of a fluid opposes the weight of an object.
5. If the buoyant force is less than the weight of an object, the object sinks.
6. The density of water is 1.0 N.
7. Air is a fluid.
8. Hydraulic devices use fluid pressure.
9. The air under the wing of a plane is moving faster than the air over the wing.
10. If the weight of a plane is more than the lift, the plane will gain altitude.

CONCEPT REVIEW: SKILL BUILDING

Use the skills you have developed in the chapter to complete each activity.

1. **Designing an experiment** Describe how you could make a sheet of aluminum foil float in water. How could you change its shape so the foil sinks?
2. **Making inferences** A barometer is a device used to measure air pressure. Explain why mercury (density 13.6 g/cm³) is usually used in a barometer instead of water (density 1.0 g/cm³).
3. **Identifying relationships** Airplanes are riveted together at the seams. The rivets are installed so they are even with the outside surface. Why is it important that the outside surface be so smooth?
4. **Applying concepts** Air exerts a downward force of 100,000 N on a tabletop, producing a pressure of 1000 N/cm².
   a. What would be the force if the tabletop were twice as large?
   b. What would be the pressure if the tabletop were twice as large?
5. **Applying concepts** A student holds two sheets of paper a few centimeters apart and lets them hang down parallel to each other. Then the student blows between the two papers. What happens to the papers? What principle is the student demonstrating? Explain your answer.
6. **Designing an experiment** The density of gold is 19.3 g/cm³. The density of pyrite, or fool's gold, is 5.02 g/cm³. Using mercury, density 13.6 g/cm³, describe an experiment by which you could tell the difference between samples of the two substances.
7. **Relating concepts** Explain why an airplane gains additional lift when the flaps at the rear of the wings are in their downward position.
8. **Applying concepts** Explain why salad dressing made of oil and vinegar must be shaken before use.

CONCEPT REVIEW: ESSAY

Discuss each of the following in a brief paragraph.

1. Explain why you seem to weigh more in air than you do in water.
2. How does an airplane wing provide lift?
3. Explain why an astronaut must wear a pressurized suit in space.
4. What is the effect on a scuba diver of increasing water depth?
5. Why does an object sink or float?
6. Using the principle of fluid pressure, explain how a medicine dropper works.

Work, Power, and Simple Machines 15

CHAPTER SECTIONS

15–1 Work

15–2 Power

15–3 Machines

15–4 Simple Machines

15–5 Compound Machines

CHAPTER OBJECTIVES

After completing this chapter, you will be able to

15–1 Define work in terms of force and distance.

15–2 Describe power and its measurement.

15–3 Classify machines.

15–3 Define and calculate mechanical advantage and efficiency.

15–4 Identify the six simple machines.

15–4 Calculate mechanical advantage for each simple machine.

15–5 Describe compound machines.

The Great Pyramid of Khufu in Egypt is one of the Seven Wonders of the World. It stands over 137 meters high. Its base covers an area large enough to hold ten football fields. More than 2 million stone blocks, each weighing about 20,000 newtons, make up its structure.

The Great Pyramid, along with the many hundreds of other pyramids built by the Egyptians more than 4600 years ago, is a tribute to human effort and ingenuity. For it is exactly these two qualities that enabled the Egyptians to chisel the stone blocks from limestone quarries, to transport them to the pyramid site and to push them to the top of the magnificent structure.

The Egyptians had only three simple machines with which to work. Their only source of power was their own human effort. Several hundred thousand people toiled for twenty years to build the Great Pyramid. Today, with modern machinery, the Great Pyramid could be built with only a few hundred workers and in one-fifth the original time!

In this chapter you will learn about work, power, and simple machines. And you will gain an understanding of how machines make work easier—certainly easier than it was for the Egyptians who built the Great Pyramid.

The Great Pyramid of Khufu at Giza, Egypt, is a tribute to human effort and ingenuity. The pyramid, made of more than 2 million stone blocks, and the Sphinx, seen in front of it, were constructed with only the simplest of machines.

15-1 Work

A scientist defines **work** as a force acting through a distance. In order for work to be done on an object, a force must move it. If there is no movement, there is no work.

Work is the product of the force applied to an object and the distance through which the force is applied. Another way of saying this is work is the amount of force applied to an object times the distance the object moves *in the direction of the force.*

$$\text{work} = \text{force} \times \text{distance}$$

As you can see from the formula, two conditions must be met in order for work to be done. One, a force must be applied. Two, the force must make an object move in the same direction as the force. If the direction of movement is *not* the same as the direction of the applied force, *no* work is done.

Suppose you push as hard as you can against a door, but the door does not move. Have you done any work? According to the two conditions, the answer is no. Although you have applied a force, there has been no movement.

Figure 15–1 *Although these lifeguards might disagree, they are not really working (left)! To a scientist, work is done when a force moves an object through a distance. The person cutting grass is working (right). Why?*

Figure 15–2 *In order for work to be done, the applied force must make an object move in the same direction as the force. The weight lifter is applying an upward force and the barbell is moving up (left). Is he doing work? The soccer player, heading the ball in a forward direction, is making the ball move forward (right). Is he doing work?*

Now suppose you are given a large box to carry. Holding the box, you walk toward the door. Have you done any work? Again the answer is no. The direction of movement is not the same as the direction of the applied force. The applied force is upward, while the direction of movement is forward. See Figure 15–3. What would you have to do with the box in order to do work?

Work does not involve time. Work only involves an applied force and movement of an object in the direction of the force. You do no work if you hold or carry a box for five minutes, ten minutes, or even an hour!

Measuring Work

Remember that work equals force times distance.

$$W = F \times d$$

Force is measured in newtons and distance in meters. So the unit of work is the **newton-meter, N-m.** One newton-meter is equal to one **joule, J.** A force of one newton exerted through a distance of one meter does one newton-meter, or one joule, of work. How many newton-meters of work are done if two newtons of force are exerted through a distance of two meters?

Figure 15–3 *In the scientific sense, why is no work being done in carrying the box (top)? Why is work being done in pushing the box (bottom)?*

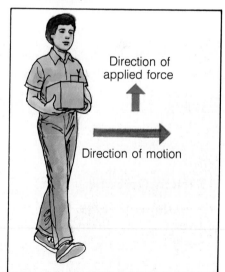

Direction of applied force

Direction of motion

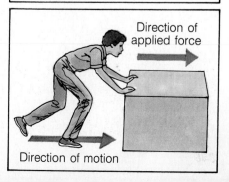

Direction of applied force

Direction of motion

A high jumper weighs 700 newtons. What work does the jumper perform in jumping over a bar 2.0 meters high?

Solution

Step 1   Write the formula

work = force × distance
W = F × d

Step 2   Substitute given numbers and units

W = 700 newtons × 2.0 meters

Step 3   Solve for unknown variable

W = 1400 newton-meters or joules

Practice Problems

1. A 900-N mountain climber scales a 100-m cliff. How much work does the climber perform?

2. A force of 200 N is required to push a lawn mower. If 4000 J of work is performed on the lawn mower, how far does it move?

SECTION REVIEW

1. What is work?
2. How are work, force, and distance related?
3. What are the units of work?
4. During a normal day's activities, would a carpenter or her supervisor be likely to perform more work? Explain your answer.

To relate work, time, and power

15–2 Power

The word **power** is like the word "work." It has different meanings for different people. But in science, power has a very specific meaning. Power indicates how fast work is done.

Power is the rate at which work is done, or the amount of work done per unit time. Power is equal to the work done divided by the time it takes to do it.

$$\text{power} = \frac{\text{work}}{\text{time}} \quad \text{or} \quad P = \frac{W}{t}$$

Looking at this formula, you can see why a bull-dozer has more power than a person with a shovel. The bulldozer does more work in the same amount of time. Can you explain why it takes more power to run up a flight of stairs than it takes to walk up?

Measuring Power

Power is the amount of work done per unit time. Since work equals force times distance, the formula for power can also be written

$$P = \frac{F \times d}{t}$$

The unit of work is the newton-meter or joule. The unit of time is the second. So the unit of power is the newton-meter per second, N-m/sec, or the joule per second, J/sec. One joule per second is also called a **watt, W.** The watt was named for James Watt, inventor of the first practical steam engine.

You are probably familiar with the watt as it is used to express electric power. Electric appliances and light bulbs are rated in watts. A 100-watt light bulb does 100 joules of work every second. Large quantities of power are measured in **kilowatts, kW.** One kilowatt equals 1000 watts. The electric company measures the electric power you use in your home in kilowatts.

Sharpen Your Skills

Work and Power

1. Determine your weight in newtons. (Multiply your weight in pounds by 4.5.)

2. Determine how many seconds it takes you to walk up a flight of stairs.

3. Determine how many seconds it takes you to run up the same flight of stairs.

4. Measure the vertical height of the stairs to the nearest 0.01 m.

5. Using the formula work = weight × height, calculate the work done in walking and in running up the stairs.

6. Calculate the power needed for walking and for running up the stairs.

Is there a difference in the work done in walking and in running? In the power?

Figure 15–4 *Both the man and the snowplow are doing work. But there is little doubt that the machine is doing more work in the same amount of time. So it has more power. How is power calculated?*

A crane lifts a car onto a junk pile in 10 seconds. What is the crane's power if 120,000 joules of work are performed?

Solution

Step 1   Write the formula

$$power = \frac{work}{time}$$

$$P = \frac{W}{t}$$

Step 2   Substitute given numbers and units

$$P = \frac{120,000 \text{ joules}}{10 \text{ seconds}}$$

Step 3   Solve for unknown variable

$$P = 12,000 \text{ joules per second} = 12,000 \text{ watts}$$

Practice Problems

1. A car performs 40,000 J of work in 20 sec. What is the power of the car?

2. A 750-N diver does a triple somersault off the 10-m platform. If it takes 1.5 sec to hit the water, what is the diver's power?

Horsepower

When James Watt built his steam engine in the 1760s, he wanted to use a unit of power that most people would recognize. Since the horse was the most common source of power in the eighteenth century, Watt decided to express steam-engine power in terms comparable to the power of a horse. Watt determined that a strong horse could move a 750-newton object one meter in one second. This represented power equal to 750 watts. So one **horsepower, hp,** was equal to 750 watts.

One horsepower is actually equal to 745.56 watts. Although horsepower is no longer measured in terms of an actual horse, it is used to measure the power of engines and motors. One horsepower is about the power of a small electric motor. The engine of your family car has about 100 horsepower. A diesel train engine can generate up to 10,000 horsepower. A nuclear power plant can produce 300,000 horsepower.

Figure 15–5 *A strong horse could lift a 750-newton object 1 meter in 1 second, or do 750 N-m of work per sec (left). A diesel train engine has about 10,000 horsepower (right). How many horses would it take to generate this power?*

SECTION REVIEW

1. What is power?
2. What is the relationship among power, work, and time? Among power, force, distance, and time?
3. What is a watt? A kilowatt?
4. A small motor does 4000 joules of work in 20 seconds. What is the power of the motor in watts? What is its horsepower?
5. Rate the following objects in terms of horsepower. Start with the object with the least horsepower. a. electric golf cart b. electric pencil sharpener c. aircraft carrier d. jet airplane

15–3 Machines

Section Objective

To describe the role of machines in doing work

For centuries, people have looked for ways to make life more enjoyable. One way of doing this is to use devices that make work easier or faster. In ancient times, people fashioned stones into tools, used tree branches to pry up heavy objects, and carried the objects in carts with wheels. These devices were some of the earliest **machines.**

A machine is a device that makes work easier. A hammer, bicycle ramp, scissors, shovel, and doorknob are examples of machines. A machine can be used to do a variety of jobs: pump water from a well, hoist a sail, plow a field, even catch a fish!

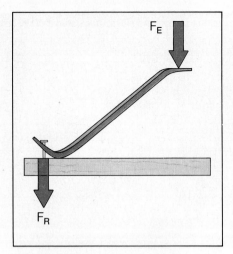

Figure 15–6 *When a machine is used, two forces always are involved. The force applied to a machine is the effort force, F_E. The force applied by the machine is the resistance force (F_R). In this diagram, what is the resistance force equal to?*

Figure 15–7 *The children pushing this merry-go-round (left) are providing the effort force. What is their work called? Those enjoying the ride represent the resistance force. What is the movement of the merry-go-round called? These crew-team members are applying an effort force to the oars, which in turn are applying a resistance force (right). The resistance force propels the boats through the water.*

Effort and Resistance

How do machines make work easier? You will recall that work equals force times distance. **Machines make work easier by changing the size or direction of the applied force.** Some machines make work easier by multiplying the applied force. For example, you need to exert less force to loosen a nail with a crowbar than you do to loosen it with your fingers. Other machines make work easier by redirecting the applied force. It is easier to raise a large object by pulling down on a rope attached to it than by lifting the object straight up.

There are always two forces involved in using a machine. The force that is applied *to* a machine is called the **effort force, F_E.** When you pull down on the handle of a crowbar, you are applying an effort force. As a result of the effort force, the crowbar moves. Work is done on the crowbar. Work done *on* a machine is called **work input, W_I.** Work must always be done on a machine if the machine in turn is to do any work.

Work input is equal to the effort force times the distance through which the force is applied, or the distance through which the machine moves. This distance is called the **effort distance, d_E.**

$$W_I = F_E \times d_E$$

The work input of the crowbar (W_I) is equal to the force you apply to the handle (F_E) times the distance the handle moves (d_E).

When the handle of the crowbar is pushed down, the claw exerts a force on the nail. The force applied *by* the machine is called the **resistance force, F_R.** Resistance force is often equal to the weight of the object being moved. Resistance force opposes effort force.

Work done *by* a machine is called **work output, W_O.** Work output is equal to the resistance force times the distance through which the force is applied, or the distance through which the object moves. This distance is called the **resistance distance, d_R.**

$$W_O = F_R \times d_R$$

The work output of the crowbar (W_O) is equal to the force the crowbar exerts on the nail (F_R) times the distance the nail moves (d_R).

Although machines make work easier, they do *not* multiply work. Machines can only multiply force. Because machines cannot multiply work, work output can never be greater than work input.

Mechanical Advantage

The number of times a machine multiplies the effort force is called the **mechanical advantage, MA.** Mechanical advantage is equal to the resistance force divided by the effort force.

$$MA = \frac{F_R}{F_E}$$

For example, if a crowbar allows you to exert only 20 newtons of force to raise a 200-newton object, its mechanical advantage is 10. The crowbar allows you to multiply your effort force ten times. By using the crowbar, you exert a force on the nail ten times greater than the force you would exert without the crowbar. That certainly makes your work easier!

The mechanical advantage of a machine is not always greater than one. Sometimes the mechanical advantage is equal to one. According to the formula, this means the resistance force is equal to the effort force. So what is the advantage of such a machine? A machine with a mechanical advantage of one changes the direction of the effort force. It

Figure 15–8 *Machines have come a long way since ancient times, as these robots at an industrial plant illustrate. Regardless of complexity, all machines have the same purpose—to make work easier.*

Figure 15–9 *In an eggbeater, the blades turn faster than the handle. Work is transferred from the handle to the blades, but the effort force is not multiplied. It is the speed that is increased. What is the mechanical advantage of an eggbeater?*

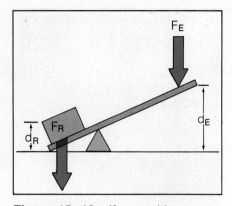

Figure 15–10 *If a machine multiplies the effort force to produce a greater resistance force, then the distance through which the effort force is applied must be greater than the distance through which the resistance force moves. In other words, to move the block, you may have to push down with less force, but you have to exert your push through a greater distance.*

does not multiply the effort force. Can you think of an example of such a machine?

Some machines have a mechanical advantage of less than one. Such a machine is used to increase the distance an object is moved or the speed with which it is moved.

Remember that work output can never be greater than work input. Even if the resistance force is greater than the effort force, which means the mechanical advantage is greater than one, work output cannot exceed work input. Something must be sacrificed. If the resistance force is greater, the distance an object is moved by this force must be smaller. Look at Figure 15–10. The effort force must travel a greater distance than the resistance force.

Efficiency

The comparison of work output to work input is called the **efficiency** of a machine. Efficiency is usually expressed as a percent. The formula for efficiency is

$$\text{Efficiency} = \frac{W_O}{W_I} \times 100$$

If a machine has high efficiency, it means that much of the work input is changed to useful work output. Low efficiency means that much of the work input is lost and a great deal of useful work output does not result.

The efficiency of a machine can never be greater than 100 percent because work output can never be greater than work input. In fact, no machine is ever 100 percent efficient. The operation of any machine always involves some friction. So some of the work the machine does is used to overcome friction. As a result, work output is always less than work input. Friction reduces the efficiency of a machine.

Role of Friction

The less friction in a machine, the higher its efficiency. The most efficient machines have the smallest amount of friction. So the efficiency of a machine can be increased by reducing friction. Keeping a machine well lubricated and in good running order reduces friction. Oil, grease, and wax are used in many machines to reduce friction. Bearings, such as those used in bicycle wheels, reduce friction.

Efficient machines are less expensive to use. They also conserve useful energy. The efficiency of an automobile engine is only about 20 percent. In other words, only one-fifth of the work input is changed to work output. The remaining work input is represented by heat loss. Engines that have high gas mileage are more efficient than gas guzzlers. Imagine what the gas mileage would be for a car that had 90 percent efficiency!

SECTION REVIEW

1. What is a machine?
2. What is effort force? Work input? The relationship between effort force, effort distance, and work input?
3. What is resistance force? Work output? The relationship between resistance force, resistance distance, and work output?
4. What is the relationship between mechanical advantage, effort force, and resistance force?
5. What is the relationship between efficiency of a machine, work input, and work output?
6. Why would a machine with 100 percent efficiency be considered an ideal machine?

Figure 15–11 *Many attempts have been made to create a machine with 100 percent or more efficiency. So far, this has proved impossible. What force reduces the efficiency of a machine?*

15–4 Simple Machines

Section Objective

To describe the six simple machines

The devices you think of when you hear the word "machine" are actually combinations of two or more simple machines. Simple machines do work with one movement. **There are six simple machines: the inclined plane, the wedge, the screw, the lever, the pulley, and the wheel and axle.**

Inclined Plane

Could you raise a car to a height of 10 centimeters? You could not do it by lifting the car straight up. But you could do it if you pushed the car up

Figure 15–12 *No matter how complex these combines (right) and hoisting devices (left) appear to be, they are actually combinations of two or more simple machines. What are the six simple machines?*

a ramp. A ramp is an **inclined plane.** An inclined plane is a slanted surface used to raise an object.

When an inclined plane is used, a smaller effort force is needed to move an object. However, the object is moved through a greater distance along the inclined plane than if it were moved straight up. To raise the car 10 centimeters, you might have to push the car several meters up an inclined plane.

The mechanical advantage of an inclined plane is the length of the plane divided by its height. Suppose you needed an inclined plane 10 meters long to raise the car 10 centimeters. The mechanical ad-

Figure 15–13 *An inclined plane is a slanted surface used to raise an object (right). An inclined plane decreases the size of the effort force needed to move an object. However, the distance through which the effort force is applied is increased (left). How is the mechanical advantage of an inclined plane calculated?*

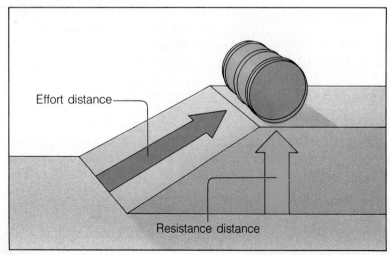

Effort distance

Resistance distance

vantage of the inclined plane would be 1000 centimeters (10 meters) divided by 10 centimeters, or 100. This means that the effort force is multiplied by 100. However, the effort distance is 100 times greater than the height to which the car is raised.

Because the length of an inclined plane can never be shorter than its height, the mechanical advantage of an inclined plane can never be less than one. This mechanical advantage, determined by dividing the length of the plane by its height, is an ideal value. Under actual circumstances, some work input is lost to friction. The friction between the object and the inclined plane has to be overcome. So the effort force in raising the car would probably be multiplied by less than 100.

Wedges and Screws

A **wedge** is an inclined plane that moves. Most wedges are made of two inclined planes. A knife, an ax, and a razor blade are examples of wedges.

A wedge is usually a piece of wood or metal that is thinner at one end. The effort force applied to the thicker end is transferred to the thinner end. As a result, a large force is exerted on a small surface.

Sharpen Your Skills

Simple Machines in Your Environment

1. Make a data table with six columns. Head each column with one of the six simple machines.

2. Walk around your house, garage, yard, and school. Identify all the simple machines you see. Record your observations on your data table.

3. Extend your observations by observing simple machines in other locations, such as a department store, supermarket, bank, and playground.

Which is the most common simple machine? The least common?

Figure 15–14 *As a wedge is moved through the object to be cut, a small effort force is able to overcome a large resistance force (left). How can the mechanical advantage of a wedge be increased? Screws come in a variety of shapes and sizes (center, right). Which of the screws shown here has the greatest mechanical advantage?*

The wedge is moved through the material to be cut or opened up.

The longer and thinner the wedge is, the less effort force is required to overcome a large resistance force. A sharpened ax requires less effort force because the end point is thinner. When you sharpen a wedge, you are increasing its mechanical advantage by decreasing the effort force that must be applied in using it.

Like the wedge, a **screw** is an inclined plane. A screw is an inclined plane wrapped around a cylinder to form a spiral. A screw rotates, and with each turn moves a certain distance up or down. A screw multiplies an effort force by acting through a long effort distance. A small effort force is needed to twist a screw into wood because of the large effort distance through which the screw is turned. The closer the threads, or ridges, of the screw, the greater the mechanical advantage of the screw.

CAREER   *Carpenter*

HELP WANTED: CARPENTER to help restore Victorian house in historic district. High school or vocational school diploma required, plus at least five years on-the-job training or experience in repairing old houses.

From the street, the old house looks haunted and deserted. Weeds and overgrown shrubs hide the low porch and the broken, weathered wooden steps. The home's new owners lead the way through the unhinged front door into a

dusty, cluttered hall. As they talk about plans for restoring the house, the **carpenter** with them thinks of all the work ahead. To make work simpler, a carpenter uses many types of simple machines.

This carpenter, for example, will need a series of ramps along which to move wheelbarrows, supplies, and other heavy objects. The pulleys and weights in the window sashes will be replaced so that the windows again glide smoothly up and down with very little effort. New slate shingles for the roof will be split by hand with a hammer and wedge. The porch columns will be raised on jacks to give the sagging porch a lift.

Most carpenters learn their trade by being an apprentice or by receiving on-the-job training. A high school or vocational school education with courses in carpentry, shop, mechanical drawing, and math are important. If you would like additional information about becoming a carpenter, contact: Home Builders Institute, National Association of Home Builders, Manpower Development and Training Department, 15th and M Streets NW, Washington, DC 20005.

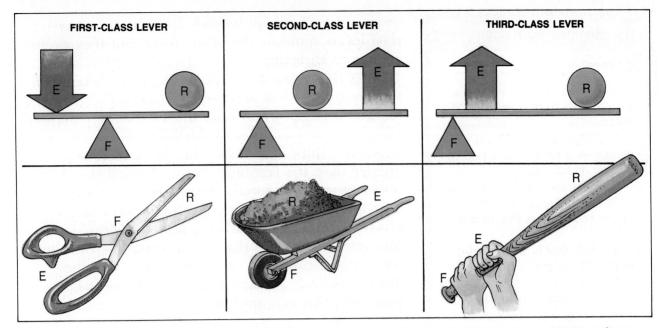

Figure 15–15 *The relative positions of the effort force, resistance force, and fulcrum determine the three classes of levers. Which lever multiplies effort force as well as changing its direction? Which lever multiplies the distance of the effort force?*

Levers

The **lever** is a simple machine that is probably quite familiar to you. A seesaw, a shovel, a nut-cracker, and a crowbar are all examples of levers. A lever is a bar that is free to pivot, or move about, a fixed point when an effort force is applied. The fixed point of the pivot is called the **fulcrum** (FUL-kruhm). When an effort force is applied to a lever, the lever moves about the fulcrum and overcomes a resistance force.

CLASSES OF LEVERS There are three classes of levers. These classes are based on the positions of the effort force, resistance force, and fulcrum. In a first-class lever, the fulcrum is between the effort force and the resistance force. See Figure 15–15. A crowbar is an example of a first-class lever. An effort force is applied to one end of the crowbar. The crowbar pivots on the fulcrum and lifts the resistance force. Pliers, scissors, and seesaws are all first-class levers. First-class levers multiply the effort force and also change its direction.

In a second-class lever, the resistance force is between the fulcrum and the effort force. See Figure 15–15. Wheelbarrows, doors, paper cutters, and

Levers

1. Tape five large washers together to form a resistance force.

2. Obtain a rigid 30-cm ruler to use as a lever and a pen to use as its fulcrum.

3. Place the washers on the 1-cm mark. Place the pen under the ruler at the 10-cm mark.

4. Push down on the ruler at the 30-cm mark. Your push is the effort force.

5. Move the pen to the 15-cm mark and again push down at the 30-cm mark.

6. Compare your effort force in steps 4 and 5.

7. Move the pen to the 20-cm mark and again push down on the 30-cm mark.

What is the effect on the effort force of decreasing the length of the effort arm? What class lever is this?

Figure 15–16 *Sometimes a lever can have a very vital use! Where is the lever in this photograph taken at Big Bend National Park?*

some nutcrackers are second-class levers. Second-class levers multiply the effort force, but they do not change its direction.

In a third-class lever, the effort force is between the resistance force and the fulcrum. See Figure 15–15 on page 361. A hoe, shovel, fishing pole, and your arm are examples of third-class levers.

With a third-class lever, the effort force is greater than the resistance force. A third-class lever does not multiply force. The advantage to a third-class lever is that it multiplies the distance of the effort force. The effort force needs to move through only a small distance to make the resistance force move through a large distance. Using the third-class lever in Figure 15–15 on page 361, explain how this fact applies.

MECHANICAL ADVANTAGE OF A LEVER The mechanical advantage of a lever, like that of any machine, is the number of times the lever increases the effort force. It is equal to the resistance force divided by the effort force. The mechanical advantage of a lever can also be calculated by using the lengths of the effort force from the fulcrum and the resistance force from the fulcrum.

The distance from the effort force to the fulcrum is called the **effort arm.** The distance from the resistance force to the fulcrum is called the **resistance arm.** The mechanical advantage of a lever is the length of the effort arm divided by the length of the resistance arm:

$$\text{mechanical advantage} = \frac{\text{effort arm length}}{\text{resistance arm length}}$$

For first- and second-class levers, the effort arm is usually greater than the resistance arm. Thus the mechanical advantage for these levers is usually greater than one. In other words, first- and second-class levers multiply the effort force.

For third-class levers, the effort arm is always less than the resistance arm. The mechanical advantage is less than one. Third-class levers do not multiply force. Third-class levers multiply distance. For example, a small movement at the handle of a shovel causes the opposite end to move in a large sweeping arc.

Pulleys

If you have ever raised or lowered a window shade, you have used another simple machine called a **pulley.** A pulley is a chain, belt, or rope wrapped around a wheel. A pulley can change either the direction or the amount of an effort force.

A pulley that is attached to a wall, ceiling, or other stationary structure is called a fixed pulley. A fixed pulley cannot multiply an effort force. But it can change the direction of an effort force and make lifting an object easier. As the effort force is used to pull the rope down, the resistance force is lifted up. It is certainly easier to pull down on a rope to raise an object than it is to lift the object directly up! Because a fixed pulley does not multiply effort force, the effort force is equal to the resistance force. So the mechanical advantage of a fixed pulley is one.

A movable pulley is hung on a rope so that it moves with the effort force. A movable pulley can multiply an effort force. But a movable pulley cannot change the direction of an effort force.

Because a movable pulley multiplies effort force, its mechanical advantage is greater than one. However, the effort distance is greater than the resistance distance. For example, to lift an object one meter with a movable pulley, you might have to pull down a two-meter length of rope.

Figure 15–17 *The fixed pulley on this boat cannot multiply force. But it can change the direction of the force and thus make moving the wooden beam easier.*

Figure 15–18 *The mechanical advantage of a pulley system is approximately equal to the number of supporting ropes. What is the mechanical advantage of the largest pulley system shown here?*

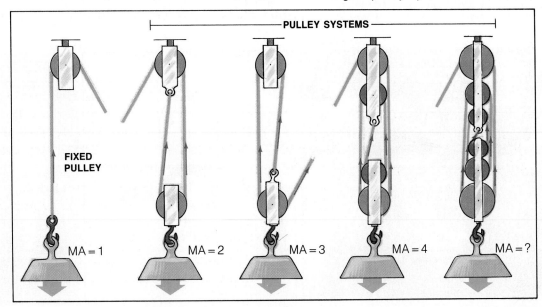

PULLEY SYSTEMS

FIXED PULLEY

MA = 1   MA = 2   MA = 3   MA = 4   MA = ?

Figure 15-19 *The block and tackle attached to the boom of the sail is an example of a pulley system. Identify the fixed and movable pulleys.*

A greater mechanical advantage can be obtained by combining fixed and movable pulleys into a pulley system. As more pulleys are used, more sections of rope are attached to the system. Each section of rope helps to support the object. This increases the mechanical advantage. You can predict the mechanical advantage of a pulley system by counting the number of supporting sections of rope. The mechanical advantage of a pulley system is approximately equal to the number of supporting ropes. This fact is illustrated in Figure 15-19. A block and tackle is an example of a pulley system used to lift heavy machinery.

Wheel and Axle

A **wheel and axle** is a lever that rotates in a circle. A wheel and axle is made of two wheels of different sizes. The axle is the smaller wheel. The larger wheel turns about the axle. The effort force is applied to the wheel. Since the wheel is a larger circular object, it always moves through a greater distance than the axle. The effort force applied to the wheel is multiplied at the axle. Bicycles, ferris wheels, water wheels, and gears are all examples of a wheel and axle.

The mechanical advantage of a wheel and axle is similar to the mechanical advantage of a lever. The effort arm is the radius of the wheel. The radius is the distance from the center of the wheel to the edge. The resistance arm is the radius of the axle.

Figure 15-20 *Each of these racers is applying an effort force to the wheel of his chair (left). Since the wheel moves through a greater distance than the axle (center), the effort force is multiplied at the axle. The same principle is responsible for the operation of a Ferris wheel (right).*

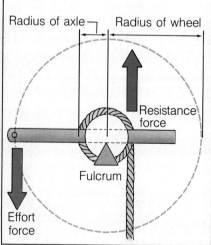

Radius of axle — Radius of wheel

Resistance force

Fulcrum

Effort force

The mechanical advantage of a wheel and axle is equal to the radius of the wheel divided by the radius of the axle.

SECTION REVIEW

1. Name the six simple machines.
2. How is the mechanical advantage of an inclined plane calculated? Of a lever?
3. What is the mechanical advantage of a pulley system with four supporting ropes?
4. How is the mechanical advantage of a wheel and axle calculated?
5. Why is the mechanical advantage of a movable pulley always somewhat less than the number of supporting ropes, not exactly equal to it?

15–5 Compound Machines

A car is not one of the six simple machines you have just learned about. The car is, however, a combination of simple machines. There are wheels and axles, a gearshift lever, a set of transmission gears, a brake lever, and a steering wheel. These are only a few of the simple machines in a car.

A car, bicycle, watch, can opener, and typewriter are examples of **compound machines.** Most of the machines you use every day are compound machines. **A compound machine is a combination of two or more simple machines.**

You are surrounded by a great variety of compound machines. How many compound machines do you have in your home? A partial list might include a washing machine, VCR, blender, sewing machine, and vacuum cleaner. Compound machines make doing work easier and more enjoyable. But remember that machines, simple or compound, cannot multiply work. You can get no more work out of a machine than you put into it!

SECTION REVIEW

1. What is a compound machine?
2. Name two different simple machines in a bicycle.

Mechanical Advantage of an Inclined Plane

Problem

How are the ideal and the actual mechanical advantage of an inclined plane determined?

Materials *(per group)*

wooden ramp at least 0.80 m long
wooden block or brick
spring scale calibrated in newtons
  (0–5 N)
meterstick
2 books
string

Procedure

1. Place one end of the wooden ramp on top of the two books.
2. Measure the length and height of the ramp. Take both measurements from the bottom of the ramp, as indicated in the accompanying figure. Record each measurement to the nearest 0.1 centimeter.
3. Tie one end of a string around the block or brick. Attach the other end of the string to the spring scale. Record the weight of the block to the nearest 0.1 newton.
4. Pull the block up the ramp with the spring scale. Read the scale while pulling the block. Record this value as the effort force to the nearest 0.1 newton.

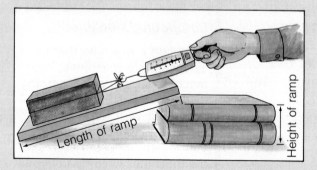

Observations

1. Calculate the work done in lifting the block without the ramp.
2. Calculate the work done in lifting the block with the ramp.
3. Calculate the ideal mechanical advantage using the formula

    IMA = length of ramp/height of ramp

4. Calculate the actual mechanical advantage using the formula

    AMA = weight of block/effort force

Length of inclined plane	cm
Height of inclined plane	cm
Weight of block	N
Effort force	N

Conclusions

1. What simple machine is the ramp? How does it make a job easier?
2. Does it require more or less force to lift the block using the ramp?
3. Is more or less work done in lifting the block when the ramp is used?
4. How does the ideal mechanical advantage compare with the actual mechanical advantage?
5. What force causes a difference in the ideal and actual mechanical advantage? How could this force be reduced?

CHAPTER REVIEW

SUMMARY

15–1 Work

❏ Work is the product of the force applied to an object and the distance through which the force is applied. W =F × d.

❏ The unit of work is the newton-meter or the joule.

15–2 Power

❏ Power is the rate at which work is done, or the amount of work done per unit time.

❏ Power equals work divided by time, $P = \dfrac{W}{t}$.

❏ The units of power are the newton-meter per second, joule per second, watt, kilowatt, and horsepower.

15–3 Machines

❏ A machine is any device that makes work easier by changing the size or direction of an applied force.

❏ Effort force is force applied to a machine.

❏ Work performed on a machine is work input.

❏ Resistance force is the force applied by a machine.

❏ Work performed by a machine is work output.

❏ Machines only multiply force, never work. Because machines cannot multiply work, work output can never be greater than work input.

❏ The number of times a machine multiplies effort force is called mechanical advantage.

❏ The efficiency of a machine is the comparison of work output to work input.

❏ Because of friction, no machine can be 100 percent efficient.

15–4 Simple Machines

❏ There are six simple machines: the inclined plane, the wedge, the screw, the lever, the pulley, and the wheel and axle.

❏ The inclined plane is a slanted surface used to raise an object.

❏ The wedge is a moving inclined plane.

❏ The screw is an inclined plane wrapped around a cylinder.

❏ The lever is a simple machine that is free to move about the fulcrum when an effort force is applied.

❏ A pulley is a chain, belt, or rope wrapped around a wheel. A fixed pulley changes the direction of an effort force. A movable pulley multiplies the effort force.

❏ A wheel and axle is a lever that rotates in a circle.

15–5 Compound Machines

❏ A compound machine is a combination of two or more simple machines.

VOCABULARY

Define each term in a complete sentence.

compound machine	inclined plane	power	watt
efficiency	joule	pulley	wedge
effort arm	kilowatt	resistance arm	wheel and axle
effort distance	lever	resistance distance	work
effort force	machine	resistance force	work input
fulcrum	mechanical advantage	screw	work output
horsepower	newton-meter		

CONTENT REVIEW: MULTIPLE CHOICE

On a separate sheet of paper, write the letter of the answer that best completes each statement.

1. If a large force is exerted on an object, no work is performed if
   a. the object moves.   b. the object does not move.
   c. the power is too large.   d. there is no friction.
2. A unit of power is
   a. the watt.   b. the kilowatt.   c. the horsepower.   d. all of the above.
3. Machines multiply
   a. work.   b. power.   c. time.   d. force.
4. The resistance force divided by the effort force is called
   a. work.   b. power.   c. mechanical advantage.   d. efficiency.
5. The efficiency of a machine is
   a. always 100 percent.   b. always greater than 100 percent.
   c. always less than 100 percent.   d. either greater or less than 100 percent.
6. The mechanical advantage of an inclined plane is found by dividing the length of the plane by its
   a. effort force.   b. resistance force.   c. effort distance.   d. height.
7. A wheelbarrow is which type of lever?
   a. first-class   b. second-class   c. third-class   d. fourth-class
8. A movable pulley has a mechanical advantage
   a. greater than one.   b. less than one.   c. equal to one.   d. equal to zero.
9. The gears in a watch are an example of a
   a. pulley.   b. lever.   c. screw.   d. wheel and axle.
10. An example of a compound machine would be a
    a. school bus.   b. crowbar.   c. pliers.   d. ramp.

CONTENT REVIEW: COMPLETION

On a separate sheet of paper, write the word or words that best complete each statement.

1. Work equals force times _____.
2. Power is work divided by _____.
3. One _____ equals 1000 watts.
4. Machines multiply a (an) _____.
5. Work done by a machine is _____.
6. _____ reduces efficiency.
7. A ramp is a (an) _____.
8. A (An) _____ is an inclined plane that moves.
9. A scissors is a (an) _____ lever.
10. A (An) _____ is a lever that rotates in a circle.

CONTENT REVIEW: TRUE OR FALSE

Determine whether each statement is true or false. Then on a separate sheet of paper, write ''true'' if it is true. If it is false, change the underlined word or words to make the statement true.

1. A unit of work is the joule.
2. Power is the rate of doing motion.
3. Machines multiply work.
4. Work output is less than work input.

368

5. The number of times a machine multiplies effort force is called mechanical advantage.
6. There are seven simple machines.
7. A screw is a lever wrapped around a cylinder.
8. The fixed point at which a lever is supported is called a fulcrum.
9. A third-class lever multiplies distance.
10. A combination of complex machines is a compound machine.

CONCEPT REVIEW: SKILL BUILDING

Use the skills you have developed in the chapter to complete each activity.

1. **Applying definitions** For each of the following situations, determine whether work is being done. Explain each answer.
   a. You are babysitting for a friend by watching the child while it naps.
   b. A television broadcaster is reporting the news.
   c. You are doing your homework by reading this chapter.
   d. You are doing your homework by writing answers to questions.

2. **Applying formulas** Two boys each weigh 800 newtons. One boy climbs a 5.0-meter rope in 10.0 seconds. The other boy climbs the same rope in 8.0 seconds.
   a. How much work is done by each boy?
   b. What is the power in watts of each boy?
   c. What is the horsepower of each boy? Hint: 1 hp = 746 watts

3. **Applying formulas** The work output of a pulley is 900 joules. The work input is 1000 joules. What is the efficiency of the pulley? How could you increase the efficiency of the pulley?

4. **Making calculations** A water wheel is 2 meters in diameter. The axle is 10 centimeters in diameter. What is the mechanical advantage of the water wheel? Hint: Watch the units!

5. **Developing a model** Suppose you have a large crate you wish to lift off the floor. To accomplish this you have been given a pulley and some rope. The crate has a hook on it, as does the ceiling. Describe two ways in which you could use this equipment to raise the crate. Accompany each description with a diagram of the setup.

6. **Relating concepts** Suppose you live on the fifth floor of an apartment building. You have just bought a new tape deck that weighs 50 newtons. To reach your apartment, which is 35 meters up, you can climb the stairs or take an elevator.
   a. If you climb the stairs, how much work do you do?
   b. If you take the elevator, is the amount of work greater, smaller, or equal to the work done in part a?
   c. If it takes you 5 minutes to climb up the stairs, what is your power? Remember, the time unit for power is seconds.
   d. Compare your power with that of the elevator if it takes 2 minutes for the elevator to reach the fifth floor.

CONCEPT REVIEW: ESSAY

Discuss each of the following in a brief paragraph.

1. The mythical god Atlas is known for the fact that he holds up a stationary Earth. Does Atlas perform any work? Explain your answer.
2. Why does the winner in a swimming race have the most power?
3. Pushing against a wall that does not move is a form of exercise. Is work done in such a case? Explain your answer.
4. Explain how machines make work easier. Use several examples in your answer.
5. Why is a bicycle a compound machine?

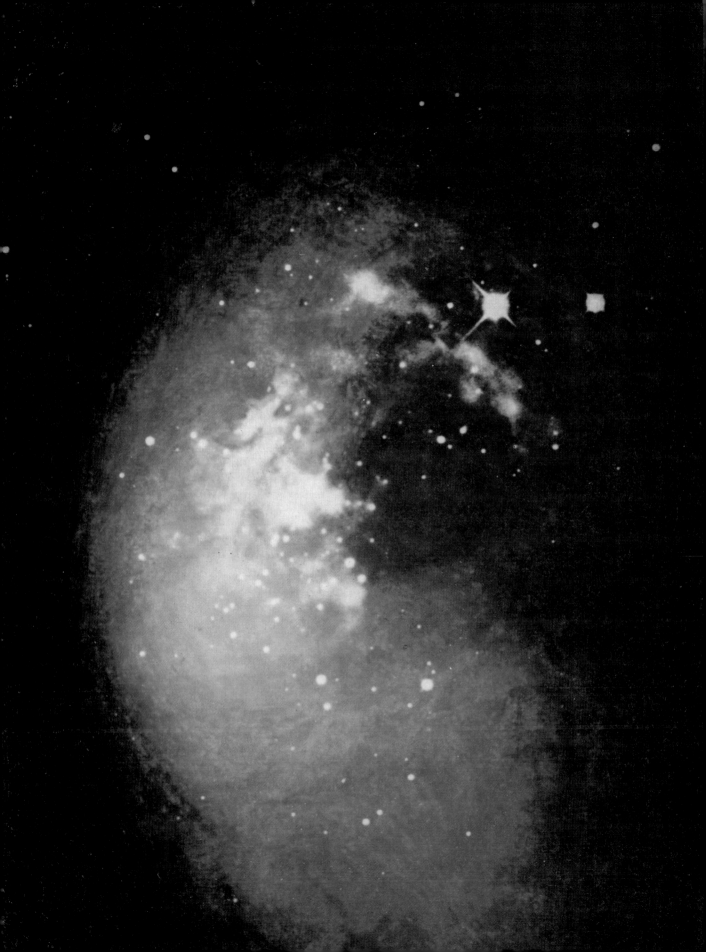

Energy

16

CHAPTER SECTIONS

16–1 Nature of Energy

16–2 Kinetic and Potential Energy

16–3 Energy Conversion

16–4 Conservation of Energy

CHAPTER OBJECTIVES

After completing this chapter, you will be able to

16–1 Define energy.

16–1 Describe five forms of energy and give examples of each.

16–2 Distinguish between kinetic and potential energy.

16–2 Explain the relationship between kinetic energy, mass, and velocity.

16–2 Calculate gravitational potential energy.

16–3 Identify several energy conversions.

16–3 Describe the energy conversions that take place in heat engines.

16–4 Explain the law of conservation of energy.

From the large, cold clouds of gas and dust, small particles begin to clump together. Their own gravity and the pressure from nearby stars cause these small clumps to form a single larger mass. Like a monstrous vacuum cleaner, gravity pulls in more and more particles of dust and gas. The gravitational force becomes so enormous that the bits of matter falling faster and faster to the center begin to heat up. The internal temperature reaches fifteen million degrees. Subatomic particles called protons collide with each other at tremendous speeds. The normal electric force of repulsion between protons is overcome by the force of the particle collisions. The protons fuse together to form helium. During this process, part of the matter is transformed into energy. A star is born!

What is energy? How can energy from our sun be changed to useful energy on the earth? Can matter really be changed into energy? Is the total energy in the universe constant? As you read further, you will find answers to these questions.

The formation of the Orion Nebula is evidence of the interaction of matter and energy. This infrared map of the nebula was created by scientists to show how the nebula would appear through a large telescope sensitive to infrared.

16–1 Nature of Energy

Figure 16–1 *The Crab Nebula in the constellation Taurus is the remains of a star that exploded in 1054. A supernova releases tremendous amounts of energy. What is energy?*

Figure 16–2 *Energy appears in many forms. Here you see two dramatic examples of the release of energy. In what form is energy released during a lightning storm? During a volcanic eruption?*

On July 4, 1054, the Chinese recorded the sudden appearance of a new star. The star shone so brightly that it could be seen even during the day. After 23 days, the distant star began to disappear. What the Chinese had observed was a supernova, an exploding star. The energy released by a supernova is capable of destroying a nearby solar system in just hours. A supernova is one of the greatest concentrations of energy in the universe.

A supernova is a very dramatic example of energy release. So, too, is a volcano. A huge amount of energy stored beneath the earth's surface is explosively released when a volcano erupts. But not all forms of energy are quite that dramatic.

You live in an ocean of energy. Energy is all around you. You hear energy as sound, see it as light, and feel it as wind. Energy creates waves on the sea, produces electricity, and keeps you warm.

What is **energy?** Energy is the ability to do work. And work involves a change in movement. Energy in its various forms is necessary for all sorts of changes. So another way of defining energy is the ability to cause change. One unit in which energy is measured is the **joule** (J).

The supernova of 1054 pushed an enormous volume of matter out into space. It did an incredible amount of work. Figure 16–1 shows the result of its great release of energy. A storm, too, releases a tremendous amount of energy. You expend energy when you turn the pages of this book.

Forms of Energy

Energy appears in many forms. All matter contains some form of energy because all matter has the ability to do work or cause change.

The five main forms of energy are mechanical, heat, chemical, electromagnetic, and nuclear. It may surprise you to learn that your body is an "energy factory" that stores and converts various forms of energy. After reading about each form of energy, see if you can describe how your "energy factory" works.

MECHANICAL ENERGY Energy associated with motion is called **mechanical energy.** Matter that is in motion has mechanical energy. Water in a waterfall has a great amount of mechanical energy. So does wind. An automobile traveling at 95 km/hr has mechanical energy. A jet plane cruising at 700 km/hr has even more! When you walk, ride a bike, or hit a ball, you use mechanical energy. As the pistons and other parts of a car engine move, mechanical energy is being used. Sound is a type of mechanical energy.

HEAT ENERGY The internal motion of particles of matter is called **heat energy.** The faster the particles move, the more heat energy is present. Rub your hands together for several seconds. Did you feel heat? You converted mechanical energy into heat energy! Heat energy often causes changes in the temperature and phase of any form of matter.

CHEMICAL ENERGY The energy that bonds atoms or ions together is called **chemical energy.** When bonds are broken, atoms are rearranged, and new bonds are formed. During this process, stored chemical energy is released. The fuel in a rocket engine has stored chemical energy. When the fuel is ignited, chemical energy is converted into heat energy.

When you start a fire in a charcoal grill, you are releasing chemical energy. When you throw a ball, you are using chemical energy stored in your muscles. This chemical energy, stored in the form of fat, comes from the food you eat.

ELECTROMAGNETIC ENERGY Moving electric charges have **electromagnetic energy.** Power lines carry

Figure 16–3 The water cascading over these rocks has the ability to do work. Therefore, the water in a waterfall has energy. What kind of energy is it?

Figure 16–4 This battery is made of 27 nickel–hydrogen cells. The battery produces energy as a result of chemical reactions within the cells. So the battery has stored chemical energy. To what other type of energy will the chemical energy likely be converted?

Figure 16–5 *Light is a form of electromagnetic energy. Each color of the rainbow (left) corresponds to a different amount of electromagnetic energy. Laser light (right) is an extremely powerful, concentrated, one-color form of electromagnetic energy.*

electromagnetic energy into your home in the form of electricity. Electric motors are driven by electromagnetic energy.

Light is another form of electromagnetic energy. Each color of light represents a different amount of electromagnetic energy. Electromagnetic energy also includes X-rays, radio waves, and laser light.

NUCLEAR ENERGY The nucleus of an atom is the source of **nuclear energy.** When a nucleus splits, nuclear energy is released in the form of heat energy and light energy. Nuclear energy is also released when lightweight nuclei collide at high speeds and fuse. The sun's energy is produced from a nuclear fusion reaction in which hydrogen nuclei fuse to form helium nuclei. Nuclear energy is the most concentrated form of energy.

SECTION REVIEW

1. What is energy?
2. Why does all matter contain energy?
3. What are the different forms of energy?
4. Copy down the first paragraph on page 371. Identify the following words or phrases in that paragraph as being one of the five forms of energy: *clump together, gravity, heat up, protons collide, electric force, protons fuse.*

16–2 Kinetic and Potential Energy

Section Objective

To classify energy as either kinetic or potential

Stretch a rubber band between your thumb and index finger. Keep the rubber band stretched without any motion. How long can you hold it this way? After a short while you begin to sense the energy in the rubber band. Yet the rubber band is not moving! The stretched rubber band has energy *stored* in it. You cannot see this energy, but you know it is there because the stretched rubber band can do work as it returns to its normal shape. Remember that energy is the ability to do work.

The energy of motion of the stretched rubber band is temporarily being stored. Energy stored in an object due to its position is called **potential** (poh-TEHN-shul) **energy.** As the rubber band is stretched, energy is put into it. In its new position, the stretched rubber band contains potential energy.

Release your thumb and the rubber band moves. Energy that a moving object has due to its motion is called **kinetic** (kih-NEHT-ihk) **energy.** As the rubber band moves back to its normal shape, it can do work.

You just learned about five forms of energy. **The five forms of energy can be classified as potential energy (energy of position) or kinetic energy (energy of motion).** Because potential and kinetic energy most often have to do with motion, they are often treated as kinds of mechanical energy.

Kinetic Energy

Kinetic energy is energy of motion. An object that moves has kinetic energy. When you walk, run, swim, and jump, you have kinetic energy. Light and heat from the sun are examples of kinetic energy. So, too, are thunder and lightning.

The faster an object moves, the more kinetic energy it has. So kinetic energy is directly related to the velocity of an object. In baseball, a fast ball has more kinetic energy than a slow curve. You have more kinetic energy when you run than when you walk. Who has more kinetic energy, a downhill skier or a cross-country skier?

Figure 16–6 *This archer in the 1984 Olympic Games is making use of potential energy, or energy stored in an object because of its position. The stretched bow has the ability to do work once it is released. The more potential energy it has, the greater will be its ability to move the arrow. How did the bow get its potential energy?*

Figure 16–7 *Kinetic energy is energy of motion. It is dependent on the mass and velocity of a moving object. Both Evelyn Ashford (top) and Fernando Valenzuela (bottom) are familiar with kinetic energy. Ashford uses it to get her across the finish line first. And Valenzuela puts it into his fast ball to pitch a strike.*

Do all objects with the same velocity have the same kinetic energy? A battleship that is moving at 40 km/hr has much more kinetic energy than a mosquito moving at the same velocity. So kinetic energy must depend on something other than just velocity. The battleship has more kinetic energy because it has greater mass. Kinetic energy depends on both mass and velocity. The mathematical relationship between kinetic energy, mass, and velocity is

$$\text{K.E.} = \frac{m \times v^2}{2}$$

According to this equation, an increase in mass or velocity will mean an increase in kinetic energy. Which of these two factors, mass or velocity, will have a greater effect on kinetic energy?

Potential Energy

Potential energy is energy of position. Imagine that you are standing on the edge of a one-meter diving board. Do you think you have any energy? You probably think you do not because you are not moving. It is true that you do not have kinetic energy. But you do have potential energy. Your potential energy is due to your position above the water.

If you were standing on a three-meter diving board, you would have three times the potential energy as on the one-meter board. Energy that is dependent on height above the earth's surface is called **gravitational** (grav-ih-TAY-shuhn-uhl) **potential energy (G.P.E.).** A waterfall, suspension bridge, and wrecking ball all have a great amount of gravitational potential energy.

Weight also determines the amount of gravitational potential energy an object has. The old saying "The bigger they are, the harder they fall" is an observation of the effect of weight on gravitational potential energy. From your own experiences, you may know that gravitational potential energy is dependent on weight. You feel a lot more gravitational potential energy with a 100-newton pack on your back than you do with a 50-newton pack.

The relationship between G.P.E., weight, and height can be expressed by the following formula:

$$\text{G.P.E.} = \text{weight} \times \text{height}$$

Figure 16–8 *Both Olympic diver Greg Louganis and the Oakland Bay Bridge have gravitational potential energy. Which has more G.P.E.?*

You can see from this formula that the greater the weight, the greater the gravitational potential energy. The higher the position above a surface, the greater the gravitational potential energy.

Although potential energy is most common in mechanical energy, it does occur in the other forms of energy. A battery contains both chemical and electric potential energy. Rocket fuel contains large amounts of chemical potential energy.

SECTION REVIEW

1. What is kinetic energy? Potential energy?
2. Use the formula for kinetic energy to describe the relationship between the kinetic energy of an object, its mass, and its velocity.
3. What is gravitational potential energy? How is it calculated?
4. The gravitational potential energy of a brick at one meter is ten joules. What is the gravitational potential energy of two bricks at two meters?

Sharpen Your Skills

Observing Gravitational Potential Energy

1. Hold a meterstick vertically, with one end on the ground.
2. Drop a tennis ball from the 50-cm mark and record the height to which it rebounds.
3. Drop the tennis ball from the 100-cm mark and record the height of the rebound.

What can you conclude about gravitational potential energy and height?

16–3 Energy Conversion

Section Objective

To describe different types of energy conversion

In an amusement park in Southern California, there is a ride called Montezuma's Revenge. A car is pulled up a steep ramp and held at the top. When the car is released, it rolls backward at a terrifying velocity. After reaching the bottom of the ramp, the car does a complete loop, returning to the bottom again. Finally, the car rolls up a ramp on the opposite side and is stopped at the top.

Changes in the forms of energy are called energy conversions. One of the most common **energy conversions** involves the changing of potential energy to kinetic energy or kinetic energy to potential energy. Montezuma's Revenge is an excellent example of energy conversion.

Kinetic–Potential Energy Conversion

Kinetic energy is energy of motion. Potential energy is energy of position. These two forms of energy are continuously being converted. Looking closely at each step in Montezuma's Revenge will help you understand this energy conversion.

At the top of the ramp, the car has maximum potential energy and zero kinetic energy. Why? As

Figure 16–9 *What are the energy changes in this ride called?*

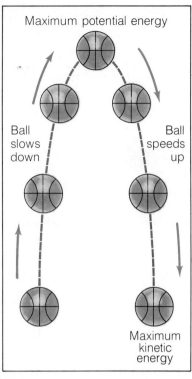

Maximum potential energy

Ball slows down

Ball speeds up

Maximum kinetic energy

Figure 16-10 *As this basketball player throws the ball in the air, various energy conversions take place. As the ball rises higher, its velocity and its kinetic energy decrease. What happens to its potential energy?*

the car rolls down the ramp, its kinetic energy increases as its potential energy decreases. Energy of position is being converted to energy of motion. The potential energy increases and the kinetic energy decreases once again as the car moves up to the top of the loop. What happens as it completes the loop and returns to the bottom? In its final step, the car's kinetic energy decreases and its potential energy increases as it rolls up the ramp.

Conversions between kinetic energy and potential energy are taking place around you every day. As an example, think of tossing a ball up into the air. When you throw the ball up, you give it kinetic energy. As the ball rises, it slows down. As its velocity decreases, its kinetic energy is reduced. But during the same process of rising higher and higher from the earth, its potential energy is increasing. At the top of its path, the ball has slowed down to zero velocity and zero kinetic energy. All of its kinetic energy from the beginning of its flight has been converted to potential energy.

Then the ball begins to fall. As it gets closer to the earth's surface, its potential energy decreases. But it is speeding up at the same time. Thus, its kinetic energy is increasing. When you catch it, it has its maximum velocity and kinetic energy. The

379

Figure 16–11 *A continuous conversion between kinetic and potential energy takes place in a pendulum. At what point is the pendulum's kinetic energy the greatest? Zero?*

Figure 16–12 *The sun's energy is converted to heat, light, and the chemical energy stored by green plants in the form of sugars and starches.*

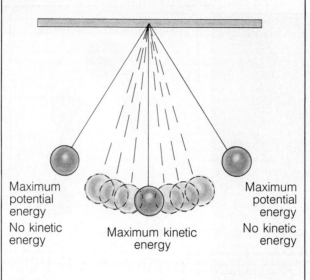

Maximum potential energy

No kinetic energy

Maximum kinetic energy

Maximum potential energy

No kinetic energy

potential energy of the ball has changed into kinetic energy. In terms of kinetic and potential energy, what happens if the ball hits the ground and bounces back up?

Figure 16–11 is a pendulum. You may have seen pendulums in large clocks. In a pendulum, there is a continuous conversion between kinetic and potential energy.

A pendulum swings in an arc. As it swings up to the top of its arc, its kinetic energy decreases and it reaches its maximum potential energy. As it then swings down, its potential energy decreases and it reaches its maximum kinetic energy. Then the pendulum gains in potential energy again as it sweeps up the opposite side. The conversion between kinetic energy and potential energy takes place over and over again. A diver springing up and down on a diving board is continuously changing potential energy to kinetic energy and kinetic energy back to potential energy.

Other Energy Conversions

Not all energy conversions involve kinetic energy and potential energy. All forms of energy can be converted to another form. For example, the sun's energy is not used merely as heat energy or light energy. It is converted to other forms of energy as well. Green plants use the energy of the sun to trigger a chemical change in which sugars and starches are made. These substances store the energy as

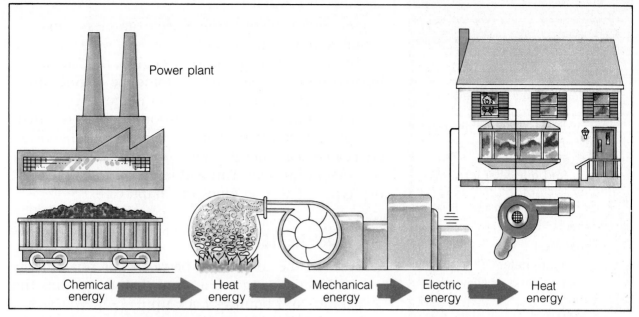

Power plant

Chemical energy → Heat energy → Mechanical energy → Electric energy → Heat energy

Figure 16–13 *A whole series of energy conversions is needed to produce the heat energy of the hair dryer. Trace the various conversions, starting with the burning of a fuel.*

chemical energy. In this process, then, light energy is converted to chemical energy.

In a battery, chemical energy is converted to electric energy. In a motor, electric energy is converted to mechanical energy. The mechanical energy of a waterfall is converted to electric energy in a generator.

Often a whole series of energy conversions is needed to do a particular job. The operation of a hair dryer is a good example of this. See Figure 16–13. The electric energy used by the dryer is generated from some fuel source, such as gas. The chemical energy from the fuel is released by burning it. The fuel provides heat energy, which in turn is changed to mechanical energy. This mechanical energy is used to make a generator do the work of providing the dryer with electric energy. When you turn the dryer on, the electric energy is changed back to heat energy.

Engines

Machines that change heat energy to mechanical energy are called **heat engines.** In a heat engine, a fuel is burned. This burning, or combustion, releases heat energy, which is then changed to mechanical energy.

Heat engines are classified according to where the fuel is burned. In an external-combustion engine, the fuel is burned outside the engine. A steam

Sharpen Your Skills

The Pendulum

1. Find a length of cord and measure off one meter. Cut the cord.
2. Tie a light mass, such as a key, to one end. Hold the other end up with one hand, so that the key is hanging.
3. Pull the key to one side. Then let the key go and observe its motion.

   a. What happened to the key when you let go?
   b. What do you think gave the key its energy?
   c. What kind of energy did it have when it was at its highest point?
   d. Where was its maximum kinetic energy?

Measuring Energy

Different units are used to measure different forms of energy. All these units are derived from the unit of work. Using reference books in the library, find out what form of energy each of the following units measures and how it is derived:

1. calorie
2. newton-meter
3. watt-second or kilowatt-hour
4. BTU

engine and a steam turbine are examples of external-combustion engines.

In an internal-combustion engine, the fuel is burned inside the engine. Automobile engines are examples of internal-combustion engines. In both external- and internal-combustion engines, the first energy conversion involves the change of chemical energy to heat energy. What does the next energy conversion involve? You will learn more about the two types of heat engines in Chapter 18.

SECTION REVIEW

1. Describe the conversion between potential energy and kinetic energy as a tennis ball drops, hits the ground, and bounces back up.
2. Describe the energy conversions that take place when a flashlight is turned on.
3. What energy conversions take place in combustion engines? What is the difference between an external-combustion engine and an internal-combustion engine?
4. Identify the various energy conversions involved in the following events: An object is raised and then allowed to fall. As it hits the ground, it stops, produces a sound, and becomes warmer.

16–4 Conservation of Energy

You have just read of many conversions of energy: kinetic and potential in the ball, heat and chemical in fuels, heat and mechanical in engines. Perhaps you have wondered if any energy is lost during such conversions. The answer is that in spite of all the changes of form, the total amount of energy remains the same.

The law of conservation (kahn-ser-VAY-shuhn) of energy states that energy can be neither created nor destroyed by ordinary means. Energy can only be converted from one form to another. So energy conversions occur without loss or gain in energy.

The law of conservation of energy is one of the foundations of scientific thought. If energy seems to disappear, then scientists look for it. Important discoveries have been made because scientists believed so strongly in the conservation of energy.

One such discovery was made by Albert Einstein in 1905. Part of his famous theory of relativity dealt with the concept that mass and energy were interchangeable. Einstein expressed this concept in the form of a mathematical equation:

$$E = mc^2$$

E is energy, **m** is mass, and **c** is the speed of light. According to this equation, the energy of any mass is equal to the product of that mass and the square of the speed of light.

With this mass–energy relationship, Einstein was saying that matter is another form of energy, or that mass and energy are two forms of the same thing and can be converted into each other. With this mass–energy relationship, Einstein modified the law of conservation of energy. He showed that if some of either matter or energy is created or destroyed, the other must make up for the change. The total amount of mass and energy is conserved.

During nuclear reactions—such as those that take place in the sun—energy and mass do not seem to be conserved. But Einstein used his famous equation to show that a loss in mass results in a gain in energy. Mass is continuously changed to energy in our sun through a process called nuclear fusion. During this process, a small loss in mass produces a huge amount of energy.

Figure 16–14 *The huge amount of energy produced by a hydrogen bomb is evidence of Einstein's mass–energy equation. Mass and energy are two forms of the same thing and can be converted into each other. What is the mathematical expression for this famous equation?*

Figure 16–15 *In 1905, Albert Einstein (1879–1955) made a major contribution to science with his theory of relativity. Part of this theory states that mass and energy are interchangeable. Here you see Einstein at Oxford University, England, in 1931, where he received the honorary degree of doctor of science.*

SECTION REVIEW

1. What is the law of conservation of energy? How do energy conversions support this law?
2. Explain the meaning of Einstein's equation $E = mc^2$.
3. Why does even a small loss in mass result in a tremendous gain in energy?
4. During certain nuclear reactions, a high-speed electron is ejected. The energy lost by the nucleus, however, does not equal the energy of the escaping electron. From this observation, scientists concluded that another undiscovered particle must also be ejected. They searched for more than 20 years before they found it. Why did the scientists believe another particle must exist?

Relating Mass, Velocity, and Kinetic Energy

Problem

How does a change in mass affect the velocity of an object if its kinetic energy is constant?

Materials (per group)

rubber band
3 thumbtacks
12 washers glued together in groups of 2, 4, and 6
wooden board, 15 cm × 100 cm
meterstick

Procedure

1. Place three thumbtacks at one end of the wooden board, as shown in the figure. Do not push the thumbtacks all the way into the board.
2. Stretch the rubber band over the three thumbtacks to form a triangle.
3. In front of the rubber band, place two washers that have been stuck together.
4. Pull the washer and rubber band back about 2 cm, as in the figure. Release the rubber band. The washers should slide about 70 to 80 cm along the board.
5. Practice step 4 until you can make the double washer travel 70 to 80 cm each time.

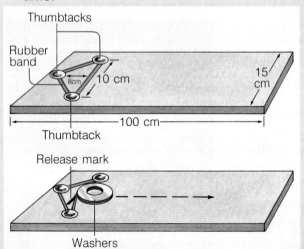

6. Mark the point to which you pulled the rubber band back to obtain a distance of 70 to 80 cm. This will be your launching point for the entire experiment.
7. Launch the double washer three times. In a data table similar to the one shown here, record the distance in centimeters for each trial. Remember to use the same launching point each time.
8. Repeat step 7 for a stack of 4 washers.
9. Repeat step 7 for a stack of 6 washers.

Observations

1. Calculate the average distance traveled by 2 washers, 4 washers, and 6 washers.

Mass	Distance (cm)			Average Distance (cm)
	1	**2**	**3**	
2 washers				
4 washers				
6 washers				

Conclusions

1. What is the relationship between the mass, or number of washers, and the average distance traveled?
2. What kind of energy was in the washers when you held them at the launching point? How do you know?
3. After launching the washers, what kind of energy did they have?
4. You launched all the washers from the same position. Was the energy the same for each launch?
5. Assume that the farther the washers slid, the greater their initial velocity. Did the heavier group of washers move faster or slower than the lighter group?
6. If the kinetic energy is the same for each set of washers, what happens to the velocity as the mass increases?

CHAPTER REVIEW

SUMMARY

16–1 Nature of Energy

❏ Energy is the ability to do work.

❏ Energy appears in many forms: mechanical, heat, chemical, electromagnetic, and nuclear.

16–2 Kinetic and Potential Energy

❏ Energy stored in an object due to its position is called potential energy.

❏ Energy that a moving object has due to its motion is called kinetic energy.

❏ Kinetic energy equals one half the product of the mass times the velocity squared.

❏ Energy that is dependent on the height of an object above the earth's surface and its weight is called gravitational potential energy.

16–3 Energy Conversion

❏ Changes in the forms of energy are called energy conversions.

❏ Machines that change heat energy to mechanical energy are heat engines.

❏ In an external-combustion engine, fuel is burned outside the engine. In an internal-combustion engine, fuel is burned inside the engine.

16–4 Conservation of Energy

❏ The law of conservation of energy states that energy can be neither created nor destroyed by ordinary means.

❏ According to Einstein's equation, $E = mc^2$, matter is another form of energy.

VOCABULARY

Define each term in a complete sentence.

chemical
  energy
electro-magnetic energy
energy
energy conversion
gravitational potential
  energy

heat energy
heat engine
joule
kinetic energy
law of conservation
  of energy

mechanical energy
nuclear energy
potential energy

CONTENT REVIEW: MULTIPLE CHOICE

On a separate sheet of paper, write the letter of the answer that best completes each statement.

1. Energy is the ability to do
   a. motion.   b. power.   c. work.   d. acceleration.
2. The unit in which energy is measured is the
   a. newton.   b. joule.   c. electron.   d. dyne.
3. X-rays, lasers, and radio waves are forms of
   a. mechanical energy.   b. heat energy.
   c. electromagnetic energy.   d. nuclear energy.
4. The sun's energy source is
   a. mechanical energy.   b. electromagnetic energy.
   c. chemical energy.   d. nuclear energy.

5. A stretched rubber band has
   a. potential energy.   b. kinetic energy.
   c. nuclear energy.   d. electromagnetic energy.

6. Energy of motion is
   a. potential energy.   b. kinetic energy.
   c. electromagnetic energy.   d. nuclear energy.

7. A 1900-kg ship traveling at 40 km/hr has kinetic energy equal to
   a. $\dfrac{1900 \times 40}{2}$.   b. $\dfrac{1900^2 \times 40}{2}$.   c. 1900×40^2.   d. $\dfrac{1900 \times 40^2}{2}$.

8. Gravitational potential energy is dependent on
   a. speed and height.   b. time and weight.
   c. weight and height.   d. acceleration and kinetic energy.

9. The energy conversions involved in heat engines are
   a. electromagnetic—mechanical—heat   b. chemical—heat—mechanical
   c. chemical—electromagnetic—heat   d. mechanical—chemical—heat

10. According to Einstein, matter is another form of
   a. energy.   b. mass.   c. time.   d. light.

CONTENT REVIEW: COMPLETION

On a separate sheet of paper, write the word or words that best complete each statement.

1. Energy is the ability to do _____.

2. The internal motion of molecules in matter is _____ energy.

3. The energy that bonds atoms or ions together is _____ energy.

4. Light is _____ energy.

5. Sound is _____ energy.

6. Energy stored in an object due to its position is called _____ energy.

7. Kinetic energy is energy of _____.

8. The equation for calculating kinetic energy is K.E. = _____.

9. Gravitational potential energy is dependent on both the _____ and _____ of an object.

10. A (An) _____ engine is a machine that changes heat energy to mechanical energy.

CONTENT REVIEW: TRUE OR FALSE

Determine whether each statement is true or false. Then on a separate sheet of paper, write "true" if it is true. If it is false, change the underlined word or words to make the statement true.

1. Energy is the ability to do <u>work</u>.

2. Gunpowder contains <u>chemical</u> energy.

3. The most concentrated form of energy is <u>mechanical</u> energy.

4. <u>Kinetic</u> energy is energy of motion.

5. In the determination of an object's kinetic energy, its <u>mass</u> has the greatest effect.

6. Gravitational potential energy depends on weight and <u>time</u>.

7. At the top of its arc, a pendulum has maximum <u>kinetic</u> energy.

8. In an external-combustion engine, the fuel is burned <u>outside</u> the engine.

9. A car engine converts chemical energy to <u>electromagnetic</u> energy.

10. Energy is neither created nor destroyed according to the <u>law of combination of matter</u>.

CONCEPT REVIEW: SKILL BUILDING

Use the skills you have developed in the chapter to complete each activity.

1. **Applying concepts** Sound is produced by vibrations in a medium such as air. The particles of air are first pushed together and then pulled apart. Why is sound considered a form of mechanical energy?

2. **Relating concepts** A bear in a zoo lies sleeping on a ledge. A visitor comments: "Look at that lazy bear. It has no energy at all." Do you agree? Explain your answer.

3. **Making calculations and graphs** The gravitational potential energy of a rock at 100 m is 1000 J. What is the G.P.E. at 50 m? At 20 m? At 1 m? At 0 m? Make a graph of height versus energy. What is the shape of your graph?

4. **Making comparisons** Body A has twice the mass of body B. Body B is moving twice as fast as body A. Is the kinetic energy of body A less than, equal to, or greater than body B? Explain your answer.

5. **Applying concepts** A book sliding across a desk loses all its kinetic energy and comes to rest. The book feels slightly warm. Was energy conserved? Explain your answer.

6. **Relating concepts** As a tennis ball bounces, there is a continuous conversion between kinetic and potential energy. But each bounce is lower than the previous bounce. Eventually, both the kinetic and potential energies of the ball disappear completely. Is energy conserved? Explain your answer.

7. **Applying concepts** Two cyclists are riding their bikes up a steep hill. Jill rides her bike straight up the hill. Jack rides his bike up the hill in a zigzag formation to conserve energy. Jack and Jill have identical masses. At the top of the hill does Jack have less gravitational potential energy than Jill? Explain your answer.

8. **Identifying relationships** The diagram below shows a golfer in various stages of her swing. Compare the kinetic and potential energies of the golf club at each labeled point in the complete golf swing.

CONCEPT REVIEW: ESSAY

Discuss each of the following in a brief paragraph.

1. List five examples of mechanical energy.
2. Compare kinetic and potential energy.
3. Describe the changes in potential and kinetic energy of a tennis ball just before, during, and just after you hit it back to your opponent with your tennis racket.
4. How does bouncing on a trampoline illustrate kinetic and potential energies?
5. Explain the following statement: "Energy can always be converted to a different form, but it is never lost."
6. Water is boiled. The resulting steam is blown against huge turbine blades. The turning blades spin in a magnetic field, producing electricity. Describe, in order, the energy conversions.

Adventures in Science

DICK RUTAN AND JEANA YEAGER: MAKING AVIATION HISTORY

"Look! Up in the sky . . . It's a bird . . . It's a plane . . . It's a very unusual plane!" This airplane, named the *Voyager*, does not look like any conventional aircraft. Its long, narrow wings are tipped with tiny upright "winglets." An extra wing streams out on either side of its nose. Two narrow fuel-filled booms suspended along either side of its body complete its design.

The *Voyager* is one of the world's newest and most extraordinary aircraft. Its 33.7-meter wingspan is greater than that of a Boeing 727. But its mass is only 8427 kilograms—just about half the mass of a small car. And although this remarkable aircraft is designed to carry up to five times its weight, it has room for only two people. But that's no surprise. For that is exactly how the *Voyager* was designed.

Burt Rutan, the plane's designer, built the *Voyager* with two particular people in mind: his brother, pilot Dick Rutan, and co-pilot Jeana Yeager. Dick and Burt Rutan have been flying airplanes since they were teenagers in Dinuba, California. Dick went on to become a fighter pilot and Burt became a designer of small innovative airplanes.

When Dick returned from a tour of duty in Vietnam, he met engineer and race pilot Jeana Yeager. A spirited Texan, Yeager had grown up training horses and sky diving. Dick introduced her to the strange planes his brother had built. Soon she began breaking speed records flying them! In their quest for aviation challenges, Dick and Jeana decided to attempt a nonstop flight around the world. Burt Rutan accepted the challenge to build a plane that could make the 40,000-kilometer trip without stopping.

For nine days, Jeana Yeager and Dick Rutan piloted their revolutionary plane *Voyager* from a tiny cockpit no larger than a telephone booth.

The *Voyager* is constructed from high-technology materials that may one day be adapted for commercial planes. Honeycombed paper is sandwiched between lightweight plastic-reinforced fibers. The combination is stronger than steel but weighs only about one-fifth as much.

The *Voyager's* light weight allows the plane to use a fraction of the fuel a normal aircraft consumes. And that is the key to the Voyager's ability to circle the globe without stopping to refuel. According to Jeana Yeager, flying in the *Voyager* is like riding on the back of an eagle.

The *Voyager* is stable but difficult to fly. And although the plane is sleek, it is not very luxurious. Its tiny cabin has one small bunk. So one pilot can sleep while the other flies. "It is like a little cocoon home," Dick Rutan once commented.

The *Voyager* broke its first long-distance record in July 1986. Dick and Jeana flew their strange craft a distance of 18,665 kilometers without landing or refueling. Because the *Voyager* travels at only 130 to 160 kilometers per hour, the flight lasted nearly five days. During the flight, the pilots were treated to a spectacular view of the earth below, since the plane rarely cruises at altitudes greater than 4500 meters. Its second record-breaking flight ended on December 23, 1986, when the *Voyager* completed its nonstop trip around the world.

In addition to flying the plane and keeping it on course, the pilot on duty must keep careful track of the 5675 liters of fuel on board. The fuel is stored in fifteen different tanks inside the *Voyager's* booms and body. As the fuel is used the remainder must be constantly shifted around to keep the plane properly balanced.

During *Voyager's* grueling flights, for which the pilots prepare at least one month in advance, Dick and Jeana cooperate by sharing responsibility. This feeling of cooperation—combined with a love of flying, a spirit of adventure, and a dedication to science—is helping this threesome make aviation history.

Issues in Science

ROBOTS: DO THEY SIGNAL AUTOMATION OR UNEMPLOYMENT?

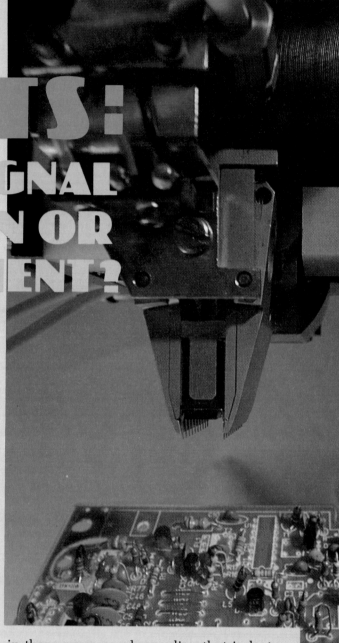

Sparks fly as a worker welds parts to an automobile body. Farther down the assembly line, another worker trims and grinds the weld joints. Beyond that, still another worker sprays paint on the car.

Up and down the assembly line, not a word is spoken as the workers perform their tasks. The workers do not pause, yawn, blink, or look at each other. "That's just not human," you might say. And you would be right. For these workers are robots!

Robots are becoming more and more common in assembly-line jobs. Dr. Harley Shaiken of the Massachusetts Institute of Technology has predicted that 32,000 robots may one day replace 100,000 automobile-industry workers. Is this prediction likely to come true?

ROBOT REVOLUTION

Already, more than 6000 robots are used in factories all over the United States. Every day more are being put to work. Several fully automated factories are now being tested. In such factories, all of the production and assembly is done by machines. One result of this "robot revolution" is increased unemployment in industrial regions. Workers in these areas are demanding that industry leaders slow down the switch to robots.

But, as many company executives point out, robots often perform jobs that are boring and repetitive, as well as jobs that may be hazardous to humans. For example, a robot may paint many thousands of cars and not be affected by inhaling paint fumes that may be dangerous for a human worker to inhale.

Other company executives point out that they must either use robots or lose business to companies that do. As Thomas B. Gunn of the Arthur D. Little Company puts it, "Are you going to reduce your work force by 25 percent by putting in robots, or by 100 percent by going out of business?" And James Baker of the General Electric Corporation puts it this way: "U.S. business has three choices in the 80s . . . automate, emigrate [leave], or evaporate [go out of business]."

NEW JOBS OR FEW JOBS?

Some industry experts believe that robots and computer systems will create many new jobs. "In the past," George Brosseau of the National Science Foundation explains, "whenever a new technology has been introduced, it has always generated more jobs than it has displaced. But we don't know whether that's true of robot technology. There's no question but that new jobs will be created, but will there be enough to offset the loss?" he adds.

James S. Albut of the U.S. National Bureau of Standards thinks so. "Robots can improve productivity and create many new jobs," he has written.

Others reply that although using robots may create more jobs in the long run, they cause job losses first. These people stress that it is up to government, business, and labor to teach people new skills and to find new jobs for workers who have been replaced by robots. Such efforts will ease some of the strain that accompanies the implementation of new and valuable technology.

Do you think United States companies should rapidly move ahead with the development and use of robots even at the risk of some unemployment and worker hardship? Or should the switch from human power to robot power be done slowly in order to lessen the impact on workers?

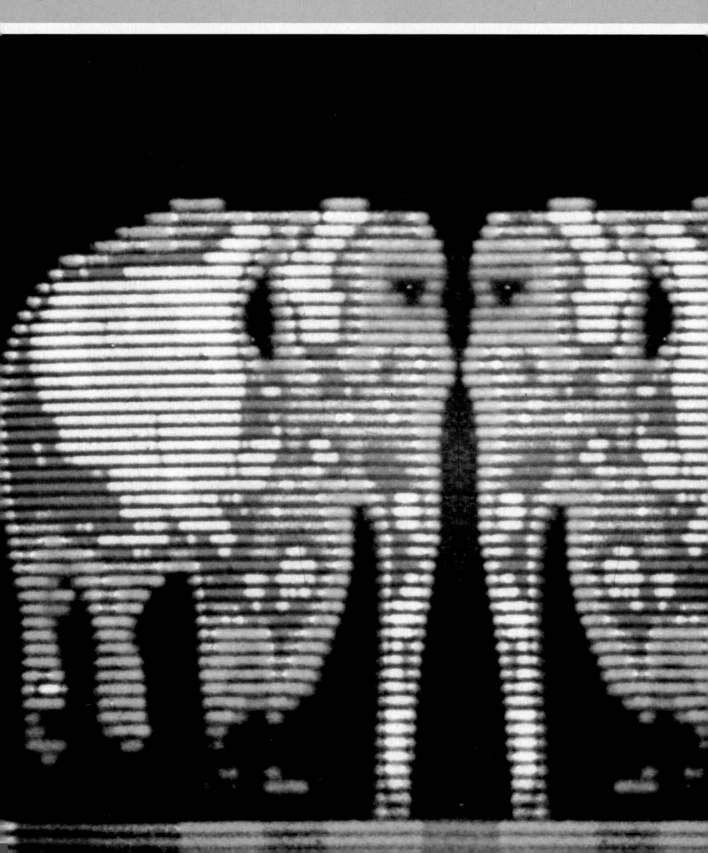

Heat Energy

Would a technique that enabled doctors to diagnose illnesses without surgery, drugs, or harmful radiation be useful? Yes, thought Lloyd Williams and Maxwell Cade. And they knew just the method that would do it—thermography. Thermography uses the heat given off by an object to produce an image on film. The image is called a thermogram. Thermography is based on the fact that all objects, including humans, give off heat energy.

At Middlesex Hospital, London, Williams and Cade worked out the design for their Pyroscan Thermographic Camera—a camera that can photograph the patterns of heat given off from skin. The infrared camera they developed is so sensitive to heat that it can record temperature differences of only one or two degrees Celsius. Variations from normal patterns of heat emission can be used to diagnose various diseases. For example, cancerous tumors are hotter than normal body tissue. So such tumors show up on a thermogram as red areas. Arthritic joints, on the other hand, are colder and appear blue in a thermogram.

Doctors now use thermography as a painless and harmless means of diagnosing certain illnesses. The Pyroscan Thermographic Camera is an important example of the way heat is being used to make human life better and more enjoyable. By reading the chapters in this unit, you will develop a larger picture of heat energy and its many applications to everyday life.

CHAPTERS

17 Heat

18 Uses of Heat

Thermography is an important application of heat energy. This thermograph of two elephants shows the relative temperature of the elephants' skin. The hottest areas are yellow and the coolest are blue.

Heat

17

CHAPTER SECTIONS

17–1 Heat: A Form of Energy

17–2 Temperature and Heat

17–3 Measuring Heat

17–4 Heat and Phase Changes

17–5 Thermal Expansion

17–6 Heat and Internal Energy

CHAPTER OBJECTIVES

After completing this chapter, you will be able to

17–1 Explain how scientists discovered that heat is a form of energy.

17–2 Define temperature in terms of the kinetic energy of molecules.

17–3 Describe how heat can be measured indirectly by measuring temperature changes.

17–4 Explain how a transfer of heat energy brings about a phase change.

17–5 Explain why thermal expansion occurs.

17–5 Describe some practical applications of thermal expansion.

17–6 Relate internal energy, work, and heat.

On September 13, 1922, the temperature in El Azizia, Libya, reached 58°C—the highest temperature ever recorded on Earth! Second to this record-breaking figure was the highest temperature ever recorded in the United States. On July 10, 1913, the temperature in Death Valley, California, soared to 57°C.

Do these temperatures sound extremely hot to you? Probably so. Yet they are bone-chillingly cold compared to the temperatures experienced in some parts of the solar system. Daytime highs on the planet Mercury, for example, often reach 427°C. Temperatures on Venus are even higher. And on the surface of the sun, the average temperature is 6000°C—more than one hundred times hotter than the hottest day on Earth!

High temperatures, of course, are the result of heat. But what exactly is heat? Where does it come from? And how does it move from one place to another? Scientists who pondered these questions hundreds of years ago thought that heat was a mysterious fluid that could flow from one object to another. In this chapter, you will find out whether these scientists were correct, as well as the answers to other questions about the nature of heat.

The deep cracks in the dry, parched mud are evidence of the tremendous heat certain places, such as this Arizona canyon, experience.

17–1 Heat: A Form of Energy

Sharpen Your Skills

The Discoveries of Rumford and Joule

The work of Count Rumford and James Prescott Joule illustrates the importance of observation and experimentation. Using books and reference materials in the library, find out more about these two scientists, their experiments, and the contributions they made toward the understanding of heat.

Have you ever toasted marshmallows over an open fire? If so, you know that the fire gives off heat. Perhaps you think that heat is some kind of substance flowing from the fire, through the air, and onto your marshmallow. Actually, that is what many eighteenth-century scientists believed. They thought that heat was an invisible, weightless fluid capable of flowing from hotter objects to colder ones. They called this substance *caloric*.

In 1798, the American scientist Benjamin Thompson, better known as Count Rumford, challenged the caloric theory. Rumford had noticed that when holes were drilled in cannon barrels, heat was produced. He devised an experiment in which he could test this observation. Holes were drilled in a cannon barrel that had been placed in a box full of water. After several hours of drilling, the water began to boil. The water boiled as long as the drilling continued. Rumford concluded that it was the drilling, not a flow of caloric, that was producing heat. Since drilling represented work being done, and energy was the ability to do work, then energy and heat must be related. Rumford concluded that heat must be a form of energy.

Molecules and Motion

Forty years after Count Rumford's experiment, British scientist James Prescott Joule investigated

Figure 17–1 *The addition of heat energy causes molecules to move faster and farther apart.*

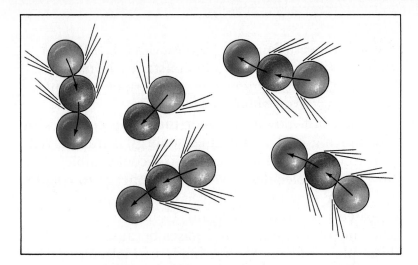

Figure 17–2 *Heat transfer by conduction involves the direct contact of molecules. As fast-moving warmer molecules collide with slow-moving cooler molecules, heat energy is transferred from the warmer to the cooler molecules. In what phases of matter can conduction take place?*

the relationship between heat and motion. He performed a series of experiments that supported the idea that objects in motion produce heat. The amount of heat produced depends on the amount of motion. You have probably noticed this effect in everyday life. For example, rubbing your hands together rapidly makes them feel warmer. Sliding too quickly down a rope can produce a "rope burn." These examples show how motion produces heat.

Scientists working at the time of Joule knew that energy is needed to produce motion. They also knew that matter is made of tiny particles called molecules. Using these facts and the experiments of Rumford and Joule, scientists concluded correctly that heat is a form of energy, and that it must somehow be related to the motion of molecules.

Heat Transfer

If you hold an ice cube in your hand for several seconds, you will notice that your hand begins to feel cold and the ice cube begins to melt. You might think that cold is being transferred from the ice cube to your hand. But there is no such thing as "coldness." Cold is simply the absence of heat. The ice cube in your hand is melting because heat is being transferred from your hand to the ice cube.

The movement of heat from a warmer object to a colder one is called **heat transfer.** There are three methods of heat transfer. **Heat energy is transferred by conduction, convection, and radiation.**

CONDUCTION In **conduction** (kuhn-DUHK-shuhn), heat is transferred through a substance, or from

Figure 17–3 *The pot of boiling water illustrates the three methods of heat transfer—conduction (black arrows), convection (blue arrows), and radiation (red arrows). Why is the handle of the pot made of plastic?*

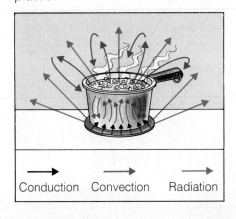

Conduction   Convection   Radiation

Sharpen Your Skills

Heat Loss

   1. Make a list of places in your home or school from which heat may be escaping.
   2. Determine whether the heat loss is due to radiation, conduction, or convection.
   3. How can the heat loss from the building be reduced?

one substance to another, by the direct contact of molecules. All molecules are constantly in motion. Because they have more energy, warmer molecules are moving faster than cooler ones.

When fast-moving warmer molecules collide with slow-moving cooler molecules, energy is transferred from the warmer molecules to the cooler molecules. Now these molecules have enough energy to collide with other slow-moving molecules. The process is repeated over and over again. Conduction can take place in solids, liquids, and gases because these three phases of matter are made of molecules.

Some substances conduct heat more effectively than other substances. These substances are called good **heat conductors.** Silver and copper are excellent heat conductors. Copper is a popular choice for cookware because it conducts heat easily.

Substances that do not conduct heat easily are called **insulators.** Glass, wood, plastic, and rubber are examples of good insulating materials. Wood and plastic handles, for example, are often used on pots and pans. The heat from the pot or pan is not easily conducted into your hand!

CONVECTION   Heat transfer by **convection** (kuhn-VEHK-shuhn) takes place in liquids and gases as molecules move in currents. These currents are caused when molecules in the heated portion of a liquid or gas speed up. As they speed up, the molecules start to spread out. The warmer part of the liquid or gas becomes less dense than the cooler part. That is, the molecules in the heated part of the liquid or gas are less closely packed. Because it is less dense than the

Figure 17–4 *Heat transfer by convection involves the motion of molecules in currents in liquids and gases. Heated molecules speed up and spread out, causing the warmer part of the liquid or gas to become less dense than the cooler part. The heated portion rises, creating currents that carry heat (left). Convection currents near the surface of the earth produce the distortion of objects seen in this photograph (right).*

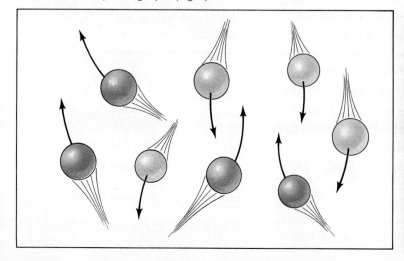

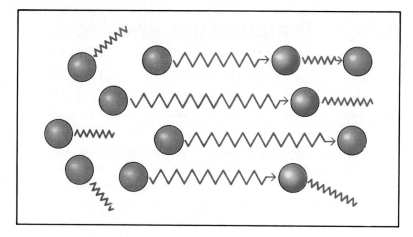

Figure 17–5 *Radiation is the transfer of heat energy in the form of invisible infrared rays. How is radiation related to the heating of the earth?*

surrounding liquid or gas, the heated portion rises, creating currents that carry heat.

As warm air near the surface of the earth is heated, it becomes less dense and tends to rise. Because cooler air is denser than warmer air, it tends to sink. As the warm air rises and the cool air sinks, convection currents are formed. These currents transfer heat. The air currents in the earth's atmosphere, which contribute to our weather, are caused by convection currents.

RADIATION When **radiation** (ray-dee-AY-shuhn) occurs, heat is transferred through space. The heat energy is in the form of invisible light known as infrared rays. Heat from the sun reaches the earth by radiation. Other familiar forms of radiation include the heat surrounding a fire or flame, the heat over a hot stove, and the heat given off by an electric heater. Now can you explain why you can toast marshmallows over a flame even if the flame does not touch the marshmallows?

SECTION REVIEW

1. How did Count Rumford's experiment support the idea that heat is a form of energy?
2. What factors caused scientists to make a connection between heat and molecular motion?
3. What type of heat transfer is illustrated by each of the following: an egg cooking in a frying pan; the roof of a house becoming hot; a warm air mass bringing a change in weather; the wire of an electric appliance becoming hot; heat from a fireplace warming a large room.

Figure 17–6 *A thermos bottle keeps liquids hot or cold by preventing heat transfer by conduction, convection, and radiation. The glass bottle reduces heat transfer by conduction. The air space between the bottles, which is a partial vacuum, prevents heat transfer by convection because there are so few air molecules to carry the heat. A silvered coating on the surface of the bottle prevents heat transfer by radiation. Why is the cap usually made of plastic?*

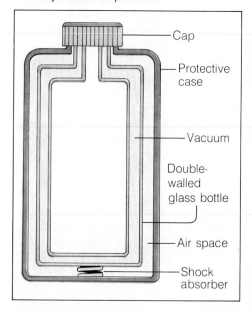

Cap

Protective case

Vacuum

Double-walled glass bottle

Air space

Shock absorber

Investigating Molecular Motion

1. Fill one beaker about two-thirds full with water at or near room temperature.

2. Fill a second beaker about two-thirds full with water that has been chilled by ice for several minutes. Remove the ice cubes once the water is cold.

3. Fill a third beaker about two-thirds full with hot water.

4. Use a dropper to place one drop of dark food coloring on the surface of the water in each beaker. Do not stir.

5. Describe the changes you see in each beaker of water. Note how slowly or quickly the changes occur in each beaker.

Explain your observations in terms of the effect of heat on the motion of molecules.

17–2 Temperature and Heat

If a weather forecast predicts temperatures between 30°C and 35°C, you know you can expect a hot day. You may think that **temperature** is a measure of heat, but it is not. Temperature and heat are related, but they are not the same thing. In order to understand the relationship between heat and temperature, you need to understand how energy and the motion of molecules are related.

Kinetic Energy

Energy of motion is called **kinetic energy.** The faster an object is moving, the more kinetic energy it has. Like all objects, molecules have kinetic energy because of their motion. When molecules are heated, their kinetic energy increases.

Temperature is a measure of the average kinetic energy of molecules. The higher the temperature of a substance, the faster the molecules in that substance are moving, on the average. Likewise, a lower temperature indicates the molecules are moving more slowly. In which pot of water would most of the molecules be moving faster, a pot at 90°C or one at 70°C?

Figure 17–7 *Heat within the earth increases the kinetic energy of water molecules so that they escape from the earth as an eruption of hot water and steam. How does this photograph of Old Faithful Geyser in Yellowstone National Park, Wyoming, illustrate the relationship between heat and temperature?*

Measuring Temperature

A **thermometer** is an instrument for measuring temperature. Most common thermometers consist of a very thin tube filled with liquid, which is usually alcohol or mercury. As the liquid in the thermometer gets warmer, the molecules move faster and farther apart. The liquid expands and rises in the tube. The reverse happens as the liquid cools. The molecules move more slowly and closer together. The liquid contracts and drops in the tube.

Along the tube of a thermometer is a set of numerals, called a scale, that allows you to read the temperature. The scale of a thermometer shows the temperature in degrees **Celsius (C).** The degree Celsius is the metric unit most often used to measure temperature. Water freezes at 0°C and boils at 100°C at sea level.

Another metric temperature scale often used by scientists is the **Kelvin scale.** On this scale, temperatures are measured in units called kelvins (K). You can convert Celsius degrees to kelvins simply by adding 273° to the Celsius temperature. For example, if a thermometer reads 10°C, the same temperature on the Kelvin scale would be 283°K (273 + 10). A temperature of −5°C would be equivalent to 268°K (273 + −5). What is the freezing point of water on the Kelvin scale? The boiling point?

One reason the Kelvin scale is useful is that its lowest reading, 0°K, is the lowest possible temperature that anything can reach. Often referred to as **absolute zero,** it is the temperature at which all molecular motion stops. What is the value of absolute zero on the Celsius scale?

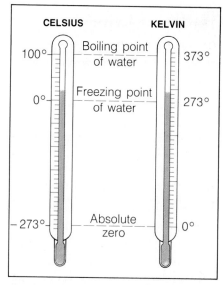

Figure 17–8 *A comparison of the Celsius and Kelvin temperature scales is shown here. What is the boiling point of water on the Kelvin scale? The freezing point?*

Figure 17–9 *At a temperature of −195.8°C, nitrogen gas becomes a liquid. A banana dipped in liquid nitrogen becomes so frozen it can be used to hammer a nail into a block of wood. What is the equivalent temperature on the Kelvin scale?*

SECTION REVIEW

1. What is temperature?
2. How does a thermometer measure temperature?
3. What is the most common scale for a scientific thermometer?
4. How would you convert a temperature in kelvins to degrees Celsius?
5. What must be true about the kinetic energy of molecules at 0°K? Can matter actually reach this temperature?

17–3 Measuring Heat

You know from cooking soup or boiling water that heat energy must be added to a substance in order to raise its temperature. Heat is needed to set molecules in motion. And temperature is a measure of that motion.

Heat cannot be measured directly. But changes in temperature provide an indirect measurement of heat. **An increase in temperature indicates the addition of heat; a decrease in temperature represents the removal of heat.**

One unit used to measure heat is the **calorie.** One calorie is defined as the amount of heat needed to raise the temperature of one gram of liquid water one degree Celsius. For example, to raise the temperature of one gram of water from 7°C to 8°C or from 33°C to 34°C, one calorie of heat is needed. Another unit used to measure heat is the joule.

The amount of heat needed for a given temperature change depends on the mass of the water being heated. For example, twenty calories will raise the temperature of one gram of water twenty degrees. But the same number of calories will raise the temperature of ten grams of water only two degrees.

Figure 17–10 *Although heat cannot be measured directly, a change in temperature provides an indirect measurement of heat. Higher temperatures indicate more heat (left). Lower temperatures indicate an absence of heat (right).*

Specific Heat Capacity

Mass is not the only factor that determines temperature change. The same amount of heat will produce a different temperature change in different substances even if their masses are the same. Some substances absorb heat energy more easily than other substances.

The ability of a substance to absorb heat energy is called its **specific heat.** The specific heat of a substance is the number of calories needed to raise the temperature of one gram of that substance one Celsius degree. The specific heat of water is 1.0 calorie per gram Celsius degree. Figure 17–11 shows the specific heat values of other substances.

Calculating Heat Energy

Specific heat can be used to calculate the amount of heat energy gained or lost by a substance. The heat gained or lost by the substance is equal to the product of its mass (m) times its change in temperature (ΔT) times its specific heat (s.h.).

Heat gained or lost = mass × change in temperature × specific heat
= m × ΔT × s.h.

TABLE OF SPECIFIC HEATS

Substance	Specific Heat (cal/g·C°)
Air	.25
Aluminum	.22
Copper	.09
Glass	.20
Ice (−20°C to 0°C)	.50
Mercury	.03
Ocean water	.93
Water	1.00
Wood	.42

Figure 17–11 *According to this table, which heats up more quickly, aluminum or mercury?*

Sample Problem

How much heat is needed to raise the temperature of 4 grams of aluminum 5C°?

Solution

Step 1   Write the formula   **Heat gained = m × ΔT × s.h.**

Step 2   Substitute given   **Heat gained = 4 grams × 5C°**
         numbers and units   **× 0.22 calories per gram Celsius degree**

Step 3   Solve for unknown   **Heat gained = 4.4 calories**
         variable

Practice Problems

1. Calculate the heat lost by 10 g of copper if it is cooled from 35°C to 21°C.

2. Ten g of a certain substance gained 16.5 cal of heat when the temperature increased from 70°C to 85°C. What is the specific heat of the substance?

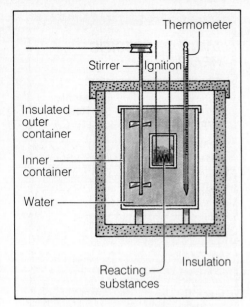

Figure 17-12 *The calorimeter is a device used to measure the heat given off during a chemical reaction. What principle of heat transfer is the basis of operation of the calorimeter?*

The Calorimeter

Within a closed system, the heat lost by one substance must equal the heat gained by another substance. A device that makes use of this principle is a **calorimeter** (kal-uh-RIHM-uh-ter).

A calorimeter is used to measure the heat given off in chemical reactions. Figure 17-12 shows the construction of a calorimeter. An insulated outer container filled with water surrounds an inner container in which a chemical reaction takes place. Since the heat given off by the reacting substances equals the heat gained by the water, the heat of the chemical reaction can be calculated. The temperature change, mass, and specific heat of the water must be known in order to make the calculation. For example, suppose the surrounding water has a mass of 300 grams. If the temperature of the water increases 5C°, then the heat given off by the chemical reaction is equal to $300 \times 5 \times 1$, or 1500 calories. How much heat would be given off by a chemical reaction that raised the temperature of 150 grams of water 10C°?

SECTION REVIEW

1. How can heat be measured?
2. What unit is used to measure heat?
3. What is specific heat?
4. Which would require more heat energy: bringing 100 grams of water at 40°C to the boiling point or raising the temperature of 1000 grams of water from 80°C to 90°C?

17-4 Heat and Phase Changes

Have you ever watched an ice cube melt in a glass of water? Heat is being transferred from the water to the ice. As the ice absorbs the heat, it melts, or changes into a liquid. Eventually all the ice will change into liquid water.

The physical change of matter from the solid phase to the liquid phase is called a **phase change.** There are several different phase changes. Phase changes occur when a solid becomes a liquid, which

Figure 17–13 *This observatory at Mt. Washington, New Hampshire, dramatically shows one important phase change—freezing. Does heat energy of a substance increase or decrease during freezing?*

is called melting, and when a liquid becomes a solid, which is called freezing. The change of a liquid to a gas, or vaporization, and the change of a gas to a liquid, or condensation, are also phase changes.

A change in phase requires a change in heat energy. When ice melts and changes into water, energy in the form of heat is being absorbed by the ice. The energy is needed to overcome the forces of attraction that hold the water molecules together in the solid phase. Where do you think this heat energy is coming from?

The amount of heat needed to change one gram of a substance from the solid phase to the liquid phase is called **heat of fusion.** The heat of fusion for ice is 80 calories per gram, 80 cal/g. In order to melt one gram of ice, 80 calories of heat is needed. What do you think happens when one gram of liquid water changes into ice? You are right if you said 80 calories of heat are lost by the one gram of liquid water as it freezes into ice.

The amount of heat needed to change one gram of a substance from the liquid phase to the gas phase is called the **heat of vaporization.** The heat of vaporization for water is 540 calories per gram, 540 cal/g. How much heat is needed to change ten grams of water to steam? How much heat is given off if ten grams of steam condensed into water?

In order for a substance to undergo a phase change, the substance must be at a certain temperature. The temperature at which a substance changes from the solid phase to the liquid phase is called its **melting point.** The temperature at which a substance changes from the liquid phase to the solid

Figure 17–14 *Here you can see water in its three phases—solid, liquid, and gas. In order to produce a phase change, heat energy must be added or removed. What phase changes involve the addition of heat? The removal?*

phase is called its **freezing point.** And the temperature at which a substance changes from the liquid phase to the gas phase is called its **boiling point.**

During a phase change, there is a change in heat energy but no change in temperature. Forces of attraction between molecules are overcome, but the average kinetic energy of the molecules remains the same. Once the melting point or boiling point of a substance has been reached, adding or removing heat will result in more of the substance changing phase, not in a change in temperature. Only after the phase change has been completed will a change in heat energy produce a temperature change.

A graph that shows how heat energy, temperature change, and phase change are related for water is called a phase-change diagram or a heating curve. See Figure 17–15. In this diagram, you can see that ice is being heated from below 0°C to its melting point. There is a temperature change. For every degree Celsius that the temperature rises, 0.5 cal/g of heat is required. At 0°C, the ice undergoes a phase change. There is no change in temperature

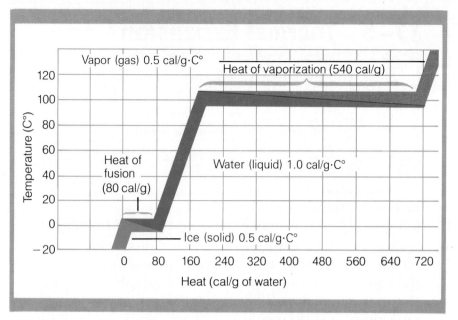

Figure 17–15 *A heating curve, or phase-change diagram, illustrates the fact that during a phase change, the addition of heat produces no change in temperature. According to the diagram, how many calories per gram are required for ice to melt? For water to vaporize?*

during a phase change. How many calories per gram are required for this phase change?

Any heat now added to the water will cause a steady increase in temperature until 100°C is reached. Then the temperature will remain at 100°C while the liquid water changes to steam. Once the phase change is complete, the temperature will begin to rise again as additional heat is added to the steam. For one gram of ice at 0°C, how many calories are needed to change it to one gram of steam at 100°C?

SECTION REVIEW

1. What is necessary for a phase change to occur?
2. What is the term used to describe the amount of heat needed to change one gram of a substance from the solid phase to the liquid phase? From the liquid phase to the gas phase?
3. What happens to temperature during a phase change? To heat energy?
4. Compare the amount of heat released when 54 grams of water freezes to ice, with the amount of heat released when 8 grams of steam condenses to water.

17–5 Thermal Expansion

Have you ever wondered why sidewalks have cracks between the squares of concrete? The reason is that concrete expands in hot weather. Without the cracks, the surface of the sidewalk would buckle. Spaces are left in bridge roadways and between railroad tracks for the same reason.

The liquid in a thermometer expands when it is heated. A tightly closed bottle of carbonated soda left out in the sun may explode or at least bubble over in a fizzy mess when opened. Automobile and bicycle tires tend to look "higher" in warm weather than in cold weather. All of these examples illustrate **thermal expansion.** Thermal expansion is the expansion of a substance due to heat. **Most substances—solids, liquids, and gases—expand when their temperature is increased.**

Expansion in Solids

A molecular model can help to explain why solids expand when heated. The molecules in a solid are arranged in fixed positions about which they vibrate. As heat energy is added to the solid, the kinetic energy of the molecules increases and their vibrations speed up. The molecules move farther away from their fixed positions and farther away from each other. This separation of molecules causes the solid to expand.

Figure 17–16 *Thermal expansion is the expansion of a substance due to heat. Solids expand when heated, so expansion links are provided in bridge surfaces (left). When the temperature is low, the gap between the metal links is large. When the temperature is high, the gap is smaller. As the soda water in this bottle warms, the gas molecules move faster (right). They eventually come out of solution as bubbles, or fizz.*

Expansion in Liquids

The molecules in a liquid also experience an increase in kinetic energy when heated. As the molecules begin to move faster, they move farther apart. So most liquids expand when heated.

There is one exception to this rule, however. Between the temperatures of 4°C and 0°C, water expands as it cools. Because of this expansion, the volume of water increases as it cools. As the volume increases, the density decreases.

Ice is less dense than liquid water. You can see evidence of this when you look at ice cubes floating in a glass of water or chunks of ice floating on top of a pond. What would be the effect on life on the earth if ice were more dense than liquid water?

Expansion in Gases

As the temperature of a gas increases, the molecules move faster and faster. They begin to collide with each other and with the sides of their container. Since the molecules in a gas have considerable freedom of motion, thermal expansion in a gas can be quite dramatic. Many explosions are caused when a tightly closed container of gas becomes too hot. Why should you never heat a gas in a closed container?

Applications of Thermal Expansion

The principle of thermal expansion can be useful in constructing heat-regulating devices. These devices make use of the fact that different solids expand at different rates.

A device that helps control temperature in an indoor area or in an appliance is called a **thermostat** (THER-muh-stat). The switch in a thermostat is a **bimetallic strip,** which consists of two different metals joined together. These two metals have different rates of expansion. When heated or cooled, one of the metals expands or contracts faster than the other, causing the strip to bend. The metal that expands more forms the outside of the curve of the bimetallic strip. The bending and unbending of the bimetallic strip opens and closes an electric circuit

Figure 17–17 *Because water expands between 4°C and 0°C, the density of ice is less than the density of water. This fact explains why ice floats. What must be true of the volume of water during this temperature interval?*

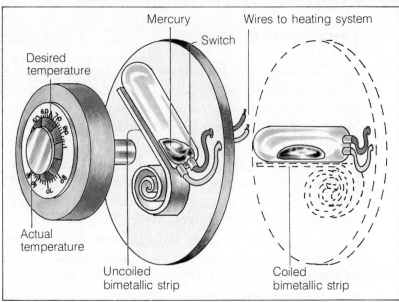

Mercury
Wires to heating system
Switch
Desired temperature
Actual temperature
Uncoiled bimetallic strip
Coiled bimetallic strip

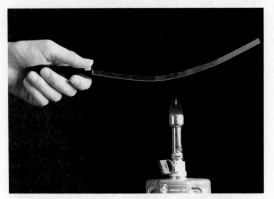

Figure 17–18 *Because the two heated metals making up the bimetallic strip expand at different rates, the strip bends (left). A bimetallic strip is an important part of a thermostat (right). When the temperature gets too cold, the bimetallic strip uncoils. This action causes a drop of mercury to close a switch and start the heating system. When the temperature reaches the desired level, the strip coils up, the mercury opens the switch, and the heat goes off. On what principle is the operation of a bimetallic strip based?*

that controls the heating or cooling device. Thermostats can be found in air conditioners, electric blankets, refrigerators, and home heating systems. What are other uses for thermostats?

SECTION REVIEW

1. What is meant by thermal expansion?
2. What happens to the molecules of a substance when the substance is heated?
3. How does a bimetallic strip make use of the principle of thermal expansion?
4. Using the formula for density, show why an ice cube floats in water.

To relate internal energy and heat

17–6 Heat and Internal Energy

Count Rumford observed that heat was produced when holes were drilled in cannon barrels. James Prescott Joule observed that objects in motion produce heat. In both cases, work was being done. You may think of work as washing dishes, babysitting, or doing homework. But when scientists speak of work, they are referring to a force acting on an object and causing it to move.

Objects in motion have kinetic energy. The molecules of any substance have kinetic energy because they are always moving. Adding heat to a substance may increase the average kinetic energy of the molecules and cause a rise in temperature. Doing work

Figure 17–19 *These runners in the 1988 Olympic Games have a great deal of kinetic energy, or energy of motion. Therefore, they have the ability to do work. The work they do involves exerting a force to move their bodies a certain distance. As a result of this work, their body temperatures increase. What then is true of their internal energy?*

on a substance also may cause a rise in temperature. The relationship between heat, motion, and work helped scientists to understand that heat is a form of energy.

Although heat can be transferred from one substance to another, a substance cannot really contain heat. Heat contained by a substance is actually energy. **Energy contained in a substance is called internal energy.** A change in temperature indicates a change in **internal energy.** When a substance receives heat or has work done on it, it gains internal energy. When a substance gives off heat or does work, it loses some of its internal energy.

SECTION REVIEW

1. What is internal energy?
2. Do work and heat have similar effects on a substance? Explain your answer.
3. A nail hit with a hammer becomes hot. When placed in a glass of water, the nail quickly becomes cool. In terms of work, heat, and energy, describe what happens to the nail.

Sharpen Your Skills

Associating Meanings

Sometimes words that have a scientific meaning also have another, more common meaning. Very often the two meanings are related. This relationship can help you remember the scientific definition.

Look up the meaning of each underlined word in the following terms. Then write one sentence that tells how the word's general meaning relates to its scientific meaning.

<u>absolute</u> zero
<u>internal</u> energy
<u>kinetic</u> energy
<u>specific</u> heat
<u>thermal</u> expansion

Temperatures of Mixtures

Problem

When hot and cold water are mixed together, what will be the temperature of the mixture?

Materials *(per group)*

3 Styrofoam cups
2 250-mL beakers
thermometer
2 100-mL graduated
  cylinders

stirring rod
several ice cubes
hot plate

Procedure

1. Place the ice cubes in one beaker and fill the beaker about two-thirds full with water. Cool the water until the temperature is 10°C or lower.
2. Fill the other beaker about two-thirds full with water and heat the beaker until the temperature is at least 75°C. Do *not* boil the water.
3. Line up the three Styrofoam cups. Place 40 mL of cold water in the first cup. Be sure that *no ice* is in the water. Place 40 mL of hot water in the second cup.
4. Measure and record the temperature of the water in each cup.
5. Pour the samples of hot and cold water into the third cup and stir. Measure and record the temperature of the mixture.

6. Pour out the water in each Styrofoam cup, but save the cups for the next steps.
7. Repeat steps 3 to 6 using 80 mL of hot water and 40 mL of cold water.
8. Repeat steps 3 to 6 using 40 mL of hot water and 80 mL of cold water.
9. For each trial, record your results in a data table similar to the one shown here.

Observations

1. For each trial, was the temperature of the mixture closer to the temperature of the hotter sample or the colder sample? How much closer?

Conclusions

1. What explanation can you offer for your observations in each trial?
2. When hot and cold water are mixed together, what is one factor that determines the temperature of the mixture?
3. What types of heat transfer are involved when the mixture is made?
4. What sources of error are present in this experiment?
5. What would you predict the approximate temperature of a mixture to be if 20 mL of water at 10°C are mixed with 100 mL of water at 80°C?

Trial	Cold Water		Hot Water		Mixture	
	Volume	*Temperature*	*Volume*	*Temperature*	*Volume*	*Temperature*
I						
II						
III						

CHAPTER REVIEW

SUMMARY

17–1 Heat: A Form of Energy

❏ The experiments of Rumford led to the conclusion that heat is a form of energy. The experiments of Joule led to the conclusion that objects in motion produce heat.

❏ Heat is a form of energy related to the motion of molecules.

❏ The three types of heat transfer are conduction, convection, and radiation.

❏ Substances that conduct heat effectively are called heat conductors. Substances that do not conduct heat easily are called insulators.

17–2 Temperature and Heat

❏ Kinetic energy is energy of motion.

❏ Temperature is the measure of the average kinetic energy of molecules.

❏ The degree Celsius is the metric unit most often used to measure temperature.

17–3 Measuring Heat

❏ Heat can be measured indirectly by measuring changes in temperature.

❏ A calorie is the amount of heat needed to raise the temperature of one gram of liquid water one degree Celsius.

❏ The ability of a substance to absorb heat energy is called its specific heat.

❏ Heat gained or lost = mass × change in temperature × specific heat (m × ΔT × s.h.).

17–4 Heat and Phase Changes

❏ A phase change requires a gain or loss of heat energy.

❏ The amount of heat needed to change a substance from the solid phase to the liquid phase is called heat of fusion.

❏ The amount of heat needed to change a substance from the liquid phase to the gas phase is called heat of vaporization.

❏ During a phase change, there is a change in heat energy but not in temperature.

17–5 Thermal Expansion

❏ Thermal expansion, the expansion of a substance due to heat, can be explained in terms of the kinetic energy of molecules.

❏ Most substances expand when heated.

❏ Between 4°C and 0°C, water expands as it cools. Ice is less dense than liquid water.

17–6 Heat and Internal Energy

❏ Adding heat to a substance increases the average kinetic energy of the molecules and may cause a rise in temperature.

❏ Energy contained in a substance is called internal energy. A rise in temperature indicates an increase in internal energy.

❏ When a substance has work done on it, it gains internal energy. When a substance does work, it loses internal energy.

VOCABULARY

Define each term in a complete sentence.

absolute zero	convection	insulator	specific heat
bimetallic strip	freezing point	internal energy	temperature
boiling point	heat conductor	Kelvin scale	thermal expansion
calorie	heat of fusion	kinetic energy	thermometer
calorimeter	heat of vaporization	melting point	thermostat
Celsius		phase change	
conduction	heat transfer	radiation	

CONTENT REVIEW: MULTIPLE CHOICE

On a separate sheet of paper, write the letter of the answer that best completes each statement.

1. Before the experiments of Rumford and Joule, scientists believed heat was
   a. an invisible fluid.   b. a form of energy.
   c. produced by work.   d. a solid substance.
2. Materials through which heat can flow easily are called
   a. insulators.   b. radiators.   c. transformers.   d. conductors.
3. A temperature of 13°C is equal to
   a. −260°K.   b. 286°K.   c. 276°K.   d. 273°K.
4. If a piece of copper (specific heat = 0.09) gains 450 calories of heat when the temperature is raised 20°C, what is the mass of the copper?
   a. 25 g   b. 250 g   c. 100,000 g   d. 900 g
5. A calorimeter is effective because
   a. in a closed system, heat lost equals heat gained.
   b. the inner container is insulated from the outer container.
   c. heat escapes easily from a calorimeter.
   d. the surrounding water reduces the heat of reaction.
6. Heat is measured in
   a. kelvins.   b. degrees Celsius.   c. specific heat units.   d. calories.
7. The amount of heat required to change a solid to a liquid is called
   a. heat of liquefication.   b. heat of vaporization.
   c. heat of fusion.   d. specific heat.
8. Substances expand when heated because the molecules
   a. stay in fixed positions.   b. move more slowly and farther apart.
   c. become larger.   d. move faster and farther apart.
9. The switch in a thermostat is a (an)
   a. calorimeter.   b. bimetallic strip.   c. joule.   d. insulator.
10. When a substance has work done on it, its internal energy
    a. increases.   b. decreases.   c. remains the same.   d. doubles.

CONTENT REVIEW: COMPLETION

On a separate sheet of paper, write the word or words that best complete each statement.

1. Heat transfer by currents of molecules is called _____.
2. _____ do not conduct heat easily.
3. Energy of motion is _____.
4. To convert degrees Celsius to kelvins, add _____ to the given Celsius temperature.
5. The temperature at which all molecular motion stops is called _____.
6. The amount of heat needed to raise the temperature of one gram of a substance one Celsius degree is called the _____ of the substance.
7. The amount of heat needed to change 40 grams of water at 100°C to steam at 100°C is _____ calories.
8. The effect of heat on the volume of a substance is called _____.
9. A (An) _____ helps control temperature in an indoor area or in an appliance.
10. Energy contained in a substance is called _____

Determine whether each statement is true or false. Then on a separate sheet of paper, write "true" if it is true. If it is false, change the underlined word or words to make the statement true.

1. When an ice cube melts, <u>coldness</u> is being transferred.
2. Heat energy from the sun reaches the earth as invisible light called <u>infrared</u>.
3. Temperature is a measure of the average <u>heat energy</u> of molecules.
4. The higher the temperature, the <u>faster</u> the molecules in a substance are moving.
5. Heat can be measured <u>directly</u>.
6. The heat needed to change 1 gram of ice to 1 gram of water is called the <u>heat of fusion</u>.
7. The amount of heat needed to change one gram of water to steam is <u>540 cal/g</u>.
8. If water cools from 3°C to 1°C, its volume <u>decreases</u>.
9. Ice is <u>less</u> dense than liquid water.
10. When an object does work, it <u>loses</u> some of its internal energy.

CONCEPT REVIEW: SKILL BUILDING

Use the skills you have developed in the chapter to complete each activity.

1. **Interpreting diagrams** Use the heating curve in Figure 17–15 to help you describe what would happen to a 10-gram ice cube at 0°C if it were to gain 5000 calories of heat.
2. **Analyzing data** A chemical reaction takes place in a calorimeter. The following data are obtained:

   mass of water   300 g
   initial temperature of water   25°C
   final temperature of water   40°C

   What is the heat in kilocalories released by the reaction? A kilocalorie is 1000 calories.
3. **Making comparisons** Compare the three methods of heat transfer in terms of how heat moves and in what kinds of substances the transfer takes place.
4. **Applying concepts** Explain why the air pressure in car tires is different after the car has been driven awhile?

5. **Interpreting diagrams**

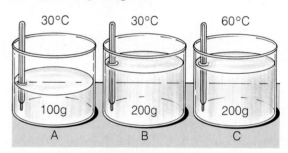

a. Which container(s) has(have) the greatest heat content?
b. In which containers is the motion of molecules the same?
c. Compare the molecular motion in containers A and C.
d. Compare the kinetic energy of containers A and B.
e. Which container needs the greatest number of calories to change the temperature by one Celsius degree?

CONCEPT REVIEW: ESSAY

Discuss each of the following in a brief paragraph.

1. Explain how Count Rumford's experiment disputed the caloric theory.
2. Explain how a thermometer makes use of the property of thermal expansion.
3. Why is there no temperature change during a phase change?
4. How are work, heat, and energy related?
5. Compare temperature and heat.

DEGREES KELVIN

243   253   263   273   283   293   303   313

Uses of Heat 18

CHAPTER SECTIONS

18–1 Heating Systems
18–2 Insulation
18–3 Cooling Systems
18–4 Heat Engines
18–5 Thermal Pollution

CHAPTER OBJECTIVES

After completing this chapter, you will be able to

18–1 Distinguish among various types of central heating systems.

18–2 Explain how insulation prevents heat loss.

18–3 Describe the operation of a cooling system.

18–4 Explain how heat engines convert heat energy into mechanical energy.

18–5 Define thermal pollution and discuss its effects on the environment.

The year is 2064. Across the Midwest, an area once called the "Breadbasket of the Nation" is covered with desert sand. In Arizona, broad-leafed evergreen trees form a continuous canopy over a region that receives an average rainfall of 260 centimeters per year.

The eastern half of New York is under water. Evening weather reports include a "glacier watch," warning citizens of northeastern seaport towns to beware of rising tides due to the melting of polar icecaps.

This scene may sound unbelievable, but it is within the realm of possibility. Scientists report that the temperature of the earth is gradually rising due to the "greenhouse effect." The greenhouse effect occurs when ultraviolet rays from the sun are absorbed by the earth, and in turn the earth radiates infrared rays back into the atmosphere. A cloud of carbon dioxide and other gases in the atmosphere absorbs the infrared rays. The infrared rays are trapped in the atmosphere. The result is a kind of "thermal blanket" wrapped around the earth.

Perhaps you are aware that heat may affect your life dramatically in the future. But did you know that heat also plays an important role in your daily life right now? In this chapter you will learn how heat is obtained, used, and controlled. As to whether predictions based on the greenhouse effect will come true, you'll just have to stick around until 2064 to find out!

This satellite map, taken by the Seasat satellite, shows average sea and land surface temperature all over the world. If the temperature of the earth continues to rise, a future map will have a decidedly different appearance.

18–1 Heating Systems

If you have ever been in a building that is too hot or too cold, you know the importance of a good heating system. Most buildings and residences in the United States have **central heating systems** that provide comfortable environments for daily activities. **A central heating system generates heat for an entire building or group of buildings from one central location.** Then the heat is delivered where it is needed.

Based on the way that heat is delivered, central heating systems are divided into two main groups: direct systems and indirect systems. A direct system circulates warm air throughout the area being heated. An indirect system circulates hot water or steam through pipes that lead to convectors or radiators. The convectors or radiators give off the heat.

Although there are different types of central heating systems, all require a source of heat, such as electricity or the burning of a fuel. All central heating systems also have automatic controls. These controls regulate the temperature of the area to be heated, turn off the system if any part of it becomes dangerously overheated, and prevent the system from starting if conditions are unsafe.

Hot Water Heating

A **hot water system** consists of a network of pipes and convectors connected to a hot water heater. Fuel burned in the hot water heater raises

Figure 18–1 *For cave dwellers, a fire represented a central heating system (right). Modern central heating systems are considerably more complex. A technician in this steam boiler control room coordinates the delivery of heat to an entire building (left). Would this central heating system be a direct or indirect system?*

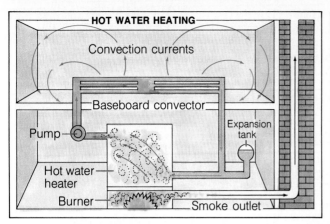

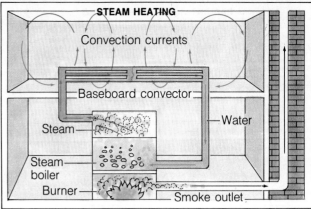

Figure 18–2 *A hot water heating system (left) and a steam heating system (right) are two common central heating systems that are quite similar. What is the major difference between the two systems?*

the temperature of the water to about 82°C. Then the water is pumped through pipes to a convector in each room. The water heats the convector. The heat given off by the convector is circulated throughout the room by convection currents. Once the water has lost its heat, it returns to the hot water heater by another pipe.

Steam Heating

A **steam heating system** is similar to a hot water system except that the water is changed to steam in a boiler. The steam is then forced through pipes to the convectors, where it gives off heat to the room. In giving off heat, the steam condenses, or changes from the gas phase to the liquid phase. The condensed steam, or water, flows back to the boiler.

Radiant Hot Water Heating

In a **radiant hot water system,** water is heated in a hot water heater and then transferred to a continuous coil of pipe in the floor of each room. As heat radiates from the pipe, a nearly uniform temperature is maintained from floor to ceiling. This means that the temperature difference between the floor and the ceiling is limited to only a few degrees. Can you think of a reason why radiant hot water heating provides a more even temperature than steam heating or hot water heating?

Radiant Electric Heating

The source of heat for a **radiant electric system** is electricity. As electricity passes through wires or cables that resist the current, heat is produced.

Sharpen Your Skills

History of Heating Systems

Listed below are several steps in the history of heating systems. Place the steps in the order that you think best illustrates the development of heating systems.

fires in crude caves
brick and tile stoves
holes in top or sides of caves to let out smoke
fireplaces
fireplace chimneys
cast iron stoves
burning of fossil fuels
electricity producing heat

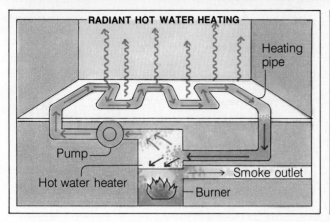

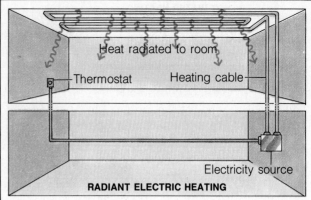

Figure 18–3 *In these central systems, heat is transferred by radiation. The source of heat in a radiant hot water system (left) is hot water. In a radiant electric system (right), the source of heat is electricity. What is radiation?*

These wires or cables can be installed in the ceiling, floor, baseboards, or walls of a room. The heat produced is radiated to all parts of the room. A thermostat, often installed in each room or local area, controls the amount of heat produced by the wires or cables.

Warm Air Heating

A **warm air system** consists of a furnace, a blower, pipelike connections called ducts, and vents that open into each room being heated. The furnace heats the air, which is then forced by the blower through the ducts to the vents. Convection currents keep the warm air moving as it transfers its heat to the surrounding air. Cool air returns to the furnace by another duct. As the air circulates, filters remove dust particles.

Heat Pump

A **heat pump system** is based on the principle that the earth or outside air contains heat that can be used to heat an area—even in cold weather! What a heat pump actually does is take heat from the outside air and bring it inside.

Figure 18–4 *In a warm air system (left), hot air from a furnace is forced through pipelike connections called ducts to vents. How is heat transferred in this system? A heat pump system (right) takes heat from the outside and brings it inside—even in cold weather! What two phase changes are involved in this heating system?*

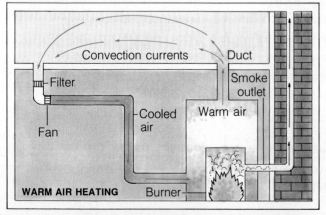

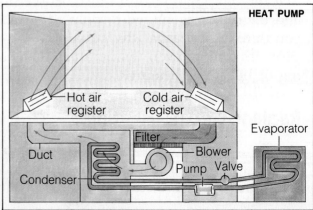

A heat pump circulates a liquid that evaporates at a low temperature through a coil *outside* the building. As the liquid passes through the coil, it picks up heat from the air or the ground. When the liquid gains enough heat, it becomes a vapor. The vapor travels into a compressor, where an increase in pressure raises its temperature. The hot vapor then passes to a coil *inside* the building where it heats the air. The warm air is forced through ducts and circulated through each room just as in a warm air system.

Once the hot vapor has given off its heat, it condenses into a hot liquid. The hot liquid is then cooled as it passes through a pressure-reducing valve. Finally, the cooled liquid is pumped into the outdoor coil to begin the process all over again. Can you see some disadvantages in this type of heating system?

Solar Heating

A **solar heating system** uses the energy of the sun to produce heat. There are two basic types of solar heating systems: **active solar heating** and **passive solar heating.**

An active solar system includes a device for collecting solar energy—called a solar collector—a place to store the heat, and a means for circulating the heat throughout the building.

Figure 18–5 shows a typical active solar heating system. The solar collector consists of a metal plate painted black on the side that faces the sun. Black absorbs sunlight better than any other color. The sunlight that is absorbed by the plate heats it. On the back of the plate is a series of metal tubing. Water, or some other liquid, circulates through the tubing. The tubing is covered by glass or clear plastic to keep it from losing heat.

As sunlight strikes the collector, it is absorbed. The heat absorbed by the collector is transferred to the water. The heated water flows through a tube to a storage tank. Here the heat from the water in the tube is transferred to the water in the tank by a heat exchanger in the tank. The hot water circulates through pipes to heat the house or to heat air blown into the house. In the meantime, a pump

Figure 18–5 *Water in the solar panel of this active solar system (top) is heated by the sun and piped to a storage tank. Here it heats water in the water tank. This heated water then circulates through pipes to heat the house (bottom). Why is the metal plate in the solar panel painted black?*

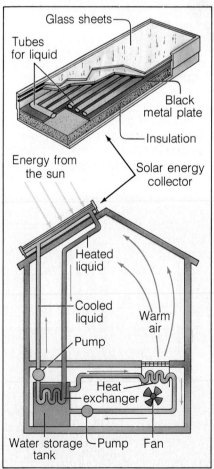

Figure 18–6 *The solar furnace at Odeille, France (left), uses hundreds of movable mirrors to focus the direct rays of the sun onto an enormous mirror. The curved mirror reflects the rays onto a single point, producing temperatures of more than 3800°C. The front side of this solar house is all windows so that the greatest amount of sunlight can be collected (right).*

Figure 18–7 *This building uses a unique central heating system. Water used to cool the computers is circulated throughout the building. Because the water has absorbed heat from the computers, it can be used to heat the building's interior.*

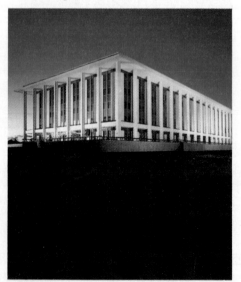

returns the cool water to the collector to be reheated by the sun. On cloudy days, when the solar collector cannot absorb enough solar energy to produce hot water and the storage system has cooled, a backup heating system is used.

In a passive solar system, a building is heated directly by the rays of the sun. To get the most heat from a passive solar system, the building must be designed with the placement, size, and orientation of windows in mind. Figure 18–6 shows a building designed for passive solar heating.

Because of the variations in the amount of solar energy received at a particular location, passive solar systems are usually not the only source of heat for a building. A backup heating system usually must be used with a passive solar system. A backup system provides heat when sunlight is not available or when the heat collected during the day is not enough for a cold night. What conditions do you think affect the amount of solar energy a location receives?

SECTION REVIEW

1. What is a central heating system?
2. How does a steam heating system differ from a hot water system?
3. Describe how a radiant electric system produces heat. Why is it different from other central heating systems?
4. What is the basic difference between an active solar system and a passive solar system?
5. Describe the heat transfers involved in a heat pump system.

18-2 Insulation

Once heat is brought into a room or building, it will quickly begin to escape if the area lacks proper **insulation.** Insulation materials reduce heat transfer because they are poor conductors of heat. **Insulation prevents heat loss by reducing the transfer of heat that occurs by conduction and convection.**

A common insulating material is **fiberglass.** Fiberglass consists of long, thin strands of glass packed together. In between the strands are air spaces. Glass is a poor conductor of heat. So is the air that is trapped between the fibers.

Insulating materials are packed beneath roofs and in the outside walls of buildings. Insulation can also be used around doors and windows. This type of insulation is called weather stripping. Weather stripping prevents heat loss by closing up spaces through which heat is transferred by convection. Double-pane window glass is another effective insulator. The air trapped between the panes of glass does not conduct heat well. And the air space is so small that convection cannot take place either.

Figure 18-8 *The long, shaggy hair of a musk ox provides insulation from the cold Arctic winter. During the fall, the ox grows an inner matting of hair, which combined with the outer coat gives a double blanket of protection.*

Figure 18-9 *Invisible heat energy, or infrared energy, can be "seen" by using a device called a thermograph. This thermogram, or heat picture, reveals heat loss from a house. Generally, the lighter and brighter the color, the greater the heat loss. How can a thermogram be useful to homeowners?*

423

Figure 18–10 *Believe it or not, blocks of ice can be used to insulate a home, as this Eskimo of the Arctic Circle well knows. How is an igloo insulated?*

A well-insulated building works as well in hot weather as it does in cold weather. In hot weather, the insulation keeps heat out. The building is kept relatively cool as heat from the outside air is prevented from entering by either conduction or convection.

SECTION REVIEW

1. What is insulation? What is its purpose?
2. How does fiberglass prevent heat loss?
3. Why is good insulation important in both hot and cold weather?
4. Explain why insulation prevents heat transfer by both conduction and convection.
5. The cardboard used for a pizza box is naturally brown in color. Explain why companies spend extra money to dye these boxes white. What else might be done to the boxes to make them more effective insulators?

To describe the operation of a cooling system

Evaporation and Cooling

1. Place a drop of water on the back of your hand. Observe how your hand feels as the drop of water evaporates.
2. Repeat step 1 but this time use a drop of rubbing alcohol. Is there any difference in the rate of evaporation?
3. Fasten a small piece of wet cotton around the bulb of a thermometer. Fan it with a sheet of cardboard. What happens to the level of mercury in the thermometer?

18–3 Cooling Systems

Have you ever stepped out of a swimming pool and felt a chill—even though you were warm before you got wet? This cooling effect is due to evaporation. As the water molecules on your skin absorb heat from your body, they change from the liquid phase to the gas phase. This absorption of heat leaves your body temperature lower than before. Evaporation is a cooling process.

The process of evaporation is used by cooling systems to remove heat energy from a room, building, or other space. Refrigerators, air conditioners, and dehumidifiers all contain **cooling systems.**

A cooling system consists of four basic parts: a **storage tank, freezer unit, compressor,** and **condenser coils.** A cooling system also includes a **refrigerant.** A refrigerant is the liquid that is to be evaporated. A refrigerant evaporates at a low temperature. Many cooling systems use **Freon** (FREE-ahn) as the refrigerant. Another common refrigerant is ammonia.

Figure 18–11 shows a typical refrigerator system. Liquid Freon in the storage tank is pumped to the freezer unit. As the liquid refrigerant evaporates here, it absorbs heat from the freezer compartment. So the inside of the refrigerator becomes cool. The Freon vapor then flows to a compressor, where the pressure of the gas is increased. The hot gaseous Freon next passes through the condenser coils, where it loses its heat and changes back into a liquid. The liquid Freon then returns to the storage tank and the process begins again.

The heat removed from the freezer compartment of a refrigerator is radiated from the condenser coils to the outside air. The condenser coils are often found on the back surface of a refrigerator. Fans are sometimes used to help blow away the air that is heated by the coils, which can become quite warm. So you must be careful not to touch these coils. Although it might sound strange, you could burn yourself on the refrigerator!

SECTION REVIEW

1. How does a cooling system use evaporation?
2. What are the basic parts of a cooling system?
3. What is a refrigerant?
4. Why is it unwise to try to cool a room by opening the door of the refrigerator?

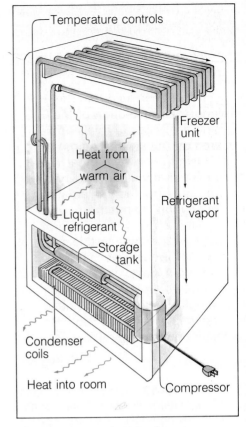

Figure 18–11 *In this diagram, you can see how the basic parts of a refrigerator work as a cooling system. What phase change takes place in the freezer unit? In the condenser coils?*

18–4 Heat Engines

Section Objective

To explain how heat engines use heat energy to do work

In Chapter 17, you learned that the experiments of Rumford and Joule showed that work produces heat. **Heat engines** make use of the reverse process. **Heat engines are machines that convert heat energy into mechanical energy in order to do work.**

All heat engines involve **combustion.** Combustion is the burning of a fuel. During combustion, a fuel is heated to a temperature at which it combines with oxygen in the air and gives off heat. Heat engines are classified into two main types according to where combustion takes place.

425

It has been said that the Industrial Revolution of the nineteenth century was powered by the steam engine.

Using books and other reference materials in the library, find out how the Industrial Revolution changed American society. What was the role of the steam engine in this revolution? Discuss your findings with your class.

Can you name some technological advances that have changed modern society? How have they changed it?

Figure 18–12 *The paddle wheels of this steamship are driven by an external-combustion engine (top). The operation of an external-combustion engine converts heat energy into mechanical energy (bottom).*

External-Combustion Engine

In an **external-combustion engine,** fuel is burned outside the engine. The steam engine is an external-combustion engine. Steam is heated in a boiler outside the engine and then passed through a valve into the engine. In early steam engines, the steam pushed against a metal plate called a **piston,** which moved back and forth in a tube called a **cylinder.** The movement of the piston passed mechanical energy to a connecting rod, which then did some kind of work, such as turning the wheels of a train or the propellers of a steamship.

Modern steam engines usually do not use a piston and cylinder. Instead, steam under great pressure is passed through holes onto paddle wheels called **turbines.** The turbines, rotating like high-speed windmills, produce mechanical energy. A steam turbine is more efficient than a piston and cylinder because it wastes less energy.

Internal-Combustion Engine

When the burning of fuel takes place inside an engine, the engine is called an **internal-combustion engine.** A familiar type of internal-combustion engine is the gasoline engine, which powers most cars.

A gasoline engine is a four-stroke engine. In the first stroke, gasoline is turned into a vapor and mixed with air in the **carburetor** (KAHR-ber-ay-ter). The mixture is then transferred through the **intake valve** to a cylinder. This process is the **intake stroke.**

Inside the cylinder is a piston. As the piston moves to the top of the cylinder, the gaseous mixture is compressed, or pushed together. The mixture

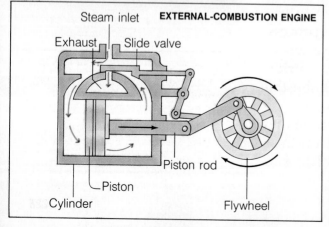

EXTERNAL-COMBUSTION ENGINE

Steam inlet
Exhaust · Slide valve
Piston rod
Piston
Cylinder
Flywheel

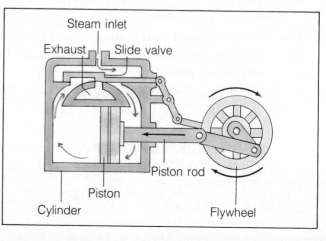

Steam inlet
Exhaust · Slide valve
Piston rod
Piston
Cylinder
Flywheel

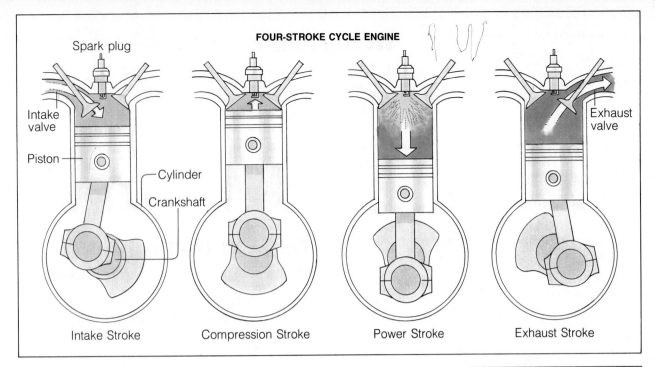

FOUR-STROKE CYCLE ENGINE

Spark plug

Intake valve

Piston

Cylinder

Crankshaft

Exhaust valve

Intake Stroke   Compression Stroke   Power Stroke   Exhaust Stroke

is reduced to one-seventh of its original volume. A **spark plug** produces an electric spark that ignites the fuel at just the right moment in the four-stroke cycle. This process is the **compression stroke.**

The explosion of hot gases increases the volume of the mixture and forces the piston back down in what is called the **power stroke.** At this point, energy is transferred from the piston to the wheels of the car by a series of shafts and gears.

Finally, the piston moves to the top of the cylinder to expel gases through the **exhaust valve.** This process is called the **exhaust stroke.** As the piston falls back down, more gas and air from the carburetor enter the cylinder to begin the four-stroke cycle again. A fixed amount of gasoline is used up in each cycle, and waste products are given off as exhaust at the end of each cycle. Figure 18–13 shows the four strokes that make up each cycle.

A **diesel engine,** like a gasoline engine, is an internal-combustion engine. But in a diesel engine, only air is taken in during the intake stroke. At the end of the compression stroke, a measured amount of fuel is injected into the compressed air in the cylinder. The compression of the gas raises its temperature high enough so that the fuel ignites spontaneously. For this reason, a diesel engine does not have spark plugs. Can you explain why a diesel engine might more correctly be called a compression–ignition engine?

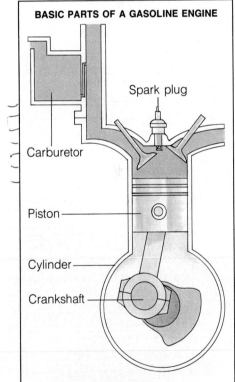

BASIC PARTS OF A GASOLINE ENGINE

Spark plug

Carburetor

Piston

Cylinder

Crankshaft

Figure 18–13 *A gasoline engine is a four-stroke internal-combustion engine. Here you see the processes involved in each stroke. During which stroke is energy transferred from the piston to the wheels of the car?*

427

SECTION REVIEW

1. How does a heat engine do work?
2. What are the two main types of heat engines? How do they differ?
3. What are the four steps in the combustion process of a gasoline engine?
4. Explain why a typical car engine is only about 30 percent efficient.

18–5 Thermal Pollution

Modern technology could not exist without the use of heat energy. Yet like many aspects of technology, the use of heat energy can be harmful to the environment.

CAREER

Ceramic Engineer

HELP WANTED: CERAMIC ENGINEER to develop laboratory equipment and pollution control devices. Applicant must have a college degree in ceramic engineering.

Perhaps the word *ceramics* brings to mind pottery and dishes. But to a **ceramic engineer,** the word means much more. For the world of ceramics goes far beyond the kitchen. A ceramic engineer develops products that are made of clay, sand, glass, and other materials that do not contain metal or plastic. These materials are all processed at high temperatures—650°C to 1650°C—in ovens called kilns.

A ceramic engineer may work in many fields, including energy development, art, pollution control, housewares manufacturing, and aerospace. A ceramic engineer may develop new types of dishes, construction materials, electric insulation, laboratory equipment, medical products, computer chips, and machine parts.

Ceramics are versatile because they are not good conductors of heat or electricity. Using ceramics, people are able to safely handle such extremely hot materials as molten metals or

high-voltage electric equipment. Also, ceramics can be made porous, waterproof, or airtight. Another advantage of ceramics is that they can be made into many different shapes—from hair-thin glass fibers for transmitting electronic messages to beautiful sculptures.

For information about a career as a ceramic engineer, contact the National Institute of Ceramic Engineers, 65 Ceramic Drive, Columbus, OH 43214.

Figure 18–14 *These cooling towers at the Three Mile Island Nuclear Power Plant in Pennsylvania are used to reduce thermal pollution of the air and water (left). Hot water from the power plant is cooled as it flows through pipes suspended in the tower (right).*

Much of the heat generated by industrial processes cannot be used. It is waste heat. This waste heat is often released directly into the atmosphere or released as hot water that gets dumped into nearby rivers and lakes. **Thermal pollution** results. **Thermal pollution occurs when waste heat damages the environment by causing an unnatural rise in temperature.**

Thermal pollution endangers the survival of fish, plants, and animals. Fish are especially vulnerable to increases in water temperature. Some species will survive only a few hours at temperatures above 25°C.

What can be done to reduce thermal pollution? One solution is the use of a **cooling tower.** In a cooling tower, hot water from a factory or power plant is cooled as it flows through pipes. By the time the water is released into a nearby river or lake, it has cooled enough so that it poses no threat to the wildlife of the area.

Figure 18–15 *The cooling system of a skating rink freezes the water to provide a smooth, hard surface for Olympic skater Jill Trenary.*

SECTION REVIEW

1. What is thermal pollution?
2. What types of wildlife are threatened by thermal pollution?
3. What is the source of the heat that causes thermal pollution?
4. According to Figure 18–14, where does the excess heat go after the water is cooled in the cooling tower?

Constructing a Solar Collector

Problem

How can solar energy be collected?

Materials *(per group)*

shoe box painted black on the inside and filled with newspaper painted black

rubber or plastic tubing, 1-mm diameter and about 1 m in length

funnel

ring stand and ring   graduated cylinder

thermometer   plastic wrap

2 250-mL beakers   pencil

container large   water
  enough to hold
  1 L of water

Procedure

1. Fill the inside of the shoe box with the crumpled newspaper. Use a pencil to punch a hole in each end of the box. See the accompanying diagram.
2. Insert the rubber or plastic tubing through the holes and position it inside the box as shown. Be sure that at least 10 cm of tubing is left sticking out of each end of the box.
3. Wrap the box tightly with plastic wrap.
4. Place the box in direct sunlight, tilting one end so that it is about 5 cm higher than the other end.
5. Attach the funnel to the tubing at the higher end of the box, using the ring stand and ring to hold the funnel in place.
6. Position one beaker at the other end of the tubing. This is the collecting beaker.
7. Fill the container with 1 L of water at room temperature. Measure and record the temperature of the water.
8. Using the graduated cylinder, pour 200 mL of water from the container to the other beaker.
9. Now pour 100 mL of water from the beaker into the funnel.

10. Repeat steps 8 and 9 so that you perform ten trials. *After every second trial, record the trial number and the temperature of the water in the collecting beaker. Remember to empty the water in the collecting beaker at the end of every second trial.*
11. Make a graph of your data. Plot the trial number along the X axis and the temperature along the Y axis.

Observations

1. How did the final water temperature compare with the initial temperature?
2. What happened to the water temperature as the number of trials increased? Does your graph support this observation?

Conclusions

1. What evidence do you have that solar energy is being collected?
2. How do you account for the different temperatures that you recorded?
3. What would happen if you placed the solar collector in direct sunlight for an hour before beginning the experiment?
4. Can you think of ways in which your solar collector might be made more effective?

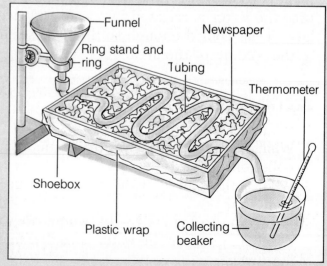

CHAPTER REVIEW

SUMMARY

18–1 Heating Systems

❏ A central heating system generates heat for a building or group of buildings from one central location.

❏ Based on the way that heat is delivered, central heating systems are classified as direct or indirect systems.

❏ Major types of central heating systems include hot water, steam, radiant hot water, radiant electric, warm air, heat pump, and solar.

18–2 Insulation

❏ Insulation prevents heat loss by reducing the transfer of heat from a building by conduction and convection.

❏ Materials that provide good insulation are poor conductors of heat.

❏ A well-insulated building works as well in hot weather as it does in cold weather.

18–3 Cooling Systems

❏ Cooling systems use the process of evaporation to remove heat from the surroundings.

❏ A cooling system consists of a storage tank, freezer unit, compressor, condenser coils, and refrigerant.

❏ A refrigerant is a liquid that evaporates at a low temperature.

❏ Two common refrigerants are Freon and ammonia.

18–4 Heat Engines

❏ Heat engines convert heat energy into mechanical energy to do work.

❏ All heat engines involve the process of combustion, or the burning of a fuel.

❏ In an external-combustion engine, fuel is burned outside the engine. The steam engine is an external-combustion engine.

❏ In an internal-combustion engine, fuel is burned inside the engine. The gasoline engine is an internal-combustion engine.

❏ The four strokes in a gasoline engine are the intake stroke, compression stroke, power stroke, and exhaust stroke.

18–5 Thermal Pollution

❏ Thermal pollution occurs when waste heat damages the environment by causing an unnatural rise in temperature.

❏ One solution to thermal pollution is the use of a cooling tower.

VOCABULARY

Define each term in a complete sentence.

active solar heating	cooling tower	Freon	passive solar heating	spark plug
carburetor	cylinder	heat engine	piston	steam heating system
central heating system	diesel engine	heat pump system	power stroke	storage tank
combustion	exhaust stroke	hot water system	radiant electric system	thermal pollution
compression stroke	exhaust valve	insulation	radiant hot water system	turbine
compressor	external-combustion engine	intake stroke	refrigerant	warm air system
condenser coil	fiberglass	intake valve	solar heating system	
cooling system	freezer unit	internal-combustion engine		

CONTENT REVIEW: MULTIPLE CHOICE

On a separate sheet of paper, write the letter of the answer that best completes each statement.

1. Which heating system involves a furnace and a blower?
a. warm air b. radiant electric c. steam d. hot water

2. Which of the following would *not* be part of an active solar heating system?
a. water storage tank b. solar collector c. fuel tank d. pipes

3. Which of the following is an insulating material?
a. Freon b. fiberglass c. copper wire d. ammonia

4. A cooling system removes heat from the surroundings through the process of
a. condensation. b. sublimation. c. insulation. d. evaporation.

5. In a cooling system, the compressor is used to
a. transfer the refrigerant to the freezer unit.
b. increase the pressure of the vaporized refrigerant.
c. remove heat from the refrigerant.
d. none of the above.

6. In a steam engine,
a. fuel is burned outside the engine. b. steam pushes against a piston or turbine.
c. steam is heated in a boiler. d. all of the above.

7. The correct order for the combustion process in a gasoline engine is
a. intake stroke, exhaust stroke, compression stroke, power stroke.
b. power stroke, intake stroke, compression stroke, exhaust stroke.
c. intake stroke, compression stroke, power stroke, exhaust stroke.
d. compression stroke, power stroke, intake stroke, exhaust stroke.

8. A diesel engine differs from a gasoline engine in that it
a. takes in only air on the intake stroke. b. has no cylinder.
c. uses no compression stroke. d. releases only air on the exhaust stroke.

9. A cooling tower reduces thermal pollution by
a. enabling factories to waste less heat.
b. cooling heated water before it is dumped into the environment.
c. cooling the air around a factory or power plant.
d. cooling bodies of water that have been damaged by waste heat.

10. Thermal pollution probably would not be a problem for
a. fish living in the ocean near a busy industrial seaport.
b. fish living in a mountain stream.
c. fish living in a lake near a power plant.
d. plant life on the bank of a river that flows past a large chemical factory.

CONTENT REVIEW: COMPLETION

On a separate sheet of paper, write the word or words that best complete each statement.

1. Hot water pumped through pipes is the basis of a _____ heating system.

2. Heat is taken from the outside air or ground in a _____ heating system.

3. Energy from sunlight is used by a _____ heating system.

4. A device for collecting solar energy is called a (an) _____.

5. Double-pane windows and weather stripping are examples of _____.
6. In a cooling system, the liquid to be evaporated is called the _____.
7. The burning of a fuel in an engine is called _____.
8. Fuel is burned outside the engine in a (an) _____ engine.
9. In a gasoline engine, gasoline is mixed with air in the _____.
10. The disposal of waste heat into the environment is called _____.

CONTENT REVIEW: TRUE OR FALSE

Determine whether each statement is true or false. Then on a separate sheet of paper, write "true" if it is true. If it is false, change the underlined word or words to make the statement true.

1. Steam gives off heat by <u>evaporating</u>.
2. In a <u>radiant hot water system</u>, hot water flows through a continuous coil of pipe in the floor of each room.
3. A building is heated naturally according to the placement of windows in an <u>active</u> solar heating system.
4. A material that helps to prevent the loss of heat from a building is called <u>insulation</u>.
5. A common refrigerant is <u>Freon</u>.
6. In a cooling system, a refrigerant loses its heat in the <u>condenser coils</u>.
7. In modern steam engines, steam pushes against a <u>piston</u>.
8. A diesel engine is an example of an <u>external-combustion</u> engine.
9. Thermal pollution is caused primarily by the disposal of <u>heated water</u>.
10. Thermal pollution can be reduced by the use of <u>insulating towers</u>.

CONCEPT REVIEW: SKILL BUILDING

Use the skills you have developed in the chapter to complete each activity.

1. **Making diagrams** Make a diagram that shows how a heat pump system gathers heat from the outside air and then uses this heat to warm the air inside a building.
2. **Applying concepts** Figure 17–6 on page 399 shows a diagram of a thermos bottle. In terms of insulation, explain the importance of the vacuum, double-walled glass bottle, air space, and cap.
3. **Classifying systems** Classify each of the following heating systems as direct or indirect: warm air, hot water, steam, heat pump, radiant hot water, solar.
4. **Applying concepts** Explain how each insulation material works: a. plastic foam used in a picnic cooler; b. aluminum foil covering a south-facing window in summer; c. goose down used in a ski jacket.

CONCEPT REVIEW: ESSAY

Discuss each of the following in a brief paragraph.

1. Choose one type of central heating system and describe how it works.
2. Explain how a cooling system operates.
3. Explain how a solar collector works.
4. Choose one type of heat engine and explain how it converts heat into mechanical energy to do work.
5. Which do you think would be *most* affected by thermal pollution: an ocean, a river, or a lake? Assume that each body of water is located near an industrial area. Explain your answer.
6. Explain why fiberglass is a good insulating material.

Adventures in Science

JENEFIR ISBISTER: *She Does*

Jenefir Isbister knelt in the blackened soil outside a Pennsylvania coal mine. With a garden trowel, she scooped some dry black soil into a plastic box. The next day, she dug up some soil from outside a coal-processing plant near the laboratory in which she works. She even scooped up a little mud from the bank of a creek in her own backyard.

Why was Dr. Isbister collecting all this soil? "My boss asked me to find a microorganism to remove sulfur from coal," she explains. And such a microorganism might make its home in coal-rich soil. Dr. Isbister is an expert on microorganisms, or living things that are too small to be seen without special equipment. Microorganisms include a variety of bacteria.

Many microorganisms—often called microbes—feed upon nature's garbage, such as fallen leaves and the remains of dead animals and plants. The microbe that Dr. Isbister was searching for was one that eats the sulfur in coal—a sulfur-eating coal bug.

But why would Isbister be looking for such a thing? As she puts it, "A coal bug could help solve the problem of acid rain." In many parts of the world, acid rain is a serious problem whose effects include the death of trees, fish, and other living things.

Acid rain often is caused by burning coal that contains high levels of sulfur. The coal smoke produced contains sulfur dioxide. Sulfur dioxide chemically combines with water in the air to form sulfuric acid, a very strong acid. The acid falls to the earth as acid rain, acid snow, and even acid fog.

One way to reduce acid rain, then, is to remove as much sulfur as possible from the coal. Washing the coal before burning is the simplest method of scrubbing out the sulfur. But coal washing is expensive and removes only some of the sulfur. Prying more sulfur out of coal requires a chemical reaction—the kind of chemical reaction microbes produce when they dine.

"A sulfur-eating microbe would let us use high-sulfur coal," Dr. Isbister explains. And high-sulfur coal is inexpensive and plentiful.

So Dr. Isbister began collecting soil in the hope of finding a microbe that eats sulfur. "Soil is the best place to look for microorganisms that will grow under many conditions," she explains. "We didn't want bugs we had to baby!"

In the first step of experimentation, Dr. Isbister and Dr. Richard Doyle, a coworker at the Atlantic Research Corporation in Alexandria, Virginia, crushed each soil sample and placed a small amount of each in separate flasks of salt solution. "The solution keeps the microbes alive while we separate them from the soil," Isbister explains.

bination that caused the microbes to eat 80 percent of the sulfur in just 18 hours. "Then we really celebrated, and Dr. Doyle and I applied for a patent on Coal Bug One." Coal Bug One is the nickname the researchers have

Dirty Work for *Cleaner* Coal

A special machine was then used to wash the bugs out of the soil in each flask. Liquid from the top of each flask was then added to another flask filled with nutrient broth. "It's a kind of soup that feeds the microorganisms," explains Isbister.

Next, the researchers added sulfur to each microbe broth. "We did lots of tests. After a long time, we found one solution that contained less sulfur than we had put in," says Isbister. The microbes in this broth had done the best job of eating sulfur. Surprisingly, the sulfur-eating microbes were the ones from her own backyard! Unfortunately, it had taken the microbes seven days to lower the sulfur level by only seven percent. "Seven percent is very little; seven days is horrible," says Isbister. "But it was a start. We had a little celebration."

Now the team added powerful chemicals to the broth, hoping to change the microbes' basic cell structure. The goal was to make the microbes hungrier for sulfur.

"I tested 250 chemical combinations," Isbister recalls. Finally, she found one com-

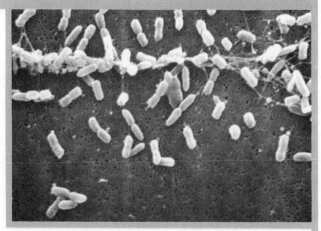

Coal Bug One, shown here in an electromicrograph (bottom), may solve the problem of burning high-sulfur coal (top).

given their sulfur-eating microbe. Two and one-half years of research had finally resulted in success.

Will Coal Bug One solve the problem of high-sulfur coal? "Coal Bug One eats just one of the many kinds of sulfur found in coal," Isbister replies. "So we'll need to find more bugs. But Coal Bug One is the first step."

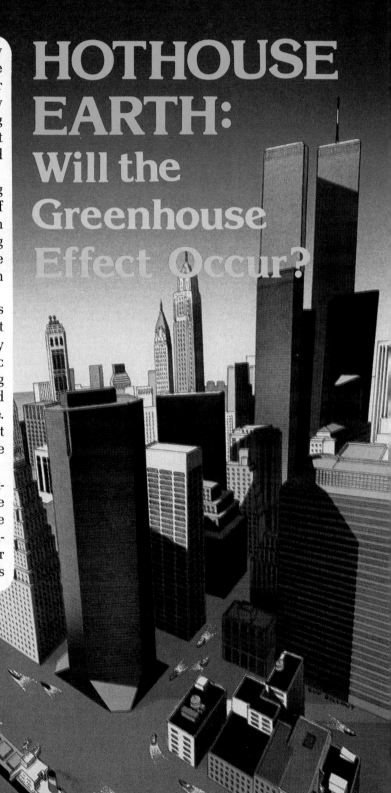

HOTHOUSE EARTH:
Will the Greenhouse Effect Occur?

The temperature has been dropping steadily all evening. So it's no surprise that you are looking forward to nestling under your blanket, where within minutes you are toasty warm. Your goose down comforter is serving its purpose. The cover traps your body heat and prevents the air that you have warmed from escaping.

Planet Earth has its own type of warming blanket. Though, of course, it is not made of feathers. The blanket is the atmosphere, which is composed of a variety of gases. By trapping heat radiated from the earth, the gases in the atmosphere act in a similar way to a down comforter.

Carbon dioxide is not the most abundant gas in the atmosphere. However it is the gas most responsible for absorbing the heat radiated by the earth. The burning of coal, oil, synthetic fuels, and natural gas is, however, adding billions of tons of carbon dioxide to the air and changing the composition of the atmosphere. This change in the thin blanket of gases that makes the earth habitable will raise worldwide temperatures.

The process of global warming by atmospheric gases has been nicknamed "the greenhouse effect." Some scientists believe that the greenhouse effect is rapidly becoming a very serious threat to the future of our planet. Over the past twenty years, researchers have watched the concentration of carbon dioxide increase considerably. A parallel increase in average global temperatures of about one-half Celsius degree has also been recorded.

To climatologists, these data represent a very strong link between the increase in atmospheric carbon dioxide and a rise in the earth's temperature. Scientists at the National Academy of Sciences agree that increased "emissions of greenhouse gases promise to impose a warming of unusual dimensions to a climate that is already unusually warm."

Scientists and climatologists are working hard to predict the possible magnitude of global warming. By using laboratory simulations and computer-generated graphs and charts, researchers have come up with this hypothesis: The average worldwide surface temperature could increase from 1.5 to 5.5 Celsius degrees by the year 2100. The consequences of such a drastic rise in the earth's temperature could be dramatic.

Polar icecaps and glaciers would melt, flooding vast tracts of land around the globe and submerging virtually all ports and harbors. At the same time, droughts would bake the grain-producing areas of the United States, Middle East, and Europe. Drinking water would be poisoned by ocean salts. Hurricanes, coastal storms, and tornadoes would occur more frequently.

As if that weren't enough, experts predict drastically altered weather patterns and changes in annual rainfall. As Robert Watson, director of NASA's upper atmospheric program, says, "Global warming is inevitable—it's only a question of magnitude and time. We can expect significant changes in climate in the next few decades."

Other researchers refuse to be so pessimistic. Recent studies by scientists at the American Geophysical Union Conference suggest that carbon dioxide buildup in the at-

If the greenhouse effect occurs, wheat fields such as these will be barren land.

mosphere might be only half as great as has been projected. There is evidence that the oceans could absorb a large amount of carbon dioxide produced by burning fossil fuels. Another cause for optimism is the discovery that an increase in atmospheric carbon dioxide causes clouds to become wetter and denser. These denser clouds reflect more sunlight than they let through. This fact suggests that ultimately there would be less heat for the atmosphere to trap and less heat to warm the globe. Some scientists theorize that the earth may even become cooler!

There is debate also over the need for immediate action. As John Hoffman of the Environmental Protection Agency proclaims, "We feel carbon dioxide is a very serious thing, but we think there is time to do research, and there is time to adapt." But others worry that time is running out and regulatory action to protect the environment must be taken now. What do you think?

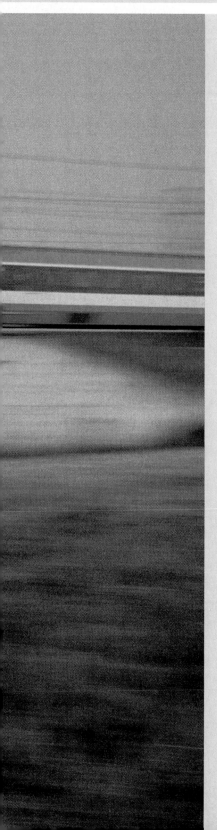

Electricity and Magnetism

Passengers journeying from Lyon to Paris on the French *Train Grande Vitesse* are riding the fastest scheduled train in the world. On a test run in 1981, the TGV easily topped 380 kilometers per hour. But what makes this train so unusual is that it is not powered by gasoline or coal. An electric current drawn from overhead wires powers the TGV along its swift course.

The TGV, however, will soon lose its place as speed champion. For engineers in Japan, West Germany, and Britain are now involved in the development of maglev trains. Maglev stands for magnetic levitation. Because a maglev train has no wheels and makes no contact with a track, it appears to levitate in midair. Although this may seem to be some sort of magic, it is actually the application of basic principles of electricity and magnetism. Maglev trains are supported and propelled by the interaction of magnets located on the train body and on the track. A Japanese test model has already achieved a speed of 516 kilometers per hour. In this unit, you will learn about the world of electricity and magnetism. And you will gain an understanding of how magnets can power a train floating above the ground.

CHAPTERS

19 Electric Charges and Currents

20 Magnetism

The Train Grande Vitesse *picks you up and leaves you off in the center of the city. There are no trips to and from airports, which are often located some distance away from a city. And, there are no delays in takeoffs and landings. Travel over short to medium distances on this train is quicker than on a plane!*

Electric Charges and Currents

19

CHAPTER SECTIONS

19–1 Electric Charge
19–2 Static Electricity
19–3 The Flow of Electricity
19–4 Electric Circuits
19–5 Electric Power

CHAPTER OBJECTIVES

After completing this chapter, you will be able to

19–1 Explain how electric charge is related to atomic structure.

19–1 Describe the forces that exist between charged particles.

19–2 Describe the effects of static electricity.

19–3 Relate voltage, electric current, and resistance.

19–3 Explain how electrochemical cells produce a flow of electrons.

19–4 Identify the parts of an electric circuit.

19–4 Compare a series and a parallel circuit.

19–5 Explain how electric power is calculated and purchased.

19–5 Describe how electricity can be used safely.

"Where were you when the lights went out?" Many people were asking each other that question the morning after November 9, 1965. On that day, shortly before the evening rush hour, a major blackout plunged the Northeastern United States and parts of Canada into total darkness. More than 200,000 square kilometers and over 30 million people were without electric power!

Electric typewriters stopped in midsentence. Elevators stopped in midair. Subways came to a screeching halt. And city traffic became a nightmare as all the traffic lights went out. Electric toothbrushes, hair dryers, toasters, refrigerators, and washing machines ceased to operate. In hospitals, doctors operated by candlelight, and auxiliary power systems kept important life-support equipment working.

For some, the blackout was an adventure—a challenge to see how well people could function without the energy they take for granted. For others, the blackout was a severe hardship. But for all, the power failure was a reminder of the importance of electricity in everyday life. It is hard to imagine a world without electricity.

Have you ever stopped to think about what electricity really is? Where it comes from and how it works? How it gets to your house and how you use it? You will learn the answers to these questions as you read this chapter. As for the blackout of 1965, perhaps someone you know was in the Northeast on that memorable day. If so, then you can ask the question, "Where were *you* when the lights went out?"

On November 9, 1965, a major blackout turned the bright, illuminated skyline of New York into darkness and left more than 30 million people in the Northeast without electricity.

19–1 Electric Charge

"It made my hair stand on end!" Perhaps you are familiar with this expression, which is often used to describe a frightening or startling experience. According to biologists, it is possible for human hair to stand on end in moments of extreme fear. But there is another force that can make hair stand on end. You probably have experienced it on a cold, dry day when your hair seemed to "fly" all around as you tried to comb it.

What you experienced was electricity. Electricity may also give you a shock if you walk along a carpet and then touch a metal doorknob. Electricity enables you to rub a balloon on your sleeve and make it stick to the wall. And electricity produces the awesome flashes of lightning in the sky.

What is electricity? Where does it come from? How does it move? To answer these questions, you must first understand atoms and charges, which are both related to electricity.

Subatomic Particles and Electricity

All matter is made up of **atoms.** An atom is the smallest particle of an element that has all the properties of that element. An element contains only one kind of atom. For example, carbon is made of only carbon atoms. Gold is made of only gold atoms.

Figure 19–1 *The metal sphere this girl is touching is part of a device called a Van de Graaff generator. This particular generator, located at the Ontario Science Center produces charges of static electricity great enough to make the girl's hair stand on end.*

Atoms are made of even smaller particles called **subatomic particles.** These subatomic particles include **protons, neutrons,** and **electrons.**

Protons and neutrons are found in the **nucleus,** or center, of an atom. Protons and neutrons account for most of the mass of an atom. Whirling around the nucleus is a cloud of electrons. Electrons occupy different energy levels, depending upon their distance from the nucleus.

Both protons and electrons have a basic property called **electric charge.** However, the kind of charge is not the same for both particles. Protons have a positive charge, which is indicated by a plus symbol (+). Electrons have a negative charge, which is indicated by a minus symbol (−). Neutrons are neutral. Neutrons have no electric charge.

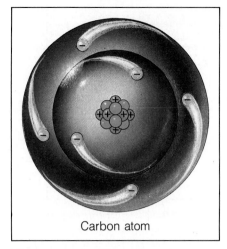

Carbon atom

Figure 19–2 *This atom of carbon shows the arrangement of the subatomic particles known as protons, neutrons, and electrons. Where is each particle found? What is the charge on each?*

Charge and Force

When charged particles come near one another, they give rise to two different forces. A force is a pull or push on an object. A force can pull objects together or it can push objects apart.

A force that pulls objects together is a **force of attraction.** A force of attraction exists between oppositely charged particles. So negatively charged electrons are attracted to positively charged protons. This force of attraction holds the electrons in the electron cloud surrounding the nucleus.

A force that pushes objects apart is a **force of repulsion.** A force of repulsion exists between particles of the same charge. So negatively charged electrons repel one another, just as positively charged protons do. **Electric charges behave according to this simple rule: Like charges repel each other; unlike charges attract each other.**

From your experience, you know that when you sit on a chair, pick up a pen, or put on your jacket, you are not attracted or repelled by these objects. Although the protons and electrons in the atoms of these objects have electric charges, the objects themselves are neutral. Why?

The number of electrons in an atom is equal to the number of protons in that atom. So the total negative charge is equal to the total positive charge. The atom is neutral. It has no overall charge.

Figure 19–3 *When charged particles come near each other, a force is produced. The force can be either a force of attraction or a force of repulsion. What is the rule of electric charges?*

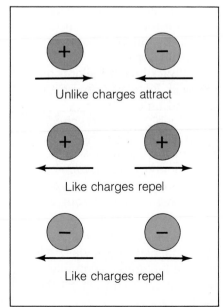

Unlike charges attract

Like charges repel

Like charges repel

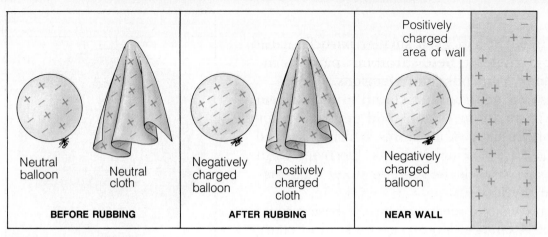

| BEFORE RUBBING | AFTER RUBBING | NEAR WALL |

Neutral balloon — Neutral cloth

Negatively charged balloon — Positively charged cloth

Positively charged area of wall — Negatively charged balloon

Figure 19–4 *Rubbing separates charges, giving the cloth a positive charge and the balloon a negative charge. When the negatively charged balloon is brought near the wall, it repels electrons in the wall. The nearby portion of the wall becomes positively charged. What happens next?*

How, then, do objects such as balloons and strands of hair develop an electric charge if these objects are made of neutral atoms? The answer lies in the fact that electrons, unlike protons, are free to move. In certain materials, the negative electrons are only loosely held by the positive protons. These electrons can easily be separated from their atoms.

Rubbing separates charges on objects. When two objects are rubbed together, one object loses electrons while the other object gains these electrons. The object that gains electrons has an overall negative charge. The object that loses electrons has an overall positive charge. Remember that *only the electrons move,* not the protons. A neutral object develops an electric charge when it either gains or loses electrons.

If you rub a balloon against a piece of cloth, the cloth loses some electrons and the balloon gains these electrons. The balloon is no longer a neutral object. It is a negatively charged object because it has more electrons than protons. As the negatively charged balloon approaches the wall, it repels the electrons in the wall. The electrons in the area of the wall nearest the balloon move away, leaving that area of the wall positively charged. Using the rule of charges, can you explain why the balloon now sticks to the wall?

Electric Fields

If two charged particles come close to each other, they will experience a force. If the two particles are alike in charge, the force will be one of repulsion. If the two particles are opposite in charge, the force will be one of attraction. The repulsion and attraction of particles occurs because charged particles have **electric fields** around them.

An electric field is the region surrounding a charged particle in which an electric force affecting other charged particles is noticeable. The electric field is strongest near the charged particle. It is weakest far away from the charged particle. The strength of an electric field depends upon the distance from the charged particle. As the distance from a charged particle increases, the strength of the electric field decreases.

SECTION REVIEW

1. What are the charged particles in an atom?
2. What is the rule of electric charges?
3. How does an object develop an electric charge?
4. A positively charged particle is placed 1 centimeter from positively charged particle X. A negatively charged particle is placed 10 centimeters from particle X. Compare the forces experienced by both the positively charged particle and the negatively charged particle.

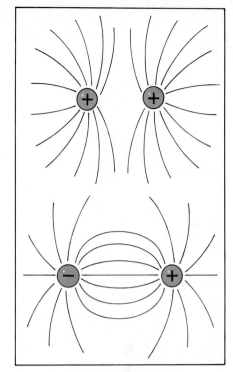

Figure 19–5 *Lines of force show the nature of the electric field surrounding two particles of the same charge (top) and two particles of opposite charge (bottom).*

19–2 Static Electricity

Section Objective

To define static electricity

When you read that the loss or gain of electrons produces an electric charge and electricity, you may have noticed that the words *electron* and *electricity* are similar. This similarity is no accident. Electricity depends upon electrons. In fact, **electricity** can now be defined as the energy associated with electrons that have moved from one place to another.

You are probably most familiar with electricity that flows through electric wires. But the movement of electrons is not always a continuous flow through a wire. Sometimes electrons can move from one object to another and then remain at rest. This type of electricity is called **static electricity.** The word *static* means "not moving," or "stationary."

Static electricity is the buildup of electric charges on an object. The electric charges build up because electrons have moved from one object to another. However, once built up, the charges do not flow. They remain at rest.

Sharpen Your Skills

Spark, Crackle, Move

1. Comb your hair several times in the same direction. Bring the comb near your hair but do not touch it.
2. Repeat step 1 but now bring the comb near a weak stream of water from a faucet.
3. In a darkened room, walk across a wool carpet and then touch the doorknob with a metal pen or rod.

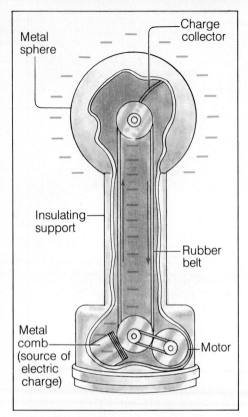

Figure 19–6 *A Van de Graaff generator produces static electricity by friction. Electrons supplied by a metal comb ride up a rubber belt to the top of the generator, are picked off by the charge collector, and transferred to the metal sphere. A large negative charge is built up and used to produce discharges of static electricity.*

Figure 19–7 *A metal rod can be charged negatively (left) or positively (right) by conduction.*

Methods of Charging

An object can become charged with static electricity in three ways: friction, conduction, and induction. Rubbing a balloon with a piece of cloth is an example of charging an object by **friction.** The motion of the cloth against the balloon causes charges on both objects to separate. Since the electrons in the cloth are more loosely held than the electrons in the balloon, electrons move from the cloth to the balloon. What is the resulting charge on the cloth? On the balloon?

If a hard rubber rod is rubbed with fur, friction separates charges on both the rod and the fur. Electrons are transferred from the fur to the rod. Because the rubber rod has gained electrons, it is negatively charged. The fur, which has lost electrons, is positively charged.

If a glass rod is rubbed with silk, electrons are transferred from the glass rod to the silk. The glass rod, which has lost electrons, is positively charged. What is the charge on the silk?

Charging by **conduction** involves the direct contact of objects. In conduction, electrons flow through one object to another object. Certain materials allow electrons to flow freely. Materials that permit electric charges to move easily are called **conductors.** Most metals are good conductors of electricity. Silver, copper, aluminum, and mercury are among the best conductors.

Materials that do not allow electrons to flow freely are called **insulators.** Insulators do not conduct electric charges well. Good insulators include

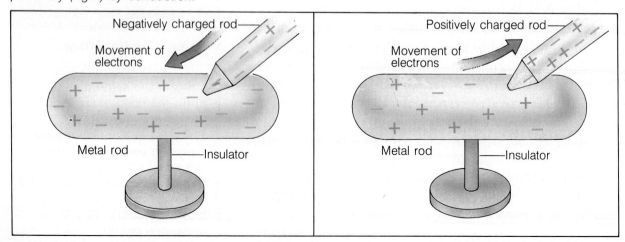

rubber, glass, wood, plastic, and air. The rubber tubing around an electric wire and the plastic handle on an electric power tool are examples of insulators. What do these insulators do?

An object can acquire a charge by **induction.** Induction involves a rearrangement of electric charges. For induction to occur, a neutral object need only come close to a charged object. No contact is necessary. For example, a negatively charged rubber rod can pick up tiny pieces of paper by induction. The electric charges in the paper are rearranged by the approach of the charged rubber rod. The electrons in the area of the paper nearest to the rod are repelled, leaving the positive charges near the rod. Because the positive charges are closer to the negative rod, the paper is attracted.

Figure 19–8 *Electric wires, often made of conductors such as copper, are covered by insulators such as rubber or plastic. Does an insulator conduct electricity?*

The Electroscope

An electric charge can be detected by an instrument called an **electroscope.** A typical electroscope consists of a metal rod with a knob at the top and a pair of thin metal leaves at the bottom. The rod is inserted in a one-hole rubber stopper, which fits into a flask. The flask contains the lower part of the rod and the metal leaves. See Figure 19–10.

In an uncharged electroscope, the leaves hang straight down. When a charged object touches the metal knob, electric charges travel down the rod and into the leaves. The leaves spread apart, indicating the presence of an electric charge. Since the charge on both leaves is the same, the leaves repel each other and spread apart.

Figure 19–9 *A charged rod brought near a conductor induces an electric charge in the conductor. Using this figure and Figure 19–7, compare the charge given to the metal rod by each charged rod when done by conduction and by induction.*

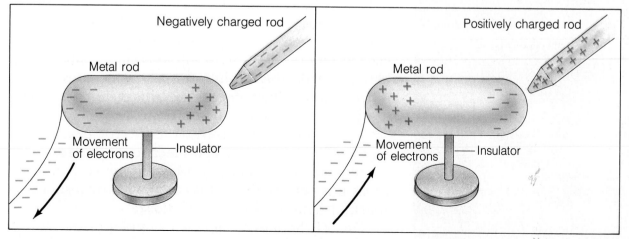

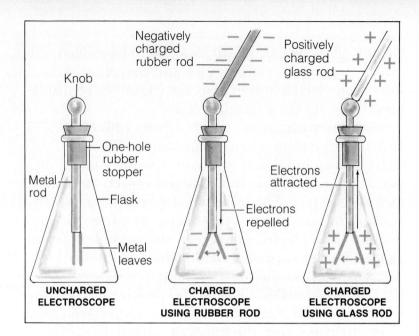

Figure 19-10 *An electroscope is used to detect electric charges. Why do the leaves in this typical electroscope move apart when either a negatively charged rubber rod or a positively charged glass rod makes contact?*

Figure 19-11 *The discharge of static electricity from one metal sphere to another can be seen as a spark (top). A more spectacular discharge of static electricity is lightning (bottom). Here lightning bolts light up the sky in Norfolk, Virginia.*

An electroscope can be charged by conduction. A charged object is brought in direct contact with the knob of the electroscope. For example, if a negatively charged rubber rod touches the knob, electrons from the charged rubber rod move to the knob of the electroscope and then down the metal rod to the thin metal leaves. The leaves gain a negative charge, repel each other, and spread apart.

If a positively charged glass rod touches the knob of the electroscope, free electrons in the leaves and metal rod are attracted by the glass rod. The metal rod and knob conduct these electrons out of the electroscope to the glass rod. The loss of electrons causes the leaves to become positively charged. They repel each other and spread apart.

Lightning

Electrons that move from one object to another and cause the buildup of charges at rest, or static electricity, eventually leave the object. Usually these extra electrons escape into the air. Sometimes they move onto another object. The charged object loses its static electricity and becomes neutral.

The loss of static electricity as electric charges move off an object is called **electric discharge.** Sometimes the discharge is slow and quiet. Sometimes it is very rapid and accompanied by a shock, a spark of light, or a crackle of noise.

One of the most dramatic examples of the discharge of static electricity is **lightning.** During a

HELP WANTED: ELECTRIC TROUBLE-SHOOTER for rural areas. High school diploma and interest in electricity required. We will train the right person.

Lightning rips the air as wind and hailstones batter the little town. Most of the area's electricity is out. The utility company sends out every available **trouble-shooter** to track down causes of the power failure.

Sometimes a trouble-shooter finds obvious problems, such as broken wires. But some-times the source of trouble is hidden, and special equipment must be used to check transformers, switches, cables, and other equipment.

After locating the problem, a trouble-shooter may climb utility poles to repair or replace damaged equipment. In order to avoid harming people or property, it is necessary to be extremely safety conscious. A trouble-shooter must know exactly how electricity is generated and conducted.

A trouble-shooter also locates and repairs electric problems in homes, hospitals, schools, and other buildings. As technology changes and utility companies install new equipment, up-to-date methods for electric repair and mainte-nance must be learned.

Training for this career may be provided by private companies or by technical schools and community colleges. If you are interested in electricity and problem solving and would like more information about a career as an electric trouble-shooter, contact the International Brotherhood of Electrical Workers, 1125 15th Street NW, Washington, DC 20005.

storm, particles contained in clouds are moved about by the wind. Charges become separated, and there are buildups of positive and negative charges. If a negatively charged cloud forms near the surface of the earth, objects on the earth become electrically charged by induction. Soon electrons are jumping from the cloud to the earth. The result of this transfer of electrons is a giant spark called lightning.

Lightning can also occur as electrons jump from cloud to cloud. As electrons jump through the air, intense light and heat are produced. The light is the bolt of lightning you see. The heat causes the air to expand suddenly. The rapid expansion of the air is the thunder you hear. Lightning contains danger-ously high amounts of electric energy. An average lightning bolt transfers 6 billion billion electrons be-tween a cloud and the earth.

One of the first people to understand lightning as a form of electricity was Benjamin Franklin. In the mid-1700s, Franklin performed experiments

---

Sharpen Your Skills

Observing Static Electricity

1. Place two books about 10 cm apart on a table.

2. Cut tiny paper dolls or some other object out of tissue paper and place them on the table between the books.

3. Place a 20 to 25-cm square piece of glass on the books so that the glass covers the paper dolls.

4. Using a piece of silk, rub the glass vigorously. Observe what happens.

Using the rule of electric charges and your knowledge of static electricity, explain what you observed.

Figure 19–12 *Benjamin Franklin's famous experiments (top) provided evidence that lightning is a form of static electricity that moves quickly through certain materials. Using these observations and the observation that pointed surfaces attract electricity, Franklin invented the lightning rod. Lightning rods attached to the tops of buildings provide a safe path for the lightning directly into the ground (bottom).*

that provided evidence that lightning is a form of static electricity, that electricity moves quickly through certain materials, and that a pointed surface attracts electricity. Franklin suggested that pointed metal rods be placed above the roofs of buildings as protection from lightning. These rods were the first **lightning rods.** Luckily for Franklin, he put a lightning rod on his roof. Shortly afterward, lightning struck his home!

Lightning rods work according to a principle called **grounding.** A discharge of static electricity usually takes the shortest path from one object to another. So lightning rods are attached to the tops of buildings and a wire connects the lightning rod to the ground. When lightning strikes the rod, which is taller than the building, it travels through the rod and the wire harmlessly into the earth.

Unfortunately, other tall objects such as trees can also act as grounders. That is why it is not a good idea to stand near a tree during a lightning storm. Why do you think it is also not a good idea to stand in an open field during an electric storm?

Voltage: The Push of Electrons

It takes energy to move an object from one place to another. Even though electrons are very small, it still takes energy to move them. When you rub a balloon against your sleeve, you apply a force. This force moves electrons from the cloth to the balloon. You are able to apply this force because you have energy. The energy you expend goes to the electrons, which move. This energy is the "push" that makes electric charges move.

A measure of the energy available to move electrons is called **voltage.** Voltage is sometimes called potential difference. Voltage can be thought of as the "push" that makes electrons move. The higher the voltage, the more energy each electron carries. The more energy each electron carries, the more energy it can deliver, and the more work it can do.

Voltage is measured in units called **volts.** The symbol for volts is the letter "V." If you see the marking "10V," you know that it means ten volts. An instrument called a voltmeter is used to measure voltage.

1. What is static electricity?
2. What are the three ways in which an object can acquire an electric charge?
3. How can you tell if an object touching an electroscope is neutral or has a charge?
4. What is lightning?
5. What is voltage? In what units is it measured?
6. What would happen if a lightning rod were made of an insulator rather than a conductor?

19–3 The Flow of Electricity

Once electrons are pushed into moving, they can be made to continue flowing provided they have a path and a source. A wire made of a suitable conducting material forms the path. A device that pumps electrons from one object to another is the source. The electrons are ready to flow. Your lamp will light, your stereo will play, your computer will work, and your oven will bake your favorite cookies!

Electric Current

The flow of electrons through a wire is called **electric current.** Current is measured according to how many electrons pass a given point during each second. The higher the electric current in a wire, the more electrons are passing through.

The symbol for current is the letter "I." The unit used to measure current is the **ampere (A),** or amp for short. One ampere is defined as the amount of current that flows past a given point per second. Among the instruments used to measure current are ammeters and galvanometers.

Resistance

Have you ever looked inside a clear light bulb and noticed a very thin piece of metal that glows when the light bulb is turned on? That piece of

Figure 19–13 *Voltage is a measure of electron energy. Current is a measure of the rate of electron flow. In this figure, how is voltage represented? How is current represented?*

LOW CURRENT AND LOW VOLTAGE

Each electron carries little energy, and there are few electrons. Little total energy is delivered per second.

HIGH CURRENT AND LOW VOLTAGE

Each electron carries little energy, but there are many electrons. Moderate total energy is delivered per second.

LOW CURRENT AND HIGH VOLTAGE

Each electron carries much energy, but there are few electrons. Moderate total energy is delivered per second.

HIGH CURRENT AND HIGH VOLTAGE

Each electron carries much energy, and there are many electrons. High total energy is delivered per second.

metal is called a filament. As electric current passes through the filament, the filament resists, or opposes, the flow of electrons. As a result of this opposition, some of the electric energy is converted into heat and light.

Opposition to the flow of electricity is called **resistance.** The symbol for resistance is the letter "R." The unit of resistance is the **ohm** (Ω).

You will remember that some materials conduct electricity better than other materials. Wires made of good conductors, such as copper, have a low resistance. So electricity flows easily through copper wires. Wires made of poor conductors, such as iron, have a high resistance. These wires offer so much resistance that almost no current can flow. What is another name for a nonconductor? For what purpose are nonconductors used in wiring?

In addition to the material used to make a wire, the resistance of a wire depends upon its thickness, length, and temperature. Electrons move more easily through a thick wire. In a thin wire, there is less room for electrons to flow. So a thin wire offers more resistance to an electric current.

A longer wire offers more resistance than a shorter wire because the electrons have a greater distance to travel. So as the length of a wire increases, the resistance increases. Temperature affects resistance because the ability of a material to conduct electricity depends to a certain extent upon temperature.

Ohm's Law

An equation called **Ohm's law** relates electric current, voltage, and resistance. **Ohm's law states that the current in a wire is equal to the voltage divided by the resistance.**

$$\text{current} = \frac{\text{voltage}}{\text{resistance}}$$

or

$$I = \frac{V}{R} \qquad \text{amperes} = \frac{\text{volts}}{\text{ohms}}$$

Looking at this equation, what do you think will happen to the current if the resistance increases and the voltage remains the same? If the resistance

What is the current through a wire that has a resistance of 30 ohms if the voltage is 45 volts?

Step 1 Write the formula

$$I = \frac{V}{R}$$

Step 2 Substitute given numbers and units

$$I = \frac{45 \text{ volts}}{30 \text{ ohms}}$$

Step 3 Solve for unknown variable

$$I = 1.5 \text{ amperes}$$

Practice Problems

1. What is the current flowing through a wire if the resistance of the wire is 20 ohms and the voltage is 40 volts?

2. A current of 0.5 amperes flows through a wire. What is the wire's resistance if the voltage is 50 volts?

decreases and the voltage remains the same? What must happen to the resistance if the voltage increases while the current remains the same?

Producing a Current

In order for a current to be produced, there must be a source of electrons. An **electrochemical cell** provides a steady supply of electric current. In an electrochemical cell, chemical energy produced by a chemical reaction is changed into electric energy.

DRY CELL The name **dry cell** is somewhat misleading, for the cell is not completely dry. It consists of a zinc can that contains a moist, pastelike mixture of chemicals. In the center is a solid carbon rod.

As a chemical reaction takes place between the zinc and the paste, electrons are released. Attached to the zinc part of the cell is a negative terminal that picks up the electrons. Attached to the carbon rod is a positive terminal that has a shortage of electrons. The difference in number of electrons between the two terminals causes an "electron pressure" that pumps the electrons.

Sharpen Your Skills

Ohm's Law

Complete the following chart.

I (amps)	V (volts)	R (ohms)
	12	75
15	240	
5.5		20
	6	25
5	110	

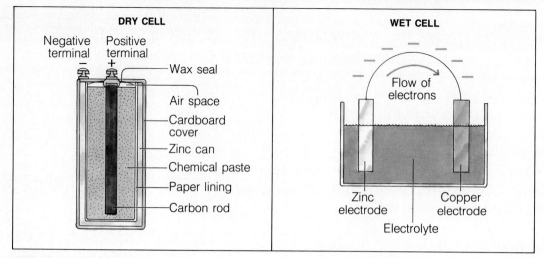

DRY CELL

Negative terminal −
Positive terminal +
Wax seal
Air space
Cardboard cover
Zinc can
Chemical paste
Paper lining
Carbon rod

WET CELL

Flow of electrons
Zinc electrode
Copper electrode
Electrolyte

Figure 19–14 *Electrochemical cells, which include dry cells and wet cells, convert chemical energy into electric energy. What is a series of dry cells called? What is another name for a wet cell?*

Figure 19–15 *The temperature difference between the hot junction and the cold junction in a thermocouple generates electricity. The greater the temperature difference, the greater the electric current. What is the energy conversion involved in the operation of a thermocouple?*

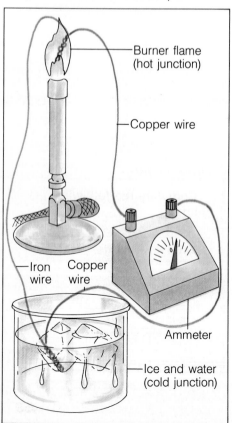

Burner flame (hot junction)
Copper wire
Iron wire
Copper wire
Ammeter
Ice and water (cold junction)

If a wire is connected to each terminal, the electrons will flow from the negative terminal through the wire to the positive terminal. As the chemical reaction continues, the electrons are pumped back to the negative terminal of the dry cell. In this way the negative terminal keeps its negative charge, and electrons can move through the complete path for a long time. A steady flow of current is established. The source of power for your portable radio or tape player is probably a dry cell such as the one just described. A series of dry cells connected to one another is called a **battery.**

WET CELL   Another type of electrochemical cell is the **wet cell,** or **voltaic cell.** A typical car battery is a series of wet cells.

In a wet cell, two different metal plates called **electrodes** are placed in a conducting liquid called an **electrolyte.** In many wet cells the electrodes are made of zinc and copper. The electrolyte is hydrochloric acid.

As the zinc reacts with the hydrochloric acid, each zinc atom releases two electrons. An excess of electrons builds up at the zinc electrode. Once again, "electron pressure" pushes the electrons from the negative zinc electrode to the positive copper electrode. A wire connecting the two electrodes provides a pathway for a steady flow of electric current.

THERMOCOUPLE   A **thermocouple** is a device that changes heat energy into electric energy. A thermocouple generates electricity as a result of temperature differences. In this device, the ends of a piece of copper wire and a piece of iron wire are joined together, forming a loop. If one iron-copper junction is heated while the other is cooled, an electric current is generated. The greater the temperature difference between the junctions, the greater the current. Figure 19–15 shows a thermocouple with an ammeter attached to measure the current.

Thermocouples are used as thermometers in cars to show engine temperature. One end of the thermocouple is placed in the engine, while the other end is kept outside the engine. As the engine gets warm, the temperature difference produces a current. The warmer the engine, the greater the temperature difference—and the greater the current. This current in turn operates a gauge that shows engine temperature. Thermocouples are also used in ovens and gas furnaces.

Current Direction

Electrons moving through a wire can move continuously in the same direction or they can change direction back and forth over and over again.

When electrons always flow in the same direction, the current is called **direct current,** or **DC.** The current in dry cells, batteries, and thermocouples is direct current.

When electrons reverse their direction regularly, the current is called **alternating current,** or **AC.** The electricity in your home is alternating current. In the alternating current in your home, electrons change direction at a rate of about 60 times per second. Alternating current is the most commonly used current.

Figure 19–16 *These electric power lines near Wagontire, Oregon, carry huge quantities of electricity to homes, offices, and other buildings in the area. What kind of current—DC or AC—is carried in these lines?*

SECTION REVIEW

1. What is electric current?
2. What is resistance?
3. How does an electrochemical cell produce an electric current?
4. How does a thermocouple differ from a dry cell or battery?
5. What is direct current? Alternating current?
6. If the design of a dry cell keeps electrons flowing steadily, why do you think a dry cell goes "dead"?

19–4 Electric Circuits

Try this experiment if you can. Connect one wire from a terminal on a dry cell to a small flashlight bulb. Does anything happen? Now connect another wire from the bulb to the other terminal on the dry cell. What happens? With just one wire connected, the bulb will not light. But with two wires providing a path for the flow of electrons, the bulb lights up.

In order to flow, electrons need a closed path through which to travel. **An electric circuit provides a complete, closed path for an electric current.**

Parts of a Circuit

An electric circuit consists of a source of electrons, a load or resistance, wires, and a switch. For a circuit that uses direct current, the source of electrons can be a dry cell or a battery. For a circuit that uses alternating current, the source of electrons is a generator at a power plant.

The load is the device that uses the electric energy. The load can be a light bulb, an appliance, a machine, or a motor. In all cases, the load offers some resistance to the flow of electrons. As a result, electric energy is converted into heat, light, or mechanical energy.

The switch in an electric circuit opens and closes the circuit. You will remember that electrons cannot

Figure 19–17 *No electricity can flow through an open circuit (left). When the switch is flipped on, the circuit is closed and electrons have a complete path through which to flow (right). What indicates a current is flowing through the circuit?*

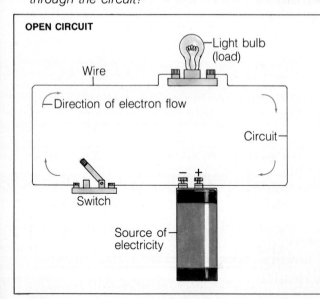

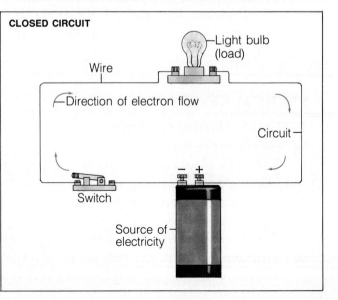

flow through a broken path. Electrons must have a closed path through which to travel. When the switch of an electric device is off, the circuit is open and electrons cannot flow. When the switch is on, the circuit is closed and electrons are able to flow. Remember this important rule: *Electricity cannot flow through an open circuit. Electricity can flow only through a closed circuit.*

Series and Parallel Circuits

As you just learned, an electric circuit consists of several parts: an electron source, a load, wires, and a switch. There are two types of electric circuits. The type depends on how the parts of the circuit are arranged.

If all the parts of an electric circuit are connected one after another, the circuit is a **series circuit.** In a series circuit, there is only one path for the electrons to take. Figure 19–19 illustrates a series circuit. The disadvantage of a series circuit is that if there is a break in any part of the circuit, the entire circuit is opened and no current can flow. Inexpensive holiday tree lights are often connected in series. What will happen if one light goes out in a circuit such as this?

In a **parallel circuit,** the different parts of an electric circuit are on separate branches. There are several paths for the electrons to take in a parallel circuit. Figure 19–19 shows a parallel circuit. If there is a break in one branch of a parallel circuit,

Figure 19–18 *When severe weather conditions damage power lines, the flow of electricity is interrupted. Why?*

Figure 19–19 *A series circuit (left) provides only one path for the flow of electrons. A parallel circuit (right) provides several paths. How are the circuits in your home wired? Why?*

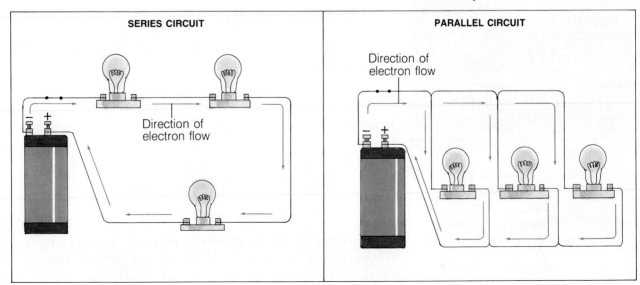

SERIES CIRCUIT

Direction of electron flow

PARALLEL CIRCUIT

Direction of electron flow

Figure 19–20 *Old types of tree lights used series circuits. Newer lights, such as these, are connected in parallel. What would happen to the lovely display if one bulb went out?*

electrons can still move through the other branches. The current continues to flow. Why do tree lights connected in parallel have an advantage over tree lights connected in series? Why do you think the electric circuits in your home are parallel circuits?

SECTION REVIEW

1. What is an electric circuit?
2. What are the main parts of an electric circuit?
3. How does a series circuit differ from a parallel circuit?
4. Do you think that a circuit could be a combination of series and parallel connections? Explain your answer.

Section Objective

To define electric power

Figure 19–21 *These familiar electric appliances need electric power to operate. Each appliance has a different power requirement, or power rating. How is electric power calculated? In what unit is it measured?*

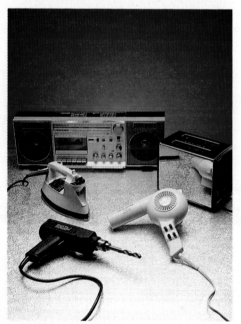

19–5 Electric Power

You probably use the word *power* in a number of different senses—to mean strength or force or energy. To a scientist, **power** is the rate at which work is done or energy is used. **Electric power is a measure of the rate at which electricity does work or provides energy.** In electric appliances, this energy is often converted to other forms of energy, such as heat, light, or mechanical energy. So electric power can be thought of as the rate at which the energy of an electric current is converted to other forms of energy.

Calculating Electric Power

Electric power can be calculated by using the following formula:

$$\text{power} = \text{voltage} \times \text{current}$$

$$\text{or}$$

$$P = V \times I$$

The unit of electric power is the **watt** (W). So the formula for power can also be written:

$$\text{watts} = \text{volts} \times \text{amperes}$$

According to this formula, one watt of power is delivered when a current of one ampere flows through a circuit whose voltage is one volt.

To measure large quantities of power, such as the power used in your home, the **kilowatt (kW)** is used. One kilowatt is equal to 1000 watts. What is the power in watts of a 0.2-kilowatt light bulb?

If you have ever looked at the label on a light bulb, hair dryer, or air conditioner, you probably are familiar with the units watts and kilowatts. Light bulbs are commonly 60, 75, or 100 watts.

Different appliances have different power ratings. As you might expect, the higher the rating, the greater the amount of electric energy needed to run the appliance. Figure 19–22 shows the power in watts for some common appliances.

Electric Energy

Have you ever noticed the electric meter in your home? This device measures how much energy your household uses. The electric company provides electric power at a certain cost. Their bill for this power is based on the total amount of energy a household uses, which is read from the electric meter.

The total amount of electric energy used depends on the total power used by all the electric appliances and the total time they are used. The formula for electric energy is

energy = power × time

or

E = P × t

Figure 19–22   *This table shows the power used by some common appliances. Which appliance would use the greatest number of watts if operated for one hour?*

POWER USED BY COMMON APPLIANCES	
Appliance	**Power Used** *(watts)*
Refrigerator/freezer	600
Dishwasher	2300
Toaster	700
Range/oven	2600
Hair dryer	1000
Color television	300
Microwave oven	1450
Radio	100
Clock	3
Clothes dryer	4000

1. For a period of several days, keep a record of every electric appliance you use. Also record the amount of time each appliance is run.

2. Write down the power rating for each appliance you list. The power rating in watts should be marked on the appliance. You can also use the information in Figure 19–22.

3. Calculate the amount of electricity in kilowatt hours that you use each day.

4. Find out how much electricity costs per kilowatt-hour in your area. Calculate the cost of the electricity you use each day.

Electric energy is measured in **kilowatt-hours (kWh).**

$$\text{energy} = \text{power} \times \text{time}$$

$$\textbf{kilowatt-hours} = \textbf{kilowatts} \times \textbf{hours}$$

One kilowatt-hour is equal to 1000 watts of power used for one hour of time. You can imagine how much power this is by picturing ten 100-watt bulbs in a row, all burning for one hour. One kilowatt-hour would also be equal to a 500-watt appliance running for two hours.

To pay for electricity, the energy used is multiplied by the cost per kilowatt-hour. Suppose the cost of electricity is 8¢ per kilowatt-hour. How much would it cost to burn a 100-watt bulb for five hours? To use a 1000-watt air conditioner for three hours?

Electric Safety

Electricity is one of the most useful energy resources. But electricity can be dangerous if it is not used carefully. Here are some important rules to remember when using electricity.

1. Never handle appliances when your hands are wet or you are standing in water. Water is a fairly good conductor of electricity. If you are wet, you could unwillingly become an alternate path for the electric current!

2. Never run wires under carpets. Breaks or frays in the wires may go unnoticed. These breaks cause short circuits. A short circuit represents a shorter and easier path for electron flow and can cause shocks or a fire.

3. Never overload a circuit by connecting too many appliances to it. Each electric circuit is designed to carry a certain amount of current safely. An overloaded circuit can cause a short circuit.

4. Always repair worn or frayed wires to avoid short circuits.

5. Never stick your fingers in an electric socket or stick a utensil in a toaster that is plugged in. The electricity could be conducted directly into your hand or through the utensil into your hand.

6. Never come close to wires on power poles or to wires that have fallen from power poles or buildings. Such wires often carry very high voltages.

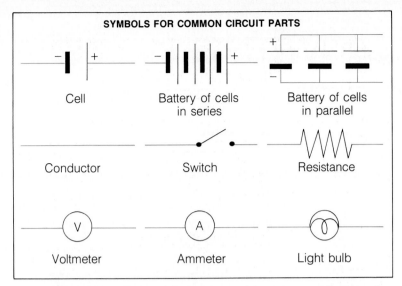

SYMBOLS FOR COMMON CIRCUIT PARTS

Cell

Battery of cells in series

Battery of cells in parallel

Conductor

Switch

Resistance

Voltmeter

Ammeter

Light bulb

Figure 19–23 *These symbols for common circuit parts are used to diagram any type of circuit— simple or complex. What are the advantages of using these symbols?*

FUSES   Your home has a great amount of electricity running through it. If too many appliances are all running at once or if the wires have become old and frayed, heat can build up in the wiring. The results can be dangerous. To protect against too much current flowing at once, your home may have **fuses** in a fuse box.

Inside each fuse is a thin strip of metal through which current flows. If the current becomes too high, the strip of metal melts and breaks the flow of electricity. So a fuse is an emergency switch.

CIRCUIT BREAKERS   Like fuses, **circuit breakers** protect a circuit from becoming overloaded. Modern circuit breakers have a switch that flips open when the current flow becomes too high. These circuit breakers can easily be reset and used again once the problem has been found and corrected. Circuit breakers are easier to use than fuses.

SECTION REVIEW

1. What is electric power? What is the formula for calculating electric power? In what unit is electric power measured?
2. What is electric energy? What is the formula for calculating electric energy? In what unit is electric energy measured?
3. Explain the purpose of fuses and circuit breakers. How is a fuse different from a circuit breaker?
4. If left running unused, which appliance would waste more electricity, an iron left on for half an hour or a television left on for one hour?

Electricity From a Lemon

Problem

Can electricity be produced from a lemon, a penny, and a dime?

Materials *(per group)*

compass
cardboard box to fit the compass
bell wire
lemon
2 pennies
dime
sandpaper
scissors

Procedure

1. Wrap 20 turns of bell wire around the cardboard box containing the compass, as shown in the accompanying figure.
2. Roll the lemon back and forth on a table or other flat surface while applying slight pressure. The pressure will break the cellular structure of the lemon.
3. Use the pointed end of the scissors to make two slits about 1 cm apart in the lemon.
4. Sandpaper both sides of the dime and two pennies.
5. Insert the pennies in the two slits in the lemon. Only half of each penny should be inserted into the lemon, and the other half should stick out.
6. Touch the two ends of the bell wire to the coins. Observe any deflection of the compass needle. Record your observations.
7. Replace one of the pennies with the dime. Repeat step 6. Observe any deflection of the compass needle. If there is deflection, observe its direction. Record your observations.
8. Reverse the connecting wires on the coins. Observe any deflection of the compass needle and the direction of deflection. Record your observations.

Observations

1. Is the compass needle deflected when the two ends of the bell wire touch the two pennies?
2. Is the compass needle deflected when the two ends of the bell wire touch the penny and the dime?
3. Is the direction of deflection changed when the connecting wires on the coins are reversed?

Conclusions

1. Is an electric current produced when two pennies are used?
2. Is an electric current produced when a dime and a penny are used?
3. What is the purpose of breaking the cellular structure of the lemon? Of sandpapering the coins?
4. What materials are necessary to produce an electric current?
5. An electric current flowing through a wire produces magnetism. Using this fact, explain why a compass is used in this investigation to detect a weak current. What other device could be used to measure the current?
6. A dime is copper with a thin outer coating of silver. What would happen if the dime were sanded so much that the copper was exposed?

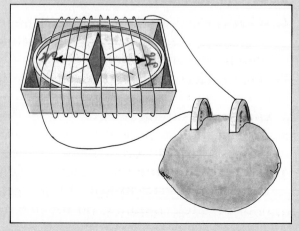

CHAPTER REVIEW

SUMMARY

19-1 Electric Charge

❏ All matter is made up of atoms.

❏ A force that pulls oppositely charged objects together is a force of attraction. A force that pushes similarly charged objects apart is a force of repulsion.

❏ An electric field is the region surrounding a charged particle in which an electric force affecting other charged particles is noticeable.

19-2 Static Electricity

❏ The buildup of electric charge is called static electricity.

❏ Objects can be charged by friction, conduction, and induction.

❏ A measure of the energy available to move electrons is called voltage (V), which is measured in units called volts (V).

19-3 The Flow of Electricity

❏ The flow of electrons through a wire is called electric current (I). Electric current is measured in units called amperes (A).

❏ Opposition to the flow of electricity is called resistance (R). Resistance is measured in units called ohms (Ω).

❏ Ohm's law states that the current in a wire is equal to voltage divided by resistance.

❏ In an electrochemical cell, chemical energy is changed into electric energy. A thermocouple changes heat energy into electric energy.

❏ In direct current (DC) electrons flow in the same direction. In alternating current (AC), electrons reverse their direction regularly.

19-4 Electric Circuits

❏ An electric circuit provides a complete, closed path for an electric current. Electricity can flow only through a closed circuit.

❏ A circuit in which there is only one path for the current is a series circuit. A circuit in which there are several paths is a parallel circuit.

19-5 Electric Power

❏ Electric power is a measure of the rate at which electricity does work or provides energy. The unit of the electric power is the watt (W). To measure large quantities of power, the kilowatt (kW) is used.

❏ Fuses and circuit breakers are used to protect against too much current flowing through a circuit at one time.

VOCABULARY

Define each term in a complete sentence.

alternating current (AC)	electric charge	electroscope	kilowatt-hour	series circuit
ampere	electric current	force of attraction	lightning	static electricity
atom	electric discharge	force of repulsion	lightning rod	subatomic particle
battery	electric field	friction	neutron	thermocouple
circuit breaker	electricity	fuse	nucleus	volt
conduction	electrochemical cell	grounding	ohm	voltage
conductor	electrode	induction	Ohm's law	voltaic cell
direct current (DC)	electrolyte	insulator	parallel circuit	watt
dry cell	electron	kilowatt	power	wet cell
			proton	
			resistance	

CONTENT REVIEW: MULTIPLE CHOICE

On a separate sheet of paper, write the letter of the answer that best completes each statement.

1. The region surrounding a charged particle in which an electric force is noticeable is called a (an)
   a. force of attraction.   b. magnetic field.   c. electric field.   d. static electricity.
2. On which pair of particles would a force of repulsion occur?
   a. proton–neutron   b. electron–electron   c. neutron–neutron   d. electron–proton
3. The three methods of giving an electric charge to an object are conduction, induction, and
   a. friction.   b. resistance.   c. direct current.   d. grounding.
4. Benjamin Franklin performed experiments to provide evidence that lightning is a form of
   a. static electricity.   b. magnetism.   c. induction.   d. voltage.
5. When electrons move back and forth reversing their direction regularly, the current is called
   a. direct current.   b. series current.   c. electric charge.   d. alternating current.
6. In a wet cell, two different metal plates are immersed in a conducting liquid called an electrolyte. These two plates are called
   a. voltaics.   b. electrodes.   c. amperes.   d. dry cells.
7. Electricity cannot flow through which of the following?
   a. series circuit   b. open circuit   c. parallel circuit   d. closed circuit
8. There are different paths for an electric current to take in a (an)
   a. series circuit.   b. open circuit.   c. parallel circuit.   d. closed circuit.
9. Circuit breakers and fuses protect a circuit from becoming
   a. discharged.   b. insulated.   c. overloaded.   d. grounded.
10. Electric energy is measured in
    a. ohms.   b. kilowatt-hours.   c. electron-hours.   d. watts.

CONTENT REVIEW: COMPLETION

On a separate sheet of paper, write the word or words that best complete each statement.

1. Protons and neutrons are contained in the _____, or center, of an atom.
2. The number of electrons in an atom is equal to the number of _____.
3. The strength of an electric field depends upon the _____ from the charged particle.
4. Rubbing a balloon with a piece of cloth charges an object by _____.
5. When a rubber rod is rubbed with fur, it becomes _____ charged.
6. The loss of static electricity is called _____.
7. The _____ is the unit in which current is measured.
8. A (An) _____ generates electricity as a result of temperature differences.
9. If all the parts of an electric circuit are connected one after another, the circuit is called a (an) _____ circuit.
10. Electric _____ is a measure of the rate at which electricity does work.

CONTENT REVIEW: TRUE OR FALSE

Determine whether each statement is true or false. Then on a separate sheet of paper, write "true" if it is true. If it is false, change the underlined word or words to make the statement true.

1. Like charges <u>attract</u> each other; unlike charges <u>repel</u> each other.
2. A neutral object develops a negative charge when it <u>gains</u> electrons.
3. Charging by <u>conduction</u> involves a rearrangement of electric charges.
4. A measure of energy available to move electrons is called <u>friction</u>.
5. Materials that do not allow electrons to flow freely are called <u>insulators</u>.
6. Ohm's law states that the current in a wire is equal to <u>resistance divided by voltage</u>.
7. Copper is a <u>good</u> conductor.
8. An electric circuit provides a complete <u>open</u> path for an electric current.
9. The total amount of electric <u>energy</u> used depends on the total power used and the total time of use.
10. If an object gets lodged in an electric socket, <u>use</u> a utensil to remove it.

CONCEPT REVIEW: SKILL BUILDING

Use the skills you have developed in the chapter to complete each activity.

1. **Applying concepts** Provide an explanation for the following observations:
   a. Clothes dried in a dryer often stick together with "static cling."
   b. Never touch both terminals at the same time when working on a car battery.
   c. It is dangerous to use a 30-amp fuse in a circuit calling for a 15-amp fuse.
2. **Making calculations** A light bulb operates at 60 volts and 2 amps.
   a. What is the power of the light bulb?
   b. How much energy does the light bulb need in order to operate for eight hours?
   c. What is the cost of operating the bulb for 8 hours at a rate of 7¢ per kilowatt-hour?
3. **Identifying relationships** Identify each of the following statements as being a characteristic of (a) a series circuit, (b) a parallel circuit, (c) both a series and a parallel circuit:
   a. $I = V/R$
   b. The total resistance in the circuit is the sum of the individual resistances.
   c. The total current in the circuit is the sum of the current in each resistance.
   d. The current in each part of the circuit is the same.
   e. A break in any part of the circuit causes the current to stop.
4. **Designing an experiment** A plastic ruler is rubbed with waxed paper. The ruler gains an unknown charge. Describe an experiment you could perform using an electroscope, a rubber rod, and a piece of fur to determine the charge on the ruler.

CONCEPT REVIEW: ESSAY

Discuss each of the following in a brief paragraph.

1. Describe the three ways in which an object can be charged.
2. Compare an insulator and a conductor. How might each be used?
3. Discuss three safety rules to follow while using electricity.
4. Describe two ways in which the resistance of a wire can be increased.

Magnetism

20

CHAPTER SECTIONS

20–1 Properties of Magnets

20–2 The Earth As a Magnet

20–3 An Explanation of Magnetism

20–4 Electromagnetism

20–5 Electromagnetic Induction

CHAPTER OBJECTIVES

After completing this chapter, you will be able to

20–1 Describe magnetism and the behavior of magnetic poles.

20–1 Relate magnetic fields and magnetic lines of force.

20–2 Describe the earth's magnetic properties.

20–2 Explain how a compass works.

20–3 Explain magnetism in terms of magnetic domains.

20–4 Describe how a magnetic field is created by an electric current.

20–5 Explain how electricity can be produced from magnetism.

20–5 Apply the principle of induction to motors, generators, and transformers.

The colored lights dance across the sky, growing bright and dim as they change shape. The choreography is never the same—each night a different cast of characters makes its entrances and exits on the darkened stage. When the show is over, the lights grow dim. For a short time, a faint glow remains. Then, once again, the sky is dark.

These colorful displays of light are called auroras. Perhaps you are more familiar with them by another name—the northern lights and the southern lights. At certain times of the year, auroras can be seen in the night sky near the Arctic Circle and the Antarctic Circle.

Auroras occur when charged particles blown out from the sun are trapped by the earth's magnetic field. As some of these particles collide with other particles in the upper atmosphere, visible light is given off.

Auroras provide evidence of how the earth behaves as a giant magnet in space. In this chapter you will learn more about the earth's magnetic field. You also will learn about magnets that can pick up everything from paper clips to huge pieces of scrap metal. And you will gain an understanding of the various applications of magnetism—applications that make your life easier and more comfortable.

A band of colors called an aurora dances across the sky in northern Alaska.

20–1 Properties of Magnets

More than 2000 years ago, the Greeks living in a part of Turkey known as Magnesia discovered a mysterious rock. This rock could attract materials that contained iron. Because the rock was found in Magnesia, the Greeks named it magnetite. The Greeks noticed another interesting thing about this peculiar rock. If they allowed it to swing freely from a string, the same part of the rock would always face in the same direction. That direction was toward a certain northern star, called the leading star or lodestar. So magnetite also became known as lodestone.

The Greeks did not know it then, but they were observing a property of matter called **magnetism.** Certain materials, such as iron, exhibit the property of magnetism. **Magnetism is a force of attraction or repulsion due to an arrangement of electrons.**

Magnetic Poles

Magnetic forces, like electric forces, involve attractions and repulsions. The magnetic forces usually are strongest at the two ends of a magnet. These ends are called **poles.**

The simplest kind of magnet is a straight bar of iron. If a bar magnet is suspended horizontally on a string and allowed to swing freely, one end of the

Figure 20–1 *Magnetite, or lodestone, is a naturally occurring rock that acts like a magnet (left). Modern magnets come in a variety of sizes and shapes, including bar magnets and horseshoe magnets (right).*

magnet will always point toward the north. The end of the magnet that points toward the north is called the **north magnetic pole.** The other end of the magnet, which points toward the south, is called the **south magnetic pole.** You have probably seen bar magnets marked with an "N" to show the north pole and an "S" to show the south pole. Perhaps you have seen horseshoe magnets too. The poles of a horseshoe magnet also are marked N and S.

When two magnets are brought near each other, they exert a force on each other. If two north poles are brought close together, they will repel each other. Two south poles will do the same thing. However, if the north pole of one magnet is brought near the south pole of another magnet, the poles will attract each other. The rule for magnetic poles is: *like poles repel each other and unlike poles attract each other.* How does this rule compare with the rule that describes the behavior of electric charges?

Magnetic Fields

Although magnetic forces are strongest at the poles of a magnet, they are not limited to the poles alone. Magnetic forces are felt around the rest of the magnet as well. The region in which magnetic forces can act is called a **magnetic field.**

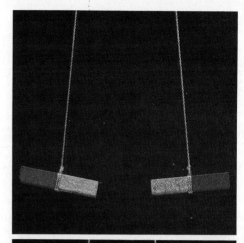
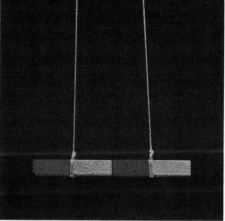

Figure 20–2 *Two bar magnets suspended by strings are free to move. What force is occurring between the magnets in each photograph? Why?*

Figure 20–3 *You can see the magnetic lines of force in the pattern formed by iron filings placed on a glass sheet over a magnet. The diagram illustrates these lines of force. Where are the lines of force strongest?*

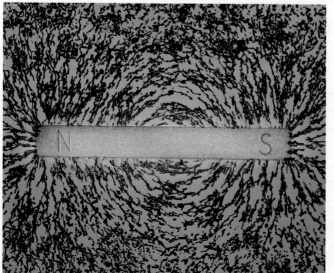
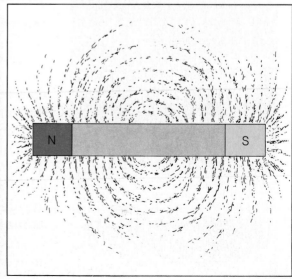

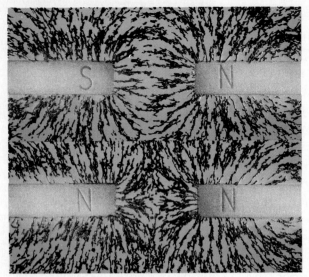

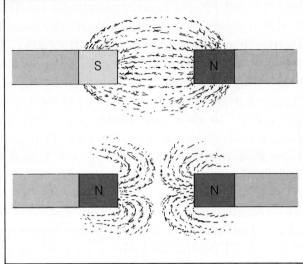

Figure 20–4 *What do the lines of force around these magnets tell you about the interaction of like and unlike magnetic poles?*

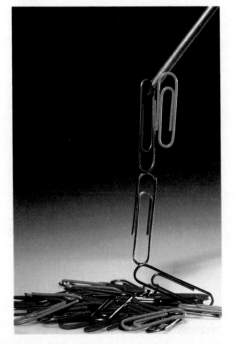

Figure 20–5 *This iron nail attracts metal paper clips. How can an iron nail be turned into a magnet? What is this process called?*

It may help you to think of a magnetic field as an area mapped out by **magnetic lines of force.** Magnetic lines of force define the magnetic field of an object. These lines of force can easily be demonstrated by sprinkling iron filings on a piece of cardboard placed on top of a magnet. Figure 20–3 on page 469 shows the lines of force that make up the magnetic field of a bar magnet. Can you explain why the lines of force form an arc between the north and south poles?

Figure 20–4 shows the lines of force that exist between like and unlike poles of two bar magnets. The pattern of iron filings shows that like poles repel each other and unlike poles attract each other. Where are the lines of force always the most numerous and closest together?

Magnetic Materials

When the Greeks discovered magnetite, or lodestone, they discovered what is known as a **natural magnet.** Natural magnets are naturally occurring substances that have magnetic properties.

Some materials can be made into magnets by stroking them in the same direction several times with strong magnets. Most of the magnets you probably have used are this type of magnet. The process by which a material is made into a magnet is known as **magnetic induction.**

You can see magnetic induction work by stroking an iron nail several times in the same direction with a strong magnet. Soon the nail itself becomes a magnet. Some materials, such as soft iron, are easy to magnetize, but they also lose their magnetism quickly. Magnets made of these materials are called **temporary magnets.** Other magnets are made of materials that are more difficult to magnetize, but which tend to stay magnetized. Magnets made of these materials are called **permanent magnets.**

Cobalt, nickel, and iron are materials from which strong permanent magnets can be made. Most permanent magnets are made of a mixture of aluminum, nickel, cobalt, and iron. This mixture, which makes a very strong magnet, is called alnico.

SECTION REVIEW

1. What is magnetism?
2. State the rule that describes the behavior of magnetic poles.
3. What is a magnetic field?
4. What is a natural magnet? A temporary magnet? A permanent magnet?
5. Suppose that a bar magnet is suspended horizontally from a string. Describe a way to make the magnet rotate in a clockwise direction without touching the magnet.

20–2 The Earth As a Magnet

Section Objective

To describe the earth's magnetic properties

Why does one pole of a bar magnet suspended from a string always point north and the other pole always point south? The first person to suggest an answer to this question was an English physician named William Gilbert. In 1600, Gilbert proposed the idea that the earth itself is a magnet. He predicted that the earth would be found to have magnetic poles.

Gilbert's theory turned out to be correct. Magnetic poles of the earth were discovered. Today, scientists know that the earth behaves as if it has a huge bar magnet buried deep within it. **The earth exerts magnetic forces on magnets and compasses and is surrounded by a magnetic field that is strongest near the north and south magnetic poles.**

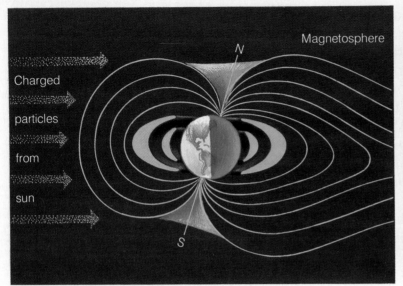

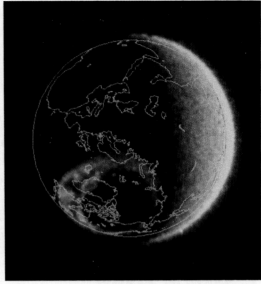

Figure 20–6 *The magnetosphere is made up of charged particles given off by the sun (left). These particles cause the formation of an aurora, such as the one shown in this photo taken by a satellite orbiting the earth (right).*

The region of the earth's magnetic field is called the **magnetosphere.** The magnetosphere, which extends beyond the atmosphere, is made up of charged particles that have been given off by the sun. Sometimes these particles collide with other particles in the upper atmosphere and light is given off. The result is the brightly colored aurora, which you read about in the introduction to this chapter.

Compasses

If you have ever used a compass, you know that a compass needle always points north. The needle of a compass is magnetized. It has a north pole and a south pole. The earth's magnetic field exerts a force on the needle just as it exerts a force on a bar magnet hanging from a string.

The north pole of a compass needle points to the north pole of the earth. As you learned, however, like poles repel and unlike poles attract. So the magnetic pole of the earth to which the north pole of a compass needle points must actually be a magnetic south pole. The same is true of the geographic south pole, which is actually a magnetic north pole. It would be too confusing, however, to try to convey this idea about the magnetism of the poles. So scientists accept the fact that the earth's magnetic north pole and magnetic south pole are named according to their locations near the geographic north pole and geographic south pole.

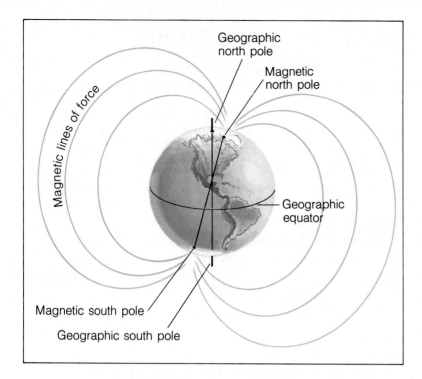

Geographic
north pole

Magnetic
north pole

Magnetic lines of force

Geographic
equator

Magnetic south pole

Geographic south pole

Figure 20–7 *You can see in this illustration that the geographic north and south poles are not located exactly at the magnetic north and south poles. Does a compass needle, then, point directly north?*

A compass needle does not point exactly to the earth's geographic poles. It points to the magnetic poles. Scientists have discovered that the magnetic north pole is located in northeastern Canada, about 1600 kilometers from the geographic north pole. The magnetic south pole is located near the Antarctic Circle. Figure 20–7 shows the locations of the earth's magnetic and geographic north and south poles.

Because a compass points to the earth's magnetic poles, it does not show true north and south. The error in a compass caused by the difference in location of the earth's magnetic and geographic poles is called **magnetic variation.** The extent of magnetic variation is not the same for all places on the earth. Near the equator, magnetic variation is slight. As you get closer to the poles, the error increases.

SECTION REVIEW

1. In what ways is the earth like a magnet?
2. How does a compass work?
3. Why is the earth's magnetic north pole really a magnetic south pole?
4. What is meant by magnetic variation?
5. Why is magnetic variation close to the equator minimal, while near the poles the error is great?

20–3 An Explanation of Magnetism

If you bring a magnet near a piece of wood, glass, aluminum, or plastic, nothing happens. In addition, none of these materials can be magnetized. Yet materials such as iron, steel, nickel, and cobalt react readily to a magnet. And all of these materials can be magnetized. Why are some materials magnetic while others are not?

Scientists believe that magnetism is due to the motion of electrons, particularly their spin. The spin of an electron sets up a magnetic field around the electron.

In most atoms, electrons occur in pairs. Each electron in a pair spins in an opposite direction. So when electrons are paired together, their opposite spins cancel each other. The magnetic field of one electron is cancelled by the magnetic field of the other electron. No magnetism results.

Some metals, however, contain atoms with unpaired electrons. Usually, these unpaired electrons have a random arrangement. They are not lined up in any one direction. Their magnetic fields extend in many different directions. The force of magnetism is not felt, and the metal is unmagnetized.

Now, if all these individual magnetic fields are arranged in the same direction—that is, all north poles facing one way and all south poles facing the other way—the strength of the total magnetic field is greatly increased. The metal is magnetized.

A region in which the magnetic fields of atoms are grouped together is called a **magnetic domain.**

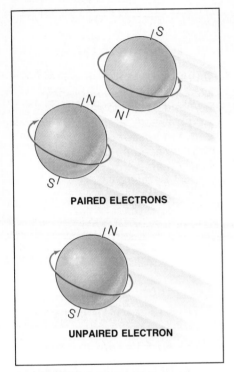

PAIRED ELECTRONS

UNPAIRED ELECTRON

Figure 20–8 *Scientists believe that magnetism is due mainly to the spin of electrons. Since all objects have electrons, why aren't all objects magnetic?*

Figure 20–9 *In an unmagnetized substance, the individual magnetic fields extend in many different directions (left). When these magnetic fields are all arranged in the same direction, the substance becomes magnetized (right). What is the name for the region in which magnetic fields of atoms are grouped together?*

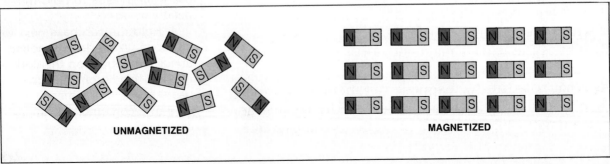

UNMAGNETIZED

MAGNETIZED

HELP WANTED: NUCLEAR MAGNETIC RESONANCE TECHNICIAN Familiarity with NMR scanner required. Must be sensitive to patients' needs. High school diploma and technical training necessary.

Aware that the patient is nervous, the technician calmly explains what is about to happen. Fear begins to disappear as the patient listens to the technician's comforting words.

The long tube-shaped machine that surrounds the patient's body, carefully explains the

nuclear magnetic resonance technician, uses a powerful circular magnet to produce clear three-dimensional images of the patient's internal organs. The painless procedure will reveal information about body structure and function that previously could be found only through surgery.

An NMR technician is trained to operate an NMR scanner. The technician must be able to follow a doctor's prescription and align the patient in the scanner so that the correct body section is imaged.

Some NMR technicians conduct laboratory research, order supplies, and handle administrative duties associated with NMR technology. Other NMR technicians are trained to examine the images produced by the NMR scanner and to recognize tumors or abnormal growths.

In some states, a license is necessary to run an NMR scanner. If you would like to find out how you can become an NMR technician, write to the American Society for Medical Technology, 330 Meadowfern Drive, Houston, TX 77067.

You can think of a magnetic domain as a miniature magnet. In an unmagnetized iron nail, for example, all the magnetic domains are pointing in different directions. See Figure 20–9. If a magnet comes near the nail, the magnetic domains temporarily line up so that like poles all point in the same direction. As soon as the magnet moves away from the nail, however, the domains go back to their original random arrangement.

Stroking the nail with a magnet will cause the domains to line up so that like poles all point in the same direction. The nail will act like a magnet. The nail will lose its magnetic properties as the domains return to a random arrangement.

The model of magnetic domains explains an interesting property of magnets. If you cut a magnet in half, the result is two smaller magnets. A piece cut from a magnet will have a north and south pole just like the original magnet. This is true no matter how many times the magnet is cut. A magnet is actually made up of thousands of smaller magnets.

Sharpen Your Skills

A Model of Magnetic Domains

1. Cut several index cards into small strips to represent magnetic domains. Label each strip with a north pole and a south pole.

2. On one sheet of posterboard, arrange the strips to represent an unmagnetized substance.

3. On another sheet of posterboard, arrange the strips to represent a magnetized substance.

Provide a written explanation for your model.

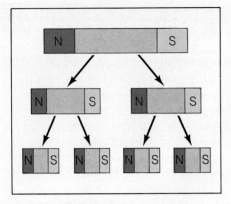

Figure 20–10 *You can see from this illustration that no matter how many times a magnet is cut in half, it retains its magnetic properties. First two and then four smaller magnets are formed. Why?*

A magnet will lose its magnetic properties if the orderly arrangement of domains is destroyed. Banging a magnet with a hammer or dropping it repeatedly on the ground will knock the domains out of line. Since heat causes the particles of a substance to move faster, heating a magnet also will disrupt the arrangement of domains.

SECTION REVIEW

1. Which subatomic particle causes magnetic properties? How?
2. What is a magnetic domain? How does the model of magnetic domains explain magnetism?
3. How can the magnetic properties of a magnet be destroyed?
4. Describe how you could make a compass needle using a steel needle. Use the model of magnetic domains in your answer.

20–4 Electromagnetism

Here is an interesting experiment for you to try. Bring a compass near a wire carrying an electric current. The best place to hold the compass is just above or below the wire, but parallel to it. Observe what happens to the compass needle when electricity is flowing through the wire and when it is not. What do you observe?

This experiment is very similar to one performed more than 150 years ago by the Danish physicist Hans Christian Oersted. His experiment led to an important scientific discovery about the relationship between electricity and magnetism.

Oersted's Discovery

In 1820, Oersted was lecturing a physics class when he noticed a wire lying above a compass. He observed that when current flowed through the wire, the compass needle was deflected, or turned, 90 degrees. When the direction of the current was reversed, the needle moved 90 degrees in the opposite direction. When no electricity flowed through the wire, the compass needle remained stationary.

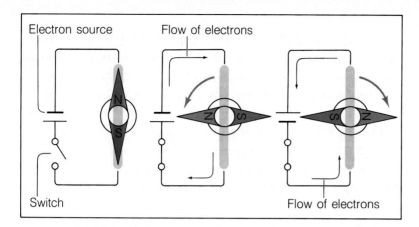

Electron source   Flow of electrons

Switch   Flow of electrons

Figure 20–11 *According to Oersted's experiment, electric current flowing through a wire gives rise to a magnetic field. In the diagram on the left, no current is flowing so the compass needle is not deflected. In the other two diagrams, the needle is deflected as current flows through the wire. What happens when the flow of electricity is reversed?*

For many years Oersted had believed that electricity and magnetism were related—now he had the evidence! As a result of his work, Oersted made a major contribution to the understanding of how electricity and magnetism are related.

An electric current flowing through a wire gives rise to a magnetic field whose direction depends upon the direction of the current. Thus, magnetism can be produced from electricity. Equally important was Oersted's discovery that a looped, or coiled, wire acted like a magnet when a current passed through it. The more coils the wire had, the stronger the magnet. It soon occurred to scientists that coiling a conductor around a piece of soft iron would produce an even more powerful magnet.

Electromagnets

The relationship between electricity and magnetism is called **electromagnetism.** Many applications of electromagnetism are part of your daily life. Powerful temporary magnets called **electromagnets** can be made by wrapping a coil of wire around a soft iron core and passing an electric current through the wire.

The strength of an electromagnet can be increased by increasing the number of loops of wire around the iron core. The electromagnet also will become stronger if the current or voltage that drives the current is increased.

An important property of an electromagnet is that it can be made to lose and then regain its magnetic properties by turning the current off and on. Can you think of a way in which this property of an electromagnet might be useful?

Figure 20–12 *An electromagnet is produced when electric current passes through a wire looped around a nail or other piece of soft iron. How can the strength of an electromagnet be increased?*

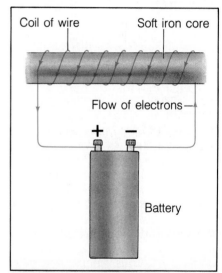

Coil of wire   Soft iron core

Flow of electrons—

+   −

Battery

Figure 20–13 *Large electromagnets can be used to pick up heavy pieces of metal. What is an important property of an electromagnet such as this?*

Figure 20–14 *As alternating current flows through the coils of wire, the poles of the movable electromagnet are reversed. The alternating attraction and repulsion between this electromagnet and the stationary electromagnet cause the movable electromagnet to spin on its shaft. Thus electric energy is converted into mechanical energy in a motor. What is the purpose of the commutator? Why would the motor not work without the commutator?*

ELECTRIC MOTOR   An **electric motor** converts electric energy into mechanical energy that is used to do work. In order to understand the operation of an electric motor, imagine the following experiment. An electromagnet is connected to a dry cell. As the current flows, one end of the electromagnet becomes the north pole and the other end becomes the south pole. A compass can be used to determine which pole is which. The connections to the dry cell are then switched. The direction of the current is reversed. The poles of the electromagnet also are reversed. So by changing the direction of a current, the poles of an electromagnet can be reversed.

An electric motor contains an electromagnet that is free to rotate on a shaft, and a permanent magnet that is held in a fixed position. The current used to run an electric motor is AC, or alternating current. Alternating current is constantly changing direction. As the current changes direction, the poles of the movable electromagnet reverse. Thus, the relationship of the rotating electromagnet to the stationary permanent magnet is one of attraction, then repulsion, then attraction again. This alternating attraction and repulsion causes the electromagnet to spin on its shaft. The mechanical energy of the spinning turns the shaft of the motor, enabling the motor to do work.

If an electric motor were made to run on DC, or direct current, the movable electromagnet would not spin continuously. So an electric motor that runs on DC has a reversing switch called a **commutator**. A commutator is attached to the movable electromagnet. As the electromagnet turns, the commutator switches the direction of current so that the mag-

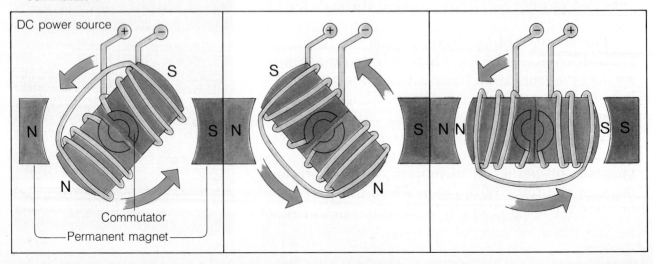

netic poles of the electromagnet reverse and the electromagnet spins. Electric current is supplied to the commutator through contacts called **brushes.** The brushes do not move, but simply touch the commutator as it spins. Electric motors are used in many household appliances—electric saws, electric can openers, food processors, refrigerators, and washing machines.

GALVANOMETER A **galvanometer** is an instrument used to detect small currents. The galvanometer consists of a coil of wire connected to an electric circuit and a needle. As current flows through the wire, the needle of the galvanometer is deflected. Because the needle will move in the opposite direction when the current is reversed, the galvanometer can be used to measure the direction of current.

Some other uses of electromagnets include doorbells, washing machines, telephones, and telegraphs. Electromagnets also are important in heavy machinery that is used to move materials such as scrap metal from one place to another.

SECTION REVIEW

1. How is magnetism related to electricity?
2. How is an electromagnet made?
3. How is an electromagnet different from a permanent magnet?
4. How does an electromagnet provide mechanical energy in an electric motor?
5. How is the effect of an electric current on a compass needle different from the effect of the earth's magnetic field on a compass needle?

20-5 Electromagnetic Induction

If magnetism can be produced from electricity, can electricity be produced from magnetism? Scientists who learned of Oersted's discovery asked this very question. In 1831, the English scientist Michael Faraday provided the answer.

Faraday discovered that an electric current could be generated, or induced, by moving a wire through

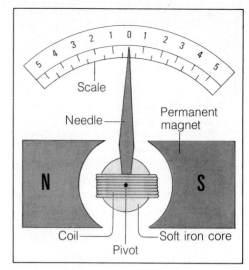

Figure 20–15 *As current flows through the coil of wire in a galvanometer, the magnet forces it to turn and the needle attached to it is deflected. The greater the current, the greater the deflection.*

Section Objective

To explain how magnetism produces electricity

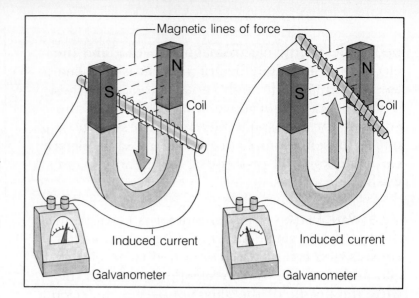

Figure 20–16 *When a conducting wire cuts across magnetic lines of force, electrons flow through the wire and a current is produced. What is this process called? What happens to the deflection of the needle in a galvanometer when the direction in which the lines of force are cut changes?*

Magnetic lines of force

Coil

Induced current

Galvanometer

Coil

Induced current

Galvanometer

a magnetic field. Faraday's discovery was duplicated at about the same time by an American scientist named Joseph Henry.

The process by which a current is produced by the motion of a conductor in a magnetic field is called **electromagnetic induction.** Electromagnetic induction involves magnetic lines of force. **When a conducting wire cuts across magnetic lines of force, a current is produced.** The same result is obtained when a magnet is moved in and out of coils of wire. It does not matter whether the conducting wire is moved or the magnet is moved. What is important is that there is motion within the magnetic field and magnetic lines of forces are cut.

Generators

An important application of electromagnetic induction is the operation of a **generator.** A generator is a device that converts mechanical energy into electric energy. How does this energy conversion compare with that in an electric motor?

A generator consists of an insulated loop of wire and a U-shaped magnet that produces a magnetic field. The loop of wire, which is attached to a power source, is placed between the poles of the magnet. As the power source rotates the loop of wire clockwise, the wire cuts the magnetic lines of force and a current is induced.

As the loop of wire continues to rotate, the wire moves parallel to the magnetic lines of force. At this point no lines of force are being cut so no current is produced. Further rotation moves the loop of wire to a place where magnetic lines of force are cut once again. But this time the lines of force are cut from the opposite direction. This means that the induced current is in the opposite direction. Because the direction of the electric current changes with each complete rotation of the wire, the current produced is AC, or alternating current.

Perhaps you own a bicycle that has a small generator attached to the back wheel to operate the lights. To turn the lights on, a knob on the generator is moved so that it touches the wheel. As you pedal the bike, you provide the mechanical energy to turn the wheel. The wheel then turns the knob. The knob is attached to a shaft inside the generator. The shaft rotates a coil of wire through magnetic lines of force. What happens to the lights when you stop pedaling? Why is this a disadvantage?

Most of the electric power you use every day comes from generators. Large generators at power plants must supply electric power for thousands of homes, offices, hospitals, schools, and stores. Turbines provide the mechanical energy for these large generators. Turbines are wheels that are turned by the force of moving steam or water. As the turbine rotates, it moves coiled wire in the generator through magnetic lines of force produced by a large and powerful magnet.

The large generators in power plants have many loops of wire rotating inside large electromagnets. The speed of the generators is controlled very carefully. The current also is controlled so that it reverses direction 120 times each second. Because two

Figure 20–17 *The force of moving water, such as this water at Hoover Dam on the Colorado River (top), is used to spin turbines (bottom) that help generate electricity by converting mechanical energy into electric energy.*

Figure 20–18 *Inside a generator (left), a loop of wire cuts magnetic lines of force to produce an electric current. What is the mechanical energy that is used to spin the generator on this bicycle?*

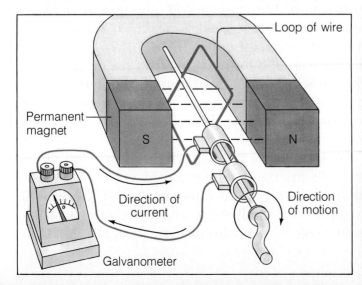

Loop of wire

Permanent magnet

S

N

Direction of current

Direction of motion

Galvanometer

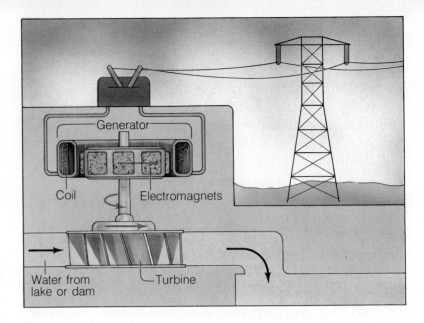

Figure 20–19 *In the operation of a generator, water spins a turbine, which in turn moves large electromagnets encased in coils of insulated wire. As the electromagnets move, the coiled wire cuts magnetic lines of force. Current is produced in the wire and conducted through power lines that eventually reach homes and other buildings.*

Generator

Coil   Electromagnets

Water from lake or dam   Turbine

reversals make one complete cycle of alternating current, the electricity generated has a frequency of 60 hertz. Alternating current in the United States has a frequency of 60 hertz.

Transformers

The processes of electromagnetism and electromagnetic induction are combined in the operation of a **transformer.** A transformer is a device that increases or decreases the voltage of alternating current. A transformer operates on the principle that a current in one coil induces a current in another coil.

A transformer consists of two coils of insulated wire wrapped around the same iron core. One coil is called the **primary coil** and the other coil is called the **secondary coil.** When an alternating current passes through the primary coil, a magnetic field is created. The magnetic field varies in direction as a result of the alternating current.

Electromagnetic induction causes a current to flow in the secondary coil. This is because the secondary coil acts as if a magnet were suddenly pushed into it. Magnetic lines of force are cut, and current is induced.

If the number of loops in the primary and secondary coils are equal, the induced voltage of the secondary coil will be the same as that of the primary coil. However, if there are more loops in the secondary coil than in the primary coil, the voltage

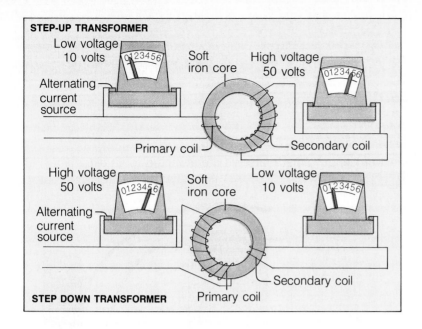

STEP-UP TRANSFORMER

Low voltage 10 volts · Soft iron core · High voltage 50 volts · Alternating current source · Primary coil · Secondary coil

STEP DOWN TRANSFORMER

High voltage 50 volts · Soft iron core · Low voltage 10 volts · Alternating current source · Secondary coil · Primary coil

Figure 20–20 *The processes of electromagnetism and electromagnetic induction are combined in the operation of a transformer. A transformer either increases or decreases the voltage of alternating current. A step-up transformer increases voltage. A step-down transformer decreases voltage. Which coil has the greater number of loops in each type of transformer?*

of the secondary coil will be greater. Since this type of transformer increases the voltage, it is called a **step-up transformer.**

In a **step-down transformer,** there are fewer loops in the secondary coil than in the primary coil. So the voltage of the secondary coil is less than that of the primary coil.

Step-up transformers are used by power companies to transmit high-voltage electricity to homes and offices. They also are used in fluorescent lights and X-ray machines. In television sets, step-up transformers increase ordinary household voltage from 120 volts to 20,000 volts or more.

Step-down transformers reduce the voltage of electricity from a power plant so it can be used in the home. Step-down transformers also are used in doorbells, model electric trains, small radios, tape players, and calculators.

Figure 20–21 *A step-down transformer is used by power companies to reduce high-voltage electricity transmitted from power plants so it can be used in homes and offices.*

SECTION REVIEW

1. What is electromagnetic induction?
2. How can electric current be produced from a magnetic field?
3. What is the purpose of a generator?
4. What is the difference between a step-up and a step-down transformer?
5. Explain what must be the position of the loop of wire in a generator when the generator provides maximum current. Minimum current.

Electromagnetism

Problem

What factors affect the strength of an electromagnet? What materials are attracted to an electromagnet?

Materials *(per group)*

dry cell
5 nails, 10 cm long
2 meters of bell wire
6 paper clips
small piece of aluminum foil
penny or copper sheet
nickel
dime
other objects to be tested

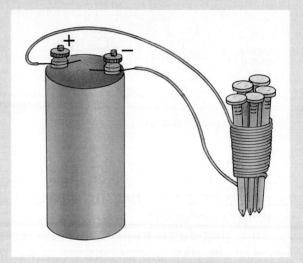

Procedure

1. Hold the five nails together and neatly wrap the wire around them. Do not allow the nails to overlap. Leave about 50 cm of wire at one end and about 100 cm at the other end.
2. Attach the shorter end of the wire to one terminal of the dry cell.
3. Momentarily touch the 100-cm end of the wire to the other terminal of the dry cell. **CAUTION:** *Do not operate the electromagnet for more than a few seconds each time.*
4. When the electromagnet is on, test each material for magnetic attraction. Record your results.
5. During the time the electromagnet is on, determine the number of paper clips it can hold.
6. Wrap the 100-cm end of wire over the first windings to make a second layer. You should use about 50 cm. There should be approximately 50 cm of wire remaining.
7. Connect the wire once again to the dry cell. Determine the number of paper clips the electromagnet can now hold. Record your results.

8. Carefully remove three nails from the windings. Connect the wire and determine the number of paper clips the electromagnet can hold. Record your results.

Observations

1. What materials are attracted to the electromagnet?
2. How many paper clips can the electromagnet hold in step 5? In step 7? In step 8?

Conclusions

1. What do the materials attracted to the magnet have in common?
2. When you increase the number of turns of wire, what effect does this have on the strength of the electromagnet?
3. How does removing the nails affect the strength of the electromagnet?
4. What general statement can be made about the factors that affect the strength of an electromagnet?

CHAPTER REVIEW

SUMMARY

20-1 Properties of Magnets

❏ Magnetism is a force of attraction or repulsion due to an arrangement of electrons.

❏ Like magnetic poles repel each other, while unlike poles attract each other.

❏ The region in which magnetic forces can act is called a magnetic field.

❏ There are three types of magnets: natural magnets, temporary magnets, and permanent magnets.

20-2 The Earth As a Magnet

❏ The earth is surrounded by a magnetic field that is strongest around the magnetic north and south poles.

❏ A compass needle does not point exactly to the earth's geographic north pole. It points to the magnetic north pole. The difference in the location of the earth's magnetic and geographic poles is called magnetic variation.

20-3 An Explanation of Magnetism

❏ Magnetism is created by electron spin.

❏ Magnetic domains are regions in which all the atoms' magnetic fields line up pointing in the same direction.

❏ A magnet will lose its magnetic properties if the orderly arrangement of the domains is destroyed.

20-4 Electromagnetism

❏ In 1820, Hans Christian Oersted discovered that a magnetic field is created around a wire that is conducting an electric current.

❏ The relationship between electricity and magnetism is called electromagnetism.

❏ An electric motor converts electric energy into mechanical energy that is used to do work.

20-5 Electromagnetic Induction

❏ In 1831, Michael Faraday discovered that an electric current can be produced from a magnetic field. This process is known as electromagnetic induction.

❏ One of the most important uses of electromagnetic induction is in the operation of a generator, which converts mechanical energy into electric energy.

❏ Electromagnetism and electromagnetic induction are combined in the operation of a transformer, which is a device that increases or decreases the voltage of alternating current.

VOCABULARY

Define each term in a complete sentence.

brush	magnetic field	north magnetic pole	step-down transformer
commutator	magnetic induction	permanent magnet	step-up transformer
electric motor	magnetic lines of force	pole	temporary magnet
electromagnet		primary coil	transformer
electromagnetic induction	magnetic variation	secondary coil	
electromagnetism	magnetism	south magnetic pole	
galvanometer	magnetosphere		
generator	natural magnet		
magnetic domain			

CONTENT REVIEW: MULTIPLE CHOICE

On a separate sheet of paper, write the letter of the answer that best completes each statement.

1. In a magnet, magnetic forces are strongest
   a. at the center.   b. at the poles.   c. around the edges.   d. in the magnetic field.
2. The region in which magnetic forces can act is called a
   a. line of force.   b. pole.   c. magnetic field.   d. field of attraction.
3. The region of the earth's magnetic field is called the
   a. atmosphere.   b. stratosphere.   c. aurora.   d. magnetosphere.
4. The idea of the earth as a magnet was first proposed by
   a. Dalton.   b. Faraday.   c. Oersted.   d. Gilbert.
5. Adjustments must be made for directions measured with a compass because
   a. a compass does not point to true north.
   b. a compass needle tends to lose its magnetism.
   c. the earth's magnetic poles are constantly changing.
   d. the earth's geographic poles are constantly changing.
6. Which of the following is not a magnetic material?
   a. lodestone   b. glass   c. cobalt   d. nickel
7. The particle responsible for an atom's magnetic properties is the
   a. electron.   b. neutron.   c. proton.   d. nucleus.
8. Which of the following will make a magnet lose its magnetic properties?
   a. stroking the magnet   b. hanging the magnet from a string
   c. dropping the magnet   d. cutting the magnet
9. A galvanometer is a device that is used to
   a. convert mechanical energy into electric energy.   b. detect electric current.
   c. convert electricity into magnetism.   d. detect a magnetic field.
10. The purpose of a generator is to
    a. convert mechanical energy into electric energy.
    b. convert electric energy into mechanical energy.
    c. use magnetism to do work.
    d. measure electric current.

CONTENT REVIEW: COMPLETION

On a separate sheet of paper, write the word or words that best complete each statement.

1. The natural magnet discovered by the Greeks is called _____.
2. The process by which artificial magnets are created is called _____.
3. The error in a compass is called _____.
4. The _____ of electrons creates a magnetic field in an atom.
5. Atomic magnetic fields group together in regions called _____.
6. The relationship between electricity and magnetism is called _____.
7. Wrapping a coil of conducting wire around a piece of iron makes a (an) _____.
8. A _____ converts electric energy into mechanical energy.
9. Current that constantly changes directions is called _____.
10. An electric current is produced from a magnetic field by _____.

CONTENT REVIEW: TRUE OR FALSE

Determine whether each statement is true or false. Then on a separate sheet of paper, write "true" if it is true. If it is false, change the underlined word or words to make the statement true.

1. The north pole of a magnet suspended horizontally from a string will point <u>north</u>.
2. Like poles of a magnet <u>attract</u> each other.
3. A naturally occurring substance with magnetic properties is a <u>permanent</u> magnet.
4. A compass needle points to the earth's <u>geographic north pole</u>.
5. Steel <u>cannot</u> be magnetized.
6. In a magnetized substance, <u>magnetic domains</u> point in the same direction.
7. Electromagnets are <u>permanent</u> magnets.
8. <u>Oersted</u> discovered electromagnetism.
9. In a generator, <u>mechanical</u> energy is converted to <u>electric</u> energy.
10. Large generators at power plants get their mechanical energy from <u>steam engines</u>.

CONCEPT REVIEW: SKILL BUILDING

Use the skills you have developed in the chapter to complete each activity.

1. **Identifying cause and effect** Explain each of the following observations:
   a. A compass needle points to the north.
   b. A compass needle is deflected 90 degrees when placed above a wire conducting an electric current.
   c. A compass needle is not deflected when a loop of wire in a generator is parallel to the magnetic lines of force.
2. **Applying concepts** The process of electromagnetic induction might seem to break the law of conservation of energy, which says that energy cannot be created. Explain why this is actually not so.
3. **Making diagrams** Use a diagram to show how the rotation of a wire loop in a generator first induces a current in one direction, then no current, then a current in the other direction.
4. **Making comparisons** How do the lines of force that arise when north and south poles of magnets are placed close together compare with the lines of force that arise when two north poles are placed close together? Use a diagram in your explanation.
5. **Applying definitions** Indicate whether each of the following characteristics describes (a) a step-up transformer, (b) a step-down transformer, (c) both a step-up and a step-down transformer.

   a. Voltage in the secondary coil is greater.
   b. Involves electromagnetism and electromagnetic induction.
   c. Voltage in the primary coil is greater.
   d. Used in doorbells and model trains.
   e. Consists of two insulated coils wrapped around opposite sides of an iron core.
   f. More loops in the secondary coil.

CONCEPT REVIEW: ESSAY

Discuss each of the following in a brief paragraph.

1. Explain how an aurora is produced.
2. Compare the three types of magnets.
3. Using the theory of magnetic domains, explain how a substance is magnetized. How it loses its magnetism.
4. Describe the discoveries of Oersted and Faraday. How are these discoveries related?
5. Explain how a galvanometer works.
6. Explain the difference between an electric motor and an electric generator in terms of energy conversion.

The Search for SUPERCONDUCTORS

Karl Mueller and Johannes Bednorz

Imagine trains that fly above their tracks at airplane speeds and powerful computers that fit in the palm of your hand. Picture unlocking the secrets of the atom, or skiing on slopes made of air. Purely imagination? Not really! All of these things—and more—have been brought closer to reality by the work of Dr. Karl Alex Mueller and Dr. Johannes Georg Bednorz. These two dedicated scientists have changed fantasy to fact through their work with superconductors.

Searching for a Better Conductor

Much of our electricity runs through copper wire. Copper is an example of a conductor, or a material that carries electricity well. However, copper is not a perfect conductor because it offers resistance to the flow of electricity. As a result of resistance, about 15 percent of the electric power passing through a copper wire is lost as waste heat.

A superconductor has no resistance. Therefore, it can conduct electricity without any loss of power. With superconductors, power plants could produce more usable electricity at lower costs and with no waste. Electric motors could be made smaller and more powerful. Superconducting wires connecting computer chips could produce smaller, faster computers.

Scientists have known about superconductors for more than 75 years. But although the principle of superconductivity was understood, the method of creating one remained a secret. . . . A secret that seemed to be "locked in a deep freeze." For until the time of Mueller and Bednorz's discovery, materials would not become superconductors unless they were chilled to at least

◄ **This magnetic cube may seem to be defying gravity. Actually, it is floating above a disk made of a superconductive material. The superconductive disk repels magnetic fields and causes the magnet to float in midair.**

−250°C! To cool materials to such extremely low temperatures, scientists had to use liquid helium, which is very costly. The supercold superconductors were just too expensive to be of general use.

If a substance could become superconducting at −196°C or higher, then it could be cooled with liquid nitrogen. Liquid nitrogen costs as little as a nickel a liter—less expensive than milk or soda pop. But what substances might become superconductors at these relatively high temperatures? That was the problem Dr. Mueller and Dr. Bednorz had to solve.

Looking in a New Direction

Many experts thought that superconductors simply did not exist at temperatures higher than −250°C. But Dr. Mueller, a highly respected physicist at IBM's research laboratory in Zurich, Switzerland, remained fascinated by high-temperature superconductors. In fact, he had already devised a new approach to finding one!

To some, his idea seemed impossible. But Dr. Mueller and his partner Dr. Bednorz were willing to follow their unusual approach under the guidance of what Dr. Mueller describes as "my intuition."

For almost three years, the two scientists mixed powders, baked them in ovens to

Superconductivity pioneers Karl Mueller (right) and Johannes Bednorz.

form new compounds, and then chilled them to see if they would lose their resistance to electricity. And for three years, the two scientists kept their work a secret. "We were sure anybody would say, 'These guys are crazy,'" Dr. Bednorz later said. But despite endless hours of hard work and dedication, none of the new compounds was the superconductor Mueller and Bednorz sought.

Then in December 1985, Dr. Bednorz read about a new copper oxide. He and Dr. Mueller thought the oxide looked promising. They decided to test it for superconductivity. On January 27, 1986, Dr. Mueller and Dr. Bednorz broke the temperature barrier to superconductivity—and broke it by a large amount. They achieved superconductivity at −243°C. By April, Mueller and Bednorz had raised the temperature of superconductivity to a new record, −238°C. Around the world, scientists began to duplicate the experiments and make even greater advances in high-temperature superconductors.

In February 1987, a team of researchers at the University of Houston led by Dr. C.W. Chu created a new oxide that shows superconductivity at −175°C. This is the first superconductor that can be cooled with liquid nitrogen—the first superconductor that might be used for everyday purposes.

Dr. Mueller and Dr. Bednorz received the 1987 Nobel Prize for Physics for their pioneering work on superconductors. Their work however does not end here. They look forward to the development of a room-temperature superconductor!

Issues in Science

NUCLEAR POWER: PROMISE OR PERIL?

A fiery explosion on April 26, 1986, rocked a city in the Soviet Union and terrified the rest of the world. The accident occurred at the Chernobyl Nuclear Power Plant, near Kiev. An explosion in a nuclear reactor blew off the roof of the plant and triggered a fire that burned for days. A cloud of radioactive particles rose into the air and was carried by winds throughout Europe. Chernobyl was the most serious nuclear accident in history.

Several people were killed instantly by the explosion at the Chernobyl plant. Others died soon after from burns or radiation poisoning. How many more will die in future years as a result of radiation remains unknown. But people may not be the only casualties of this explosion. The future of nuclear power in the United States has been gravely threatened by the accident at Chernobyl.

BENEFITS VERSUS RISKS

The popularity of nuclear power in the United States had begun to decline long before the Chernobyl accident. Rising costs, delays in obtaining government licenses, and construction problems had plagued the nuclear power program. Public fears about the safety of nuclear power and the health hazards associated with nuclear wastes had prompted people to ask, "Is nuclear power worth it?" Accidents such as the one at Chernobyl have caused many people to answer, "No!"

People who are in favor of nuclear power say this attitude is not realistic. They argue that nuclear power is needed as a source of energy. Fossil fuels such as coal, oil, and natural gas presently supply most of the energy required to meet worldwide needs. But someday fossil fuels will run out. Once used up, these *nonrenewable* energy resources will be gone forever.

Critics of nuclear power say we can develop alternative energy resources. Energy from the sun, wind, rushing water, tides, and the earth's inner heat could meet our energy needs. These *renewable* resources could lessen our dependence on fossil fuels and nuclear energy. But proponents of nuclear power stress that these resources alone cannot satisfy the increasing energy needs of an increasing world population.

THE SAFETY ISSUE

People in favor of nuclear power claim that despite the Chernobyl accident, nuclear technology has a better safety record than coal, oil, and hydroelectric technology. To support this position, they cite the thousands of deaths caused by coal mine accidents, oil-drilling accidents, and dam failures.

Critics of nuclear power argue that the risks of conventional energy technologies are known and understood, while the dangers of nuclear power are not fully defined. They say that the possibility of more serious nuclear disasters exists, as the Chernobyl accident, unfortunately, has hinted at.

"Once again," says Robert Pollard, a nuclear power expert with the Union of Concerned Scientists, "this accident has brought home the idea that when you build a commercial nuclear power plant, you decide to accept the risk, however small, of killing a few thousand people."

Many critics add that large-scale accidents are not the only dangers of nuclear power. Small radiation leaks from nuclear plants, nuclear fuels, and nuclear waste dumps pose long-term health hazards to millions of people. These critics contend that no more nuclear power plants should be built until all the risks are known.

Supporters of nuclear power point to the progress of implementing safety procedures in nuclear power plants. Their prediction is that nuclear power plants of the future "will be perfectly safe."

Do you think the benefits of nuclear power outweigh the risks? Or are nations jeopardizing their future safety by turning to nuclear power? If nuclear energy becomes a dead issue, will it cause hardship or encourage the development of alternative energy resources?

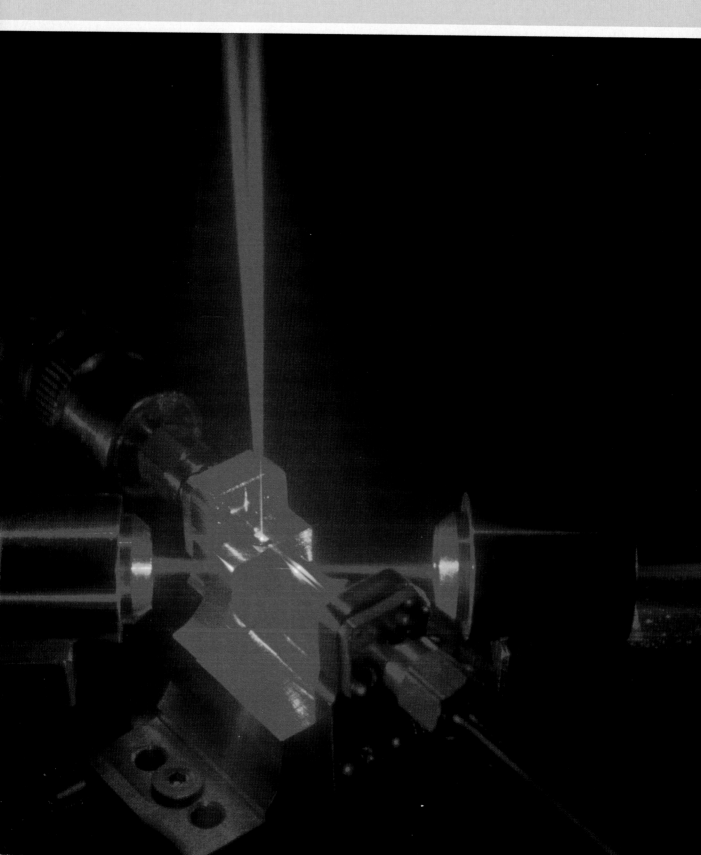

Waves: Sound and Light

In 1979, Gary Finkle's world changed dramatically. A severe spinal-cord injury suffered in a swimming accident left Gary virtually without any feeling or movement below his shoulders. Everyone assumed he had no chance for an independent life. But they were wrong! A unique combination of light energy and a clever monkey gave Gary a new lease on life.

Gary became a charter member of a nonprofit organization that trains capuchin monkeys to help people such as himself increase their self-reliance and independence through the use of light. Here is how this unusual method works. Gary uses his mouth to control a small laser-beam pointer mounted on his wheelchair. With it he can direct his monkey, Jo, to do a number of tasks. Responding to the laser-beam signals, Jo brings Gary his snacks and even cleans away the scraps.

Gary's heart-warming story is just one of the many important applications of light. From primitive signal fires to modern fiber-optic technology and holograms, human beings have used light waves for communication. As you read the chapters in this unit, you will learn about light and another important wave—sound. And you will explore their many uses in your everyday world.

CHAPTERS

21 Waves

22 Sound

23 Light

24 Light and Its Uses

Laser light, a concentrated beam of coherent light, has many important and practical uses.

Waves

21

CHAPTER SECTIONS

21–1 Nature of Waves

21–2 Types of Waves

21–3 Characteristics of Waves

21–4 Speed of Waves

21–5 Interactions of Waves

CHAPTER OBJECTIVES

After completing this chapter, you will be able to

21–1 Define a wave.

21–1 Describe the medium of a wave.

21–2 Compare transverse and longitudinal waves.

21–3 Identify the basic characteristics of waves.

21–4 Relate the speed, frequency, and wavelength of a wave.

21–5 Describe reflection, refraction, diffraction, and interference of waves.

This was it! The wave of the day. He had waited all morning for this one, passing up several good rides. But this wave belonged to him. It was as if it had traveled several thousand kilometers from the Arctic to the Pipeline in Hawaii just for him.

A couple of quick strokes and he was up on his surfboard. He drove down the face of the wave in an S-shaped turn. He drove again for distance and then hit full speed as he reached the bottom. The wave towered over him. The water thundered around him. He felt its awesome energy and knew if he could not keep ahead of the crushing weight of the water, he would be pulled under. But success was his this time. With a sense of accomplishment and an appreciation of nature's power, he rode the wave all the way to shore.

What is a wave? Where does a wave get its energy? How can a wave travel several thousand kilometers? As you read this chapter, you will find the answers.

A wave such as the ''Pipeline'' in Hawaii is an exhilarating reminder of nature's awesome energy.

21–1 Nature of Waves

Drop a pebble into a still pond and observe the circular waves moving outward. Watch the waves moving across tall grass on a windy day. Observe the huge waves in the ocean during a storm. These examples illustrate wave motion. You might be surprised to discover that sound and light are also examples of wave motion. But sound waves and light waves are difficult to observe.

Waves and Energy

When a pebble is dropped into a still pond, the surface of the water is disturbed. The disturbance moves outward along the surface of the water as a series of **waves.** The disturbance is caused by energy traveling through the water. What is the source of this energy?

The pebble that is dropped into the water has kinetic energy because it is moving. Kinetic energy is energy of motion. When the pebble hits the water, some of its kinetic energy is transferred to nearby particles of water. These particles start to move as a result of the energy. Their movement transfers energy to neighboring water particles, which in turn move. As the water particles move, a wave is produced across the surface of the water. Energy is transferred from one place to another.

A wave is a disturbance that transfers energy through matter or space. A wave is always the result

Figure 21–1 *A pebble thrown into a still pond creates a disturbance that moves outward along the surface of the water as a wave (left). The small drop seen in the air will fall back creating more waves. The waves generated by a hurricane along the coast of Boca Raton, Florida, are very powerful and dramatic (right). What is common to both these waves?*

of energy moving from one place to another. It is important to note that when a wave moves through matter, the particles of matter do *not* move along with the wave. Only the energy that produces the wave moves with the wave.

Waves Through a Medium

A **medium** is any substance or region through which a wave is transmitted. Water is a medium for ocean waves. Air is a medium for sound waves. All phases of matter can act as a medium. For certain waves, a medium of matter is not required. These waves can be transmitted through a vacuum. Light is such a wave. Light from the sun, for example, travels to the earth through the vacuum of space.

A medium transfers wave energy but has no overall motion itself. The particles of the medium vibrate, or move, in small circles. The energy is transmitted from one place to another. But there is no movement of matter between these places. In other words, energy is transmitted *without* the movement of the medium as a whole.

If you have ever watched an object floating on water, you will understand wave motion and the transfer of energy. As the waves move past the object, the object bobs up and down. The waves continue to move forward, but the object remains in approximately the same place. Energy is transmitted, but matter is not.

Two properties of a medium affect the speed of a wave. One property is density. A wave moves more slowly in a denser medium. As the density of a medium increases, the speed of a wave decreases. Why? A denser medium has more inertia to overcome. It is harder to get the particles of a denser

Figure 21–2 *These wheat fields in Montana illustrate wave motion. The stalks of wheat sway back and forth as their energy is transmitted as waves. The stalks, however, do not move with the wave. What is the medium for these waves?*

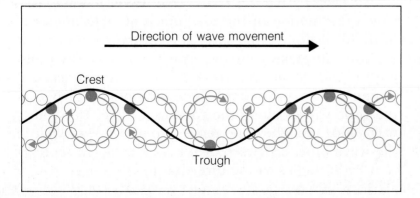

Direction of wave movement

Crest

Trough

Figure 21–3 *As a wave moves through the medium of water, the individual water particles move in circles. The energy of the wave is transmitted without the movement of the medium as a whole. If you were viewing an object on the leftmost circle, how would its motion appear?*

medium to respond to the energy of the wave and to start moving.

Another property of a medium that affects the speed of a wave is elasticity. Elasticity refers to the ability of a medium to return quickly to its original shape after being disturbed. A wave moves faster in a more elastic medium. For example, the speed of sound in steel is greater than it is in air. The elasticity of steel is greater than that of air.

SECTION REVIEW

1. What is a wave? What is a medium?
2. How does a wave move through a medium?
3. What two properties of a medium affect the speed of a wave?
4. At 25°C, the speed of sound in air is 346 m/sec. At 0°C, the speed of sound in air is 332 m/sec. Explain why the speed decreases as the temperature decreases.

Sharpen Your Skills

Earthquake Waves

Earthquakes produce three types of waves. Using books and other reference materials in the library, find out about earthquake waves. Write a report on your findings. Include a diagram of each type of wave. What two types can you easily identify?

21–2 Types of Waves

All waves are not the same. Ocean waves are a different type of wave from sound waves. Why? Although they both transfer energy through a medium, the movement of the disturbance through the medium is quite different. **Depending on the motion of the medium as compared to the movement of the wave, waves are classified as either transverse or longitudinal.**

Transverse Waves

An ocean wave is a **transverse wave.** A wave in which the motion of the medium is at right angles to the direction of the wave is a transverse wave.

You can make your own transverse wave by pulling up and down on a rope that has been attached at one end to a doorknob. The energy you give to the rope travels along the rope as a wave. But you will notice that the rope moves up and down while the wave moves forward. Your up-and-down motion is at right angles to the direction of the wave.

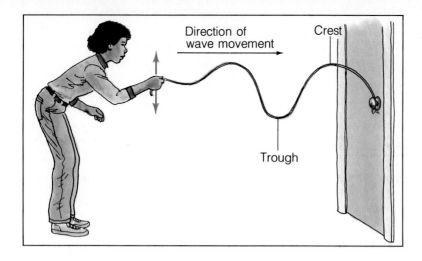

Figure 21–4 *A rope attached at one end to a doorknob and pulled up and down will generate a transverse wave. How does the movement of the rope compare to the direction of wave movement?*

Two important parts of a transverse wave represent the up-and-down motions of the particles of the medium. The **crest** of a wave is the high point. The crest represents the maximum displacement upward of a particle of the medium. The **trough** represents the maximum displacement downward of a particle of the medium. The trough is the low point of a wave. See Figure 21–4.

CAREER

Geophysicist

HELP WANTED: Experienced **GEOPHYSICIST** to lead an expedition in search of new sources of oil and natural gas. Knowledge of sonar devices helpful. College degree in geology required.

The first rays of sunlight draw long shadows of the people climbing into two trucks. The trucks roll out across the desert as the sun and the temperature steadily rise. A typical day for a **geophysicist** might begin this way.

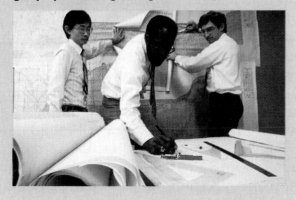

The geophysicists' trucks carry devices that help detect underground oil. One device, called a thumper truck, carries a huge vibrator on its underside. As the truck slowly moves across the desert sand, the vibrator pounds the earth, sending sound waves downward through rock.

The sound waves from the thumper truck are reflected from the rock layers beneath the sand back to the earth's surface. Another device, called a seismograph, records the time it takes for the waves to travel. The geophysicist then studies the wave speeds to determine if the rock layers contain pockets of oil.

Geophysicists perform similar tests in the oceans to detect oil, gas, or minerals buried there. Other geophysicists use sound waves to make maps of the earth's surface and to study earthquakes and water and soil conditions.

If you would like information about a career as a geophysicist, contact the American Geophysical Union, Meetings and Members Program, 2000 Florida Avenue NW, Washington, DC 20009.

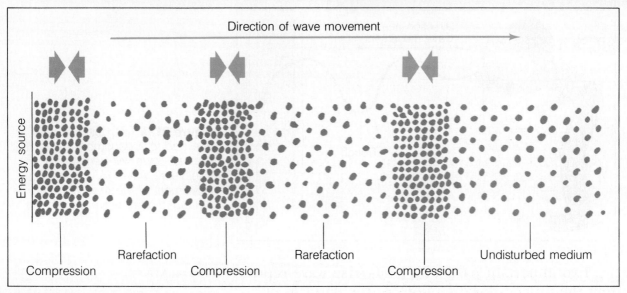

Figure 21–5 *A longitudinal wave is a series of compressions and rarefactions. The motion of the molecules of the medium is parallel to the direction of wave movement. What happens to the molecules of the medium in a compression? In a rarefaction?*

Longitudinal Waves

Clap your hands together near your face. You hear a clap. Do you also feel any air striking your face? When you clap your hands, you crowd the air molecules together, causing a **compression** (kuhm-PREHSH-uhn). A compression is a space in the medium in which the molecules are crowded together. See Figure 21–5. This compressed band of air then moves forward. As it does, it leaves behind a space that contains much fewer molecules. A space in the medium in which there are fewer molecules is called a **rarefaction** (rair-uh-FAK-shun). See Figure 21–5.

As the compressed air molecules move forward, they collide with the air molecules next to them. These molecules also become compressed. Each layer of molecules pushes the next layer as the compressions move forward through the medium. Each compression is followed by a rarefaction. So rarefactions also move forward. As the layers move back and forth through the medium, compressions and rarefactions develop and "move" in a regular, repeating way. Energy is transmitted as a wave.

A wave that consists of a series of compressions and rarefactions is a **longitudinal** (lahn-juh-TYOOD-uhn-uhl) **wave.** In a longitudinal wave, the motion of the medium is parallel to the direction of the wave. In other words, the molecules of the medium move in the same direction the wave moves. Sound waves are longitudinal waves.

SECTION REVIEW

1. What is a transverse wave?
2. What is a compression? A rarefaction?
3. What is a longitudinal wave?
4. Suppose that a long line is formed at a movie theater. Someone in back gives a big push. Everyone moves forward as this "push" moves toward the front. As people regain their balance, they move back. Which type of wave is generated? Explain your answer.

21–3 Characteristics of Waves

Section Objective

To describe the characteristics of a wave

There are many different kinds of waves. Sound waves, light waves, radio waves, microwaves, and ocean waves are but a few examples. All waves, however, share certain basic characteristics. **All waves have amplitude, wavelength, and frequency.**

Amplitude

A wave is a disturbance in a medium. The molecules in the medium are moved from their normal, or rest, position. The maximum distance the molecules are displaced from their rest position is called the **amplitude** (AM-plih-tyood) of the wave. The amplitude of a wave indicates the energy of that

Figure 21–6 *The basic characteristics of a wave are shown here. What is the high point of a wave called? The low point? What does wave amplitude measure?*

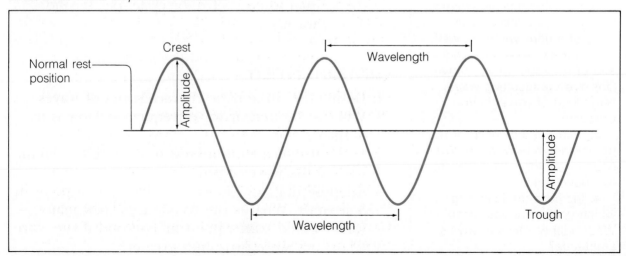

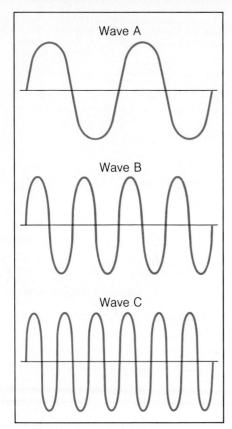

Figure 21–7 *Frequency is the number of complete waves per unit time. What is the frequency of Wave A? Wave B? Wave C?*

wave. As the energy that generates a wave increases, the amplitude of the wave also increases. What happens to the crest and trough of a wave as amplitude increases?

Wavelength

The distance between two consecutive crests or troughs of a wave is called the **wavelength.** Actually, the wavelength can be measured from any point on a wave as long as it is measured to the *same point* on the next wave. Wavelength is usually measured in meters or centimeters. The symbol for wavelength is the Greek letter lambda (λ).

Frequency

The number of complete waves, or complete cycles, per unit time is called **frequency** (FREE-kwehn-see). For a transverse wave, you can think of frequency as the number of crests *or* troughs produced per unit time. For a longitudinal wave, frequency is the number of compressions *or* rarefactions produced per unit time. For example, if 100 complete cycles of compressions and rarefactions—100 compressions and 100 rarefactions—are carried by a medium in one second, the frequency of the wave is 100 cycles per second.

The unit used to measure wave frequency is called the **hertz (Hz).** This unit is named after Heinrich Hertz, who was one of the first scientists to study certain types of waves. A frequency of one hertz is equal to one wave, or cycle, per second: 1 Hz = 1 wave/sec.

SECTION REVIEW

1. Define the three basic characteristics of waves.
2. What is the unit of wave frequency? How is it defined?
3. If the distance from a crest to a trough is 0.5 m, what is the wavelength?
4. Suppose that you notice 15 waves pass a point in 3 seconds. What is the frequency? How many waves would pass a point in 1 second if the wave frequency were two times greater?

21-4 Speed of Waves

Section Objective

To relate wave speed, frequency, and wavelength

You have learned that the speed of a wave depends on the medium in which it travels. In a given medium, however, the speed of a wave is constant. The speed of a wave is determined by the number of waves passing in one second and the length of the wave. **The speed of a wave is equal to the frequency times the wavelength.**

speed = frequency × wavelength

When the frequency of a wave is measured in hertz and the wavelength is measured in meters, the speed of the wave is measured in meters per second.

A wave with a frequency of 4 Hz and a wavelength of 2 m has a speed of 8 m/sec (4 Hz × 2 m = 8 m/sec). If the frequency of the wave were increased to 8 Hz, the wavelength would decrease to 1 m in the same medium. Why? In a given medium, the speed of a wave is constant. The speed must still be 8 m/sec. If the frequency is now 8 Hz, then the wavelength must be 1 m (8 Hz × 1 m = 8 m/sec). An increase in frequency requires a corresponding decrease in wavelength. What would happen to the frequency if the wavelength were increased?

Sample Problem

What is the speed of a wave with a frequency of 100 hertz and a wavelength of 15 meters?

Solution

Step 1 Write the formula	**speed = frequency × wavelength**
Step 2 Substitute given numbers and units	**speed = 100 hertz × 15 meters**
Step 3 Solve for unknown variable	**speed = 1500 meters/second**

Practice Problems

1. A sound wave has a frequency of 110 Hz and a wavelength of 3.0 m. What is the speed of the wave?

2. What is the frequency of a wave that has a wavelength of 5.0 m and a speed of 250 m/sec?

SECTION REVIEW

1. If the frequency and wavelength of a wave are changed, what happens to the speed? Why?
2. What is the relationship between wave speed, frequency, and wavelength?
3. A wave has a frequency of 10 Hz and a wavelength of 30 m. What is its speed?
4. If the frequency of the wave in question 3 were 20 Hz, what would be the wavelength?

21–5 Interactions of Waves

Waves traveling in the same medium move at a constant speed and direction. What would happen, however, if the waves encountered a different medium, reached an obstacle, or met another wave? Depending on the conditions, the waves would interact in a certain way with the medium. **The four basic wave interactions are reflection, refraction, diffraction, and interference.**

Reflection

Figure 21–8 shows water waves striking a barrier and bouncing back. This interaction is called **reflection** (rih-FLEHK-shuhn). Reflection is the bouncing back of a wave after it strikes a boundary that does *not* absorb the wave's energy. Imaginary

Figure 21–8 *Reflection is the bouncing back of a wave after it strikes a boundary that does not absorb its energy. According to the law of reflection, the angle of incidence equals the angle of reflection (right). This laser beam dramatically illustrates the reflection of light as it strikes a mirrored surface (left).*

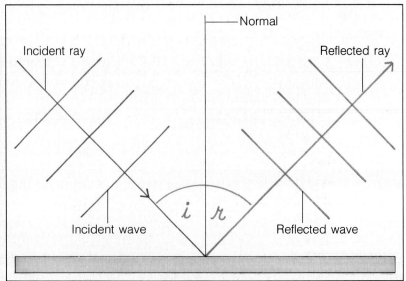

rays have been added to the diagram to show the direction of the incoming waves and the waves that are bounced back.

The incoming wave is called an **incident wave.** The wave that is bounced back is called a **reflected wave.** The angle formed by the incident ray and a line perpendicular to the barrier is called the **angle of incidence, i.** The angle formed by the same perpendicular line and the reflected ray is called the **angle of reflection, r.** The line perpendicular to the barrier is called the **normal.** The **law of reflection** states that the angle of incidence is equal to the angle of reflection.

Refraction

Waves do not bend as they travel through a medium. Waves travel in straight lines. However, when waves pass *at an angle* from one medium to another—air to water or glass to air, for example—they bend. The waves bend because the speed of the waves changes as the waves travel from one medium to another.

The bending of waves due to a change in speed is called **refraction** (rih-FRAK-shuhn). Refraction occurs because waves move at different speeds in different mediums. As waves pass at an angle from one medium to another, they may speed up or slow down.

You can see the results of the refraction of light. Place a pencil diagonally in a glass of water. The

Figure 21–9 *This diagram illustrates how waves bend as they pass from air to water. The effect of refraction is shown in the accompanying photograph. Look back at Figure 21–8. Can you find evidence of refraction?*

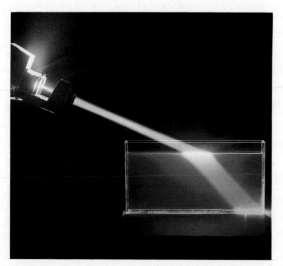

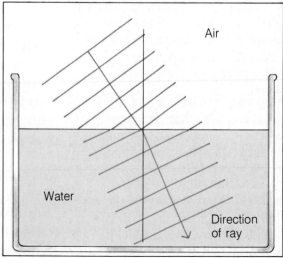

Figure 21–10 *The refraction of light as it passes from one medium to another makes this flower stem look as if it were broken. Why does refraction occur?*

Sharpen Your Skills

Law of Refraction

Assemble the following materials:

2 rubber or wooden wheels firmly attached to an axle large piece of velvet cloth or coarse sandpaper

1. Roll the wheels and axle across a smooth tabletop. Describe the direction of motion.

2. Place the velvet cloth or the coarse sandpaper on the table.

3. Roll the wheels again but in such a way that only one wheel moves across the rough surface. Describe the motion. What effect does this motion have on the direction of the wheels? What causes this to happen?

Explain how this activity illustrates refraction of waves.

pencil appears to be split into two pieces. The light waves traveling through air are slowed down and bent when they travel through water. You can observe refraction in another way. Place a coin in the bottom of an empty cup. Move the cup so that the coin is out of your line of sight. Then fill the cup with water. Does the coin become visible?

Diffraction

The bending of waves around the edge of a barrier is called **diffraction** (dih-FRAK-shuhn). Diffraction is a result of a new series of waves being formed when the original waves strike a barrier. Perhaps you are familiar with the diffraction of sound waves. You can hear a band playing before you actually see them march around the corner into your line of sight. The sound waves reach you by bending around the corner of the building.

Interference

Suppose that you and a friend are holding the ends of a piece of rope. You both snap the ends at the same time. Two waves are sent toward each other. What will happen when the waves meet at the middle of the rope?

When two or more waves arrive at the same point at the same time, they interact with each other in a process called **interference.** The two waves combine to produce a single new wave. The two waves can combine in two different ways.

CONSTRUCTIVE INTERFERENCE If waves combine in such a way that the crests of one wave meet the crests of the other, **constructive interference** occurs. The crests of the two waves add together to form a single wave. The amplitude of the single wave is equal to the sum of the amplitudes of the two original waves. See Figure 21–11.

DESTRUCTIVE INTERFERENCE If waves combine in such a way that the crests of one wave meet the troughs of the other, **destructive interference** occurs. The crests and troughs combine by subtracting from each other to form a single wave. The ampli-

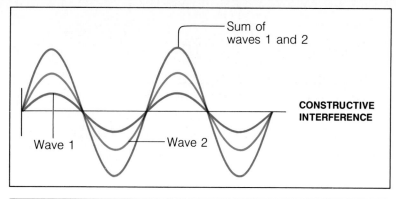

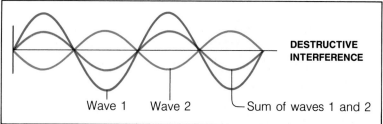

Figure 21–11 *When two waves arrive at the same place at the same time, they interfere with each other. The interference can be constructive or destructive. Which type of interference increases wave amplitude? Which type decreases wave amplitude?*

tude of this wave is the difference between the amplitudes of the original waves. See Figure 21–11.

ANTINODES AND NODES A point at which constructive interference causes maximum energy displacement is called an **antinode.** Any crest or trough may be called an antinode. A point at which destructive interference results in no energy displacement is called a **node.**

If both you and a friend continuously shake the ends of the rope up and down, something interesting occurs. Several points along the rope will not move. These are nodal points. Between the nodal points there are maximum displacements of the rope upward and downward. These are antinodal points. When constructive interference and destructive interference produce stationary nodes and antinodes, the resulting wave is called a **standing wave.**

SECTION REVIEW

1. What is the law of reflection?
2. What is refraction? Diffraction?
3. Compare constructive and destructive interference.
4. What is a standing wave?
5. Except for a connecting door, two rooms are separated by a soundproof wall. Explain why a sound produced in any part of one room can be heard anywhere in the other room.

Observing Wave Properties of a Slinky®

Problem

What are the characteristics of a wave?

> **Materials** *(per group)*
>
> Slinky®, or other coiled spring

Procedure

1. On a smooth floor, stretch the spring to about 3 meters. Have one person hold the spring at each end. **CAUTION:** *Do not overstretch the spring.*
2. Make a loop at one end of the spring as shown in the accompanying figure.

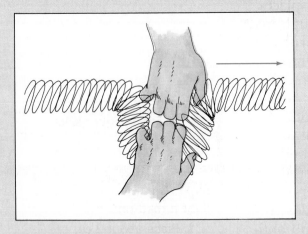

3. Release the loop and observe the motion of the wave. Observe the reflected wave.
4. Move one end of the spring back and forth on the floor. Draw a diagram of the wave you observe.
5. Repeat step 4, but this time increase the rate at which you move the spring back and forth.
6. Now squeeze together the first 20 cm of the spring, as shown in the accompanying figure.

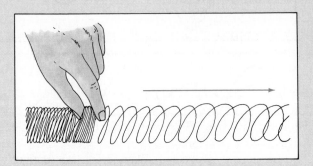

7. Release the compressed section of the spring and observe the wave as it moves down the spring.

Observations

1. In step 3, is the reflected wave on the same or the opposite side as the original wave?
2. What happens to the frequency when you increase the rate at which the spring is moved back and forth?
3. What happens to the wavelength when you increase the rate at which the spring is moved back and forth?

Conclusions

1. Are the waves generated in steps 1 to 5 transverse or longitudinal? Explain your answer.
2. Are the waves generated in steps 6 and 7 transverse or longitudinal? Explain your answer.
3. What is the relationship between the rate at which the spring is moved back and forth and the frequency? And the wavelength?
4. What are three characteristics of a wave?

CHAPTER REVIEW

21–1 Nature of Waves

❏ A wave is a disturbance that transfers energy through matter or space.

❏ A medium is any substance or region through which a wave is transmitted.

21–2 Types of Waves

❏ A transverse wave is one in which the motion of the medium is at right angles to the direction of the wave.

❏ A crest is the maximum displacement upward of a particle of the medium.

❏ A trough is the maximum displacement downward of a particle of the medium.

❏ Molecules crowded together cause a compression. A rarefaction is a space in the medium in which there are fewer molecules.

❏ In a longitudinal wave, the motion of the medium is parallel to the direction of the wave.

21–3 Characteristics of Waves

❏ Amplitude is the maximum distance the molecules are displaced from their rest position.

❏ Wavelength is the distance from any point on a wave to the same point on the next wave.

❏ Frequency is the number of waves, or complete cycles, per unit time.

❏ The unit used to measure frequency is the hertz (Hz).

21–4 Speed of Waves

❏ The speed of a wave equals frequency times wavelength.

21–5 Interactions of Waves

❏ Reflection is the bouncing back of a wave after it strikes a boundary that does not absorb the wave's energy.

❏ The law of reflection states that the angle of incidence equals the angle of reflection.

❏ Refraction is the bending of waves due to a change in speed.

❏ Diffraction is the bending of waves around the edge of a barrier.

❏ Constructive interference adds waves together to form a single wave whose amplitude is the sum of the amplitudes of the original waves.

❏ Destructive interference combines waves to form a single wave whose amplitude is the difference between the amplitudes of the original waves.

❏ A standing wave is a wave with stationary nodes and antinodes produced by constructive interference and destructive interference.

VOCABULARY

Define each term in a complete sentence.

amplitude	constructive interference	hertz	medium	refraction
angle of incidence	crest	incident wave	node	standing wave
angle of reflection	destructive interference	interference	normal	transverse wave
antinode	diffraction	law of reflection	rarefaction	trough
compression	frequency	longitudinal wave	reflected wave	wave
			reflection	wavelength

CONTENT REVIEW: MULTIPLE CHOICE

On a separate sheet of paper, write the letter of the answer that best completes each statement.

1. An example of a medium for a wave is
   a. air.   b. water.   c. space.   d. all of the above.
2. A medium transfers
   a. matter.   b. energy.   c. molecules.   d. air.
3. An ocean wave is an example of a
   a. transverse wave.   b. longitudinal wave.   c. standing wave.   d. stationary wave.
4. The maximum distance the molecules of a medium are displaced from their rest position is the
   a. amplitude.   b. wavelength.   c. frequency.   d. speed.
5. Wavelength is the distance between
   a. two consecutive crests.   b. two consecutive troughs.
   c. one point to the same point on the next wave.   d. all of the above.
6. In a given medium, if the frequency increases,
   a. the wavelength increases.   b. the speed increases.
   c. the speed remains constant.   d. the speed decreases.
7. The bending of waves due to a change in speed is called
   a. reflection.   b. refraction.   c. diffraction.   d. interference.
8. The bending of waves around the edge of a barrier is called
   a. reflection.   b. refraction.   c. diffraction.   d. interference.
9. The interaction of waves that meet at the same point at the same time is called
   a. reflection.   b. refraction.   c. diffraction.   d. interference.
10. A point where constructive interference produces maximum energy is called a (an)
    a. node.   b. antinode.   c. medium.   d. rarefaction.

CONTENT REVIEW: COMPLETION

On a separate sheet of paper, write the word or words that best complete each statement.

1. A wave is a disturbance that transfers _____.
2. In a transverse wave, the particles of the medium move _____ to the direction of the wave.
3. In a longitudinal wave, the particles of the medium move _____ to the direction of the wave.
4. The energy of a wave can be indicated by the _____.
5. The distance from any point on a wave to the same point on the next wave is called _____.
6. Frequency is measured in _____.
7. In the same medium, an increase in the frequency of a wave will cause a decrease in the _____ of the wave.
8. The law of reflection states that the angle of _____ equals the angle of reflection.
9. When two waves add together to form a single wave, the type of interference is _____.
10. A point of no energy displacement due to destructive interference is a (an) _____.

CONTENT REVIEW: TRUE OR FALSE

Determine whether each statement is true or false. Then on a separate sheet of paper, write "true" if it is true. If it is false, change the underlined word or words to make the statement true.

1. A medium transfers wave <u>matter</u>.
2. The <u>crest</u> of a wave is the maximum displacement upward.
3. Molecules spread out in <u>rarefaction</u>.
4. A <u>transverse</u> wave is a series of compressions and rarefactions.
5. The distance between two consecutive crests is one <u>amplitude</u>.
6. Frequency is measured in <u>hertz</u>.
7. The incoming wave is the <u>standing</u> wave.
8. The bending of waves due to a change in speed is called <u>reflection</u>.
9. When two waves combine to subtract from each other, <u>destructive</u> interference occurs.
10. Constructive interference and destructive interference producing stationary nodes and antinodes is called a <u>diffraction</u> wave.

CONCEPT REVIEW: SKILL BUILDING

Use the skills you have developed in the chapter to complete each activity.

1. **Applying concepts** Waves travel slower through a denser medium. Although water is denser than air, sound waves travel faster in water. Explain why.
2. **Making calculations** Complete the following table.

Speed (m/sec)	Frequency (Hz)	Wavelength (m)
150	2.0	
	250	1.5
200		0.5
	200	1.0

3. **Identifying relationships** State the effect on the frequency and speed of a wave if the amplitude is increased; wavelength is increased; wavelength is decreased.

4. **Interpreting diagrams** Answer the following questions using these diagrams.

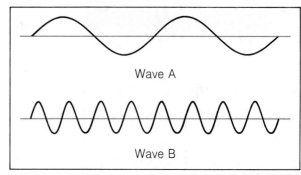

Wave A

Wave B

a. Which wave has the largest amplitude?
b. Which wave has the shorter wavelength?
c. Which wave has a higher frequency?

CONCEPT REVIEW: ESSAY

Discuss each of the following in a brief paragraph.

1. How do density and elasticity of a medium affect the speed of a wave?
2. Distinguish between transverse and longitudinal waves.
3. The frequency of a wave is decreased in a given medium. Describe what happens to the wavelength and speed.
4. Describe what happens to an incident wave after hitting a barrier at an angle.
5. Describe how a standing wave is produced.
6. Sometimes when a jet plane flies over your house you can actually feel the rooms shake. Explain why.

Sound

22

CHAPTER SECTIONS

22–1 Wave Model of Sound

22–2 Properties of Sound

22–3 Wave Interactions

22–4 Sounds You Hear

22–5 How You Hear

CHAPTER OBJECTIVES

After completing this chapter, you will be able to

22–1 Define sound.

22–1 Describe the transmission of sound.

22–2 Identify the properties of sound.

22–3 Classify wave interactions.

22–4 Distinguish between noise and music.

22–5 Explain how sound is heard.

Dawn broke over the Mojave Desert in California as Captain Chuck Yeager climbed into a tiny rocket plane called the X-1. On this Tuesday, October 14, 1947, Yeager was to attempt to break the sound barrier.

The speed of sound, which is called Mach 1, is 1056 kilometers per hour at an altitude of 12,000 meters. All previous attempts to reach this speed had ended in disaster. Many engineers claimed it was impossible to fly faster than the speed of sound. They said any plane that attempted to break the sound barrier would be torn apart.

At 9000 meters the B-29 mother plane dropped the X-1 from the bomb bay opening. Yeager fired the four rocket chambers and began climbing at a 45-degree angle. The acceleration was so violent that he had to strain to move his hands a few centimeters forward to the controls. The needle reached 0.96 Mach and then went clear off the scale. On the ground, the observers heard a tremendous explosion—the sonic boom. The X-1 had broken through the sonic wall! The plane and pilot were safe, and scientists had conquered yet another frontier.

In this chapter, you will learn about sound: What sound is, how it travels, how you hear. Also, you will learn more about those sounds most familiar to you—noise and music.

The pioneering flight of Chuck Yeager (inset) has made possible the now everyday flights of planes such as this at more than three times the speed of sound.

22-1 Wave Model of Sound

A large boulder breaks loose from a high cliff and crashes to the bottom of a canyon. No one is present to hear the crash. Is there any sound? Perhaps you would answer no. But a scientist would likely disagree. In order to understand why, you must know more about the nature of sound.

Sound is a form of energy that causes molecules of a medium to vibrate back and forth. The molecules of the medium vibrate back and forth in a series of compressions and rarefactions. This series of compressions and rarefactions produces a wave in which the sound energy is transmitted. The motion of the molecules of the medium is parallel to the direction of movement of the wave. So sound travels through a medium as a longitudinal wave.

Is there sound produced when the boulder crashes to the canyon floor? The answer is yes. The crashing boulder causes compressions and rarefactions of the molecules of the air. These vibrations of molecules are transmitted through the air in the form of longitudinal waves.

Would sound be produced if the boulder crashed to the bottom of a canyon on the moon? Because the moon has no atmosphere, there is no medium to carry the sound waves. There are no molecules present to be compressed and rarefied. So there is no sound on the moon.

Figure 22–1 *Sound is a form of energy that causes molecules of a medium to vibrate back and forth, as you can clearly see from the splashes of water created by a vibrating tuning fork (left). If there are no molecules of a medium present, such as on the moon, there will be no sound. So astronaut Harrison Schmitt explores a lunar boulder in the silent world of the moon (right).*

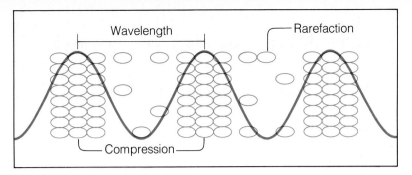

Figure 22–2 *A periodic series of compressions and rarefactions moves through a medium in the form of a longitudinal sound wave. In this diagram, a compression corresponds to a wave crest and a rarefaction to a wave trough. What is the distance between consecutive crests called?*

Transmitting Sound

Because a sound wave is a series of compressions and rarefactions of molecules, materials that are elastic transmit sound easily. Elastic materials are those that return quickly to their original shape.

Solids are generally more elastic than either liquids or gases. The molecules in a solid do not move very far and bounce back very quickly as the compressions and rarefactions of a sound wave go by. Sound travels more easily through solids than it does through liquids or gases. Metals such as iron and nickel are very elastic and are, therefore, excellent transmitters of sound. Lead is not very elastic. How well do you think lead transmits sound?

Most liquids are not very elastic. Sound is not transmitted as well in liquids as it is in solids. Gases are even more inelastic than liquids. So gases are the poorest transmitters of sound.

Another way of determining how well a medium transmits sound is to consider the arrangement of the molecules of the medium. The molecules of a solid are the most closely packed. Vibrations are most easily passed from one molecule to another in a solid. That is why you put your ear to a door to hear sounds on the other side. How would you describe the transmission of sound in a liquid and in a gas based on their molecular arrangement?

Speed of Sound

The speed of sound in air is about 340 meters per second. This is considerably slower than the speed of light, which is almost one million times as great as the speed of sound. A familiar illustration of the difference in speeds of sound and light is a thunder-and-lightning storm. The sound of thunder reaches you *after* the light from a flash of lightning,

Figure 22–3 *Dolphins can "talk" and "listen" to each other because sounds are easily transmitted through water (top). When sound waves strike a hard surface, they are reflected (bottom). A reflected sound is called an echo. What is true about the series of compressions and rarefactions in an echo and in the original wave?*

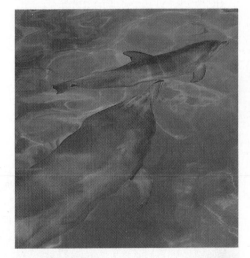

SPEED OF SOUND

Substance	Speed (m/sec)
Rubber	60
Air at 0°C	331
Air at 25°C	346
Cork	500
Lead	1210
Water at 25°C	1498
Sea water at 25°C	1531
Silver	2680
Copper	3100
Brick	3650
Wood (Oak)	3850
Glass	4540
Nickel	4900
Aluminum	5000
Iron	5103
Steel	5200
Stone	5971

Figure 22–4 *The speed of sound varies in different mediums. In what medium does sound travel the fastest? The slowest?*

even though both are produced at the same time! So if lightning occurs at a distance of 340 meters, it will take one second for you to hear the sound of thunder. How long would it take if the lightning were 3400 meters away?

The speed of sound in a medium is determined by two factors. One factor that affects the speed of sound is temperature. You learned that the speed of sound in air is about 340 m/sec. This value is for air at a temperature of about 15°C. At 25°C, sound travels at 346 m/sec. And at 0°C, sound travels at only 331.5 m/sec.

As the temperature of a medium increases, the speed of sound increases. Sound travels faster at higher temperatures. When Chuck Yeager broke the sound barrier, he was flying at an altitude of 12,000 meters and a speed of 293 m/sec. At 12,000 meters the temperature is so cold that the speed of sound is only 290 m/sec. If you were watching a baseball game on a cold day, would the time difference between seeing the bat hit the ball and hearing it be greater or lesser?

The nature of the medium also affects the speed of sound. Sound travels fastest in the most elastic materials. The speed of sound in water is 1500 m/sec. The speed of sound in steel is 5200 m/sec.

In materials in the same phase of matter, the speed of sound is slower in the denser material. Because the more massive molecules of the denser material have greater inertia, they do not move as quickly as the less massive molecules of the less dense material. The speed of sound in dense metals such as lead and gold is much less than the speed in steel or aluminum. Lead and gold are also less elastic—another reason why the speed of sound is slower in these metals.

SECTION REVIEW

1. What is sound? What kind of wave is it?
2. Compare the transmission of sound waves in solids, liquids, and gases.
3. What two factors affect the speed of sound?
4. Thunder is heard five seconds after a flash of lightning is seen. How far away is the lightning if the speed of sound in air is 340 m/sec?

22-2 Properties of Sound

Many different sounds reach your ears every hour of every day. Some sounds are pleasant. Some are unpleasant. Some sounds are loud, others soft. And some sounds, such as a song played on a guitar, are instantly recognizable and different from other sounds. There are many kinds of sounds, and each sound has its own special properties.

In Chapter 21 you learned about the characteristics of waves. All waves have amplitude, frequency, and wavelength. Since sound travels in longitudinal waves, it has these three characteristics. You will recall that amplitude indicates the energy of a wave. Frequency is the number of waves per unit of time.

In addition to amplitude and frequency, sound waves have the characteristic of interaction. **Amplitude, frequency, and wave interaction determine the properties of sound known as intensity, frequency, and quality.** The effects of these properties on the ear are loudness, pitch, and timbre (TAM-ber).

Intensity and Loudness

What is the difference between the sound of thunder and the sound of a handclap? The thunder has a great deal more energy than a handclap. The amount of energy in a wave is called **intensity.** Energy moves molecules of a medium from their rest positions. So intensity of a sound is determined by the amplitude of the sound wave. The larger the amplitude, the greater the intensity.

Figure 22-5 *You hear a variety of sounds every hour of every day. Some sounds are pleasant (left), others are unpleasant (right). All sounds have three basic properties. What are these properties?*

Viewing Vibrations

Sound is caused by vibration. You can observe this by experimenting with a tuning fork.

1. Strike the prongs of a tuning fork with a pencil and then hold the fork close to your ear. What happens? What happens when you touch the prongs of the fork?

2. Next, strike the prongs of the tuning fork and place the ends of the prongs in a glass of water. What happens?

3. Tie a small piece of cork to a string and hold the string in one hand so the cork can swing freely. Strike the prongs of the tuning fork and hold one prong against the cork. Observe what happens.

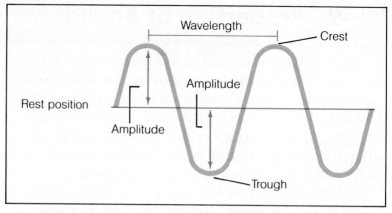

Figure 22–6 *Some of the basic characteristics of a sound wave can be seen in this diagram. What three characteristics can you identify?*

Intensity determines the loudness of a sound. The greater the intensity of a sound, the louder the sound is to the ear. Thunder sounds louder than a handclap because the intensity of thunder is much greater than the intensity of a handclap.

Intensity is measured in units called **decibels.** A sound with an intensity of 0 decibels is so soft that it can barely be heard. Thunder, on the other hand, has an intensity of 120 decibels. Thunder is a very loud sound. Sounds with intensities greater than 120 decibels can actually cause pain in human beings. A jet engine has an intensity of about 170 decibels. This sound is very painful to human ears. So

Figure 22–7 *Decibel levels of some familiar sounds are shown in this table. Which sounds would be considered painful?*

INTENSITY OF SOUND

Sound	Decibels	Sound	Decibels
Threshold of human hearing	0	Heavy street traffic	70–80
Rustling leaves	10	Vacuum cleaner	75–85
Whisper	10–20	Loud music	90–100
Very soft music	30	Rock concert	115–120
Classroom	35	Threshold of pain	120
Average home	40–50	Jet engine	170
Conversation	60–70	Rocket engine	200

ground crews exposed to this sound must wear special ear protection to avoid painful injuries. Music with an intensity above 85 decibels also can cause ear damage.

Frequency and Pitch

Sing the notes of the musical scale to yourself. Do you notice that the first "do" is a low note and the last "do" is a high note? Each note has its own **pitch.** The pitch of a sound is how high or low the sound is. Do not confuse high and low with loud and soft.

The pitch of a sound depends on how fast the molecules of a medium vibrate. Each complete vibration—one compression and one rarefaction—makes up a wave. So the pitch of a sound depends on the number of waves produced in a given time.

Frequency is the number of waves per unit time. The greater the frequency, the greater the number of waves in a given period of time. So pitch can now be defined as the property of sound that depends on the frequency of waves.

Sound waves that have a high frequency are heard as sounds of high pitch. A piccolo produces high-pitched sounds. Sound waves that have a low frequency are heard as sounds of low pitch. A tuba produces low-pitched sounds. A high note sung by a soprano may have a frequency of 1000 hertz. A low note sung by a bass may have a frequency of 70 hertz. A whistle has a high pitch because its frequency is about 1000 hertz. Thunder has a low pitch—its frequency is less than 50 hertz. You will recall that a frequency of one hertz is equal to one wave, or cycle, per second.

The human ear can hear sounds that range from about 20 hertz to about 20,000 hertz. Sounds with frequencies higher than 20,000 hertz are called **ultrasonic** (uhl-truh-SAHN-ihk) sounds. Most humans cannot hear ultrasonic sounds, but many animals can. Dogs can hear sounds with frequencies up to 25,000 hertz. Porpoises can hear sounds with frequencies up to 150,000 hertz! And bats actually produce ultrasonic sounds and then use their echoes to locate prey or to avoid bumping into objects. In this way, bats can fly about safely in the dark.

Figure 22–8 *The pitch of a sound depends on the frequency of the waves. How would you describe the frequency of the high-pitched sound of a flute? Of the low-pitched sound of a tuba?*

DOPPLER EFFECT Have you ever listened to the sound of a race-car engine as the car moves past you? As the race car approaches you, the pitch of the sound becomes higher. The pitch then becomes lower as the race car moves away from you.

The same effect occurs if you are on a train moving past a railroad crossing that has warning bells. The pitch of the bells increases, or gets higher, as you approach the crossing. The pitch of the bells decreases, or gets lower, as you move past the crossing. In either case, what you are observing is a change in the pitch of a sound due to the motion of either the sound source or the listener. A change in the frequency and pitch of a sound due to the motion of either the sound source or the observer is known as the **Doppler effect.**

When there is relative motion between a sound source and an observer, the frequency of the waves changes. As the sound source approaches the observer, compressions and rarefactions are generated from points that become closer and closer. Waves reach the observer sooner than they would have if the source had been producing them from its original position. The wave cycles reach the observer's ear more frequently. More waves per second mean a higher frequency and pitch.

When the source is moving away from the observer, sound waves are farther apart. The sound waves reach the observer later than they would have if the source were not moving. Fewer waves reach the observer. The decrease in frequency produces a sound of lower pitch.

Figure 22–9 *As the train approaches the crossing (top), the listener hears a sound of higher pitch. As the train leaves the crossing (bottom), the listener hears a sound of lower pitch. What do the people in the train hear?*

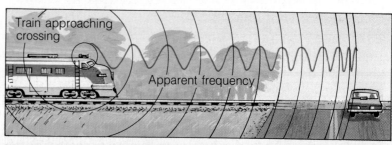

Train approaching crossing

Apparent frequency

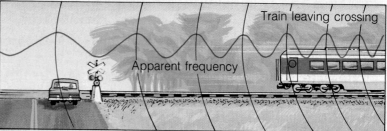

Train leaving crossing

Apparent frequency

SONAR High-frequency ultrasonic waves are used in a system called "*so*und *n*avigation *a*nd *r*anging," or **sonar.** Sonar is used by ships to locate objects in the water or to determine underwater distances. In a sonar system, high-frequency waves sent out by instruments on a ship reflect off any solid object in the water. A detector on the ship picks up the reflected waves. The distance to the object is calculated by multiplying the speed of sound waves in water by one-half the time it takes the waves to make a round trip, or to go from the ship to the ocean floor and back to the ship.

Sound Quality

Why can you tell the difference between the sound of a trumpet and the sound of a flute even when they are both playing the same note? The instruments have a different sound **quality.** Sound quality is called **timbre.**

Why does each different sound source have a unique timbre? Sounds are produced by a source when it vibrates at a certain frequency. Actually, most objects that produce sound vibrate at several different frequencies at the same time. Each frequency produces a sound with a specific pitch. The blending of the pitches gives the sound its timbre.

How can a single source produce more than one frequency? Look at Figure 22–12 on page 522. The top diagram shows the *whole string* vibrating. When the whole string vibrates, the note produced is called the **fundamental tone.** The fundamental tone has the lowest possible frequency and pitch. At the same time, sections of the string are vibrating two times and four times faster than the fundamental tone, and producing sounds of higher pitch. This is

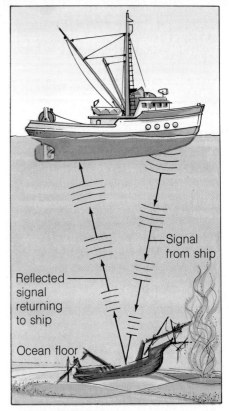

Figure 22–10 *Sonar is used to locate objects or determine distances under water. What two pieces of information must be known in order to calculate the distance from the ship to the object on the ocean floor?*

Figure 22–11 *Sound waves can be converted into electric signals, which are displayed as a pattern of light on a screen. Here you can see the pattern produced by a harmonica (left) and a recorder (right) both sounding the same note. Notice the differences in the amplitude, wavelength, and frequency of the two sounds.*

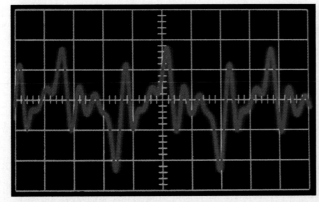

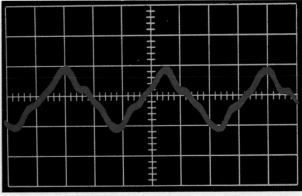

Figure 22–12 *A fundamental tone is produced when the whole string vibrates (top). When sections of the string vibrate faster than the fundamental tone, notes called overtones are produced (bottom). How does the pitch of overtones compare with that of the fundamental tone?*

Fundamental tone

String

Overtones

String

shown in the bottom diagram. The sounds of higher frequencies are called **overtones.** Sounds always have a fundamental tone and one or more overtones. The blending of the fundamental tone and the overtones produces the characteristic quality, or timbre, of a particular sound.

Without overtones, a trumpet and a flute would sound exactly the same. In fact, a violin, a clarinet, and your friend's voice would all have the same sound quality if it were not for overtones. Timbre is so unique for each person's voice that voice prints have been used to identify a person.

The talents of a **piano tuner** are needed to make a piano sound wonderful. The piano tuner first compares the pitch of one note on the piano with the pitch of a tuning fork. Then each string is tightened or loosened so that the tone is correct.

A piano tuner also adjusts the many parts that work together to produce the piano's beautiful tones. This may require realigning or replacing worn hammers, replacing broken strings, or rebuilding the wooden board that amplifies the strings' vibrations. Some piano tuners even rebuild pianos.

A piano tuner must have good hearing and manual dexterity. If you would like information about a career as a piano tuner, contact the Piano Technicians Guild, 9140 Ward Parkway, Kansas City, MO 64114.

SECTION REVIEW

1. Compare intensity and loudness.
2. How are frequency and pitch related?
3. What is the Doppler effect?
4. What is timbre?
5. What is a fundamental tone? An overtone?
6. The speed of sound in ocean water is 1530 m/sec. If it takes three seconds for an ultrasonic wave to make a round trip from a sonar device, what is the distance to the reflecting object?

22–3 Wave Interactions

Section Objective

To describe resonance and interference

Suppose that you are in your room listening to the stereo. The station starts playing your favorite song, so you turn up the volume. Whenever a particular note is made by the lead guitar, the glass on your desk starts vibrating. The glass might even shatter! Why?

Resonance

Sound is produced by vibrations in a medium. Every medium has its own frequency of vibration, or **natural frequency.** For example, one object may vibrate at 250 hertz, while another object vibrates at 510 hertz. So the first object has a natural frequency of 250 hertz, and the second object has a natural frequency of 510 hertz.

An object vibrating at its natural frequency can cause a nearby object to start vibrating *if that object has the same natural frequency.* The second object picks up some of the vibration energy of the first object and vibrates "in sympathy" with it. The glass on your desk absorbs some of the energy of the guitar when the two frequencies are the same. The glass vibrates in sympathy with the guitar. **The ability of an object to vibrate by absorbing energy of its own natural frequency is called resonance.** A singer can shatter glass by singing a clear, strong, high-pitched note. If the natural frequency of the glass is the same as the natural frequency of the note sung by the singer, the glass will vibrate due to **resonance.** Glass is not very flexible.

523

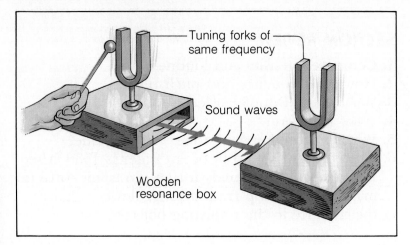

Figure 22–13 *When one tuning fork is set in motion it begins to vibrate at its natural frequency. These vibrations travel through the air and the wooden resonance box, which strengthens them. The tuning fork on the right will begin to vibrate "in sympathy" because it absorbs energy of its own natural frequency (right). Resonance caused the collapse of the Tacoma Narrows Bridge in November 1940 (left).*

So if the intensity of the sound is great enough, the glass will shatter.

You are applying the principle of reasonance every time you turn on your radio. Each radio station broadcasts at a specific frequency. When you turn the dial and tune in to a station, you are matching the frequency of your radio with the frequency of the broadcasting station. Can you think of some other examples of resonance?

Combining Sounds

In Chapter 21, you learned that waves produced at the same time can combine, or interact. You will remember that this combining of waves is called interference. Interference of waves can be constructive or destructive.

Sound waves produced at the same time from different sources can interfere constructively or destructively. When the sound waves are in phase, they combine to produce constructive interference. As a result of constructive interference, the intensity of the sound is increased. The sound is louder. Outdoor amphitheaters use band shells to amplify the music through constructive interference.

When the sound waves are out of phase, they combine to produce destructive interference. As a result of destructive interference, the intensity of the sound is decreased. The sound is softer. Destructive interference actually can produce "dead" spots in which no sound can be heard.

Dead spots are especially troublesome in large halls that have hard surfaces that bounce sounds back into the room. These reflected sounds

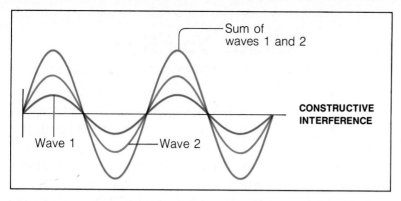

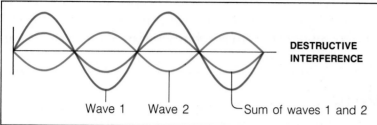

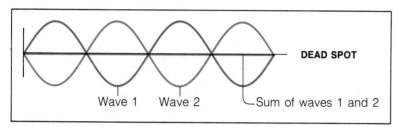

Figure 22–14 *Sound waves that are in phase can combine to produce constructive interference. Sound waves that are out of phase can combine to produce destructive interference. In some instances, destructive interference can produce "dead" spots. How do the intensities of the resulting sounds compare in these three types of wave interference?*

interfere destructively and cancel each other. Engineers who work in **acoustics,** or the science of sound, try to design concert halls and auditoriums with no dead spots. Acoustical engineers must carefully design the shape, position, and materials of an auditorium to eliminate interference problems and provide the best possible sound.

Acoustics is also concerned with the occurrence of **reverberations** (rih-ver-buh-RAY-shuhnz). A reverberation is a combination of many reflected waves. During a long reverberation time, musical sounds can blend properly and produce a pleasing sound.

SECTION REVIEW

1. What is natural frequency?
2. What is resonance?
3. Distinguish between constructive and destructive interference in terms of sound intensity.
4. Describe constructive and destructive interference in terms of the combining of crests and troughs and the resulting amplitude.

Figure 22–15 *This amphitheater at Lincoln Center in New York City is designed to eliminate interference problems and produce the best possible sound.*

To distinguish between music and noise

Figure 22–16 *A stringed instrument produces sound when the strings are set in motion by plucking or bowing. This traditional African drum is a percussion instrument, which vibrates when struck. A brass instrument such as the marching bugle tuba produces sound when a column of air is made to vibrate.*

22–4 Sounds You Hear

What is the difference between screaming and singing? Between the honk of a car horn and the high note of a violin? Screaming is noise; singing is music. The honk of a horn is noise; the note of a violin is music. Is the difference between noise and music simply a matter of personal taste? Perhaps you might be tempted to answer yes. After all, your music might be someone else's noise, and vice versa. But to a scientist, three characteristics of music set it apart from noise.

Music

A sound is music if it has a pleasing quality, a definite identifiable pitch, and a definite repeated timing called rhythm. Musical instruments produce sounds in several different ways. In woodwind and brass instruments—such as flutes, clarinets, trumpets, and trombones—columns of air are made to vibrate at various frequencies within the instruments. Percussion instruments, such as drums and cymbals, are set vibrating by being struck.

Stringed instruments are either plucked or rubbed to produce regular vibrations. The guitar, violin, and harp produce music in this way. The vibration produced has a certain frequency, and thus a certain pitch. But by changing the length, tightness, or thickness of the string, the string can be made to produce different pitches.

A shorter string vibrates at a higher frequency and produces a sound of higher pitch. The short strings of a ukulele produce higher pitched notes than the longer strings of a cello. The vibrating length of a string can be changed by the proper positioning of the fingers along the string. Musicians do this to produce the pitches they desire.

The more tension in a string, the higher the frequency of vibration and the higher the pitch. A stringed instrument is tuned by either tightening or loosening each string on the instrument. If a string is tightened, it produces a higher pitched sound. If loosened, it produces a lower pitched sound.

The strings on a bass guitar are thicker than the strings on a lead guitar. Thicker strings vibrate at a lower frequency than thinner strings. So thicker strings produce lower pitched sounds. What kinds of sounds do thinner strings produce?

Noise

Why is the squeak of chalk on a chalkboard so unpleasant? It is noise. Noise is basically unwanted sound. Noise has no pleasing quality, no identifiable pitch, and no definite repeating pattern. Look at Figure 22–17. The four pictures are wave patterns of sound. A and B were produced by musical tones. Notice the repeating wave patterns. What were C and D produced by? Is there a repeating pattern?

When noise reaches a level that causes pain or damages body parts, it becomes noise pollution. Noise pollution has become a major concern of society. For noise pollution can have a serious effect on people's health. The stress from listening to loud noises can raise a person's blood pressure and cause nervous tension. Studies of guinea pigs exposed to loud noises over a prolonged period of time show that noise can damage delicate tissues of the ear.

What can you do about noise pollution? In many countries, laws have been passed to prohibit noise pollution. People are not allowed to bring loud radios into public places. Of course, you don't have to wait for a law to follow this example. In your home, you can look for sources of noise pollution. Then you can determine which sources are within your control. You may not want to stop a loud appliance

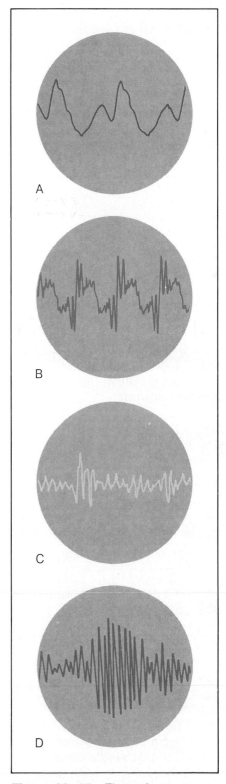

Figure 22–17 *These four wave patterns illustrate both music and noise. What distinguishes music from noise?*

in your kitchen. But placing a rubber pad under the appliance will lessen its noise level. In what other ways can you help prevent noise pollution?

SECTION REVIEW

1. What is music?
2. Describe how a string can be made to produce different pitches.
3. Distinguish between music and noise.
4. Sounds with decibel levels between 60 and 100 can be annoying. Sounds above 100 decibels can cause damage to hearing. Classify the following sounds as either annoying or damaging: snowmobile, food blender, power mower, jet plane, loud rock band, subway train, police siren.

Sharpen Your Skills

Sound Through Bones

The bones in your body are excellent conductors of sound, and you can prove it.

1. Gently strike the prongs of a fork on the table and quickly place the handle of the fork against the bone behind your ear. What happens? Repeat this procedure using other bones in your body.

2. Again strike a fork on the table. Put the handle of the fork between your teeth and bite down. Is the sound transmitted? Which is the better conductor, bone or teeth? How is this fact related to the operation of a hearing aid?

22–5 How You Hear

Do you remember the question posed at the beginning of this chapter about a boulder crashing to the bottom of a canyon? You learned that even if no one is around to hear the crash, a sound is still produced. For sound is a form of energy that causes molecules of a medium to vibrate back and forth.

If the question had been whether a sound is *heard*, the answer would have been no. In order for a sound to be heard, three things are needed. One, there must be a source that produces the sound. Two, there must be a medium to transmit the sound. And three, there must be an organ of the body that detects the sound. **In humans, the organ of the body that detects sound is the ear.**

How do you hear a series of compressions and rarefactions? Look at Figure 22–18. Hearing begins when sound waves enter the **outer ear.** The outer ear acts as a funnel for the sound waves. The waves move through the **ear canal** and strike a tightly stretched membrane called the **eardrum.** The vibrating air molecules cause the eardrum to vibrate very much like a musical drum.

Vibrations from the eardrum enter the **middle ear.** The middle ear contains the three smallest bones in the body. The first bone, the **hammer,** picks up the vibrations from the eardrum. The

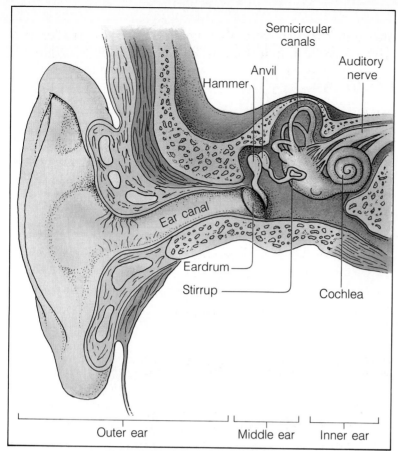

Hammer Anvil Semicircular canals Auditory nerve

Ear canal

Eardrum

Stirrup

Cochlea

Outer ear | Middle ear | Inner ear

Figure 22–18 *This illustration shows the structure of the human ear. What are the three main parts of the ear?*

hammer passes the vibrations to the second bone, the **anvil.** The anvil transmits the vibrations to the third bone, the **stirrup.** The stirrup then sets another membrane vibrating. This membrane transmits the vibrations to a liquid-filled **inner ear.**

The vibrations in the inner ear are channeled into the **cochlea** (KAHK-lee-uh). The cochlea is shaped like a snail shell and contains a special liquid and hundreds of special cells attached to nerve fibers. The nerve fibers join together to form one nerve that goes to the brain. The special cells detect movements in the liquid of the cochlea and convert them to electric impulses. The nerve fibers transmit the electric impulses to the brain, where they are interpreted as sound.

SECTION REVIEW

1. Name the three main parts of the ear.
2. What is the function of the eardrum?
3. Where are the nerve impulses interpreted as sound?
4. What would happen if the eardrum were torn?

Sharpen Your Skills

Model of a Wave

1. Using the wax from a lighted candle, attach a straight pin to one prong of a tuning fork.
2. Set up the apparatus as shown below.

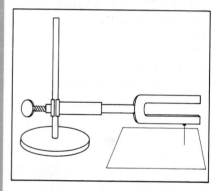

3. Place a sheet of carbon paper under the pin. Carefully adjust the height of the pin to lightly touch the paper.
4. Tap the opposite prong of the tuning fork.
5. Slowly and steadily pull the carbon paper under the pin. You may have to practice several times.
6. After several trials, cut out your best wave model and tape it to a sheet of paper.

Identify the basic wave characteristics. Explain why tapping the opposite prong produced a wave. Would the wave model be different if the prongs were reversed?

Speed of Sound in Air

Problem

Can the speed of sound in air be calculated?

> **Materials** *(per group)*
>
> 1000-mL graduated cylinder
> hollow glass tubing, approximately
> 2.5 cm × 45 cm
> tuning fork of known frequency
> meterstick
> water

Procedure

1. Fill the graduated cylinder with water to about 3 cm from the top.
2. Hold the hollow tubing in the water.
3. Strike the tuning fork against the heel of your shoe. Quickly place the fork just over the top of the hollow tube, as shown in the accompanying figure.
4. Move the hollow tube up and down until the *loudest* sound is heard. If there is more than one position in which the sound appears the loudest, choose the position in which the length of the tube above the water's surface is the shortest.
5. Record the length, L, of the air column to the nearest 0.1 cm.
6. Measure and record the inside diameter of the hollow tube to the nearest 0.1 cm.
7. Record the frequency of the tuning fork.

Observations

1. Calculate the wavelength of the tuning fork using the following formula:

   wavelength = (4 × L) + (1.6 × D)
    where L = length of the air column
     D = diameter of the tube

2. Calculate the speed of sound in air using the following formula:

   speed of sound = frequency ×
      wavelength

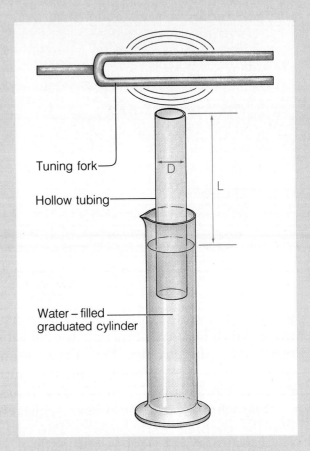

Tuning fork—

Hollow tubing—

Water – filled — graduated cylinder

Conclusions

1. The speed of sound in air is about 34,500 cm/sec. How close is your calculation to this value?
2. How do you account for differences between your calculated value and the given value?
3. If a tuning fork with a different frequency were used, would you expect a different value for the speed of sound? Explain your answer.
4. If this investigation were performed at a temperature of 5C° above or below the actual temperature, would the speed of sound be different? Explain your answer.

CHAPTER REVIEW

SUMMARY

22–1 Wave Model of Sound

❏ Sound is a form of energy that causes molecules of a medium to vibrate back and forth.

❏ Sound is a longitudinal wave.

❏ The speed of sound in air is about 340 meters per second at about 15°C.

22–2 Properties of Sound

❏ The amplitude of a sound wave determines the intensity, or loudness, of the sound.

❏ The frequency of a sound wave determines the pitch of the sound.

❏ The Doppler effect is a change in the frequency and pitch of a sound due to the relative motion of the source or the observer.

❏ The interaction of different frequencies in a sound wave determines the timbre.

❏ The lowest frequency of a vibrating object is called its fundamental tone. The higher frequencies are called its overtones.

22–3 Wave Interactions

❏ Every object has its own natural frequency of vibration.

❏ The ability of an object to vibrate by absorbing energy of its own natural frequency is called resonance.

❏ The intensity, or loudness, of a sound can be increased by constructive interference.

❏ The intensity, or loudness, of a sound can be reduced by destructive interference.

❏ Acoustics is the science of sound.

22–4 Sounds You Hear

❏ Music is sound that has a pleasing quality, a definite identifiable pitch, and a repeated pattern called rhythm.

❏ Noise is sound that does not have a pleasing quality, an identifiable pitch, or a repeating pattern.

❏ Over a period of time, loud noises can damage the ears and have other harmful effects on a person's health.

22–5 How You Hear

❏ In humans, the body organ that detects sound is the ear.

❏ The outer ear collects sound waves and sends them into the ear canal.

❏ The waves cause the eardrum to vibrate at the same frequency as the sound wave.

❏ The vibrations of the eardrum are transmitted to three small bones in the middle ear and then into the fluid in the cochlea.

❏ Special cells inside the cochlea detect the vibrations in the liquid and change them to electric nerve impulses.

❏ Nerve fibers carry the nerve impulses to the brain, where they are interpreted as sound.

VOCABULARY

Define each term in a complete sentence.

acoustics	eardrum	natural frequency	resonance
anvil	fundamental tone		reverberation
cochlea	hammer	outer ear	sonar
decibel	inner ear	overtone	stirrup
Doppler effect	intensity	pitch	timbre
ear canal	middle ear	quality	ultrasonic

CONTENT REVIEW: MULTIPLE CHOICE

On a separate sheet of paper, write the letter of the answer that best completes each statement.

1. The speed of sound is fastest in a
   a. vacuum.　　b. gas.　　c. liquid.　　d. solid.
2. An increase in the speed of sound is related to an increase in the
   a. temperature.　　b. crests.
   c. amplitude.　　d. wavelength.
3. The loudness of a sound wave depends upon its
   a. frequency.　　b. medium.　　c. amplitude.　　d. pitch.
4. Pitch is related to
   a. amplitude.　　b. interference.　　c. speed.　　d. frequency.
5. The quality of a sound depends upon its
   a. fundamental pitch.　　b. amplitude.　　c. overtones.　　d. natural frequency.
6. A change in frequency due to motion of source and observer is known as
   a. sonar.　　b. the Doppler effect.　　c. overtones.　　d. resonance.
7. The lowest frequency at which an object can vibrate is called its
   a. timbre.　　b. resonance.　　c. first overtone.　　d. fundamental tone.
8. The science of sound is called
   a. acoustics.　　b. overtones.　　c. sonar.　　d. resonance.
9. Vibrations from the eardrum enter the
   a. outer ear.　　b. middle ear.　　c. inner ear.　　d. brain.
10. Loud noises that continue for a prolonged period can cause
    a. ear injury.　　b. nervous tension.　　c. high blood pressure.　　d. all of the above.

CONTENT REVIEW: COMPLETION

On a separate sheet of paper, write the word or words that best complete each statement.

1. Sound is a (an) _____ wave.
2. Sound travels best in a (an) _____.
3. Light travels _____ than sound.
4. The _____ of a sound is determined by the amplitude.
5. The _____ of a sound determines its pitch.
6. _____ sounds have frequencies too high for the human ear to hear.
7. Timbre is a mixture of _____.
8. _____ is the science of sound.
9. _____ is sound that has rhythm.
10. Sound vibrations in the inner ear are changed to _____.

CONTENT REVIEW: TRUE OR FALSE

Determine whether each statement is true or false. Then on a separate sheet of paper, write "true" if it is true. If it is false, change the underlined word or words to make the statement true.

1. A sound wave is a series of <u>compressions</u> and <u>rarefactions</u>.
2. The speed of sound in hydrogen gas is <u>faster</u> than the speed of sound in oil.
3. An increase in temperature <u>decreases</u> the speed of sound.
4. As the energy in a sound wave increases, the <u>frequency</u> of the wave also increases.

5. Loudness is measured in <u>hertz</u>.
6. Sonar uses <u>ultrasonic</u> waves.
7. Frequencies higher than the fundamental tone are called <u>overtones</u>.
8. Constructive interference increases the <u>frequency</u> of a sound wave.
9. <u>Noise</u> has a definite repeating pattern.
10. The organ that detects sound is the <u>ear</u>.

CONCEPT REVIEW: SKILL BUILDING

Use the skills you have developed in the chapter to complete each activity.

1. **Making comparisons** List the following materials from best to worst as transmitters of sound: a. steel b. oxygen gas c. soup d. wood.
2. **Making calculations** How long would it take to hear the thunder from a flash of lightning 6800 meters away? Assume the speed of sound in air is 340 m/sec.
3. **Designing an experiment** How could two observers on opposite banks of a river use sound to measure the river's width?
4. **Applying concepts** Automatic garage doors are operated by radio signals from a device that the driver has in the car. Explain why a garage door sometimes opens when an airplane overhead is communicating by radio with the control tower.
5. **Making graphs** Plot a graph showing how the speed of sound in air varies with the temperature, using the following data:

Temperature °C	Speed m/sec
−10	325
0	331
10	337
20	343

6. **Interpreting graphs** From your graph in question 5, determine the speed of sound in air a. at 18°C b. at 25°C. By how much does the speed of sound change for a change in temperature of 1°C?
7. **Relating concepts** Sometimes a whistling sound is heard in a room when a window is slightly open on a windy day. How is this observation related to the principle of a wind instrument?
8. **Identifying relationships** Draw a wave diagram to illustrate each of the following sounds: a. high-pitched and loud b. low-pitched and soft c. low-pitched and loud.
9. **Making predictions** The part of the ear that is outside the head collects the energy of sound waves and funnels it into the ear canal. What would be the effect on the loudness of sounds if you held the mouthpiece of a megaphone to your ear?
10. **Applying definitions** Overtones that sound well together are said to be in harmony. In order for sounds to be harmonic, their overtones must have frequencies that are whole-number multiples of the fundamental. Which of the following frequency combinations will produce harmonic sounds? What will the other combinations produce?
    a. 256, 512, 768, 1024 Hz b. 128, 256, 1024 Hz c. 288, 520, 2048 Hz d. 128, 288, 480 Hz e. 512, 1024, 4096 Hz

CONCEPT REVIEW: ESSAY

Discuss each of the following in a brief paragraph.

1. If you were sitting in the last row of an auditorium during a concert, why might you see the drummer hit the drum before you actually heard it?
2. Trace the path of the sound of a handclap from the moment the clap is made to the moment you interpret the sound.
3. Describe the sound of a car whose horn has become stuck as it approaches you and then passes you.

Light

CHAPTER SECTIONS

23–1 Nature of Light

23–2 Electromagnetic Spectrum

23–3 Particle, Wave, or Both?

23–4 Reflection of Light

23–5 Refraction of Light

23–6 Color

23–7 How You See

CHAPTER OBJECTIVES

After completing this chapter, you will be able to

23–1 Explain the relationship between light energy and the atom.

23–1 Describe the properties of electromagnetic waves.

23–2 Identify the parts of the electromagnetic spectrum.

23–2 Describe the uses of electromagnetic waves of different frequencies.

23–3 Distinguish between the particle and wave properties of light.

23–4 Compare regular and diffuse reflections.

23–5 Describe the process of refraction.

23–6 Account for the color of opaque and transparent objects.

23–6 Distinguish between colors of light and colors of pigments.

23–7 Explain how you see.

The year is 1926. Albert Michelson is making a final check of his instruments. He has been working on this project for two long years. All his planning and preparation will be put to the test. Tonight he will accurately determine the speed of light.

Michelson has spent most of his career trying to obtain an accurate value for the speed of light. The method Michelson has chosen has made it necessary for him to determine the distance between two mountains in Southern California. Throughout the previous year, he supervised a team whose task it was to measure that distance. Descending the slope of Mount Wilson and ascending the slope of Mount San Antonio, the team finally made the measurement. It had taken more than a year to determine that the distance was exactly 25 kilometers!

Now that Michelson has an accurate value for the distance, he needs to measure the time it takes light to travel that distance. Light from a rotating mirror on Mount Wilson is transmitted to a mirror on Mount San Antonio. Then the light is reflected back to the rotating mirror on Mount Wilson. Michelson is able to measure the time it takes for the light to make the trip.

Once Michelson knows how long it takes the light to make a round trip, he can determine the actual speed of light by dividing the distance traveled by the travel time. But why would a scientist devote two years to measuring the speed of light? One reason is that the exact speed of light is important to an understanding of modern physics. Another reason is that like most scientists, Michelson was curious.

In this chapter you will learn more about the nature and properties of light. And you will gain an understanding of the important role light plays in your life—just as it did in Michelson's.

A laser beam arcs toward the moon from the McMath Solar Telescope on Kitt Peak, Arizona, and is reflected back to a telescope on the earth. Because the speed of light is known—thanks to Albert Michelson—the distance to the moon can be accurately measured.

23–1 Nature of Light

What do a microwave oven and a light bulb have in common? Are you surprised to learn that they both produce light? When you think of light, you probably think only of what you can see—rainbows, sunlight, city lights, fireworks, and television, for example. You probably do not think of radio waves, microwaves, infrared rays, ultraviolet rays, X-rays, and gamma rays. Yet these waves are all forms of light—invisible light.

Light Energy

The atom is the source of all forms of light, whether visible or invisible. According to modern atomic theory, tiny electrons moving about the nucleus of an atom are located in different energy levels within the electron cloud. Electrons located in a certain energy level have a specific amount of energy. However, an electron can absorb more energy. When energy is absorbed by an electron, the electron moves up to a higher energy level.

The location of an electron in a higher energy level is an unstable condition. So eventually the

Figure 23–1 *Fireworks, amusement park lights, and moonlight are forms of light you are probably most familiar with (left). But they are not the only forms of light. All forms of light—visible and invisible—have their source in the atom. As a neutral atom absorbs energy, it becomes excited. Some of its electrons capture the energy and then release it in tiny packets (right). What are these packets called?*

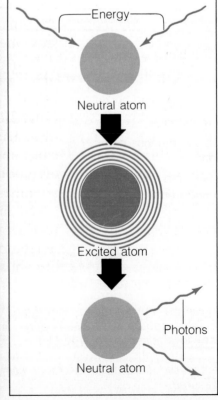

electron loses its extra energy and falls back to its original energy level. As it does so, the electron releases its absorbed energy in the form of a tiny packet, or bundle, of energy called a **photon** (FOH-tahn). The photon contains the exact amount of extra energy that the electron absorbed.

Light is made up of a stream of photons, or tiny packets of energy. Some photons contain more energy than others. The energy of a photon depends on how much energy an electron in an atom absorbs and then releases. The amount of energy in a photon determines the kind of light wave produced. For example, photons of visible light contain a moderate amount of energy. X-ray photons, on the other hand, contain a good deal more energy. They are high-energy photons. Radio waves do not contain as much energy as visible light. Radio waves are made up of low-energy photons.

Electromagnetic Waves

Now you know two differences between light waves. Some light waves are visible while others are not, and the photons of different forms of light waves contain different amounts of energy. However, all light waves share several characteristics.

The speed of light is the same for all forms of light. The speed of light in a vacuum is 300,000 kilometers per second, 300,000 km/sec. The speed of all forms of light is slower in air, water, glass, and other materials.

All light waves are transverse waves. You will recall that in a transverse wave, the direction of wave energy is at right angles to the movement of the molecules of the medium. With a light wave, however, there are no moving molecules of the medium. There are only moving photons of energy.

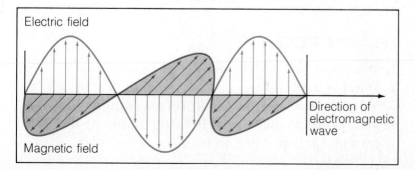

Figure 23–2 *In a transverse wave, the direction of the wave energy is at right angles to the electric and magnetic fields.*

Hole in Your Hand

Here is an optical illusion for you to try.

1. Roll a sheet of notebook paper into a tube and hold one end of it up to your right eye.

2. Place the side of your left hand against the tube with palm toward you at a distance of 15 centimeters from your eye.

3. Keep both eyes open and look at a distant object. Describe what you see.

The moving photons of energy generate electric and magnetic fields. This is the reason light waves are called **electromagnetic waves.** An electromagnetic wave is both electric and magnetic in nature. The electric and magnetic fields are at right angles to each other and to the direction of wave energy. See Figure 23–2 on page 537.

Electromagnetic waves are different from other waves because they can travel in a vacuum. Electromagnetic waves do not need a medium through which to travel. Light can be transmitted with or without a medium. Sound needs a medium.

Polarized Light

Light that you can see contains transverse waves that are vibrating in many directions. If the light is passed through a special filter, light in which the waves vibrate in a certain uniform pattern is produced. This light is called **polarized light.** Polarized light is light whose waves vibrate along a single plane.

Polarizing filters contain a large number of parallel slits. Only those waves vibrating in the same plane as the slits pass through the filter. All other waves are reflected or absorbed. One of the most common uses of polarizing filters is in sunglasses. Polarized sunglasses cut down on glare.

Figure 23–3 *Light waves that vibrate in all directions can be passed through a special filter to produce light waves that vibrate along a single plane only. This light is called polarized light. What is a common use of polarizing filters?*

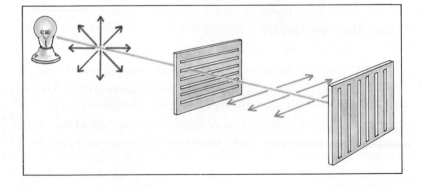

SECTION REVIEW

1. What are the various forms of light?

2. What is a photon?

3. What characteristics do all forms of light share?

4. Do you think light travels faster in air or in water? Explain your answer.

23–2 Electromagnetic Spectrum

Section Objective

To identify the waves that make up the electromagnetic spectrum

The different forms of electromagnetic waves are arranged in a particular order according to certain characteristics. These characteristics are photon energy, wave frequency, and wavelength. Since all electromagnetic waves travel at the same speed, speed is not used as a characteristic.

The arrangement of electromagnetic waves in order of their wavelengths, and thus their frequencies, is called the **electromagnetic spectrum.** See Figure 23–4. **The electromagnetic spectrum consists of radio waves, infrared rays, visible light, ultraviolet rays, X-rays, and gamma rays.**

Waves with the longest wavelengths have the lowest frequencies. Waves with the shortest wavelengths have the highest frequencies. Electromagnetic waves in the spectrum range from very short-wavelength, high-frequency gamma rays to very long-wavelength, low-frequency radio waves. Visible light is the small portion of the spectrum that you can detect with your eyes. The rest of the electromagnetic spectrum is invisible.

Figure 23–4 *The various forms of light that make up the electromagnetic spectrum are arranged according to their increasing frequency and decreasing wavelength. What happens to the photon energy of the waves as their frequency increases?*

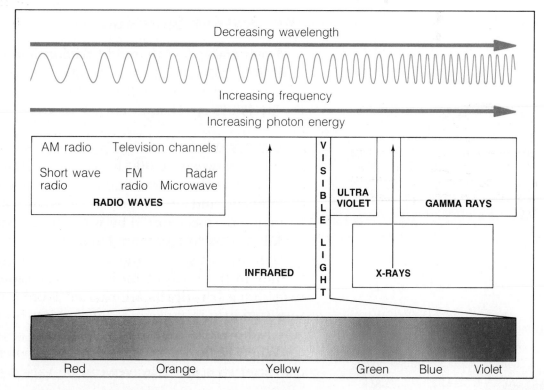

Figure 23–5 *The visible spectrum is the portion of the electromagnetic spectrum to which your eyes are sensitive. As white light passes through this diamond it is broken up into the colors of the visible spectrum. What are these colors?*

The Visible Spectrum

As you look at the diagram of the electromagnetic spectrum in Figure 23–4 on page 539, notice that only a very small portion of the spectrum is visible light. The **visible spectrum** is the portion of the electromagnetic spectrum to which your eyes are sensitive. Although you may think of most light as being white light, you can see that the visible spectrum is broken down into different colors. White light is made up of many different colors of light.

The visible spectrum consists of light waves with frequencies between 430 trillion hertz and 760 trillion hertz. This range of frequencies includes all the colors of white light—red, orange, yellow, green, blue, and violet. Each color has a certain frequency.

Red has the lowest visible frequency at 430 trillion hertz. Red photons also have the lowest energy. Violet light has the highest visible frequency at 760 trillion hertz. Violet photons have the highest energy. Moving along the spectrum from red to violet, the frequency of the waves and the energy of the photons increase. What happens to the wavelength? Which color has the longest wavelength? The shortest?

The Invisible Spectrum

Frequencies less than 430 trillion hertz or greater than 760 trillion hertz are invisible to the eye. Waves with frequencies that fall into this range make up the **invisible spectrum.**

RADIO WAVES Electromagnetic waves with frequencies between 10,000 hertz and 1 trillion hertz are called **radio waves.** Radio waves have the lowest frequencies and the longest wavelengths in the electromagnetic spectrum. The wavelengths vary from 30 kilometers to less than 1 millimeter.

The main use of radio waves is communication, usually in the form of radio and television broadcasts. Such broadcasts are carried from a transmitting station to a receiving station by two methods: AM radio waves and FM radio waves.

When radio waves are transmitted, one of two characteristics of the waves can be varied—either

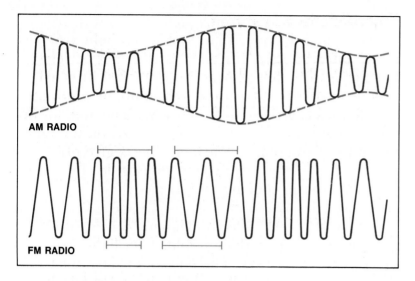

AM RADIO

FM RADIO

Figure 23–6 *AM radio waves are amplitude-modulated waves. FM radio waves are frequency-modulated waves. Because AM waves have longer wavelengths, they can bend around hills and buildings. The shorter wavelength FM waves are blocked by large objects. If you were traveling by car through the Rocky Mountains, which type of wave would be easier to receive on your radio?*

the amplitude of the wave or the frequency. The variation in either amplitude or frequency of a wave is called **modulation** (mahj-uh-LAY-shuhn). AM means amplitude modulation and FM means frequency modulation.

Information is carried by AM radio waves as a pattern of changes in amplitude. See Figure 23–6. AM radio waves have frequencies between 500,000 hertz and 2 million hertz. Many radio stations transmit AM waves. The sound portions of most television broadcasts are carried as AM waves.

Information is carried by FM radio waves as a pattern of changes in frequency. See Figure 23–6. All FM radio waves have frequencies between 87 million hertz and 108 million hertz. Many radio stations transmit FM waves. The picture portions of most television broadcasts are carried as FM waves.

Because AM radio waves have longer wavelengths, they can bend around hills and buildings. The shorter-wavelength FM radio waves are blocked by large objects.

Radio waves with frequencies between one billion hertz and one trillion hertz are called **microwaves.** Microwaves are the highest-frequency radio waves. The wavelengths of microwaves are only a few centimeters. Microwaves are used for communication and for cooking.

Short-wavelength microwaves are used in **radar.** Radar, which stands for *radio detecting and ranging*, is used in locating objects, calculating distances to objects, and monitoring automobile speed.

Figure 23–7 *Because microwaves are absorbed by most foods, they are used in cooking. Microwaves cause the molecules of the food substance to vibrate. This vibration increases the kinetic energy of the molecules, and so the temperature of the food increases. How do you think the speed of microwave cooking compares with other conventional methods?*

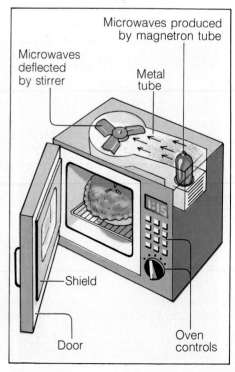

Microwaves produced by magnetron tube

Microwaves deflected by stirrer

Metal tube

Shield

Door

Oven controls

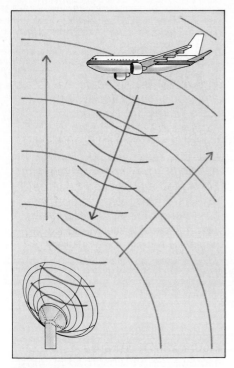

Figure 23–8 *In a radar device, a radio transmitter sends out high-frequency waves that bounce off objects and return as "echoes" picked up by a receiver.*

INFRARED RAYS Electromagnetic waves with frequencies slightly lower than visible red light are called **infrared rays.** Infrared rays cannot be seen, but they can be felt as heat. You can feel infrared rays as heat from the sun, a light bulb, or a stove.

All objects give off infrared rays. The amount of infrared given off by an object depends on the temperature of the object. Warmer objects give off more infrared rays than colder objects do. Infrared rays are used in cooking and in medicine.

ULTRAVIOLET RAYS Electromagnetic waves with frequencies just higher than visible violet light are called **ultraviolet rays.** The energy of ultraviolet photons is great enough to kill living cells. So ultraviolet lamps are often used in hospitals to kill germs and in processing plants to destroy bacteria and preserve food.

Ultraviolet rays are present in sunlight. When your body absorbs sunlight, ultraviolet rays cause

Figure 23–9 *Infrared light cannot be seen, but it can be detected as heat and used to produce a thermogram, or heat picture (left). Hotter areas appear as white, while cooler areas appear as blue and black. Note the dog's cold nose! When rocks containing fluorescent minerals are exposed to invisible ultraviolet light, they glow (center). X-rays are used to produce pictures of bones (right), such as these that show the growth of a hand from 2 years to 60 years.*

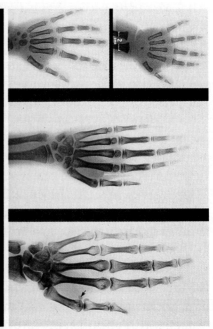

your skin cells to produce vitamin D. Vitamin D is needed to make healthy bones and teeth. Ultraviolet rays can also make your skin tan. However, too much ultraviolet light can burn your skin.

X-RAYS Electromagnetic waves with frequencies just above ultraviolet are called **X-rays.** The energy of X-ray photons is great enough to pass easily through many materials, including your skin. Denser materials, however, absorb X-rays. Bone absorbs X-rays. When an X-ray picture of a part of your body is taken, the bones absorb the rays and the soft tissue does not. The picture that results shows the bones as white areas and the soft tissue as black. As you might expect, too much exposure to X-rays can be very harmful. Lead absorbs almost all the X-rays that strike it. Can you think of an important use of lead based on this property?

GAMMA RAYS The highest-frequency electromagnetic waves are called **gamma rays.** Gamma rays have the highest-energy photons and shortest wavelengths of all the electromagnetic waves. Certain radioactive materials emit gamma rays. Gamma rays also come from outer space.

Gamma rays have tremendous penetrating ability—even greater than X-rays. The energy of gamma rays is so great that the photons can penetrate up to three meters of concrete! Gamma rays are used in medicine in the treatment of cancer. Excessive exposure to gamma rays, however, can cause severe illness.

SECTION REVIEW

1. What is the electromagnetic spectrum? List the kinds of waves that make it up.
2. In what three ways do forms of light differ?
3. What color has the lowest visible frequency? The highest visible frequency?
4. Moving along the spectrum from radio waves to gamma rays, what happens to frequency, wavelength, and photon energy?
5. Ultraviolet lights, or blacklights, give a violet glow. Are you seeing ultraviolet rays when you see ultraviolet light? Explain your answer.

Sharpen Your Skills

X-Rays

Wilhelm Röntgen discovered X-rays in 1896. Within a few months, X-rays were being used in hospitals. Using books and other reference materials in the library, find out about Röntgen and his work with X-rays. Write a report on your findings. Include information on the benefits and dangers of X-rays.

Figure 23–10 *This gamma camera image of the heart was produced when a patient was injected with a substance that gives off gamma rays. The camera detects the gamma rays and with the help of a computer creates an image. What kind of photon energy do gamma rays have?*

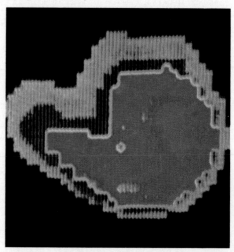

23–3 Particle, Wave, or Both?

Throughout this chapter, you have read about light as a wave and about the properties of light waves. The wave model of light, which has been the prevailing theory since the early 1800s, successfully explains most of the properties and behavior of light. However, in the early 1900s, scientists discovered something rather unusual about light, something that made them modify their wave theory.

Scientists shone violet light onto the surface of certain metals. The energy carried by photons of violet light was absorbed by electrons in the atoms of the metal plate. This photon energy knocked electrons out of the atoms in the metal plate. In fact, enough electrons were knocked off the metal plate to cause an electric current to flow. Since the experiment involved electrons and photons, this result came to be known as the **photoelectric effect.** The photoelectric effect is the production of electrons by photons of light.

Next, the scientists repeated the experiment with red light. Nothing happened! No matter how long the red light was shone or how bright it was, no electrons were ever knocked out of the metal's atoms. The dimmest violet light produced electrons, but the strongest red light did not!

As you know, photons of red light have less energy than photons of violet light. According to the wave theory, however, if red light strikes a metal plate as a continuous wave, then eventually the electrons should "soak up" enough energy so that they

Figure 23–11 *The energy of individual photons of violet light can produce an electric current. The energy of individual photons of red light cannot (left). The production of electrons by photons of light is called the photoelectric effect. Solar cells, such as these large arrays on a satellite in orbit around the earth, are one application of the photoelectric effect. What theory of light explains this effect?*

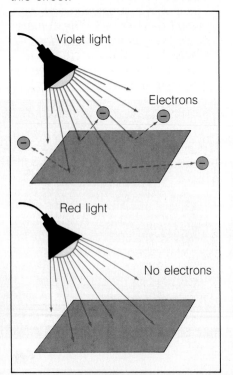

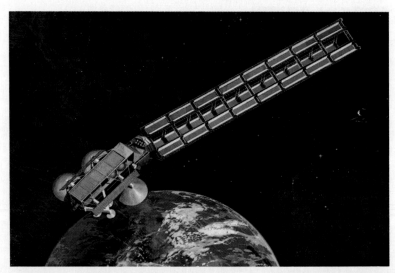

Figure 23–12 *When two beams of light from two slide projectors intersect, they pass through each other without colliding. The images produced on each screen are clear. What theory of light explains this behavior?*

can escape from their atoms. That does not happen. But suppose, in this case, light acts more like a stream of particles than like a wave. Then each individual red light photon, acting on its own, can never knock an electron from an atom. No single red light photon contains enough energy to do the job, no matter how long the light is on or how bright it is. On the other hand, violet light photons carry more energy than red light photons. So a single violet light photon can knock an electron right out of its atom. In the photoelectric effect, it certainly appears as if light acts more like individual particles than like a continuous wave!

The photoelectric effect can only be explained by a particle theory of light. The property of light waves known as interference can only be explained by a wave theory of light. Confused? Don't be. Scientists today describe light as both particlelike and wavelike. Scientists have not yet found a final solution to the problem of whether light is a particle or a wave. But this problem provides a good opportunity for you to remember that science is a way of explaining observations; it is not absolute knowledge.

SECTION REVIEW

1. What convinced scientists that light is a particle?
2. Why is light said to have a dual nature?
3. Which of the following electromagnetic waves would you expect to produce a photoelectric effect: radio waves, infrared waves, ultraviolet rays, X-rays, gamma rays?

23–4 Reflection of Light

What happens to light when it strikes the surface of an object? Some of the light is absorbed by the object. The remaining light bounces off the surface of the object. Light that bounces off the surface of an object is said to be reflected.

The type of surface light strikes determines the kind of reflection that is formed. No matter what type of surface light strikes, however, the angle formed by the incident ray and the normal equals the angle formed by the reflected ray and the normal. This is the law of reflection.

Kinds of Reflection

Why can you see your reflection in a mirror but not in a wall? In both cases light is reflected off a surface. In both cases, the angle of incidence equals the angle of reflection. So why is there a difference?

A mirror has a very smooth surface. The incident rays are always parallel to each other. Because the mirror has a smooth surface, the reflected rays will also always be parallel to each other. There is very little scattering of reflected light. The image formed is clearly defined and looks exactly like the object. This type of reflection is called a **regular reflection.**

The surface of a wall is not very smooth. A surface that is not smooth is often described as irregular. The incident rays are still parallel to each other. But because of the irregular surface, the reflected

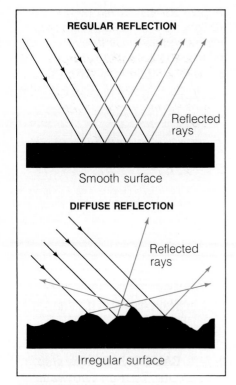

Figure 23–13 *Reflection from a smooth surface, or regular reflection, does not produce much scattering of light rays. Reflection from an irregular surface produces considerable scattering of light rays. The result is a diffuse reflection.*

Figure 23–14 *The castle you see is actually an image of the real thing, produced by light rays reflected from the surface of the water. What is reflection?*

rays are scattered in all directions. See Figure 23–13. The image formed is not clearly defined. Instead, it looks a bit "fuzzy," and the outlines of the image keep changing. Reflected light that is scattered in many different directions due to an irregular surface is called a **diffuse** (dih-FYOOS) **reflection.**

Although diffuse reflections are not desirable for seeing your image, they are rather important. If the sun's rays were not scattered by reflecting off uneven surfaces and dust particles in the air, you would see only those objects that are in direct sunlight. In addition, the glare of the sunlight would be so strong that you would have difficulty seeing.

SECTION REVIEW

1. What is a regular reflection? How is it formed?
2. What is a diffuse reflection? How is it formed?
3. One example of a simple mirror is a still pool of water. Explain the difference in reflections from a still pool and a rippled pool.

CAREER   *Photographer*

HELP WANTED: PHOTOGRAPHER to work inside and outside the studio. Experience with light filters and a variety of lighting conditions preferred. Must be able to develop and print all materials. High school diploma required. Technical training or college preferred.

"Turn toward me just a bit and . . . hold it!" The shutter snaps and the **photographer** directs the model for another shot.

A photographer uses a variety of film, color filters, and lenses to adjust the camera to light conditions and to produce various images of the subject or model. Using light, color, and shadow, a photographer captures on film the mood or personality of the subject.

Photography plays an important role in fashion, science, journalism, and engineering. Some photographers work in studios where models or clients go to be photographed. Most photographers also must be ready to travel to other places to work. For science photographers this may mean frequent trips to laboratories. Photojournalists must often quickly catch action

shots at news events. Photography combines artistic ability with technical skill. Some knowledge of science, engineering, mathematics, or chemistry usually is necessary to prepare for a career in scientific, industrial, or journalistic photography. So a college education may be useful to a photographer.

If you would like to find out more about a career as a photographer, contact Professional Photographers of America, Inc., 1090 Executive Way, Des Plaines, IL 60018.

To explain the process of refraction

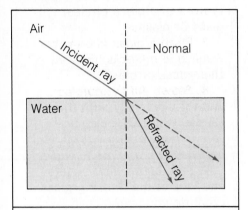

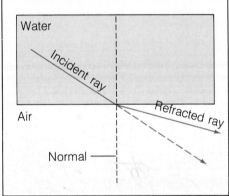

Figure 23–15 *As light passes from a less dense medium to a more dense medium, its speed decreases and it is refracted toward the normal (top). As light passes from a more dense medium to a less dense medium, its speed increases and it is refracted away from the normal (bottom). What do you think happens when light enters either medium parallel to the normal?*

Figure 23–16 *The index of refraction is a comparison of the speed of light in air with the speed of light in a certain material. In which substance does light travel the slowest?*

Light does not bend as it travels through a medium. Light travels in straight lines. What happens then when light passes from one medium to another? When light passes at an angle from one medium to another—air to water, glass to air, for example—it bends. The bending of light occurs because the speed of light changes. **The bending of light due to a change in its speed is called refraction.**

Refraction occurs because light moves at different speeds in different mediums. As it passes from one medium to another, it either speeds up or slows down. When light passes from a less dense medium to a more dense medium, it slows down. This is the case when light passes from air to water. When light passes from a more dense medium to a less dense medium, it speeds up. This is the case when light passes from glass to air. See Figure 23–15.

As you just read, light moves at different speeds in different mediums. Because its speed changes, light is refracted. The amount by which a material refracts light is measured by its **index of refraction.** The index of refraction is the comparison of the speed of light in air with the speed of light in a certain material. Since the speed of light in air is always greater than in any other material, the index of refraction of a certain material is always greater than one. The larger the index of refraction, the more the light rays are bent. Figure 23–16 gives the index of refraction for some substances.

INDEX OF REFRACTION OF SOME COMMON MATERIALS			
Material	**Index of Refraction**	**Material**	**Index of Refraction**
Air	1.00	Glass (ordinary)	1.52
Ice	1.31	Salt crystals	1.54
Water	1.33	Calcite	1.66
Methanol	1.33	Diamond	2.42

Bending and Separating

You learned that white light is made up of all the visible colors. Each color corresponds to a particular frequency. If white light passes from air to glass, its speed changes and it is refracted. Each frequency of light is refracted by a different amount. Red, with the lowest frequency, is refracted the least. Violet, with the highest frequency, is refracted the most. Because each color is refracted a different amount, each color bends at a different angle. The result is a separation of white light into the six colors of the spectrum, or rainbow. See Figure 23–17.

The piece of glass that forms a spectrum is called a **prism** (PRIHZ-uhm). Notice that the light bends as it enters the prism and as it leaves it. The bending occurs as the light leaves the prism because the speed of light changes again as the light passes from glass back to air. At this point, which color is refracted the most? The least?

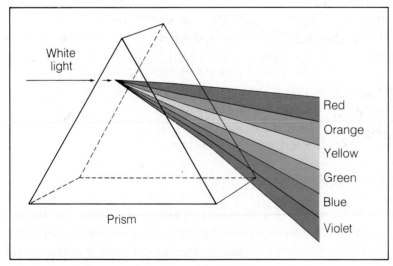

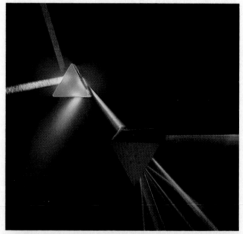

Figure 23–17 *As white light passes through a prism, it is refracted. Since each frequency is bent a different amount, the white light breaks up into the colors of the spectrum (left and top right). Water droplets in the air act as tiny prisms, forming the visible spectrum better known as a rainbow (bottom right).*

White light

Red
Orange
Yellow
Green
Blue
Violet

Prism

SECTION REVIEW

1. What is refraction?
2. What is the index of refraction?
3. Which color is refracted the most? The least?
4. Are longer or shorter wavelengths refracted at a greater angle?

23–6 Color

Here is something for you to try: Describe the clothes you are wearing today as precisely as you can *without* using colors. Pretty difficult, isn't it? The world you live in is full of colors. Just look around you and enjoy the colorful scenery!

When Light Strikes

In order to understand why objects have color, you must know what happens when light strikes the surface of an object. **When light strikes any form of matter, the light can be transmitted, absorbed, or reflected.**

When light is transmitted, it passes through the substance it strikes. If the light is transmitted readily, the substance is said to be **transparent.** Objects seen through transparent substances are very clear. Glass, water, and air are transparent. With transparent substances, there is no scattering of light.

If light is transmitted through a substance that scatters the light, the image seen is unclear and lacks detail. A substance that transmits light but no detail of that light is said to be **translucent** (tranz-LOO-suhnt). Waxed paper and frosted glass are translucent substances. A translucent substance produces a fuzzy image when you look through it.

A substance that does not transmit light is said to be **opaque** (oh-PAYK). A block of wood, a sheet of metal, and a piece of black cloth are opaque substances. When light strikes an opaque substance, it is either reflected or absorbed.

Figure 23–18 *A transparent substance transmits light readily, so objects seen through it are very clear (top). A translucent substance does not transmit light readily, so objects seen through it are unclear and lack detail (bottom). Which substance produces the most scattering of light?*

The Color of Objects

Why is grass green, an apple red, and a daffodil yellow? The answer to this question depends on the color of the light striking the object and whether the object is opaque or transparent.

OPAQUE OBJECTS An opaque object does not allow any light to pass through it. The light falling on the object is either reflected or absorbed. If the light is absorbed, can it reach your eyes? Obviously not. Only the light that is reflected reaches you. So the color of an opaque object is the color it reflects.

Think for a moment of a red apple. A red apple reflects red and absorbs all other colors. You see the red apple only by the light it reflects. What color do the green leaves on the stem of the apple reflect?

Now think about an object that is white. White is the presence of all the colors of the visible spectrum. So what is being reflected from a white object? You are right if you said *all* the colors are reflected. No color is absorbed.

If all the colors are absorbed, then no color is reflected back to you. The object appears black. Black is the absence of color. Most objects reflect more than one color, however. These colors combine and produce a great variety of color mixtures.

TRANSPARENT OBJECTS Transparent objects allow light to pass through them. The color that is transmitted is the color that reaches your eyes. The other colors are absorbed. So the color of a transparent object is the color of light it transmits. Red glass absorbs all colors but red, which it transmits. Green glass transmits only green light. Ordinary window glass transmits all colors and is said to be colorless.

Primary and Complementary Light

Each color of the visible spectrum has its own wavelength and frequency. All the colors that you see are a result of how your eyes respond to various mixtures of three frequencies of light.

The three colors that can be mixed to produce light of any color are called the **primary colors.** The primary colors of light are red, blue, and green. Any color of light can be made by mixing red, blue, and green light in different ways.

Look at Figure 23–20 on page 552. You can see that if red light, blue light, and green light are mixed together, the result is white light. When the three primary colors are mixed together in equal amounts, the result is white light. All other shades of color can be produced by mixing the primary colors in different proportions. The color pink has more red light than blue and green light.

Any two colors that combine to form white light are called **complementary colors.** Yellow and blue are complementary colors, as are cyan and red. What is the third pair of complementary colors?

Figure 23–19 *The color of an opaque object is the color it reflects. In white light, this apple appears red because it reflects red light (top). If only green light shines on it, it appears black (bottom). Why?*

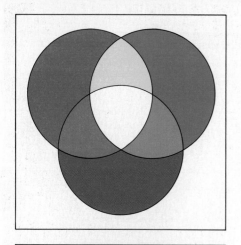

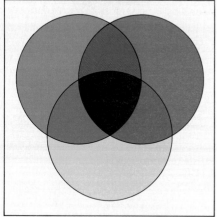

Figure 23–20 *The primary colors of light—red, blue, and green—combine to form white light (top). The primary pigments—yellow, cyan, and magenta—combine to form black (bottom). What is the relationship between the primary pigments and the complements of the primary colors of light?*

Primary and Complementary Pigments

You just learned that blue *light* and yellow *light* produce white *light*. Have you ever mixed blue paint and yellow paint? Was the mixture white? Definitely not. The mixture was green.

Paints are not sources of light. Paints are pigments. And the blending of pigments is different from the way your eyes blend the various colors of light. Pigments have a certain color because they absorb certain frequencies of the visible spectrum and reflect others.

The **primary pigments** are yellow, cyan, and magenta. Figure 23–20 shows how the primary pigments absorb and reflect light. When the three primary pigments are mixed in equal amounts, all colors are absorbed and the result is black. By looking at this figure, you may have noticed something interesting: The primary pigments are the complements of the three primary colors of light.

SECTION REVIEW

1. Compare transparent, translucent, and opaque substances.
2. Why would a green tree appear black under a blue light?
3. What are the primary colors of light? Of pigments? The complementary colors of each?
4. What happens when the primary colors of light are mixed in equal amounts? When the primary pigments are mixed in equal amounts?

Section Objective

To describe how you see

23–7 How You See

You have learned what light is and how it is reflected and refracted. You know why an apple is red. And you can distinguish between the colors of light and of pigments. But how do you see light?

You see light through a series of steps that involves the various parts of the eye and the brain. Light enters the eye through an opening called the **pupil.** The colored area surrounding the pupil, called the **iris,** controls the amount of light that

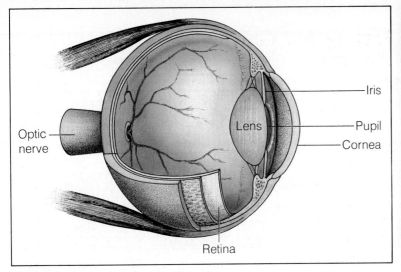

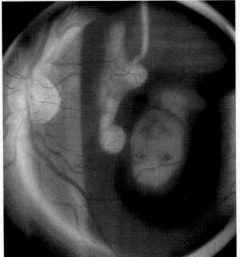

Figure 23–21 *The eye is the organ of sight (left). This photograph (right) is an actual image as it is formed on the retina.*

enters the pupil. A lens in the eye refracts the light and makes it converge on the **retina.** Muscles attached to the lens adjust its shape so that you can see objects both near and far away. The image that falls on the retina is inverted and smaller than the object.

The retina is made of light-sensitive nerves that transfer the image to the brain. The brain interprets the image as right-side up. Some of the nerve cells in the retina are called **rods.** Rods are sensitive to light and dark. Other nerve cells called **cones** are responsible for your seeing colors. Each cone is sensitive to a particular primary color.

Ideally, the image formed by the lens should fall directly on the retina. If the eyeball is too long, the image forms in front of the retina. A person has difficulty seeing objects at a distance but no trouble seeing objects nearby. This condition is called **nearsightedness.**

If the eyeball is too short, the image is focused behind the retina. The person can see distant objects clearly but has difficulty with nearby objects. This problem is called **farsightedness.** You will learn more about these conditions and how to correct them in Chapter 24.

SECTION REVIEW

1. What is the function of the iris? The pupil?
2. Where in the eye is the image formed?
3. What causes color blindness?

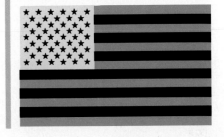

Regular Reflection

Problem

What is the relationship between the angle of incidence and the angle of reflection for regular reflection?

Materials *(per student)*

plane mirror
wood block
rubber band
4 straight pins
corrugated cardboard, 30 cm × 20 cm
graph paper cut to fit cardboard
metric ruler
protractor

Procedure

1. Tape the graph paper to the cardboard.
2. Draw a horizontal line one-third the distance from the top of the graph paper.
3. Attach the mirror to the wood block with a rubber band.
4. Place the *back edge* of the mirror on the line you drew in step 2.
5. Use the rubber band to attach a straight pin at the center of the mirror. Label this point A. See the accompanying figure.
6. Position a second pin approximately 10 cm in front of pin A. This pin must be in a direct line with pin A and with the image it produces in the mirror. Push the pin into the cardboard and label this point B.
7. Position another straight pin about 5 cm to the left of point B. Push the pin into the cardboard and label this point P.
8. Position a fourth pin so that it lines up with the image of pin A and the image of pin P. Push this pin into the cardboard and label the point R.
9. Remove all the pins and the mirror from the cardboard.
10. Draw a line from point B through point A to the horizontal line you drew in step 2.

Label the intersection of these two lines point C.
11. Draw another line from point P to point C.
12. Draw a third line from point R to point C.
13. Use a protractor to measure the angle PCB and the angle RCB. Record these measurements.

Observations

1. What is the size in degrees of angle PCB?
2. What is the size in degrees of angle RCB?

Conclusions

1. What is line BC called?
2. What is line PC called? Angle PCB?
3. Which line is the reflected ray? Which angle is the angle of reflection?
4. The law of reflection states that the angle of incidence is equal to the angle of reflection. Do your data verify this law? Explain your answer.
5. How do you account for any error in your results?

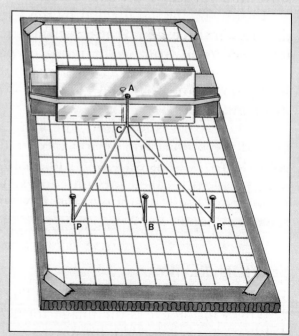

CHAPTER REVIEW

SUMMARY

23–1 Nature of Light

❏ Light is made up of a stream of photons, or tiny packets of energy.

❏ All light energies are transverse electromagnetic waves.

❏ Polarized light is light whose waves vibrate along a single plane.

23–2 Electromagnetic Spectrum

❏ The electromagnetic spectrum includes radio waves, infrared waves, visible light, ultraviolet rays, X-rays, and gamma rays.

❏ The higher the frequency of an electromagnetic wave, the higher its photon energy and the shorter its wavelength.

23–3 Particle, Wave, or Both?

❏ Light can be explained as both particlelike and wavelike.

23–4 Reflection of Light

❏ The angle of incidence equals the angle of reflection.

❏ Regular reflection produces a clearly defined image that looks exactly like the object.

❏ Diffuse reflection is reflected light that has been scattered in many different directions.

23–5 Refraction of Light

❏ Refraction is the bending of light.

❏ The index of refraction is a measure of the amount by which a material refracts light.

❏ A prism separates white light into the six colors of the visible spectrum.

23–6 Color

❏ The color of an opaque object is the color of light it reflects.

❏ The color of a transparent object is the color of light it transmits.

❏ The primary colors of light are red, blue, and green. Primary colors combine to produce white light.

❏ Complementary colors of light combine to produce white light.

❏ Primary pigments are yellow, cyan, and magenta. Primary pigments combine to produce black.

23–7 How You See

❏ Nearsightedness occurs when the image falls in front of the retina.

❏ Farsightedness occurs when the image falls behind the retina.

VOCABULARY

Define each term in a complete sentence.

complementary color

cone

diffuse reflection

electromagnetic spectrum

electromagnetic wave

farsightedness

gamma ray

index of refraction

infrared ray

invisible spectrum

iris

microwave

modulation

nearsightedness

opaque

photoelectric effect

photon

polarized light

primary color

primary pigment

prism

pupil

radar

radio wave

regular reflection

retina

rod

translucent

transparent

ultraviolet ray

visible spectrum

X-ray

CONTENT REVIEW: MULTIPLE CHOICE

On a separate sheet of paper, write the letter of the answer that best completes the statement.

1. All light energies
   a. travel the same speed in a vacuum.   b. are transverse waves.
   c. are electromagnetic waves.   d. all of the above.
2. Each color of light has a different
   a. frequency.   b. energy.   c. wavelength.   d. all of the above.
3. The highest energy photons are
   a. radio waves.   b. infrared waves.   c. X-rays.   d. gamma rays.
4. Both wave and particle theory can explain how light
   a. reflects.   b. diffracts.   c. interferes.   d. all of the above.
5. The angle of reflection
   a. is sometimes less than the angle of incidence.
   b. equals the angle of incidence.
   c. is always greater than the angle of incidence.
   d. equals the angle of refraction.
6. The color that is refracted at the greatest angle is
   a. red.   b. yellow.   c. green.   d. violet.
7. An object that will *not* transmit any light is
   a. transparent.   b. translucent.   c. opaque.   d. all of the above.
8. The primary colors of light are
   a. red, yellow, blue.   b. red, green, blue.
   c. yellow, green, blue.   d. red, yellow, orange.
9. The primary colors of pigments are
   a. red, yellow, blue.   b. red, green, blue.
   c. yellow, cyan, magenta.   d. blue, cyan, magenta.
10. To see an object clearly, the image must fall exactly on the
   a. retina.   b. iris.   c. lens.   d. pupil.

CONTENT REVIEW: COMPLETION

On a separate sheet of paper, write the word or words that best complete each statement.

1. The _____ is the source of all forms of light.

2. The _____ spectrum contains all the colors you see.

3. Short-wavelength microwaves are used for _____.

4. The highest energy photons are _____.

5. _____ rays are felt as heat.

6. The _____ theory of light explains the photoelectric effect.

7. A clearly defined image is called _____ reflection.

8. A distorted image is produced by _____ reflection.

9. The bending of light is called _____.

10. _____ materials will only reflect or absorb light.

Determine whether each statement is true or false. Then on a separate sheet of paper, write "true" if it is true. If it is false, change the underlined word or words to make the statement true.

1. A particle of light is called a photon.
2. Light waves travel in a vacuum.
3. The invisible spectrum contains all the colors of the rainbow.
4. Ultraviolet radiation can be felt as heat.
5. Frequencies just above ultraviolet are called gamma rays.
6. The production of electrons by photons of light is called the photoelectric effect.
7. Reflected light that is scattered is called diffuse reflection.
8. A piece of glass that forms a spectrum is called a lens.
9. When all three primary pigments are mixed, the result is black.
10. Light enters the eye through the iris.

Use the skills you have developed in the chapter to complete each activity.

1. **Relating concepts** Two electrons drop from a higher energy level to a lower energy level. The first electron releases twice as much energy as the second electron. Which electron emits the higher frequency photon? Explain your answer.
2. **Applying concepts** A prism separates white light into the colors of the spectrum. What would happen if a second prism were placed in the path of the separated colors. Use a diagram in your answer.
3. **Identifying relationships** Using your knowledge of color and the behavior of light, answer the following:
   a. Why are roadways made of materials that are black or gray?
   b. Why is clothing worn for sports such as tennis usually white?
   c. How can traffic lights, which use white light bulbs, produce different colors?
4. **Making predictions** Cyan is a mixture of blue and green light. What color would result if cyan light were mixed with red light? What color would result if cyan pigment were mixed with red pigment? Explain your answers.
5. **Applying definitions** Using the table in Figure 23–16, answer the following:
   a. Does light go faster or slower when moving from methanol to glass?
   b. When light travels from diamond to air, is it bent toward or away from the normal?
   c. Light undergoes a greater velocity reduction going from air into which material, glass or calcite?
6. **Making diagrams** Explain why the sun you see setting has already set. Use a diagram in your answer.

Discuss each of the following in a brief paragraph.

1. What characteristics are common to all light waves?
2. Explain why the wave theory of light cannot explain the photoelectric effect.
3. How is a rainbow produced?
4. Describe how the surface light strikes is related to the type of reflection produced.
5. Describe how you see.

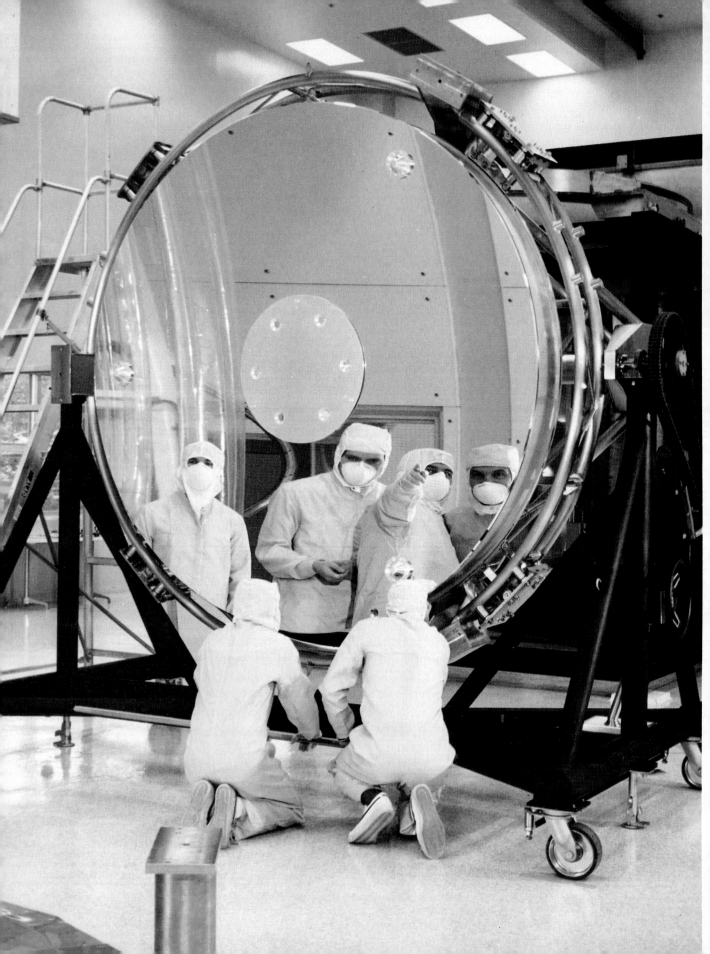

Light and Its Uses 24

CHAPTER SECTIONS

24–1 Sources of Light

24–2 Reflection and Mirrors

24–3 Refraction and Lenses

24–4 Optical Instruments

24–5 Light and Technology

CHAPTER OBJECTIVES

After completing this chapter, you will be able to

24–1 Distinguish between luminous and illuminated objects.

24–1 Describe incandescent, fluorescent, and neon light.

24–2 Explain how concave and convex mirrors form images.

24–2 List several uses of concave and convex mirrors.

24–3 Explain how convex and concave lenses form images.

24–3 Relate the images formed by convex and concave lenses to their uses.

24–4 Describe the operation and uses of several optical instruments.

24–5 Identify new applications of light technology.

What do the following numbers have in common: 14 billion light-years, 300,000 kilometers per second, 2.4 meters, and $1.5 billion? The answer is the Hubble Space Telescope, NASA's latest and most ambitious contribution to the study of the universe.

The Space Telescope is simply a 13-meter cylinder with a 2.4-meter mirror at one end—if that can be called simple! Built at a cost of more than $1 billion, the Space Telescope can gather light from stars too distant or too dim to be studied clearly from the earth.

The new astronomical "eye in the sky" was carried into space in April 1990 aboard the space shuttle *Discovery* and was placed in orbit 500 kilometers above the earth's surface. The Space Telescope's reflecting mirror can gather light from objects in the universe as far away as 14 billion light-years. Light travels at 300,000 kilometers per second. In one year, light travels a distance of more than 9 trillion kilometers. This distance is called a light-year. The light the Space Telescope gathers might have left its source 14 billion years ago—about the time the universe was born!

The universe that scientists see will be expanded 350 times by the Space Telescope. The view the Space Telescope provides is almost to the edge of the universe and the beginning of time!

In this chapter, you will learn more about telescopes and other instruments that use light. You will gain an understanding of how mirrors and lenses work. And you will look at some "light tools" whose future applications are as exciting and ambitious as those of the Hubble Space Telescope.

Technicians working on the 2.4-meter primary mirror of NASA's Hubble Space Telescope wore masks and special suits to maintain absolute cleanliness.

24-1 Sources of Light

Almost all of the natural light the earth receives comes from the sun. The sun and other stars are called **luminous** (LOO-muh-nuhs) objects. A luminous object gives off its own light. Light bulbs, candles, campfires, and even fireflies are luminous objects.

Objects such as the moon can be seen because light shining on them is reflected, or bounced off. An object that can be seen only by reflected light is called an **illuminated** (ih-LOO-muh-nayt-ehd) object. You see the moon because sunlight is reflected off its surface. The moon does not give off its own light. How would you describe the pages of this book? The lamp in your room?

As you learned in Chapter 23, light is a form of energy. A luminous object produces light when the electrons in its atoms give off energy. There are three different ways in which a luminous object can be made to give off energy in the form of light. These three ways determine the type of light produced. **A luminous object can produce incandescent light, fluorescent light, or neon light.**

Incandescent Light

Certain objects can be heated until they glow, or give off light. Light produced from heat is called **incandescent** (ihn-kuhn-DEHS-uhnt) light. An object

Figure 24-1 *The aurora borealis, or northern lights, as seen over Fairbanks, Alaska (left), is a luminous light source. The light is produced when particles in the earth's upper atmosphere absorb and then release the energy of subatomic particles shot from the sun. Although the moon is shining brightly over the Sawtooth Mountains of Sun Valley, Idaho (right), it is doing so by reflected light. The moon is an illuminated object.*

Figure 24–2 *This light bulb is incandescent because it produces light when electricity flows through the thin tungsten filament inside (left). If colored filters are placed over an incandescent light source, a variety of colors is produced (center). Certain living organisms, such as glowworms, are bioluminescent (right). They can produce light through chemical reactions in their bodies.*

that gives off incandescent light is said to be incandescent. Ordinary light bulbs in your home are incandescent lights. They produce light when electricity is applied to them.

Inside the glass bulb of a light bulb is a thin wire filament made of the metal tungsten. Tungsten can be heated to over 2000°C without melting. When the light is switched on, electrons flow through the tungsten wire. Because the filament is thin, there is resistance to the electron flow. Electric resistance produces heat. Enough heat will cause the tungsten to glow as photons of visible light are emitted.

Fluorescent Light

Light that is produced by the electron bombardment of gas molecules contained at low pressure is called **fluorescent** (floo-REHS-uhnt) light. Fluorescent light is cool light that uses much less electricity than incandescent light.

Fluorescent tubes, usually long and narrow or circular in shape, contain mercury vapor and argon gas. When electricity flows through the tube, electrons collide with the atoms of mercury vapor. The collisions produce photons of ultraviolet light. You cannot see this ultraviolet light. However, the inside of the tube is coated with special substances called **phosphors.** Phosphors absorb ultraviolet photons and begin to glow, producing visible light. The color that a fluorescent bulb produces depends on the phosphors used.

Sharpen Your Skills

Heat and Light

1. Place a thermometer on a dinner plate.
2. Position an incandescent light bulb 10 cm above the thermometer.
3. Turn on the bulb. After about 5 minutes record the temperature.
4. Repeat the procedure, but this time use a fluorescent bulb.

Which light source operates at a higher temperature? Why is this an advantage?

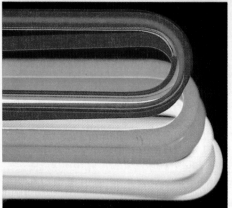

Figure 24-3 *The tubes lining the tunnel are producing fluorescent light (top). Tubes filled with neon and other gases produce different-colored light (bottom). Fluorescent light and neon light are often called gas discharge light.*

Neon Light

When electrons pass through glass tubes filled with gas, light is produced. The most common type of gas discharge light is **neon** light. Similar to fluorescent light, neon light is cool light. Neon light is bright red light. If other gases are added, however, different colors are produced.

Mercury vapor produces a greenish-blue light that does not create much glare. So mercury vapor lamps are used to light streets and highways. Sodium vapor lamps, which give off a bright yellow-orange light, use less electricity than mercury vapor lamps. In many locations, sodium vapor lamps are replacing mercury vapor lamps.

SECTION REVIEW

1. What is a luminous object? An illuminated object?
2. How does an incandescent bulb produce light?
3. How does a fluorescent source produce light?
4. Indicate whether the following are luminous or illuminated objects: incandescent light; the planet Mars; the planet Earth; neon light.

To classify mirrors according to the shape of their surfaces

Figure 24-4 *By using a series of mirrors correctly placed, an almost infinite number of images is produced by the reflection of light. What type of mirror is being used?*

24-2 Reflection and Mirrors

You learned in Chapter 21 that reflection is the bouncing back of waves when they strike the surface of an object. The most common surface from which light waves are reflected is a **mirror.** Any smooth surface that reflects light and forms images can be used as a mirror. The surface of a mirror can be perfectly flat or it can be curved. **Based on the shape of its surface, a mirror is classified as plane, concave, or convex.**

Plane Mirrors

A mirror with a perfectly flat surface is a **plane mirror.** Figure 24–5 shows how an image of an object is formed in a plane mirror. Observe that the image appears to be behind the mirror. You know that this cannot be so, since the mirror is opaque

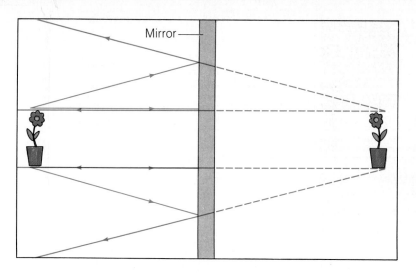

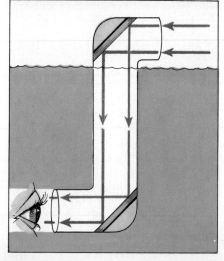

Figure 24–5 *This diagram shows how an image is formed in a plane mirror. The reflected rays never really meet in front of the mirror. But if extended in back of the mirror, they come together and an image is formed. What kind of image is formed by a plane mirror? What characteristics of the image are illustrated here?*

Figure 24–6 *These people are using an optical instrument known as a periscope to see an event that is actually blocked from their view (top). Light enters at the top of the periscope, is reflected from one mirror to the other, and then to the viewer's eye (bottom).*

and no light can pass through it. As you can see from the figure, the reflected rays never really meet in front of the mirror. But if extended in back of the mirror, they come together and an image is formed.

The image formed by a plane mirror is rightside up, or erect, the same size as the object, and as far in back of the mirror as the object is in front of the mirror. The image is also reversed. Stand in front of a mirror and raise your *left* hand. Which hand of your image appears to be raised?

The image formed by a plane mirror is called a **virtual image.** The word virtual means "not real." A virtual image only seems to be where it is. In other words, it can be seen only in the mirror. A virtual image cannot be projected onto a screen.

Concave Mirrors

A mirror can be curved instead of flat. If the surface of a mirror curves *inward*, the mirror is called a **concave mirror.** Most images formed by concave mirrors are inverted, or upside down. You can experiment with a concave mirror by looking at the inner surface of a shiny metal spoon. Move the spoon back and forth and observe what happens to your image.

Look at Figure 24–7 on page 564, which shows how a concave mirror forms an image. Notice the straight line drawn through the center of the mirror. This line is called the **optical axis.** Light rays

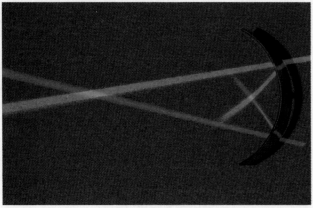

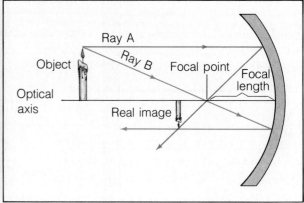

Figure 24–7 *A concave mirror reflects light rays so that they converge at a point called the focal point (left). You can see how an image is formed by a concave mirror by following ray A and ray B as they strike the mirror's surface and are reflected (right). What type of image is formed by a concave mirror? What is its size and position?*

Figure 24–8 *If a light source is placed at the focal point, the reflected rays are all parallel to one another (left). No image is formed, but a concentrated beam of light, such as that produced in a searchlight, results (right). Where else are concave mirrors used to produce a powerful beam of light?*

striking a concave mirror parallel to the optical axis are all reflected through the same point in front of the mirror. The point in front of the mirror where the reflected rays meet is called the **focal point.** The distance between the center of the mirror and the focal point is called the **focal length.** Follow ray A to see how it is reflected through the focal point.

Ray B passes through the focal point before it strikes the mirror's surface. Notice that it is reflected parallel to the optical axis. Light rays passing through the focal point before reaching the mirror are all reflected parallel to the optical axis. Where reflected rays A and B meet, an image is formed. The image is upside down, smaller than the object, and in front of the mirror. The image is a **real image.** A real image can be projected onto a screen because the light actually passes through the point where the image appears.

When a light source is placed exactly at the focal point of a concave mirror, something interesting

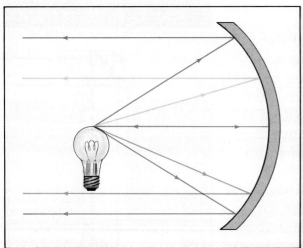

happens. All the light waves are reflected back parallel to one another, and to the optical axis, in a concentrated beam of light. See Figure 24–8. If you open a flashlight, you will find a concave mirror behind the bulb. The bulb is placed at the focal point of the mirror so that the reflected light forms a powerful beam. Concave mirrors are placed behind car headlights to focus the light beam. Concave mirrors are used in searchlights and in spotlights.

If a light source is placed closer to a concave mirror than the focal point, none of the reflected rays meet. So a real image cannot be formed. Under such conditions, a concave mirror forms only a virtual image. The virtual image is larger than the object. This makes concave mirrors useful as shaving or makeup mirrors.

Convex Mirrors

The surface of a **convex mirror** curves *outward* like the surface of a ball. Reflected rays spread out from the surface of a convex mirror, as you can see in Figure 24–9. The image formed by a convex mirror is always erect and smaller than the object. Like the image formed by a plane mirror, the image formed by a convex mirror appears behind the mirror.

Convex mirrors provide very large areas of reflection. For this reason, they are used in automobile side-view and rear-view mirrors to obtain a wider view. They are also used in stores to provide

Figure 24–9 *Because a convex mirror spreads out reflected light rays from its very large area of reflection (right), it is often used to increase traffic visibility (left). What type of image does a convex mirror form?*

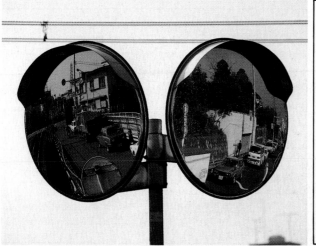

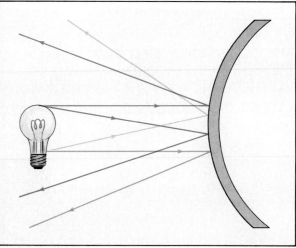

security guards with a complete view of shopping areas. However, convex mirrors give a distorted indication of distance. Objects appear to be farther away than they actually are. Why is this an important concern when using a car mirror?

SECTION REVIEW

1. Describe the surface of a plane mirror. A concave mirror. A convex mirror.
2. Describe the image formed by a plane mirror. By a concave mirror. By a convex mirror.
3. What are some uses of each type of mirror?
4. Why are convex mirrors not used for telescopes?

24–3 Refraction and Lenses

Have you ever used a magnifying glass, a camera, or a microscope? If so, you were using a **lens** to form an image. A lens is any transparent material that refracts light. The light is said to be focused through the lens. Most lenses are made of glass or plastic and have either one or two curved surfaces. As parallel rays of light pass through the lens, they are refracted so that they either come together or

Figure 24–10 *A convex lens converges light rays because parallel rays of light are refracted toward the center—the thickest part—of the lens (left). What is the point at which the rays converge called? The degree to which the lens is curved determines the amount of refraction (right). How does the focal length of a very curved lens compare with the focal length of a slightly curved lens?*

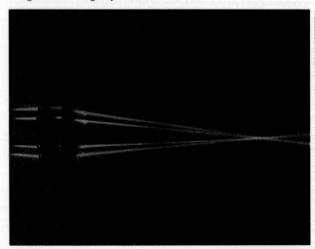
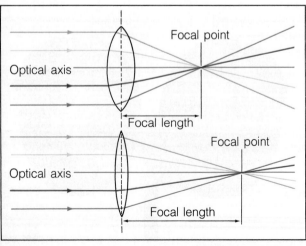

spread out. **A lens that converges, or brings together, light rays is a convex lens; a lens that diverges, or spreads out, light rays is a concave lens.**

Convex Lenses

A lens that is thicker in the center than at the edges is called a **convex lens.** As parallel rays of light pass through a convex lens, they are bent toward the center—the thickest part of the lens. The light rays converge. The point at which the light rays converge is the focal point.

Light is refracted as it enters a lens and again as it leaves the lens. The amount of refraction depends on the degree to which the lens is curved. A very curved lens will refract light more than a lens whose surface is only slightly curved. In a very curved lens, the converging rays will meet at a focal point closer to the lens. Thus, the focal length of a very curved lens is shorter than that of a slightly curved lens.

Because a convex lens converges light, it can form a real image. However, a convex lens can also

A

B

C

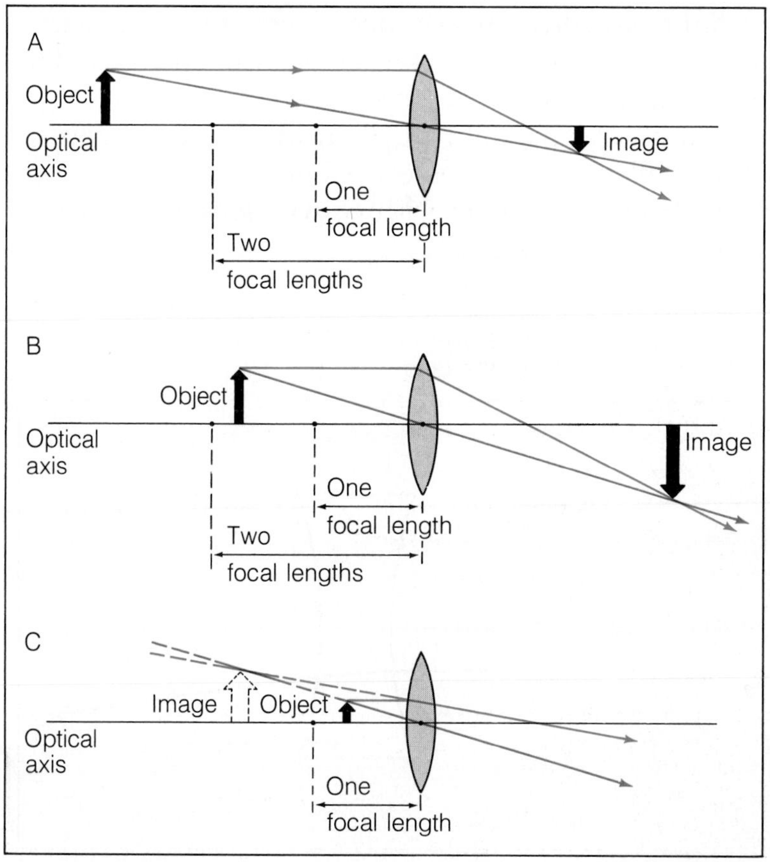

Figure 24–11 *The type of image formed by a convex lens depends on where the object is placed in relation to the focal length of the lens. What type of image is formed in A and B? In C?*

form a virtual image. The kind of image a convex lens forms depends on the position of the object.

If an object is placed at more than two focal lengths beyond a convex lens, the image formed is inverted and smaller than the object. The lens of a camera and the lens in your eye produce this type of image. See Figure 24–11 on page 567.

If an object is placed more than one focal length but less than two focal lengths beyond a convex lens, the image formed is inverted and larger than the object. This type of image is formed by the convex lens in a microscope or slide projector. See Figure 24–11 on page 567.

If an object is placed between a convex lens and its focal point, a virtual image is formed. The virtual image is erect and larger than the object. For this reason, convex lenses can be used as magnifying glasses. See Figure 24–12.

Concave Lenses

A lens that is thicker at the edges and thinner in the center is called a **concave lens.** As parallel rays of light pass through a concave lens, they are bent toward the edges—the thickest part of the lens. The light rays diverge.

All images produced by concave lenses are erect and smaller than the object. Concave lenses are most often used along with convex lenses to help form a sharper image.

Figure 24–12 *A convex lens can be used as a magnifying lens when an object is placed between the lens and its focal point (top). Droplets of water act as convex lenses. Notice how they magnify the stem of this leaf (bottom).*

Figure 24–13 *A concave lens diverges light rays because parallel rays of light are refracted toward the edges—the thickest part—of the lens.*

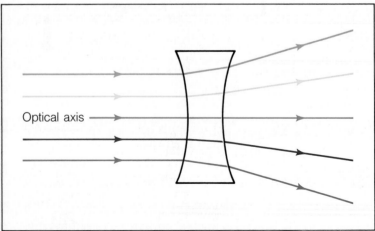

Optical axis

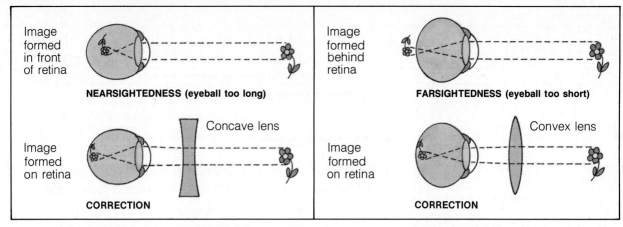

Figure 24-14 *Nearsightedness is corrected by using a concave lens. Why? Farsightedness is corrected by using a convex lens. Why?*

Lenses and Vision

The lens of your eye is a convex lens. It is not a hard and rigid lens, but rather a soft and flexible one. So it can easily change shape to allow you to see clear images of objects both near and distant. Small muscles attached to the lens either relax or tighten and thereby control the curvature of the lens in order to focus images directly on the retina. How do you think the muscles move to allow you to see nearby objects? Distant objects?

NEARSIGHTEDNESS Ideally, the image formed by the convex lens of the eye should fall directly on the retina. In certain cases, the image falls in front of the retina because the eyeball is too long. This condition is called nearsightedness. A nearsighted person has difficulty seeing distant objects clearly but no trouble seeing nearby objects.

The lens of a nearsighted person is too convex. The rays of light converge at a point in front of the retina. A correcting lens would have to make the light rays diverge before they enter the eye. So a concave lens is used to correct nearsightedness. See Figure 24-14.

FARSIGHTEDNESS If the eyeball is too short, the image is focused behind the retina. This condition is called farsightedness. A farsighted person can see distant objects clearly but has difficulty seeing nearby objects. These objects appear blurred.

The lens of a farsighted person is not convex enough. The rays of light converge at a point behind the retina. A correcting lens would have to make the light rays converge before they enter the eye. So a convex lens is used to correct farsightedness. See Figure 24–14 on page 569.

SECTION REVIEW

1. Compare a convex lens and a concave lens.
2. What kind of lens is used to correct nearsightedness? Farsightedness? Explain your answer.
3. If you wished to examine a small object using a lens, would you choose a converging or diverging lens? Name the lens you would choose.

Section Objective

To identify several optical instruments

24–4 Optical Instruments

An optical instrument produces images by the reflection or refraction of light. **An optical instrument uses mirrors or lenses to produce images.** What optical instruments can you name?

Cameras

Just like the eye, a camera works by allowing light to enter through a lens. A camera lens, however, may be made up of several separate lenses. And the image produced by a camera lens falls on photographic film that contains chemical substances that are sensitive to light. Where does the image produced by the eye fall?

Figure 24–15 *These three photographs were taken with lenses of different focal lengths. The size of the image depends on the focal length of the lens. Which photograph was taken with a camera lens of short focal length? Of long focal length?*

A camera contains a convex lens. The image formed by a camera is real and inverted. It is also smaller than the object. The size of the image formed on the film depends upon the focal length of the lens. A lens with a short focal length produces a small image. But because the image of the object being photographed is small, a wider area of the surroundings is included.

A lens with a long focal length produces a large image. With this kind of lens, the area of the surroundings is decreased as the size of the image is increased. See Figure 24–15.

The opening in the camera through which light enters is called the aperture. The size of the aperture controls the amount of light that passes through the lens and reaches the film.

Telescopes

Telescopes are used to view objects that are very far away. By using mirrors and lenses, telescopes produce enlarged images of distant objects.

A refracting telescope uses a series of lenses to focus and magnify light from distant objects. The larger the lenses used in a refracting telescope, the greater the light-gathering power. The refracting telescope at Yerkes Observatory in Wisconsin has a light-gathering power about 40,000 times greater than that of the human eye. The diameter of its largest lens is about 100 centimeters.

Figure 24–16 *The refracting telescope at Yerkes Observatory in Wisconsin (left) uses a series of lenses to form an image of a distant object (right). The Yerkes Observatory telescope is the world's largest refracting telescope.*

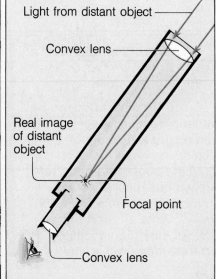

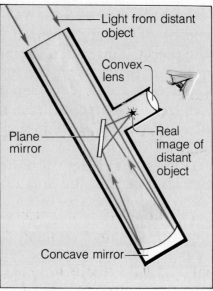

Light from distant
object

Convex
lens

Plane
mirror

Real
image of
distant
object

Concave mirror

Figure 24–17 *The Hale Telescope at Mount Palomar in California (left) is one of the world's largest reflecting telescopes. Light rays from a distant object are reflected from one mirror to another to produce an image (right). What is the purpose of the convex lens?*

A reflecting telescope uses a series of plane and concave mirrors to gather light from distant objects. The image formed by these mirrors is, however, relatively small. So a lens inside the eyepiece is used to magnify the image. The "200-inch" Hale telescope at Mount Palomar in California is one of the world's largest reflecting telescopes.

Microscopes

A microscope uses two convex lenses to magnify extremely small objects. One lens of the microscope is placed at the end of the tube. The other lens is in the eyepiece. The total magnification produced by the microscope is the product of the magnification of the two lenses.

SECTION REVIEW

1. Name three optical instruments. Explain what each does.
2. Compare a refracting and a reflecting telescope.
3. Which type of camera lens would be called a wide-angle lens—one with a short focal length or one with a long focal length? Which type would be called a telephoto lens?

Sharpen Your Skills

Color Photography

Color film is sensitive to the various frequencies of light. It can record the colors of an object.

Using books and other reference materials in your library, find out how color film works. Write a report that describes how the various colors are recorded on the film.

24–5 Light and Technology

Today, scientists have developed new and exciting ways to use light—from looking inside the human body to cutting through the body to producing three-dimensional images of body parts. **New developments in light technology include lasers, holography, and fiber optics.**

Lasers

Unlike white light, which is a mixture of all the frequencies of the visible spectrum, light from a **laser** is made up of only one frequency. Laser light is **coherent light,** or light that is in phase. This means that the crests and troughs of the light waves all move in the same direction at the same time. Light from a laser, then, travels in almost parallel lines with very little spreading. These characteristics make laser light an extremely powerful single-color light.

Different kinds of gases, liquids, and crystals are used to make lasers. One of the most common lasers is a ruby laser. A ruby laser consists of a solid rod made of ruby crystals. At each end of the rod is a mirror. One of these mirrors is a partial mirror. It does not reflect all the light that strikes it.

Wrapped around the rod is a tube called a flash tube, which provides energy in the form of bright flashes of light. The light is focused on and absorbed by atoms in the ruby crystals. When atoms absorb energy, their electrons move to higher energy levels. But the electrons do not stay there. Instead, they quickly drop back to their original levels. In the process of dropping back, the electrons give off the energy they absorbed. This energy is given off in the form of photons of light. All of the photons emitted have the same frequency and wavelength. They are all photons of the same color!

The process is repeated over and over so that a large number of photons are released. The photons are reflected back and forth between the mirrored ends of the rod, causing even more photons to be released. In this way, the light intensifies, or amplifies. When the light becomes intense enough, it passes through the partial mirror as a narrow beam of concentrated light.

Figure 24–18 *A laser produces an intense beam of coherent, single-color light (top). Such a beam of light can be used to diagnose eye diseases by monitoring the flow of blood through vessels in the retina (bottom).*

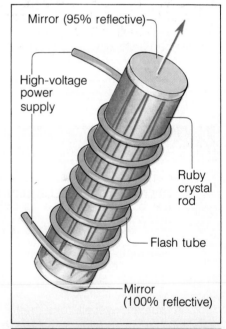

Mirror (95% reflective)

High-voltage power supply

Ruby crystal rod

Flash tube

Mirror (100% reflective)

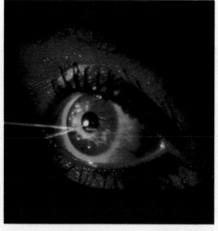

Figure 24–19 *This hologram, or three-dimensional image of an object, was the first all-color hologram to be created. What kind of light is used in holography?*

Lasers have uses in medicine, manufacturing, communication, surveying, entertainment, and even measuring the distance to the moon. Lasers are used in audio and video disks, computers, and printers. In the future, lasers may be used to produce an almost limitless supply of nuclear fusion energy.

Holography

One of the newest and most exciting uses of laser light is in **holography.** Holography is a technology that uses laser light to produce a three-dimensional image of an object or scene. The image is called a **hologram.**

Holograph systems are used with laser beams to scan the universal bar codes on grocery store items. Holograms have many other possible uses. They can store a tremendous amount of data in a limited space, give details of structural flaws in machine parts, display the interior of body organs, and bring three-dimensional TV pictures into your home.

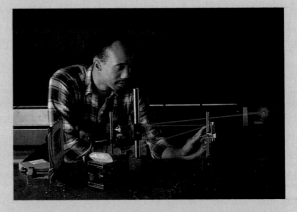

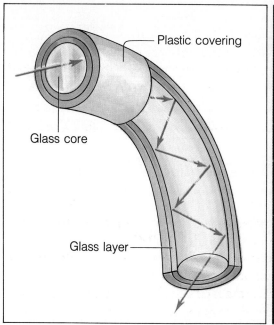
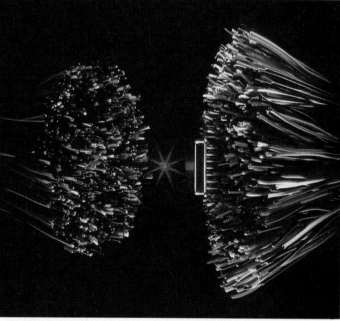

Plastic covering

Glass core

Glass layer

Figure 24–20 *Optical fibers are like "light pipes" because, through a series of continuous reflections, light is transported from one place to another (left). The single optical-fiber cable in the center of the photograph can carry as many messages in the form of high-intensity laser light as all the electric wires combined (right).*

Fiber Optics

Imagine a doctor being able to see inside a patient's body without having to perform surgery. Advances in the field of **fiber optics** have made this possible. Fiber optics deals with the transfer of light through long, thin flexible fibers of glass or plastic called **optical fibers.**

An optical fiber is like a "light pipe." A ray of light enters the fiber and is reflected so that it zigzags its way through the length of the fiber. See Figure 24–20.

Optical fibers are rapidly replacing electric wires in communication systems such as telephone systems. A single optical fiber can carry thousands of messages in the form of high-intensity laser light with extraordinary clarity. Optical fibers are also used in medicine, television signal transmission, and data processing.

SECTION REVIEW

1. Name three uses of lasers.
2. What is a hologram? An optical fiber?
3. Distinguish between white light and laser light.

Convex Lenses

Problem

What kinds of images are formed by a convex lens?

Materials *(per group)*

convex lens
lens holder
meterstick
light bulb and socket
blank sheet of paper

Procedure

1. Place the convex lens in the lens holder and position them at least 2 meters in front of the *lighted* bulb.
2. Position the paper behind the lens so a clear image of the bulb can be seen on the paper. The sheet of paper must be positioned vertically. Record the position and the relative size of the image.
3. Measure the distance from the lens to the paper. This is the focal length of the lens. Record the distance in centimeters.
4. *Turn off the light bulb when moving it.*
5. Move the bulb to a position that is greater than twice the focal length of the lens. Turn the bulb on. Record the position and relative size of the image.
6. Move the bulb to a position that is exactly twice the focal length. Record the position and relative size of the image.

7. Move the bulb to a position equal to the focal length. Record the position and relative size of the image.
8. Move the bulb to a position between the lens and the paper. This position is less than one focal length. Record the position and relative size of the image.

Object Distance (bulb to lens)	Image Position (erect or inverted)	Image Size

Focal length of lens _____

Observation

Describe the image formed in each step of the procedure for which you have made observations.

Conclusions

1. Is the image formed by a convex lens always erect? If not, under what conditions is the image inverted?
2. What happens to the size of the image as the bulb moves closer to the focal length? To the position of the image?
3. What happens to the size of the image as the bulb moves to less than the focal length? To the position of the image?

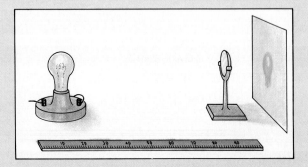

CHAPTER REVIEW

SUMMARY

24-1 Sources of Light

❏ Luminous objects produce their own light.

❏ An illuminated object is seen only by reflected light.

❏ Light produced from heat is called incandescent light.

❏ Light that is produced by the electron bombardment of gas molecules contained at low pressure is called fluorescent light.

❏ Neon light is produced when electrons pass through glass tubes filled with neon gas.

24-2 Reflection and Mirrors

❏ A plane mirror has a perfectly flat surface and produces an image that is erect and the same size as the object.

❏ Concave mirrors curve inward and produce images that are usually inverted and magnified.

❏ Convex mirrors curve outward and produce images that are erect and smaller than the object.

24-3 Refraction and Lenses

❏ A convex lens converges light rays and produces real or virtual images, depending on the position of the object.

❏ A concave lens diverges light rays and produces erect images that are smaller than the object.

❏ To correct nearsighted vision, concave lenses are used. To correct farsighted vision, convex lenses are used.

24-4 Optical Instruments

❏ An optical instrument uses mirrors or lenses to produce images.

❏ A camera works by allowing light to enter through a convex lens.

❏ The image formed by a camera is real, inverted, and smaller than the object. The size of the image depends upon the focal length of the lens.

❏ A refracting telescope uses a series of lenses to focus and magnify light.

❏ A reflecting telescope uses a series of plane and concave mirrors to gather light.

❏ A microscope uses lenses to magnify extremely small objects.

24-5 Light and Technology

❏ Light from a laser is coherent, has a single frequency, and forms a very intense and concentrated beam.

❏ A hologram is a three-dimensional picture made from laser light.

❏ Optical fibers are long, thin, flexible fibers of glass or plastic that transmit light.

VOCABULARY

Define each term in a complete sentence.

coherent light	fluorescent	laser	phosphor
concave lens	focal length	lens	plane mirror
concave mirror	focal point	luminous	real image
convex lens	hologram	mirror	virtual image
convex mirror	holography	neon	
fiber optics	illuminated	optical axis	
	incandescent	optical fiber	

CONTENT REVIEW: MULTIPLE CHOICE

On a separate sheet of paper, write the letter of the answer that best completes each statement.

1. A flashlight beam is seen because the light is
   a. luminous.   b. illuminated.   c. fluorescent.   d. neon.
2. Which of the following does *not* belong?
   a. luminous   b. illuminated   c. incandescent   d. fluorescent
3. The filament in an incandescent light bulb is
   a. steel.   b. copper.   c. tungsten.   d. tin.
4. The photons released in a fluorescent light bulb are
   a. infrared.   b. ultraviolet.   c. X-ray.   d. gamma.
5. The point in front of a mirror where reflected rays meet is the
   a. focal length.   b. focal point.   c. aperture.   d. vertex.
6. As compared to the object, the image formed by a convex mirror is
   a. erect and larger.   b. inverted and smaller.
   c. inverted and larger.   d. erect and smaller.
7. The Hale telescope has a 5-meter
   a. plane mirror.   b. convex mirror.   c. concave lens.   d. concave mirror.
8. The image formed by a convex lens in a telescope is
   a. erect and enlarged.   b. inverted and enlarged.
   c. inverted and smaller.   d. erect and smaller.
9. Farsightedness is corrected by a
   a. convex mirror.   b. convex lens.   c. concave mirror.   d. concave lens.
10. Crests and troughs of each wave are lined up with all other waves in
   a. incandescent light.   b. fluorescent light.   c. neon light.   d. laser light.

CONTENT REVIEW: COMPLETION

On a separate sheet of paper, write the word or words that best complete each statement.

1. The sun is a (an) _____ object.
2. A _____ mirror is perfectly flat.
3. A _____ mirror curves inward.
4. A _____ mirror curves outward.
5. A _____ lens diverges light.
6. The opening in the camera through which light enters is called the _____.
7. Light produced from heat is _____.
8. _____ is concentrated light with a single frequency.
9. A (An) _____ is a three-dimensional picture made with laser light.
10. A (An) _____ is a thin, flexible glass tube that transmits light.

CONTENT REVIEW: TRUE OR FALSE

Determine whether each statement is true or false. Then on a separate sheet of paper, write "true" if it is true. If it is false, change the underlined word or words to make the statement true.

1. The moon is said to be <u>luminous</u>.
2. Cool light is <u>fluorescent</u> light.
3. A plane mirror forms a <u>virtual</u> image.
4. Reflecting telescopes use <u>convex</u> mirrors.

5. <u>Concave</u> mirrors give an extra wide view.
6. <u>Concave</u> lenses are used in magnifying glasses.
7. The lens of the eye is a <u>concave</u> lens.

8. A camera lens produces an image that is inverted and <u>smaller</u>.
9. All laser light is <u>in phase</u>.
10. <u>Holograms</u> are three-dimensional images.

CONCEPT REVIEW: SKILL BUILDING

Use the skills you have developed in the chapter to complete each activity.

1. Applying concepts Suppose you are building an incubator and you need a source of heat. Would you use an incandescent or fluorescent light bulb? Explain your answer.

2. Relating concepts What characteristics of laser light can be used to explain the following statements:
   a. Laser light is never white.
   b. Laser light is useful in surveying.
   c. Laser stands for *l*ight *a*mplification through *s*timulated *e*mission of *r*adiation.

3. Applying definitions The lens at the end of a microscope tube has a magnification of 10×. The eyepiece lens has a magnification of 6×. What is the total magnification achieved by the microscope?

4. Making calculations When a convex lens produces a real image, the following relationship applies:

$$\frac{d_o}{d_i} = \frac{s_o}{s_i} \quad \text{or}$$

$$\frac{\text{object distance}}{\text{image distance}} = \frac{\text{object size}}{\text{image size}}$$

   a. What is the size of the image formed at 15 centimeters from a lens if the object is 4 centimeters tall and located 20 centimeters from the lens?
   b. An image measuring 2.5 centimeters is formed 10 centimeters from a lens. How large is the object if its distance from the lens is 20 centimeters?
   c. At what distance is a 2-centimeter image located if a 6-centimeter object located 75 centimeters from the lens produces this image?

5. Making comparisons Compare the structure and operation of a camera to that of the eye.

6. Expressing an opinion The technology is now available to place a series of mirrors in orbit. These mirrors would reflect light back to Earth in order to illuminate major urban areas at night. What do you think are some of the problems and the benefits that would result from such a project?

CONCEPT REVIEW: ESSAY

Discuss each of the following in a brief paragraph.

1. List five examples of luminous light.
2. How is light produced in an incandescent light bulb? In a fluorescent light bulb?
3. Compare a real image and a virtual image. Which type of mirror forms a real image? Which type of lens forms a real image?
4. Explain why when white light passes through a single convex lens different colors of the visible spectrum are focused at different points. Use a diagram to illustrate your explanation.
5. Describe the two vision problems. How is each corrected?
6. Describe how an optical fiber transmits light.

Adventures in Science

JOHN CAULFIELD'S
WONDERFUL WORLD OF
HOLOGRAPHY

Welcome to the wonderful world of holography! Or, as Isaac Asimov has described it, "the greatest advance in imaging since the eye." With a wide range of applications, holography is fast becoming a tool of the artist, scientist, surgeon, and city planner alike. What exactly is holography?

According to Dr. John Caulfield of the University of Alabama, holography is an unusual photographic technique that records a three-dimensional image so accurately that the image often appears to be real. Little wonder then that the term coined for this exciting technique comes from the Greek words *holos* and *gramma*, which mean "the whole message."

Conventional photography records images in two dimensions, producing photographs that appear flat. But holography adds a third dimension. So a holographic image, or hologram, has the same details of depth and texture that the original object has. In a series of steps, holography recreates the complex pattern of light that reflects off an object and makes it visible.

First, a laser beam is directed at an object. The beam bounces off the object and onto a photographic plate. Another laser beam is directed at the plate. Together, the two beams form a pattern of light interference that looks like gray smudges. When still another laser beam is aimed at the plate in the second step of the process, the blurry message is unscrambled. Color is added by the artist, photographer, or scientist. The reconstructed image of the original scene or object is so real the temptation is to reach out and touch it.

"An interesting characteristic of the hologram," says Caulfield, who is a leader in the field of holographic applications, "is that the observer is able to see many different views of the image. It is like viewing a three-dimensional scene through a window. By moving to different parts of the window, we see the same scene from new angles."

This innovative technology is actually not that new. Holography was invented in 1947 by the Hungarian scientist Dennis Gabor. But because his techniques were unrefined, Gabor's experiments were ignored for nearly fifteen years. With the introduction of the laser in 1960, the field of holography bloomed. Today, holography is a growing technology with uses in fields as different as engineering and tennis! And John Caulfield is one scientist who intends to be in the forefront of this exciting science.

Caulfield's research includes developing images of things that *do not* exist or perhaps *cannot* exist! Such images are called synthetic holograms. Synthetic holograms have many important uses. For example, engineers can use them to design more efficient and pollution-free motors for cars and machines. Architects can use synthetic holograms to design buildings and to determine their best location in the actual landscape. And doctors can view computer-generated holograms of parts of the human body before performing surgery.

More practical applications of holography include the use of printed synthetic holograms on credit cards and the use of holographic optical instruments to scan product codes on grocery items.

Holographic images of an airplane's instrument panel are projected directly in front of pilots as part of their training. And a recent development uses holography to guide aircraft through fog by creating holograms of the airport.

The world of holography grows as Dr. Caulfield and other scientists refine and expand the technology. With his interest in the technique of holography and his belief in its infinite applications, Caulfield is helping to prepare future scientists for the challenges that lie ahead. Holography is a young science with a bright, exciting future. As Caulfield notes, "We haven't yet seen the whole message of holography!"

Working in a laboratory at the University of Alabama, Dr. Caulfield deflects a laser beam toward an object for pulsed laser holography.

Issues in Science

HYPERSONIC TRAVEL:

Is Faster Better?

Picture yourself as a busy New York rock star. Tough demands on your time are nothing new, but tomorrow's schedule seems impossible. You must attend an important breakfast meeting in London, sign contracts over lunch in New York, and perform before a sellout crowd at 8 P.M. in Los Angeles.

Can you do it?

You can if you prepare yourself for an exhausting twenty-six-hour trip that includes two supersonic flights and one subsonic flight. Aboard the supersonic transport, better known as the SST, travel is about twice the speed of sound, or 2400 kilometers per hour. Subsonic jetliners cruise at speeds between 800 and 1000 kilometers per hour. Thirty years ago, speeds such as these were only a dream. Today, they are a reality. But by the year 2000, they may be just a memory!

Need for Speed

By the year 2000, the wish of many travelers to go faster and faster may come true. The United States, Great Britain, and France are working on *hypersonic* airliner designs. Hypersonic transports, or HSTs, would fly at from five to eight times the speed of sound. In an HST, travel time from Los Angeles to Tokyo would be reduced from about ten hours to as few as two. And a flight from New York to San Francisco would be a mere 16 minutes—not five hours. Future predictions for the HST include round-the-world flights lasting no more than four hours!

Different Views

Some people believe that faster air travel could improve trade and cultural links between nations. And that's one reason why government and industry officials are urging the United States to build and use hypersonic airliners. Ben Rich of Lockheed Corporation says, "Routine hypersonic flights between nations will be a reality by the end of the century."

Several aviation experts disagree, however. They feel that supersonic flight is not very practical and that hypersonic flight may be even less practical. These experts say commercial flights at speeds faster than the speed of sound have several drawbacks. One is cost. Planes burn more fuel at supersonic speeds. At faster speeds, the fuel use will be even greater and the costs higher. Another factor that adds to cost is the stress put on a plane's structure at supersonic speeds. As a result of this stress, supersonic planes require more frequent maintenance.

Furthermore, the critics argue, part of the speed advantage of hypersonic flights may be lost due to heavy traffic over and around major airports. A hypersonic plane might cross the Atlantic in less than an hour and then spend another half-hour waiting to land.

Another potential obstacle to commercial hypersonic flight is noise pollution. When an aircraft flies faster than sound, it creates shock waves in the air. These waves produce "sonic booms" that can be felt and heard on the ground. To protect people from sonic-boom effects, the U.S. Federal Aviation Administration (FAA) prohibits commercial supersonic flights over the United States.

Supporters of the hypersonic plane have no problem with the FAA limitation. As they see it, most of the HST flights would be over the ocean between the United States and the Far East. Trade between countries that rim the Pacific Ocean is greatly increasing. As a result, more and more people are flying between the United States and Japan, China, Singapore, and Australia.

To counter the argument of increased cost, supporters of the hypersonic plane claim that a significant portion of each trip could take

A long line of cars forms part of a protest march at Kennedy International Airport in New York. The target of the protest is the supersonic transport, or SST, whose noise level upon takeoff and landing has angered residents of the area.

place at higher altitudes than those used by conventional aircraft. Flying at higher altitudes uses less fuel and reduces operational costs.

No doubt, developing and building a hypersonic plane will be expensive. Aerospace industry specialists estimate that one hypersonic plane may cost $5 billion to $10 billion. Critics say it may cost twice that amount. But since HSTs may have uses outside the commercial-flight industry, supporters of the HST think that the high cost of developing the plane is justified. They support their position with the belief that the development effort would keep the United States in the forefront of the aviation industry.

Will the possible benefits to world trade, more efficient flight, and aviation advancement balance the costs in money and pollution? What do you think?

Physical Science and Technology

Most countries mine coal and oil to produce energy. But Iceland, a small island nation in the North Atlantic, mines "volcanic fires." Iceland sits atop a volcanic belt covering one-third of its territory. The heat generated from this geothermal belt provides Icelanders with 30 percent of their total energy needs and 70 percent of their space-heating requirements.

In the past, Icelanders have used geothermal energy for hot springs bathing and laundering. Today, the uses have been expanded to include home heating, electricity production, and industrial manufacturing. No wonder Icelanders say, "Think well of the glowing embers."

Iceland's use of geothermal energy demonstrates how clean, inexpensive alternative energy sources can be used to meet people's energy needs. But the "glowing embers" are only one example. As you read the chapters in this unit, you will learn about alternative energy sources. And you will also learn how the union of science and technology promises to provide exciting and important developments for your future.

CHAPTERS

25 Energy Resources

26 Energy and the Environment

27 Chemical Technology

28 Electronics and Computers

Solar energy can be used any time and place the sun shines. Geothermal energy comes from within the earth. It can be used even when the sun does not shine. The steam rising from the ground is produced when water is heated underground.

585

Energy Resources 25

CHAPTER SECTIONS

25–1 Fossil Fuels

25–2 Solar Energy: Direct and Indirect

25–3 Nuclear Energy

25–4 Alternative Energy Sources

CHAPTER OBJECTIVES

After completing this chapter, you will be able to

25–1 Explain how fossil fuels formed on the earth.

25–1 Define hydrocarbon and combustion.

25–2 Describe several direct uses of solar energy.

25–2 Explain how power derived from moving water and wind is related to the sun.

25–3 Compare the processes of nuclear fission and nuclear fusion.

25–3 Describe the parts of a nuclear reactor.

25–4 Discuss the importance of alternative energy resources.

25–4 List several potential alternative energy resources.

The time: 75,000 years ago. Huddled together in a dim cave, the hunters prepare for a long, cold night. A smoldering fire provides the only warmth as a chilling darkness settles over the land. One member of the group agrees to keep the fire going while the others sleep. The hunters do not know how to start a fire. They have carried the glowing embers for this fire from the remains of a forest fire started by lightning.

The night is quiet. The fire-keeper's eyes grow heavy. Soon he is asleep. The fire goes out. The hunters have lost their only source of light and heat. It is humankind's first energy crisis.

The time: 1973. Cars line up for at least 4 kilometers. As the sun peeks over the horizon, a young man selling coffee and doughnuts makes his way through the sea of automobiles. The more sociable motorists use the opportunity to visit with neighbors. Others read the morning paper or try to sleep. The rest just sit in their cars and scowl.

An early morning traffic jam? No, the first experience with an oil shortage for the United States. Shipments of oil to the United States have been drastically reduced. Motorists wait in line for what has become a most precious commodity—gasoline.

Fortunately, the oil crisis of 1973 did not last long. The discovery of new oil fields plus efforts to conserve fuel produced a relative abundance of oil by 1986. But the shortages of the 1970s were dramatic indications of how dependent people are on fuel and how dangerously close they are to running out of it.

Every day you use energy from fuel to heat your home, power your car, operate appliances, and cook your food. What would your life be like if that energy were not available? In this chapter, you will learn about various energy resources for present and future use. With that information, you should be better able to answer the question.

Early people used fire for cooking, for light and heat, and to ward off dangerous animals.

25–1 Fossil Fuels

Most of the energy you use every day comes from **fossil fuels.** Fossil fuels formed hundreds of millions of years ago when layers of dead plants and animals were buried beneath sediments such as mud, sand, silt, or clay. Over millions of years, heat and great pressure changed the sediments into rock and the plant and animal remains into fossil fuels. **The three main fossil fuels are coal, oil, and natural gas.**

The reason fossil fuels are so useful as energy sources is due to their chemical makeup. Fossil fuels are rich in **hydrocarbons.** Hydrocarbons are substances that contain the elements hydrogen and carbon. When hydrocarbons in fossil fuels are combined with oxygen at high temperatures, heat and light energy are released. This process—which you probably call burning—is known as **combustion.**

Other types of fuels also give off heat and light during combustion. People have burned wood as a fuel ever since they learned how to start a fire. But wood and other fuels do not produce as much energy as fossil fuels. A kilogram of coal, for example, provides twice as much heat as a kilogram of wood. The heating values of oil and gas are more than three times that of wood. In addition, fossil fuels are easier to transport, store, and use.

Coal

Coal is a solid fossil fuel. There are four types of coal, each of which represents a different stage in the development of coal. Each can be used as a fuel.

The first type of coal is **peat.** Peat is a soft substance made of decayed plant fibers. When peat undergoes pressure from rocks piled above it, it is converted into **lignite** (LIHG-night). Lignite, the second type of coal, is soft and has a woody texture.

If even more pressure is applied to lignite, it turns into **bituminous** (bigh-TOO-muh-nuhs) **coal.** Bituminous coal, the third type of coal, is often called soft coal. Bituminous coal is the most plentiful type of coal on the earth. It takes tremendous pressure to change bituminous coal into **anthracite** (AN-thruh-sight), the fourth type of coal. Anthracite

Figure 25–1 *Before early people learned how to start fires, they used fires started by lightning and erupting volcanoes. How might a fire started by a volcano have been transported?*

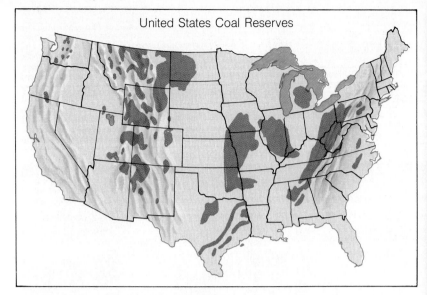

United States Coal Reserves

is very hard and brittle. Few deposits of anthracite are located in the United States.

Oil and Natural Gas

Unlike coal, the plants and animals from which oil and natural gas formed probably lived in the earth's oceans. When they died, they sank to the ocean floor and were covered by sediments. In time, the layers of sediments changed into sandstone, limestone, or shale. Pressure from these rock layers, in addition to great heat and the action of certain bacteria, changed the plant and animal remains into oil and natural gas.

Rocks such as sandstone and limestone have tiny pores through which oil and gas can seep. When oil and natural gas were first formed, they probably seeped through the sandstone and limestone layers. In time, the oil and gas that were covered by harder rocks through which they could not seep formed pools. The oil and gas became trapped in natural "pockets" under the harder rocks.

Oil that is drilled from beneath the earth is called crude oil, or petroleum. Some of the fuels that can be obtained from petroleum are gasoline, kerosene, heating oil, and jet fuels. In Chapter 27, you will read about other petroleum products.

Although almost all of the petroleum used in the world today is obtained from oil wells, some petroleum is located near the surface of the earth. Two sources of this petroleum are tar sands and oil

Figure 25–2 *Coal miners dig for coal in deep mine shafts under the earth (right). Major coal reserves are located throughout the United States (left). Where is the coal deposit nearest your home located?*

Figure 25–3 *Petroleum and natural gas are often found in the same deposit. Why is natural gas usually found above petroleum?*

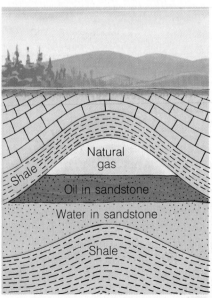

Natural gas

Shale

Oil in sandstone

Water in sandstone

Shale

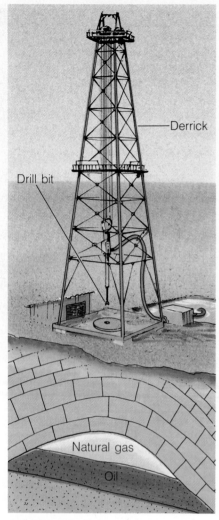

Figure 25-4 *To obtain petroleum and natural gas, geologists drill through rock layers covering the fuel deposits (left). The petroleum obtained from deposits in Alaska is piped through the Alaska pipeline (right).*

Sharpen Your Skills

Where Is the Oil?

Using books and other reference materials in the library, find out where the major oil fields in the world are located. Make a map showing these oil fields. Be sure to include oil fields that have recently been discovered, as well as areas that are presently believed to contain oil.

shale. Tar sands are layers of sand soaked with thick, gooey petroleum. Oil shale is a gray rock that can contain droplets of oil within the rock. Unfortunately, obtaining oil from both tar sands and oil shale is not economical.

Natural gas is usually found along with petroleum. Because natural gas is less dense than petroleum, it often is located above petroleum deposits. The most common natural gas is methane. Methane and other types of natural gas are used as fuels to heat homes. Methane also is used in gas stoves.

Fossil Fuel Shortages

Fossil fuels are **nonrenewable resources.** Nonrenewable resources are formed by nature over millions of years. Once they are used up, they cannot be replaced. So the gasoline lines of 1973 could return. Even worse, some scientists believe that if people continue to use oil at the present rate, the United States may be out of oil by the year 2060. The worldwide supply of oil may be used up by 2080. A resource that took hundreds of millions of years to form will be used up in the span of a few thousand years. Do you now understand why conservation of nonrenewable resources such as fossil fuels is such an important topic—not just for scientists but for everyone throughout the world?

SECTION REVIEW

1. What are the three main types of fossil fuels?
2. What is the name for substances made of the elements hydrogen and carbon?
3. Why is natural gas usually found on top of petroleum deposits?
4. Most scientists believe that oil and natural gas formed beneath the ocean floor. However, a great amount of oil and natural gas are now found beneath dry land. Explain how this could have occurred.

Figure 25–5 *Oil shale may contain enough oil to be ignited.*

25–2 Solar Energy: Direct and Indirect

Section Objective

To describe direct and indirect uses of solar energy

Life on earth could not exist without the energy given off by the sun. Without this **solar energy,** plants would not grow, rain would not fall, and wind would not blow. Planet Earth would be so cold and dark that nothing could survive.

Scientists estimate that the amount of solar energy falling on a 200-square-kilometer plot near the equator is enough to meet the world's energy needs! As you can see, tapping this solar energy certainly would help conserve fossil fuels. **Solar energy can be used directly from the sun or indirectly, such as using wind or water power to produce usable energy.**

Direct Solar Energy

Direct solar energy means taking energy straight from the sun and using it. The main problem with direct solar energy is that it is difficult to collect, convert, concentrate, and store.

PASSIVE SOLAR ENERGY Direct solar energy can be either passive or active. An example of passive use would be positioning windows in a house so that the

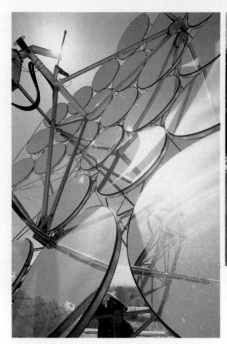

Figure 25–6 *These solar collectors reflect the sun's rays toward a tower of water, where enough heat energy is absorbed to heat the water (left). The solar collectors on the roof of this school in Denver, Colorado, supply most of the school's energy (right). Are these solar collectors an example of the direct or indirect use of solar energy?*

Figure 25–7 *A solar cell, or photovoltaic cell, converts sunlight directly into electricity.*

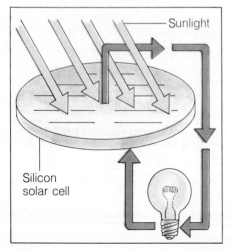

amount of sunlight absorbed would be enough to heat the house. The obvious problem with passive solar energy for home heating is that when the sun stops shining, the source of heat is removed.

ACTIVE SOLAR ENERGY Active solar energy involves collecting the sun's energy in a device called a **solar collector.** In a typical solar collector, a large, dark surface covered with glass or plastic absorbs energy from the sun. Water is actively pumped through pipes or a large, flat surface inside the collector. The water is warmed by the sun's energy. The warm water is then stored to provide heat and hot water for some future time. What advantage does active solar heating have over passive solar heating?

Although the use of passive and active solar heating has been successful in many homes, it has not gone far to meet the energy needs of society as a whole. In order to provide energy for offices, schools, factories, hospitals, and apartment complexes, some type of central solar power plant must be designed.

SOLAR CELLS A solar cell, or **photovoltaic cell,** is a device that converts sunlight directly into electricity. Most solar cells are "sandwiches" of very thin layers of silicon and metal. When sunlight strikes the surface of this sandwich, electrons flow across the layers. This flow of electrons is electric current, which can be used to do work. Unfortunately, the amount of electricity produced by a single solar cell is very small. Huge numbers of cells are needed to produce useful amounts of electricity.

Solar cells were first used on a large scale in 1959 to generate electricity aboard the United States space vehicle *Vanguard I*. Since then, they have been used to generate electricity on most spacecraft. Can you think of a reason why solar cells would be especially effective in space?

One disadvantage of solar cells has been their cost. In 1959, electricity from solar cells cost about $500 per watt. Now it is down to $6 per watt. Although the efficiency of solar cells has been greatly improved, energy experts say that the cost will have to be lowered to $1 per watt in order to compete with the cost of electricity obtained from fossil fuels.

Indirect Solar Energy: Water Power

Energy from the sun causes water to evaporate from oceans and lakes. This water vapor condenses to form clouds in the atmosphere. When the water vapor falls back to the earth as rain or snow, it produces rushing rivers and streams.

There is tremendous power in moving water. Since ancient times, people have used that power to turn mill wheels. By the late 1800s, most water mills had been replaced by steam engines. But with the invention of the electric light bulb in 1879, water power became important once again as a means of generating electricity. Why is water power an indirect use of solar energy?

The mechanical energy in falling or flowing water is used to generate usable electricity in a **hydroelectric** power plant. Hydroelectric means "using water to produce electricity." At a hydroelectric plant, dams hold back millions of tons of water. Some of the water is allowed to pass through pipes and is then channeled past turbines within the plant. The rushing water spins the blades of a turbine in an electric generator to produce electricity. Although new plants are built each year, the number of areas in which a dam can be built is limited. In this sense, hydroelectric power is limited.

In the past few years, another way of producing hydroelectric power has been developed. This method, often referred to as **tidal power,** involves using the rise and fall of tides. In areas where the difference between high and low tides is great, the

Sharpen Your Skills

Dinosaur Power

Almost 100 million years ago, a dinosaur called *Stegosaurus* roamed the earth. Some scientists believe *Stegosaurus* used solar energy in an unusual way.

Using books and other reference materials in the library, find out what the *Stegosaurus* looked like. Then predict what part of its body might have been used to absorb solar energy.

Figure 25-8 *Inside a generator at a hydroelectric plant, the mechanical energy of moving water is used to spin a turbine. The spinning turbine, in turn, causes large electromagnets to spin. The spinning electromagnets generate electricity. What energy conversion is involved in this process?*

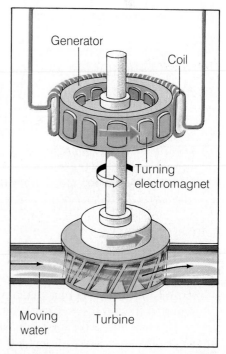

Generator

Coil

Turning electromagnet

Moving water

Turbine

Figure 25–9 *For centuries, the mechanical energy of moving water has been used to turn water mills (left). Today, falling water at Boulder Dam is used to generate electricity (right). Are water mills and hydroelectric plants direct or indirect uses of solar energy?*

movement of water during changes in the tides can be used to spin a turbine and generate electricity. Tidal power plants are in use in France, Canada, and the Soviet Union. However, tidal power as an energy resource is quite limited since there are relatively few areas in the world in which tidal power plants can be built.

CAREER   *Hydroelectric Plant Operator*

HELP WANTED: HYDROELECTRIC PLANT OPERATOR Must have mechanical skills or power-plant operation experience. Work includes maintaining equipment and supervising other employees. High school diploma required.

A huge, light-green water pipe extends from one reservoir at the top of a cliff to another reservoir at the bottom of the cliff. During the day, gravity pulls water down through the pipe to turn turbines and generate electricity. At night, water from the lower reservoir is pumped back into the upper reservoir.

A **hydroelectric plant operator** oversees the daily flow of millions of liters of water up and down through the pipe. The operator makes sure that the electric generating plant's turbines and other equipment are working properly. The operator monitors meters and gauges and records the amount of water that is released from the upper reservoir or that is pumped from the lower reservoir.

The operator routinely checks safety devices. During power failures, the operator may

have to start up or reverse the flow of water or repair faulty equipment. A hydroelectric plant operator must have mechanical skill and the ability to deal with emergencies quickly and efficiently.

Most hydroelectric power plant operators have a high school diploma plus several years of technical training. If you would like to learn more about this career, contact the International Union of Operating Engineers, 1125 17th Street NW, Washington, DC 20036.

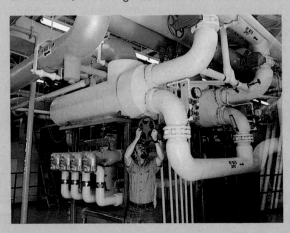

Indirect Solar Energy: Wind Power

Solar energy does not heat the earth evenly. It is the uneven heating of the earth by solar energy that causes winds to blow. Throughout history people have used the wind to propel sailing ships, turn mill wheels, and pump water. Why is wind power an indirect use of solar energy?

In 1890, a Danish inventor developed a windmill that could generate electricity. The movement of the wind caused the windmill to spin. The spinning windmill was connected to a turbine in a small electric generator. As the wind blew, an electric current was generated. Wind generators became very popular with American farmers. They were widely used until the 1940s. But wind generators had some serious disadvantages. Can you think of what some of these disadvantages might be?

When the United States faced serious oil shortages in the 1970s, interest in wind energy was renewed. The use of new materials and designs made possible the development of tough, efficient wind generators. Some of these look like giant egg beaters. Others look like weather vanes. Still others look like huge cylinders. Most can adjust to changing wind conditions, and all can withstand storms.

Energy planners do not expect wind energy to meet the energy needs of the world. But they do believe that the increased use of wind generators will save fuel and reduce air pollution.

Sharpen Your Skills

Timing Tides

At Cape May, New Jersey, along the shore of the Atlantic Ocean, there is a high tide every 24 hours and 50 minutes. If this high tide occurs at 6:00 A.M. on Tuesday, at what time will it occur on Wednesday? Thursday?

Figure 25–10 *This experimental windmill "farm" at Altamont Pass in California consists of several thousand windmills that generate electricity. Is this a direct or indirect use of solar energy?*

595

SECTION REVIEW

1. List three ways in which solar energy is used directly.
2. What is the relationship between hydroelectric power and solar energy?
3. In what ways is solar energy used in your home? Considering the region in which you live, what other forms of solar energy might be appropriate for use in your home?

Section Objective

To explain how energy is released during nuclear fission and nuclear fusion

25–3 Nuclear Energy

You may recall that the nucleus of an atom contains protons and neutrons. The force that binds protons and neutrons in the nucleus is called the **strong force.** Scientists have long known that if the strong force could be broken, vast amounts of nuclear energy would be released. In other words, if the nucleus of an atom could be split, a new and powerful energy source would be found. This energy, called **nuclear energy,** is the energy locked within the nucleus by the strong force.

Nuclear Fission

In 1938, the first **nuclear fission** (FIHSH-uhn) reaction was carried out. **Fission is the splitting of an atomic nucleus into two smaller nuclei, during which nuclear energy is released.** A fission reaction does not happen on its own. It must be made to happen. The most common fission reaction involves the splitting of a uranium-235 nucleus.

Figure 25–11 *In this diagram of a chain reaction, a uranium-235 nucleus is bombarded by a neutron "bullet." What are the products of this fission reaction?*

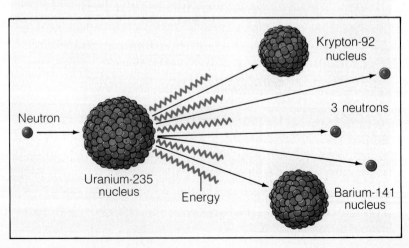

Krypton-92 nucleus

Neutron

3 neutrons

Uranium-235 nucleus

Energy

Barium-141 nucleus

To split a uranium-235 nucleus, scientists must shoot a "nuclear bullet" into the nucleus. The nuclear bullet in a fission reaction is a neutron. When a neutron strikes the uranium-235 nucleus, the nucleus is split into a krypton-92 nucleus and a barium-141 nucleus. During this process, two or three more neutrons are released from the uranium-235 nucleus. Energy is released as well. See Figure 25–11.

Each neutron released during a fission reaction is capable of starting another fission reaction by splitting another uranium-235 atom. The neutrons released by each of these reactions then split several more atoms. One neutron striking one uranium-235 atom initiates a chain of nuclear fission reactions. The process in which the splitting of one atom causes the splitting of additional atoms is called a **nuclear chain reaction.**

If a nuclear chain reaction is uncontrolled, the resulting energy that is released will create an atomic explosion. That is just what happens in an atomic bomb. However, if the chain reaction is carefully controlled, the energy that is released can be a valuable energy resource. Controlled chain reactions take place in nuclear power plants.

Nuclear Power Plants

The energy produced during nuclear fission is mostly heat energy. In a nuclear power plant, this heat energy is used to convert water into steam. The steam then passes through a turbine in an electric generator. The steam spins the blades of the turbine. So nuclear power plants produce electricity from the energy locked within the nucleus.

Fission reactions in a nuclear power plant are produced and controlled in nuclear reactors. The three main parts of a nuclear reactor are the **core, moderator,** and **control rods.**

CORE   The core is the central part of a nuclear reactor. It is within the core that nuclear fission takes place. To begin a fission reaction, nuclear fuel rods are placed in the core. The most common nuclear fuel is uranium-235. When neutrons strike the rods of uranium-235, nuclear fission begins. If the

Figure 25–12 shows the design of a typical nuclear reactor. Labels: Concrete, Cadmium control rods, Cooling water, Heated water, Steam pipe, Electric generator, Uranium fuel rods, Steam generator.

Figure 25–12 *This illustration shows the design of a typical nuclear reactor. How is the heat that is produced during a chain reaction converted into electricity?*

Figure 25–13 *Before being placed in a reactor, nuclear fuel rods are carefully checked (top). If the nuclear fuel rods are placed at just the right distance from one another, a chain reaction will occur (bottom). What is the most common fuel for nuclear fuel rods?*

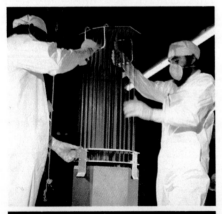

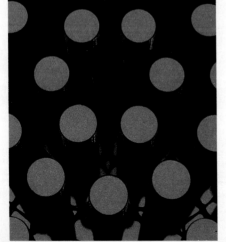

fuel rods are placed at just the right distance from one another, a chain reaction occurs. It is important to note that the nuclear fuel rods in a nuclear reactor cannot explode due to fission. That is, a nuclear explosion similar to an atomic bomb is impossible in a nuclear reactor.

MODERATOR The neutrons released during fission move very fast—too fast to be absorbed by other uranium nuclei. So the neutrons must be slowed down. A material that slows down neutrons is called a moderator. The most common moderator used in the United States is water.

CONTROL RODS In order for a nuclear reaction to produce useful energy, the overall speed of the reaction must be carefully controlled. This task is accomplished with control rods. In most reactors, the control rods are made of the element cadmium. Cadmium rods have the ability to "soak up" neutrons. By placing control rods deep in the reactor core, extra neutrons are absorbed and the fission process is slowed down. By pulling the control rods out of the reactor a bit, the fission reaction is speeded up as more neutrons become available to split uranium-235 nuclei.

There was a time not too long ago when energy experts predicted that nuclear power would become the world's leading source of energy. Just one 1.25-centimeter pellet of uranium-235 can produce as much energy as 615 liters of fuel oil. And eight such pellets would be enough to supply all your home energy needs for one year. Yet the experts' predictions did not come true. What went wrong?

Aside from the potential safety problems associated with nuclear power plants, the main reason nuclear power has not become a more important energy resource is an economic one. The costs of building such plants have risen tremendously in the last decade. Electricity derived from nuclear power plants costs *more* than electricity derived from other sources. And it is estimated that the costs will go even higher.

Is nuclear power from fission a lost cause? Not at all. Scientists are trying to find ways to make nuclear power safer and cost effective. If they succeed, nuclear power may become an even greater source of energy in the future.

Nuclear Fusion

Just as splitting an atomic nucleus releases energy, so does combining two atomic nuclei. **The combining of atomic nuclei is called fusion.** In fact, **nuclear fusion** produces far more energy than nuclear fission. It is fusion that produces the energy given off by stars such as our sun.

Within the sun, enormous heat and pressure cause the nuclei of hydrogen atoms to fuse into a helium atom. During this process, some of the mass of the hydrogen nuclei is converted into energy. Scientists have found a way to produce energy through nuclear fusion. However, the energy produced is uncontrolled and destructive. The explosion of a hydrogen bomb is a nuclear fusion reaction.

To be able to produce a controlled fusion reaction that generates useful energy is a long-standing dream of many scientists. But it is very likely that by the year 2000 nuclear fusion will become a reality. Since a nuclear fusion reactor would use hydrogen from water, an unlimited supply of fuel would be available. This fact, plus the fact that nuclear fusion likely will be nonpolluting, explains why scientists want this dream to become a reality.

Figure 25–14 *Three Mile Island in Pennsylvania was the site of a serious nuclear power plant accident. Radiation escaped into the atmosphere when the reactor's cooling system failed and the nuclear core overheated.*

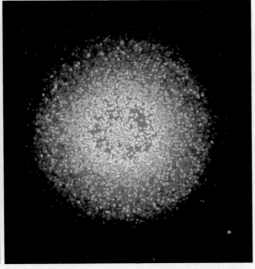

Figure 25–15 *Tiny hydrogen pellets placed in the chamber of an experimental fusion device are bombarded with a beam of electrons (left). When a pellet reaches temperatures of more than 70 million degrees Celsius, it undergoes nuclear fusion (right). If it could be fully developed, why would nuclear fusion be a source of energy that could meet worldwide needs?*

SECTION REVIEW

1. What type of nuclear reaction involves splitting an atomic nucleus? Combining two atomic nuclei?
2. What is the "bullet" used in a fission reaction?
3. How is the rate of the chain reaction in a nuclear reactor controlled?
4. Why would safe economical nuclear power provide a good alternative to the dwindling supply of fossil fuels?

25–4 Alternative Energy Sources

Today, there are enough energy resources to meet the world's needs. Why then must people be concerned about conserving energy resources? The answer is twofold. One reason people must look for new, clean sources of energy is pollution. There are several pollution problems associated with many energy resources. You will read about some of these pollution problems in Chapter 26. The other reason people must develop new energy resources is the future energy needs of society. The present available supply of energy resources cannot be used up today without preparing for tomorrow. Today's generation must use energy wisely to ensure its availability for future generations. **Throughout the world, scientists are working to develop alternative energy resources, such as gasohol, geothermal energy, biomass, and hydrogen power.**

Gasohol

Almost all cars in the United States are powered by gasoline. During the gas shortages of the 1970s, however, scientists began looking for alternatives to gasoline. One alternative that was developed was **gasohol.** Gasohol is a mixture of gasoline and alcohol. Ethanol, or ethyl alcohol, is the alcohol commonly used. Gasohol is widely used today in South America.

Ethanol is obtained by the action of yeast cells on various grains such as corn, wheat, and barley. The yeast converts the sugar in the grain into ethanol and carbon dioxide in a process called **fermentation** (fer-muhn-TAY-shuhn). Today, scientists are experimenting with cars that run entirely on ethanol. How does gasohol conserve fossil fuels?

Geothermal Energy

You may not realize it, but there is a lot of energy beneath your feet. Molten rock deep within the earth has an average temperature of about 1800°C. This heat is called **geothermal energy.** You do not

Figure 25–16 *Grains such as corn are combined with yeast cells to produce ethanol. What is the name of this process?*

Figure 25–17 *This geothermal well in Iceland is a source of hot water (left). In a geothermal power plant, cold water is pumped into the earth where it is heated, returned to a power plant, and used to generate electricity (right). How else might the cold water pumped into the earth be used to generate electricity?*

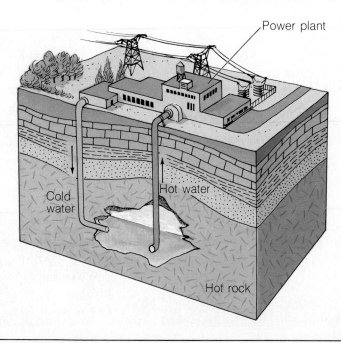

notice this heat because you are shielded by about 64 kilometers of the earth's crust.

In some places, there are cracks and weak spots in the earth's crust. These cracks and weak spots are often called hot spots. Water in hot spots becomes heated by contact with hot rocks. Frequently, this water bursts forth from the earth in fountains of steam and boiling water known as **geysers.** Geysers and hot groundwater are used in Iceland to heat homes and greenhouses. In Italy, New Zealand, the Soviet Union, and the United States, water heated underground is used to spin turbines and generate electricity.

Hot spots can be used to produce geothermal energy in another way. Cold water is often pumped into hot spots in the earth. The heat in the hot spots turns the water into steam. Because the number of hot spot regions on the earth is limited, however, it is unlikely that geothermal energy can keep pace with the world's growing energy needs.

Biomass

Any material that can be burned is a combustible material. Combustible materials can be used in a variety of ways. They can be used to heat water and produce steam. The steam can then be passed through a turbine to generate electricity. Combustible materials also can be burned to generate heat for homes and factories. One group of combustible

Figure 25–18 *From sugar cane grown in Hawaii (left), tiny pellets of fibrous wastes are formed (center). These fuel pellets can then be burned in a factory (right). What general term is used to describe combustible materials that come from living things?*

materials is known as **biomass.** Biomass includes plants, animal wastes, and all other forms of matter that come from living things.

Biomass has been used as a fuel for heating purposes for thousands of years. Wood is the main form of biomass used for combustion. Other forms of combustible vegetation include corn husks, waste fibers from sugar cane, sunflowers, and seaweed. In many parts of the world, animal wastes are dried in the sun and used as heating fuel.

One advantage of biomass is that it is renewable. Biomass fuels can continually be grown. Scientists are experimenting with ways to use biomass more economically and efficiently. However, as long as fossil fuels remain relatively inexpensive, biomass will not be a major source of energy worldwide.

Hydrogen Power

The only truly unlimited energy source on earth, other than sunlight, is hydrogen. Oceans, rivers, and lakes all contain hydrogen in the form of water. Hydrogen can be burned in place of fossil fuels. The problem with using the hydrogen in water is that it is bound to oxygen atoms. A water molecule, you may recall, contains 2 hydrogen atoms bonded to 1 oxygen atom.

To obtain hydrogen for combustion, a water molecule must be decomposed. The decomposition of water usually is done by passing an electric current through water. The process of decomposing water is called **electrolysis.** However, it takes more electricity to produce hydrogen during electrolysis than can be obtained by burning hydrogen at an electric generating plant. So at this time, hydrogen power does not appear to be a major energy source.

SECTION REVIEW

1. What is gasohol?
2. Use the definition of geothermal energy to explain the meaning of the prefix *geo-* and the suffix *-thermal.*
3. What is biomass? How can it be used to produce electricity?
4. How would building a house partially beneath the earth's surface help conserve energy?

Figure 25–19 *This chart shows the sources of energy used in the United States. How much energy is presently obtained from fossil fuels?*

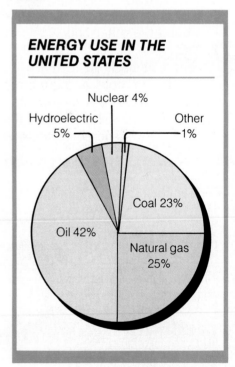

ENERGY USE IN THE UNITED STATES

Nuclear 4%
Hydroelectric 5%
Other 1%
Coal 23%
Oil 42%
Natural gas 25%

Solar Heating

Problem

Does the color of an object affect the amount of solar energy it absorbs?

Materials *(per group)*

black and white construction paper
2 metal or plastic containers with
   plastic lids
2 Celsius thermometers
water
scissors and tape
clock or watch

Procedure

1. Tape two layers of black paper around one container. Tape two layers of white paper around the other one.
2. Using the scissors, carefully punch the center of each lid to make a hole large enough to hold a thermometer. **CAUTION:** *Handle the scissors carefully.*
3. Fill each container with water at room temperature and cover them with plastic lids.

4. Carefully insert a thermometer through the hole in each lid. Make sure the bulb of the thermometer is just below the surface of the water. **CAUTION:** *Be careful when handling the thermometer.*
5. Place the containers on a sunny windowsill. Make sure each is in direct sunlight.
6. Record the temperature of the water in each container every 3 minutes for 36 minutes. Place your data on a data table.

Time (min)	3	6	9	12	15	18	21
Temperature (°C)							

Observations

1. During which time interval did the temperature in the black container begin to rise? During which time interval did the temperature in the white container begin to rise?
2. What was the final temperature of the water in the black container? In the white container?
3. Make a graph of your data, plotting temperature on the vertical axis and time intervals on the horizontal axis.

Conclusions

1. How effectively did the sun's solar energy heat the water in the containers?
2. Does the color of an object affect the amount of solar energy it absorbs?
3. What hidden variable might have an effect on your results?
4. Based on this experiment, what color clothing would you be likely to wear in the winter? In the summer?

CHAPTER REVIEW

SUMMARY

25–1 Fossil Fuels

❏ The three main types of fossil fuels are coal, oil, and natural gas.

❏ Fossil fuels have high heating values because they are rich in hydrocarbons.

❏ The four types of coals are peat, lignite, bituminous, and anthracite.

❏ Many fuels are produced from petroleum.

❏ Natural gas usually is found above deposits of petroleum. The most commonly used natural gas is methane.

❏ Fossil fuels are a nonrenewable resource whose supplies are running out.

25–2 Solar Energy: Direct and Indirect

❏ Energy given off by the sun is called solar energy.

❏ Solar energy can be used directly or indirectly.

❏ Active and passive solar heating systems are examples of direct solar energy.

❏ Solar cells, or photovoltaic cells, convert sunlight into electricity.

❏ Hydroelectric power is power derived from moving water.

❏ At a hydroelectric plant, moving water is used to spin a turbine and produce electricity.

❏ The movements of tides can be used to generate electricity.

❏ Windmills connected to a generator use the power of the wind to produce electricity.

❏ Both hydroelectric power and wind power are indirect uses of solar energy.

25–3 Nuclear Energy

❏ Nuclear energy is the energy locked within the atom by the strong force.

❏ Fission is the splitting of an atomic nucleus into two smaller nuclei.

❏ In a nuclear power plant, a nuclear chain reaction produces heat energy that can be used to convert water into steam and spin a turbine.

❏ The three main parts of a nuclear reactor are the core, moderator, and control rods.

❏ The combining of atomic nuclei is called nuclear fusion.

25–4 Alternative Energy Sources

❏ Gasohol is a mixture of gasoline and ethanol.

❏ Heat from deep within the earth is called geothermal energy.

❏ The burning of biomass can be used to convert water into steam, which can then spin a turbine and produce electricity.

❏ Hydrogen found in water represents an unlimited supply of hydrogen fuel.

❏ At the present time, it takes more energy to produce hydrogen from water than can be obtained by burning hydrogen.

VOCABULARY

Define each term in a complete sentence.

anthracite	electrolysis	hydrocarbon	nuclear chain reaction	photovoltaic cell
biomass	fermentation	hydroelectric	nuclear energy	safety system
bituminous coal	fossil fuel	lignite	nuclear fission	solar collector
combustion	gasohol	moderator	nuclear fusion	solar energy
control rod	geothermal energy	nonrenewable resource	peat	strong force
core	geyser			tidal power

CONTENT REVIEW: MULTIPLE CHOICE

On a separate sheet of paper, write the letter of the answer that best completes each statement.

1. Fossil fuels do *not* include
   a. coal.   b. shale.   c. petroleum.   d. natural gas.
2. Which of the following has the lowest heating value?
   a. coal   b. natural gas   c. wood   d. petroleum
3. The most plentiful type of coal is
   a. peat.   b. lignite.   c. bituminous.   d. anthracite.
4. A direct use of the sun's energy would be
   a. burning biomass.   b. a solar cell.   c. hydroelectric power.   d. a windmill.
5. Most solar cells are "sandwiches" of metal and
   a. plastic.   b. hydrogen.   c. silicon.   d. oxygen.
6. Most of the world's electricity is produced from which source of energy?
   a. solar   b. hydroelectricity   c. nuclear   d. biomass
7. The most typical nuclear fuel in a nuclear reactor is
   a. uranium-238.   b. uranium-235.   c. plutonium.   d. hydrogen.
8. Neutrons are slowed down in a nuclear reactor by
   a. uranium-235.   b. a moderator.   c. control rods.   d. concrete casings.
9. The combining of atomic nuclei is called
   a. fission.   b. geothermal energy.   c. fusion.   d. strong force.
10. Yeast converts sugar into alcohol through the process of
    a. fermentation.   b. electrolysis.   c. combustion.   d. biomass.

CONTENT REVIEW: COMPLETION

On a separate sheet of paper, write the word or words that best complete each statement.

1. Combustion of hydrocarbons produces _____ and _____.
2. Coal is a (an) _____ fossil fuel.
3. _____ is the hardest form of coal.
4. A (An) _____ resource cannot be replaced once it is used up.
5. _____ is energy from the sun.
6. A device that converts energy from the sun into electricity is a (an) _____.
7. A (An) _____ is the nuclear "bullet" used in a fission reaction.
8. In a nuclear reactor, extra neutrons are "soaked up" by _____, which are usually made of _____.
9. _____ is heat produced within the earth.
10. Water is decomposed into hydrogen and oxygen in a process called _____.

CONTENT REVIEW: TRUE OR FALSE

Determine whether each statement is true or false. Then on a separate sheet of paper, write "true" if it is true. If it is false, change the underlined word or words to make the statement true.

1. Combustion is the burning of hydrocarbons.   2. The first stage in coal formation is lignite.

3. Natural gas is usually found <u>below</u> petroleum.
4. Collecting solar energy and storing it in the form of hot water is an example of <u>passive</u> solar heating.
5. Hydroelectric power is an <u>indirect</u> use of solar energy.
6. Windmills are a <u>direct</u> use of solar energy.
7. Fission is the <u>combining</u> of atomic nuclei.
8. An accident at a nuclear power plant <u>can</u> cause an atomic explosion.
9. <u>Geysers</u> are fountains of steam and boiling water that gush from within the earth.
10. <u>Fermentation</u> is the process of decomposing water molecules into hydrogen and oxygen.

CONCEPT REVIEW: SKILL BUILDING

Use the skills you have developed in the chapter to complete each activity.

1. **Making predictions** Using your imagination and the information provided in this chapter, think about how primitive people may have discovered fire and how they learned to start fires. Prepare a colorful diagram to illustrate your supposition.
2. **Classifying resources** Classify each of the following resources as renewable or nonrenewable: coal, natural gas, wood, hydroelectric power, sugar cane, geothermal energy, hydrogen, nuclear energy, petroleum, tar sands.
3. **Making inferences** Based on the description of control rods, what do you think would happen if the control rods in a nuclear reactor failed to function?
4. **Making maps** Choose geothermal energy or tidal energy. Find out where in the world these energy resources are used. Make a map to display these locations.
5. **Making observations** Over a period of several days, keep a list of the ways in which you use energy produced by fuels. Be sure to identify the fuel that produces each type of energy.
6. **Expressing an opinion** Write a short essay that expresses your opinion about the following statement: "These dire predictions about running out of oil are greatly exaggerated. And even if we do run out, I feel confident that human beings, with all their resourcefulness, will find another way to produce the energy they need."
7. **Classifying solar energy** Classify each of the following as a direct or indirect use of solar energy: solar cell, fossil fuel, geothermal energy, hydroelectric power, biomass, hydrogen power, solar heating.
8. **Drawing conclusions** In 1937, the German airship *Hindenburg* exploded in midair. As a result of the combustion of the gas that filled the *Hindenburg,* water formed. What can you conclude about the gas that filled the *Hindenburg* airship?

CONCEPT REVIEW: ESSAY

Discuss each of the following in a brief paragraph.

1. Discuss the advantages and disadvantages of a solar cell.
2. Explain how a nuclear reactor controls a fission reaction.
3. Explain what is meant by a nuclear chain reaction.
4. What is the greatest advantage of direct solar energy over other energy sources?
5. Do you agree with the statement, "Just because a resource is abundant does not make it a valuable resource"? Explain your answer.
6. Should petroleum be conserved and saved for future generations?

Energy and the Environment

26

CHAPTER SECTIONS

26–1 Pollution—What Is It?

26–2 Land Pollution

26–3 Air Pollution

26–4 Water Pollution

26–5 Pollution—What Can Be Done?

CHAPTER OBJECTIVES

After completing this chapter, you will be able to

26–1 Define pollution.

26–2 Describe the ways in which obtaining and using energy can cause land pollution.

26–3 Describe the ways in which obtaining and using energy can cause air pollution.

26–3 Relate the burning of fossil fuels to the formation of acid rain.

26–4 Describe the ways in which obtaining and using energy can cause water pollution.

26–4 Discuss other sources of water pollution.

26–5 Discuss how conservation and new technologies can reduce land, air, and water pollution.

The first sign of danger came with the southeast wind. Instruments at a Swedish nuclear power plant detected twice as much radioactivity in the atmosphere as usual on April 28, 1986. At first the Swedes feared a malfunction in their own plant. But it soon became apparent that the excess radioactivity was being carried by winds from the Soviet Union.

It was not long before the story broke. An explosion and fire at the Chernobyl nuclear power plant in the Russian Ukraine had released a huge cloud of radioactive dust. The cloud was blown by winds across Poland and into Scandinavia. Later the wind shifted and blew the deadly cloud over Switzerland and Italy. Everywhere the cloud was blown, people were warned to avoid contaminated water, vegetables, and milk. About 25 people in the vicinity of Chernobyl died. Thousands more may develop serious health problems.

The accident at Chernobyl undoubtedly will have an effect on the further development of nuclear power. Once thought to be the energy solution of the future, nuclear power is now viewed with skepticism.

Our society could not exist without sources of energy. Yet we must keep in mind that using energy brings with it certain pollution problems. In this chapter, you will learn about some of the causes of pollution as well as some of the solutions to pollution. Despite its tragic outcome, the accident at Chernobyl has had one important effect. It has made people more aware than ever before of the necessity to reduce pollution.

The fire at the Chernobyl nuclear power plant in the Soviet Union resulted in a cloud of radioactivity that spread over neighboring countries. How many people will be affected by this radioactivity will not be known for at least twenty years.

26–1 Pollution—What Is It?

Our environment is like a great treasure house—in it we have everything we need for life. Air, water, food, and energy all exist in such abundance that it is hard to imagine ever being without them. Yet that is just what might come to pass. For despite the richness of natural resources, a delicate balance between plenty and want exists in our environment.

The balance in our environment can be upset by the way in which we obtain and use our natural resources. If we use renewable resources faster than they can be replaced, the balance will be upset. If we too quickly consume nonrenewable resources, which cannot be replaced, the balance will be upset. If in the process of obtaining or using one resource we pollute another resource, the balance will be upset. It is this problem of pollution that needs our attention.

Pollution is the release of substances into the environment that changes the environment for the worse. Most pollution is the result of human activities. Although pollution cannot be blamed entirely on the use of energy resources, a great deal of pollution is directly tied to energy use. Our heavy dependence on fossil fuels has made pollution a major concern in the last several decades. In obtaining and using the energy we need, people have polluted the land, air, and water.

Figure 26–1 *Keeping our natural resources beautiful is something everyone is interested in (left). Yet litter discarded by careless people can quickly upset the balance in our environment (right). How can such littering be prevented?*

SECTION REVIEW

1. Compare renewable and nonrenewable resources.
2. What is pollution?
3. How might an increase in the use of renewable energy sources help maintain a balanced environment?

26–2 Land Pollution

Section Objective

To relate energy use to land pollution

The use of coal as a fuel was an important step in the industrialization of our nation. Yet our environment has often paid heavily for the use of coal.

Coal near the surface of the ground is obtained by a process called **strip mining.** In strip mining, entire hills are cut apart by large earth-moving machines. This process badly damages the land. In addition to scarring the landscape, strip mining can cause land pollution.

During the strip-mining process, fertile topsoil is buried under piles of rock. When the rock is exposed to moisture and rain, acids and other dangerous chemicals seep out of the rock. Rainwater carries the acids into the ground, polluting nearby soil. The acids also may be carried into nearby streams, causing water pollution as well.

This pollution, however, need not occur. Coal mining companies can take steps to restore the land to its original condition. The process of restoring the land is called **land reclamation.** See Figure 26–2. In 1978, Congress passed a law that required mine owners to reclaim the land whenever possible.

Figure 26–2 *Strip mining of coal can destroy the land (left). But the land can be restored and returned to its natural beauty (right). What is this process of land restoration called?*

Figure 26–3 *One of the most serious causes of land pollution is the leaking of toxic wastes from improperly stored or maintained barrels (left). As proof of the danger, notice the special equipment the scientists must wear while examining leaking wastes in a toxic waste dump in New Jersey (right). How does the leaking of toxic wastes cause water pollution as well as land pollution?*

Figure 26–4 *Low-level nuclear wastes are being buried at this dump site in Hanford, Washington.*

Obtaining and using certain energy resources can pollute the land. Strip mining is but one example. Another example involves solid wastes from factories. Solid wastes from factories may contaminate the land with **toxic,** or poisonous, chemicals. Factories that produce fuels and petrochemicals from petroleum are a major source of this type of land pollution. When improperly stored in barrels buried under the soil, toxic wastes can seep into the land.

Perhaps the most threatening form of land pollution today is the disposal of **nuclear wastes.** Nuclear wastes are radioactive substances associated with the use of radioactive materials or the production of nuclear power.

Nuclear wastes are classified as either low-level or high-level wastes. Low-level wastes have relatively short half-lives. The half-life of a radioactive substance is a measure of its rate of decay. Low-level wastes decay quickly. The disposal of these wastes usually does not cause major pollution problems. The wastes can be isolated from the environment until they are no longer radioactive.

High-level wastes, however, have half-lives of about 10,000 years or more. Isolating these substances from the environment for that length of time is practically impossible. A common practice has been to seal these wastes in concrete or glass containers and then bury the containers deep within the earth. The problem with this procedure is that the containers may eventually corrode or leak. The nuclear wastes can then escape, polluting the land. As the radioactive substances seep out, they also can find their way into underground water sources and contaminate the water supply.

HELP WANTED: RANGE MANAGER to specialize in environmental impact due to oil, gas, and coal operations. College degree in range management required.

It is a short helicopter ride to the densely wooded hills. From the air, the **range manager** compares the landscape below with the geologic maps of the area. A petroleum company for which the range manager works plans to mine the coal and natural gas buried within these rolling hills.

A range manager develops conservation plans for the area that is to be mined. A range manager writes an environmental impact statement. This is a report that outlines the possible effects of mining activities on the environment. The report explains what could happen to the land, air, water, plants, people, and wildlife of the area.

After mining or drilling operations are complete, a range manager develops a plan to restore or reclaim the area to a natural and productive site. Occasionally, a former mining site is turned into a recreation area or park. A range manager oversees this type of recreational land development.

To become a range manager, a college student studies many subjects. These include science, economics, communications, computers, and resource management. If you would like information about a career as a range manager, write to the U.S. Department of Agriculture, Soil Conservation Service, 14th and Independence Avenue SW, Dept. 0054, South Building, Washington, DC 20250.

SECTION REVIEW

1. Describe two ways in which strip mining damages the land.
2. What term is used for nuclear wastes that have very long half-lives?
3. Describe how a pollutant buried underground in one area might cause pollution many kilometers away from the burial site.

26–3 Air Pollution

Section Objective

To identify and describe major sources of air pollution

Imagine a place where the sky is always gray, the buildings are blackened by smoke, and the air smells like rotten eggs. Do you think people would choose to live in such a place? The people of Donora, Pennsylvania, did in the 1940s.

The city of Donora boasted one of the largest steel mills in the world. The economy of the city

Greenhouse Effect

The carbon dioxide released into the air by motor vehicles and the burning of fossil fuels by industry have created what scientists call the greenhouse effect. Using reference books in the library, write a report on the greenhouse effect. Include in your report how adding carbon dioxide to the atmosphere increases the greenhouse effect. Also include predictions made by scientists about how the greenhouse effect may change the earth's climate, as well as the results of such changes.

was thriving as mills and factories operated 24 hours a day. Millions of tons of coal were burned every hour to provide energy for this growing industrial center. And the people of Donora reasoned that the gray sky, the smoke, and the smell were the price they had to pay for progress.

But in October 1948, the price became too high. The air had become almost unbreathable. Noontime looked like late evening. People could barely see. A temperature inversion had settled over the city.

A **temperature inversion** occurs when cool air near the earth's surface becomes trapped under a layer of warmer air. Normally, air near the surface is able to rise, taking pollutants with it. But during a temperature inversion, pollutants are trapped in the layer of cool air near the earth. The temperature inversion in Donora lasted four days.

Since the Donora disaster, which caused the death of 20 people and the hospitalization of thousands more, cities and states have passed laws to help control emissions of pollutants from factories and power plants. Yet the problems associated with burning coal and other fossil fuels still remain.

Coal and other fossil fuels contain sulfur impurities. When a fossil fuel is burned, sulfur combines

Figure 26–5 *During a temperature inversion, cool air containing pollutants becomes trapped near the ground under a layer of warm air (left). Temperature inversions are a serious problem in some major cities, such as Los Angeles (right). What group of people might be particularly affected by a temperature inversion?*

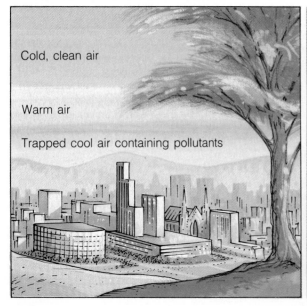

Cold, clean air

Warm air

Trapped cool air containing pollutants

with oxygen in the atmosphere to form various sulfur oxides. When sulfur oxides react with moisture in the air, droplets of weak sulfuric acid form in the atmosphere. The droplets eventually mix with rainwater to form **acid rain.** You will learn more about acid rain and its relationship to water pollution in the next section.

Although much air pollution comes from the industrial burning of coal and other fossil fuels, the most significant source of air pollution is motor vehicles. Gasoline and diesel fuels do not burn completely in the engines of cars, buses, and trucks. Unburned fuel vapors and carbon dioxide are released into the atmosphere. These pollutants can burn and irritate the eyes. They also can damage the lungs, particularly of people who already have breathing problems. Air pollution due to motor vehicles also can damage plant life.

Other pollutants contained in the exhausts of motor vehicles are nitrogen oxides. Nitrogen oxides are compounds in which nitrogen is combined with oxygen. In the atmosphere, nitrogen oxides may combine with water vapor to form droplets of weak nitric acid. The nitric acid may fall to the earth as acid rain in much the same way sulfuric acid does.

Figure 26–6 *Air pollution in Japan can become so severe that a warning bell is rung to alert people to stay indoors. Why do you think these people are wearing masks?*

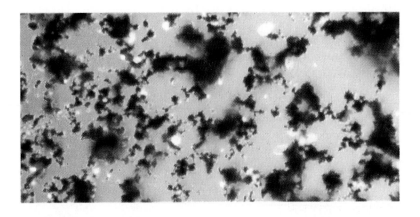

Figure 26–7 *Some of the pollutants released in car exhaust fumes are shown in this unusual photograph of auto exhaust particles. How can this type of pollution be decreased?*

SECTION REVIEW

1. What is the chief source of air pollution?
2. How does a temperature inversion increase the damaging effects of pollutants released into the atmosphere?
3. What problems would be caused for a city such as Donora, Pennyslvania, if the activities of factories were curbed?

26–4 Water Pollution

To identify and describe the major sources of water pollution

The lake, once teeming with life, now seems strangely empty. The surrounding land is quiet—too quiet. Nearby plants and trees have withered. Animals who once depended on the lake area for food have left or died. This lake and its inhabitants are victims of acid rain.

In the last section, you read how emissions from factories and motor vehicles can cause droplets of sulfuric acid and nitric acid to form in the atmosphere. When these droplets fall to the earth as acid rain or acid snow, they change the acidity, or pH level, of the waterways fed by the acid rain. Most organisms can survive in only a narrow range of water acidity. By increasing the water's acidity, acid rain kills many of the organisms living there. At the same time, acid rain damages the plant life on which the rain falls. Throughout parts of the United States, lakes and forests are being destroyed by acid rain.

Acid rain begins as air pollution. As rain falls to the earth the problem becomes water pollution. Then as the acid rain seeps into the soil, land pollution results. In this example of a "pollution chain," all aspects of the environment are damaged.

Figure 26–8 *Acid rain can severely damage the plants and animals living in lakes and ponds (left). This photograph shows the pollutants in a single drop of acid rain (right). What are the two acids contained in acid rain?*

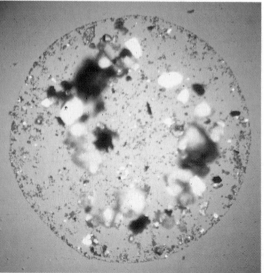

Figure 26-9 *This oil spill occurred when a supertanker ran aground in the Delaware River near Philadelphia, Pennsylvania. The oil killed many plants and animals in the river and polluted nearby shores.*

Fossil Fuels and Water Pollution

Strip mining for coal releases pollutants into the soil and water. Burning fossil fuels creates water pollution by producing acid rain. Unfortunately, there are even other ways in which our energy needs contribute to water pollution.

Both obtaining and using energy resources are major causes of water pollution. Here is one example. Petroleum is often found under the sea floor. To obtain petroleum, offshore oil wells are constructed. And although great precautions are taken, drilling accidents do occur. As a result of such accidents huge amounts of oil spill into oceans and lakes. Oil spills also occur when tankers carrying oil are damaged so that they leak their oil into the surrounding water.

Oil spills are also an environmental disaster. Plants and animals that come in contact with the oil are often destroyed. If the oil reaches the shore, it contaminates beaches and may contribute to the death of shore-dwelling organisms. Despite improved cleanup technology, oil spills remain one of the most difficult types of water pollution to remedy.

Nuclear Power and Water Pollution

A great amount of hot water is generated in a nuclear power plant. The heat from this water is usually transferred to a nearby body of water, such

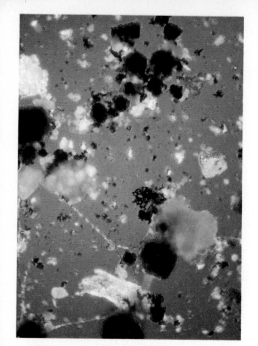

Figure 26–10 *In this photograph, you can see some of the emissions given off at a nuclear power plant. Although such emissions often leak into the air, they can pollute the land and water as well. How?*

as a lake or stream. The temperature of the body of water rises. The increase in temperature in bodies of water such as lakes is called **thermal pollution.** Most water-dwelling organisms can survive only in a narrow temperature range. When the water temperature rises, many organisms are destroyed. In what ways are thermal pollution and acid rain similar?

You have read how radioactive wastes from nuclear power plants and other uses of radioactive materials can pollute the land. In much the same way, radioactive wastes can pollute our water supplies. Radioactive wastes stored in containers dumped into the sea may leak out of the containers and become a long-term water pollutant.

Other Sources of Water Pollution

Although using and obtaining energy is a major source of water pollution, it is by no means the only source. Many factories dump solid wastes directly into nearby water or onto land that has water underground. Such dumping is especially serious because groundwater is the most important source of drinking water in the United States. Sewage, too, is often released into rivers and streams. Chemicals used on farmlands to improve the growth of plants or to kill harmful insects also may enter and pollute the groundwater.

Water pollution limits the amount of wildlife that can live in the water, affects supplies of drinking water, and destroys recreational areas. To prevent further water pollution, federal laws have been passed to prohibit industry from dumping certain

Figure 26–11 *Although it may look like this sewage is being dumped into a nearby river, the sewage has actually been treated at a sewage treatment plant so that it is safe to discharge. Do you think sewage treatment should be mandatory? Give reasons for your answer.*

chemical wastes into the earth's waters. Wastewater treatment systems are being constructed to remove pollution from rivers and lakes. What other steps might be taken to stop water pollution and save one of the earth's most important natural resources?

SECTION REVIEW

1. How does acid rain damage organisms living in lakes or streams?
2. Using acid rain, describe the relationship between burning fossil fuels and the pollution of water, air, and land.
3. Why would an ocean be much less affected by thermal pollution than a lake?

26–5 Pollution—What Can Be Done?

Section Objective

To discuss ways in which pollution can be reduced

The problems of environmental pollution will not go away. To the contrary, they will worsen as population increases. But there is something that can be done about pollution. **Pollution can be reduced by conserving energy, by finding cleaner ways to use energy, and by using alternative clean energy sources.**

Conservation

Conservation is the wise and careful use of resources. When we conserve our energy resources, we benefit the environment in two ways. First, our nonrenewable resources will last longer. Second, pollution will be reduced.

There are many ways that energy can be conserved at home. Doing full loads in the washing machine or dishwasher instead of several small loads will save energy. Turning the thermostat down a few degrees in the winter and turning the air conditioner up a few degrees in the summer will save energy. And making sure that a house or apartment is well insulated also will save energy.

Because a great amount of energy is used by motor vehicles, changing driving habits can make a

Sharpen Your Skills

The Year 2050

Write a short story that describes what you think life will be like in the year 2050. The focus of your story should be the kinds of energy resources used and the environmental problems that may exist.

Figure 26–12 *Many tons of paper are being recycled at this recycling center. Recycling will help save many trees, from which paper is made. What materials do you recycle?*

Sharpen Your Skills

Car Pooling

Select a *safe* spot where you can observe cars as they go by. Be sure you can see into each car. Do not use a busy highway because there would be no way to check every car. Try to be at your site at different times each day for several days. Keep a record for ten minutes each day of the number of people in each car that goes by. Make a chart to present your findings.

1. How many cars have only the driver? At what times of day? How many have one, two, three, or more passengers?

2. How might the environment benefit from car pooling?

real difference in the quality of our environment. The use of car pools and public transportation saves fuel and reduces air pollution. So does keeping a car well tuned and in good operating condition. And don't forget the most ancient form of transportation—walking!

A form of conservation that has received considerable public attention is **recycling.** You probably have a recycling center in your neighborhood or town. In recycling, substances that can be used again from discarded articles are reclaimed and sent to factories. Recycling has been very successful in reclaiming paper, glass containers, and aluminum cans.

New Technologies

New technologies can reduce pollution by creating cleaner and more efficient ways of obtaining and using energy resources. Technology also can help develop alternatives to fossil fuels.

The burning of coal has been made less damaging to the environment by the use of scrubber systems. A scrubber system works like a shower. As sulfur oxides are released from burning coal, a high-pressure spray of water dissolves them before they can react with water in the atmosphere. Scrubber systems and other antipollution systems can be placed in smokestacks to prevent the release of pollutants into the atmosphere.

Pollution from automobile exhaust has been reduced by equipping cars with pollution-control

Figure 26–13 *Pollutants released into the air from factory smokestacks cause acid rain and other forms of air pollution. Can such pollution be decreased without having to close the factory?*

devices. This type of pollution could be further reduced by the development of engines that burn fuel more completely.

Scientists are working on new methods of ocean-drilling for oil in order to reduce the possibility of underwater leaks. In addition, several new methods have been developed for dealing with oil spills. These include vacuum systems that can pump oil out of the water and certain types of absorbents that can soak up oil near the shore.

In Chapter 25, you learned about ways in which scientists are working to find alternatives to fossil fuels. If a clean, renewable source of energy such as solar energy or nuclear fusion could be used on a large scale, many of our pollution problems would be solved.

Everyone's Responsibility

At the beginning of this chapter, you read that pollution is caused mainly by the activities of people. It is important to realize that the activities of people can also stop pollution. And everyone—young or old, scientist or nonscientist—can help.

SECTION REVIEW

1. What is conservation?
2. How can new technologies reduce pollution?
3. How does recycling reduce pollution and conserve important resources?
4. In what ways can you personally reduce pollution?

Figure 26–14 *Almost everyone is opposed to pollution. These people have taken to the streets of Washington, D.C., to protest against the pollution due to toxic wastes.*

Observing Air Pollution

Problem

How can you observe solid particles in the atmosphere that cause air pollution?

Materials *(per group)*

6 petri dishes	1 petri dish cover
petroleum jelly	glass-marking pencil
graph paper	magnifying lens

Procedure

1. Coat the flat surface of each petri dish with a thin layer of petroleum jelly.
2. Immediately place the cover over one of the petri dishes. Put this dish aside.
3. Place the other five petri dishes in locations where they will be exposed to the outside air yet will not be disturbed.
4. Use the marking pencil to write the name of the location on the side of each dish.
5. Do not disturb the dishes for three days.
6. Collect the dishes after three days. Place each dish, one at a time, on the graph paper. Use the magnifying lens to count the number of particles in each part of the graph paper grid. Total the number of par-

ticles in each dish. Record your data on a data table similar to the one on this page.

Observations

1. Compare the data from each location.
2. Compare your data with data from other groups. Record the locations of the data from other groups, as well as the number of solid particles counted in each dish.

Conclusions

1. Which dish was the control in this investigation? Explain your answer.
2. The solid particles you counted were evidence of air pollution. How can you account for the difference in the number of particles at the various locations?
3. How can you explain the difference in the number of particles found in other locations by your classmates?
4. Make a graph of your data, plotting location on the horizontal axis and number of particles counted on the vertical axis. What conclusions can you draw?

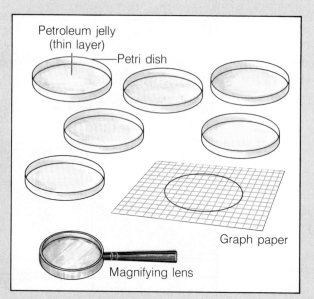

Petroleum jelly (thin layer)

Petri dish

Graph paper

Magnifying lens

Dish	Number of Particles
1	
2	
3	
4	
5	
6	

CHAPTER REVIEW

SUMMARY

26-1 Pollution—What Is It?

❑ The balance in our environment can be easily upset by the ways in which we obtain and use energy resources.

❑ Pollution is the release of unwanted substances into the environment.

26-2 Land Pollution

❑ Strip mining causes land pollution by burying fertile topsoil under rocks and by the action of acids that seep out of the rocks when exposed to water.

❑ Land damaged by strip mining can be restored by land reclamation.

❑ Both obtaining and using energy resources contribute to land pollution.

❑ High-level nuclear wastes may take many thousands of years to decay and become non-radioactive. Because of their long half-lives, such wastes are difficult to store safely.

26-3 Air Pollution

❑ Burning fossil fuels releases many polluting emissions into the atmosphere.

❑ During a temperature inversion, pollutants are trapped in a layer of cool air near the earth's surface.

❑ Most air pollution is due to motor vehicle exhausts.

❑ Sulfur oxides and nitrogen oxides released during the burning of fossil fuels can combine with water in the atmosphere to form droplets of sulfuric acid or nitric acid. These acids fall to earth as acid rain.

26-4 Water Pollution

❑ Acid rain has damaged many lakes, streams, and other waterways, as well as plant life near such bodies of water.

❑ Both obtaining and using energy resources are major causes of water pollution.

❑ Thermal pollution occurs when bodies of water, often near nuclear power plants, are heated above their normal temperatures. Thermal pollution can destroy plant and animal life in such bodies of water.

❑ Aside from using energy resources, water can be polluted by the dumping of solid wastes, litter, sewage, fertilizers, and pesticides.

26-5 Pollution—What Can Be Done?

❑ Conservation is the wise and careful use of natural resources.

❑ Pollution can be reduced by conservation of energy resources.

❑ Recycling useful solid wastes can help reduce pollution?

❑ New technologies are being developed to lessen pollution due to fossil fuels.

❑ Alternative energy sources also can help lessen fossil fuel pollution.

❑ Reducing pollution is not just a task for scientists, it is a job for everyone.

VOCABULARY

Define each term in a complete sentence.

acid rain
conservation
land
  reclamation
nuclear waste

pollution
recycling
strip mining
temperature
  inversion

thermal
  pollution
toxic

CONTENT REVIEW: MULTIPLE CHOICE

On a separate sheet of paper, write the letter of the answer that best completes each statement.

1. Pollution has become a major problem largely because of the
   a. abundance of natural resources. b. dependence on fossil fuels.
   c. use of renewable resources. d. decrease in energy consumption.
2. Obtaining and using energy resources have resulted in pollution of
   a. land. b. air. c. water. d. all of these.
3. Coal near the surface of the ground is obtained through
   a. power shovels. b. deep mine shafts. c. strip mining. d. land reclamation.
4. Poisonous wastes that contaminate the land are called
   a. nuclear fuels. b. toxic wastes. c. low-level wastes. d. petrochemicals.
5. High-level nuclear wastes are difficult to dispose of because they
   a. are large and bulky. b. are poisonous.
   c. have long half-lives. d. have short half-lives.
6. A temperature inversion occurs when
   a. winds do not blow. b. warm air is trapped under cool air.
   c. cool air is trapped under warm air. d. warm air rises above cool air.
7. The major source of air pollution is
   a. nuclear wastes. b. burning coal. c. industrial wastes. d. motor vehicles.
8. The release of excess heat into nearby bodies of water is called
   a. thermal pollution. b. acid rain.
   c. groundwater pollution. d. toxic waste pollution.
9. Water pollution
   a. limits wildlife. b. limits drinking-water supplies.
   c. destroys recreational areas. d. all of these.
10. The burning of coal has been made less polluting due to
    a. offshore drilling. b. recycling.
    c. scrubber systems. d. motor vehicle antipollution devices.

CONTENT REVIEW: COMPLETION

On a separate sheet of paper, fill in the word or words that best complete each statement.

1. The release of unwanted substances into the environment is called _____.
2. _____ can be obtained by strip mining.
3. Radioactive products of a nuclear power plant are called _____.
4. A _____ occurs when a layer of cool air is trapped under warmer air.
5. Sulfur oxides combine with water in the atmosphere to form droplets of _____, which fall to the earth as _____.
6. Nitric acid forms in the atmosphere when _____ combine with _____.
7. An accident or leak in a petroleum tanker at sea may result in a (an) _____.
8. A rapid increase in the temperature of a lake or river may be caused by _____.
9. Reclaiming materials from glass and aluminum containers and paper is called _____.
10. _____ is the wise and careful use of natural resources.

CONTENT REVIEW: TRUE OR FALSE

Determine whether each statement is true or false. Then on a separate sheet of paper, write ''true'' if the statement is true. If it is false, change the underlined word or words to make the statement true.

1. Pollution is the release of <u>any</u> substance.
2. Resources that can be replaced once used up are called <u>nonrenewable</u> resources.
3. Nuclear wastes that have a short half-life are called <u>high-level</u> wastes.
4. The air pollution in Donora, Pennsylvania, was caused by the burning of <u>natural gas</u>.
5. The impurity in coal that leads to acid rain is <u>sulfur</u>.
6. Gasoline burns <u>completely</u> in a car engine.
7. Oil released into the ocean <u>is not</u> fatal to sea plants and animals.
8. The release of <u>sewage</u> into waterways is an example of water pollution.
9. Conservation is the wise use of <u>nonrenewable</u> resources.
10. <u>Solar energy</u> is an example of a renewable resource.

CONCEPT REVIEW: SKILL BUILDING

Use the skills you have developed in the chapter to complete each activity.

1. **Making diagrams** Make a chart or diagram that shows a pollution chain in which acid rain begins as air pollution and then becomes water and land pollution.
2. **Making maps** Find out where coal is mined around the world. Make a map that shows each area of coal mining. Use different colors to show coal deposits that have high-sulfur content or low-sulfur content.
3. **Relating cause and effect** Identify a possible cause for each of the following:

   a. acid rain forms
   b. temperature of a lake rises dramatically
   c. United States runs out of oil
   d. more and more people use car pools
4. **Expressing an opinion** Write a brief essay that either supports or refutes the following statement:
   ''I think this whole environmental thing has gone too far. Once industrial profits go down because of all this government interference, the country will be worse off than before.''
5. **Relating concepts** Write a short report in which you discuss how each of the following groups might react to the problem of acid rain in a certain area:

   a. tourists
   b. owners of industry
   c. wildlife preservationists
   d. fishermen
6. **Applying concepts** One serious form of land pollution is garbage and litter. Instead of being disposed of in solid-waste dumps, garbage and litter can be burned. Why is burning garbage not an environmentally sound idea? How could it become an environmentally sound idea?

CONCEPT REVIEW: ESSAY

On a separate sheet of paper, discuss each of the following in a brief paragraph.

1. How can you conserve energy in the home?
2. Explain how the balance in our environment is related to obtaining and using energy resources.
3. Explain why land, water, and air pollution cannot really be separated from one another.
4. How is conservation related to reducing pollution?

Chemical Technology 27

CHAPTER SECTIONS

27–1 Fuels from Petroleum
27–2 Petrochemical Products

CHAPTER OBJECTIVES

After completing this chapter, you will be able to

27–1 Identify the major fractions of petroleum.

27–1 Describe the process of fractional distillation.

27–2 Explain how polymers are formed from monomers.

27–2 Describe the process of polymerization.

27–2 List some important natural and synthetic polymers.

Somewhere near Prudhoe Bay on the bone-chilling north coast of Alaska, four scientists stand on a vast barren plain. The view is awesome. All that meets the eye is a white landscape dotted with icy shades of green and blue. But the landscape was not always this stark. Millions of years ago this region was covered with forests. Animals and microscopic organisms made their homes among the trees, grasses, and giant ferns. A hot sun beat down on the lush vegetation.

Over millions of years, the plants and animals that flourished in the forests of Alaska died out and were buried. Time, heat, and the pressure of layers of sediment transformed the remains of these organisms into a black, thick liquid. Oil!

The scientists who stand on the ice and snow of Prudhoe Bay are looking for oil. Oil is one of the world's most important and valuable resources. Oil is a source of energy that warms homes and powers cars, planes, trains, and ships. Oil is a source of chemicals used to manufacture clothing, medicines, paints, records and cassette tapes, and thousands of other products used every day.

How does a gooey, black fluid from inside the earth get to be a pair of sneakers, an aspirin, or a tape that holds Bruce Springsteen's voice? In this chapter, you will find out more about the important role oil plays in making your life more comfortable and enjoyable.

Millions of years ago, this area on the north coast of Alaska was covered by a lush tropical forest. Today, it is covered by a blanket of ice and snow. Yet deep beneath the surface, the remains of organisms that once lived in the tropical forest have collected as droplets of oil.

Section Objective

To describe how fractional distillation separates petroleum into its various components

The oil that gushes from deep within the earth is a mixture of chemicals called crude oil, or **petroleum.** Petroleum is usually black or dark brown. But it can be green, red, yellow, or even colorless. Petroleum may flow as easily as water or it may ooze slowly like thick tar. The color and density of petroleum depend on the substances that make it up. By itself, petroleum is almost useless! But the different parts, or **fractions,** of petroleum are among the most useful chemicals in the world.

Petroleum is separated into its useful parts by a process called fractional distillation. The process of **distillation** involves heating a liquid until it vaporizes and then allowing the vapor to cool until it condenses back into a liquid. The different fractions of petroleum have different boiling points. So each fraction vaporizes at a different temperature. The temperature at which a substance boils is the same as the temperature at which it condenses. Thus, each fraction will condense back to a liquid at a different temperature. By drawing off each fraction as it condenses, petroleum can be easily separated into its various parts.

Fractional distillation of petroleum is done in a **fractionating tower.** The process of separating petroleum into its fractions is called refining. At a

Figure 27–1 *Geologists drill through the earth's surface to find crude oil, which is then recovered by devices such as an oil rig (left). The first oil well in the United States was drilled in 1859 in Pennsylvania (right). What is another term for crude oil?*

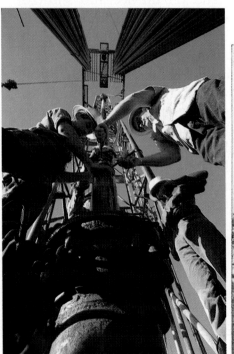

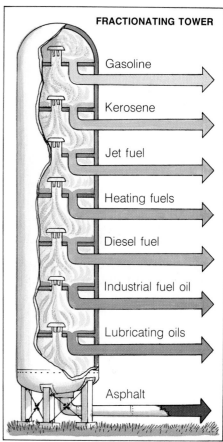

Figure 27–2 *Petroleum is separated into fractions in fractionating columns in an oil refinery (left). Each fraction condenses at a different temperature and is drawn off in collecting vessels located at fixed points along the column (right).*

refinery, fractionating towers may rise 30 meters or more. Petroleum is piped into the base of the fractionating tower and heated to about 385°C. At this temperature, which is higher than the boiling points of most of the fractions, the petroleum vaporizes.

Figure 27–2 shows a typical fractionating tower. When the petroleum vaporizes, the fractions rise up the tower. As they rise, they cool and condense. Some fractions condense at high temperatures. These fractions condense near the bottom of the tower and are drawn off to collecting vessels. Other fractions continue to rise in the tower. As they rise, they cool even more before they condense. These fractions are drawn off at higher levels in the tower. As a result of this vaporization–condensation process, the various fractions of petroleum are separated and collected.

You will notice in Figure 27–2 that asphalt is collected at the bottom of the fractionating tower. Asphalt vaporizes at a temperature that exceeds the temperature in the tower. When the other fractions vaporize, asphalt is left behind as a liquid that simply runs out of the bottom of the tower. Which fraction in the tower condenses at the lowest temperature?

Figure 27–3 *This illustration shows the amount, or percent yield, of each fraction that can be obtained from a barrel of crude oil. Which fraction represents the highest percent yield?*

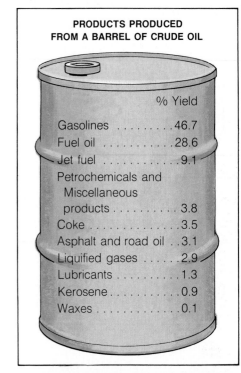

PRODUCTS PRODUCED
FROM A BARREL OF CRUDE OIL

	% Yield
Gasolines	46.7
Fuel oil	28.6
Jet fuel	9.1
Petrochemicals and Miscellaneous products	3.8
Coke	3.5
Asphalt and road oil	3.1
Liquified gases	2.9
Lubricants	1.3
Kerosene	0.9
Waxes	0.1

SECTION REVIEW

1. What physical property forms the basis of fractional distillation?
2. Why do substances with low boiling points condense near the top of a fractionating tower?
3. How would you separate three substances—A, B, and C—whose boiling points are 50°C, 100°C, and 150°C, respectively?

27–2 Petrochemical Products

Ride a bicycle down your street and you are probably gliding along on a product of petroleum, or a petrochemical product. The rubber in the inner tube is made from petrochemicals. Put on your winter jacket and you are probably keeping yourself warm with a petrochemical product—the lining of your jacket is made from petrochemicals.

Polymer Chemistry

One simple definition of chemistry is the "making and breaking of bonds." In a chemical reaction, the chemical bonds that hold atoms together in molecules are broken. The atoms are rearranged, different bonds are formed, and new molecules are produced. The petrochemical products that are part of your life come from the making and breaking of chemical bonds in petrochemicals. A general term for this process is polymer chemistry. And polymer chemistry involves **polymers** (PAHL-ih-merz).

The term polymer comes from the Greek words *polys*, meaning "many," and *meros*, meaning "parts." The word "parts" refers to a grouping of atoms called a molecular unit. A molecular unit alone is not a polymer. But many molecular units strung together in a series form a unique polymer.

The individual molecular units that form a polymer are called **monomers** (MAHN-uh-merz). You can think of a polymer as a series of monomers all bonded together one after another. The type of monomers and the length and shape of the polymer chain determine the physical properties of the polymer.

Figure 27–4 *A polymer is made up of a series of monomers. What factors distinguish one polymer from another?*

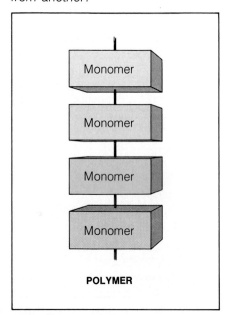

POLYMER

Methane

Figure 27–5 *Substances produced from methane include Plexiglas, antifreeze, fire extinguisher foam, and Teflon (top). Ethylene products include plastic laser disks, aspirin, plastic wrap, and synthetic fibers (bottom).*

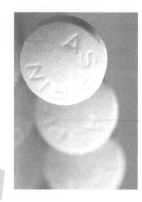

Ethylene

Natural Polymers

Most of the polymers you will read about in this chapter are made from petrochemicals. Some polymers, however, occur in nature. Cotton, silk, wool, and natural rubber are all natural polymers. Cellulose and lignin, important parts of wood, are natural polymers. In fact, all living things contain polymers. Protein, an essential ingredient of living matter, is a polymer. The monomers from which proteins are made are called **amino acids.** Combined in groups of one hundred or more units, amino acid monomers form many of the parts of your body—from hair to heart muscle.

Synthetic Polymers

Although the term polymer may be new to you, the polymers produced from petrochemicals are probably quite familiar. Polymers produced from petrochemicals are called synthetic polymers. Petrochemical products such as rubber and plastic wrap are synthetic polymers. Synthetic polymers are used to make fabrics such as nylon, rayon, orlon, and dacron. Plastics, used in many products from kitchen utensils to rocket engines, are petrochemical products made of polymers. The list goes on and on.

The first polymer was manufactured in 1909. Since then, **polymerization** (puh-lihm-uhr-ih-ZAY-shuhn) has come a long way. **Polymerization is the process of chemically bonding monomers to form polymers.** Most early polymers consisted of fewer

Life Science Library/Giant Molecules. Photograph by John Zimmerman © 1986 Time, Inc. Time-Life Books, Inc. Publisher
Life Science Library/Giant Molecules. Photograph by Donald Miller © 1986 Time, Inc. Time-Life Books, Inc. Publisher

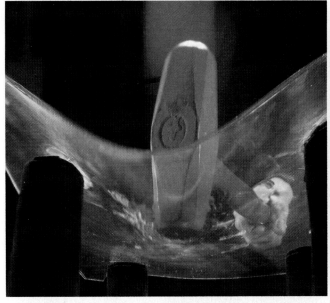

Figure 27–7 *Polymer technology has produced some amazing materials. This sheet of plastic simply bends no matter how hard it is struck by a hammer (left). This extra-thin sheet of plastic is not damaged by temperatures over 1000°C. But as you can see from the boiling water, it does allow the transfer of heat (right).*

than two hundred monomers. Today's polymers may contain thousands of monomers. The numerous ways in which these monomers can be linked may be very complex. They include single chains, parallel chains, intertwining chains, spirals, loops, and loops of chains!

Polymer chemistry has produced synthetic materials that are strong, light, heat resistant, flexible, and long lasting. These properties give polymers a wide range of uses. For example, polymers are used as substitutes for human tissue, such as bones and arteries. These polymers must last a lifetime and withstand the wear and tear of constant use. Polymer adhesives, rather than thread, are often used to hold clothes together. Polymers are replacing glass, metal, and paper as containers for food. The cup of hot chocolate you may have held today did not burn your hand because it was made of a white insulating polymer. Polymer materials also are used for rugs, furniture, wall coverings, and curtains. Look around you and see how many polymers you can spot. And remember to thank petroleum for all these useful polymers.

Figure 27–8 *Polymers are used to build artificial body parts such as this artificial heart (top) and this artificial knee joint (bottom). What important properties must polymers used in artificial body parts have?*

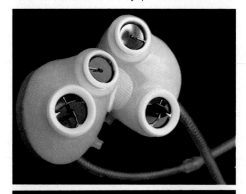

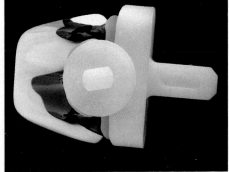

On July 4, 1986, a figure that represents freedom to people of the United States and most of the world was honored with a huge birthday party. The figure is the Statue of Liberty. Almost everywhere you looked that day there were replicas of the one hundred-year-old statue. The replicas were cast from almost every material imaginable: chocolate, ice, aluminum, glass, plastic, concrete, plaster, and—like the original statue—copper.

Producing the molds from which these statues were formed kept many **patternmakers** busy for months before the celebration. A patternmaker produces molds for new car parts, new board game pieces, machine parts, and many other products.

Using blueprints that show how the finished product should look, a patternmaker first makes a model of the new product. The model is usually made of clay, wood, or plaster. The model is then pressed into clay, sand, plaster, or other materials to make a hollow mold. The finished piece is then cast, or formed, from this mold.

Frequently, a mold is used to shape new synthetic materials. So a patternmaker must be familiar with the chemical technology that is used to develop new materials. A high school diploma and courses in art, math, mechanical drawing, and metalworking are required to become a patternmaker. Usually a patternmaker learns the skills of the trade through a five-year apprenticeship. For information about a career as a patternmaker, contact the American Foundrymen's Society/Cast Metals Institute, Inc., Golf and Wolf Roads, Des Plaines, IL 60016.

Polymer materials also can be mixed and matched to produce substances with unusual properties. Different plastics and synthetic fibers are combined to make punctureproof tires and bulletproof vests. Layers of polymer materials can be combined to make waterproof rain gear.

Polymer chemistry also is important in the transportation industry. Each year the number of polymer parts in cars, planes, and trains increases. A plastic car engine has been built and tested. This engine is lighter, more fuel efficient, and more durable than a metal engine.

Figure 27–9 *Synthetic fibers are one of the many products formed from polymers. What is the name of the process of chemically bonding monomers to form polymers?*

Figure 27–10 *The scientist is holding a thin strand of Kevlar, a polymer five times stronger than steel (right). Ropes of Kevlar have replaced steel in lines used to hold ships at dock (left).*

Devices that produce electricity also are being improved with polymers. Polymer batteries and solar electric cells will soon be available. These developments are expected to increase the use of solar energy and improve energy conservation. Recently, a new polymer was developed that can conduct electricity almost as well as metals such as copper. One of the scientists who developed this polymer described its possible use "as a lightweight, rechargeable battery about as thick as a sheet of paper." As you can see, polymers made from petroleum are extremely important today. And they will be even more important in the future.

SECTION REVIEW

1. What is the relationship between a monomer and a polymer?
2. List three examples of natural polymers.
3. What is the name of the process in which monomers are chemically bonded to form polymers?
4. What might be some of the economic side effects of increased use of polymers in automobiles?

Comparing Natural and Synthetic Polymers

Problem

How do natural and synthetic polymers compare in strength, absorbency, and resistance to chemical damage?

> **Materials** *(per group)*
>
> 12 Styrofoam cups   marking pen
> liquid bleach   scissors
> water   paper towel
> oil   rubber gloves
> medicine dropper   metric ruler
> mild acid (lime juice, vinegar, or lemon juice)
> 3 samples of natural polymer cloth: wool, cotton, linen
> 3 samples of synthetic polymer cloth: polyester, nylon, acetate

Procedure

1. Record the color of each cloth.
2. Label six Styrofoam cups with the names of the six cloth samples. Also write the word "bleach" on each cup.
3. Cut a piece about 2 square centimeters from each cloth. Put each piece in its cup.
4. Wearing rubber gloves, carefully pour a small amount of bleach into each cup.
5. Label the six remaining cups with the names of the six cloth samples and the word "acid." Then pour a small amount of the mild acid into each and repeat step 3.
6. Set the cups aside for 24 hours. Meanwhile, proceed with steps 7 through 9.
7. Using the remaining samples of cloth, attempt to tear each.
8. Place a drop of water on each material. Note whether the water forms beads or is absorbed. If the water is absorbed, record the rate of absorption.

9. Repeat step 8 using a drop of oil.
10. After 24 hours, carefully pour the liquids in the cups into the sink or into a container provided by your teacher. Dry the samples with a paper towel.
11. Record any color changes.

Observations

1. Which material held its color best in bleach? In acid?
2. Which materials were least resistant to chemical damage by bleach or mild acid?
3. Which material has the strongest fiber or is hardest to tear?
4. Which materials are water repellent?

Conclusions

1. Compare the natural and synthetic polymers' strength, absorbency, and resistance to chemical damage.
2. Which material would you use to manufacture a laboratory coat? A farmer's overalls? A raincoat? An auto mechanic's shirt?

CHAPTER REVIEW

SUMMARY

27–1 Fuels from Petroleum

❏ Crude oil, or petroleum, is made up of different parts called fractions.

❏ Although petroleum has no practical uses, its fractions have many important uses.

❏ Petroleum is separated into its components through a process called fractional distillation.

❏ During fractional distillation, petroleum is heated to a temperature at which most of its fractions vaporize. As the fractions rise up the fractionating tower, they cool and condense at different temperatures. The liquid fractions are drawn off and separated at different levels in the tower.

27–2 Petrochemical Products

❏ Substances derived from petroleum are called petrochemicals.

❏ Most petrochemical products are polymers.

❏ A polymer is a series of molecular units called monomers.

❏ The process of chemically combining monomers to make a polymer is called polymerization.

❏ Natural polymers include cotton, silk, wool, natural rubber, cellulose, lignin, and protein.

❏ Proteins are made of amino acids.

❏ Synthetic polymers include rubber, plastics, and fabrics such as nylon, orlon, rayon, and dacron.

❏ Polymers are usually strong, lightweight, heat resistant, flexible, and long lasting.

❏ Polymers can be mixed and matched to form substances that are waterproof, puncture-proof, or electrically conductive.

VOCABULARY

Define each term in a complete sentence.

amino acid	fractionating tower	petroleum
distillation	monomer	polymer
fraction		polymerization

CONTENT REVIEW: MULTIPLE CHOICE

On a separate sheet of paper, write the letter of the answer that best completes each statement.

1. Crude oil is
   a. a single substance. b. gasoline. c. asphalt. d. a mixture.
2. The physical property used to separate petroleum into its parts is
   a. melting point. b. boiling point. c. density. d. solubility.
3. The highest temperature in a fractionating tower is about 385°C because that is
   a. below the boiling point of most petroleum fractions.
   b. above the boiling point of most petroleum fractions.
   c. equal to the boiling point of most petroleum fractions.
   d. below the melting point of most petroleum fractions.
4. Of the following, the least likely to vaporize in a fractionating tower is
   a. kerosene. b. gasoline. c. asphalt. d. heating fuel.

5. The process of distillation involves
   a. vaporization and condensation.　　b. freezing and melting.
   c. vaporization and melting.　　d. freezing and condensation.
6. A polymer is made up of a series of
   a. atoms.　　b. monomers.　　c. fuels.　　d. synthetic molecules.
7. An example of a natural polymer is
   a. wool.　　b. plastic.　　c. crude oil.　　d. copper.
8. An example of a synthetic polymer is
   a. natural rubber.　　b. protein.　　c. rayon.　　d. cotton.
9. The process of chemically bonding monomers to form polymers is called
   a. distillation.　　b. fractionation.　　c. polymerization.　　d. refining.
10. An example of a polymer product is
   a. lead tubing.　　b. crude oil.　　c. water.　　d. plastic.

CONTENT REVIEW: COMPLETION

On a separate sheet of paper, write the word or words that best complete each statement.

1. Oil that gushes from deep within the earth is called crude oil, or _____.
2. The process of _____ involves heating a liquid until it vaporizes and then allowing it to cool until it condenses.
3. To separate crude oil into its useful components, a _____ tower is used at a _____.
4. Each fraction of petroleum has a different _____.
5. _____ are products made from petroleum.
6. A polymer consists of many _____ bonded together.
7. The natural polymers _____ and _____ are important components of wood.
8. _____ are the monomers from which proteins are made.
9. _____ is the process in which monomers are chemically bonded to form polymers.
10. Polymers manufactured from petroleum are called _____ polymers.

CONTENT REVIEW: TRUE OR FALSE

Determine whether each statement is true or false. Then on a separate sheet of paper, write "true" if it is true. If it is false, change the underlined word or words to make the statement true.

1. Petroleum taken directly from the earth is called asphalt.
2. Petroleum can be separated into its different parts, or fractions.
3. The process of separating petroleum into its components is called boiling.
4. Heating a liquid to its boiling point turns it into a vapor.
5. When a vapor evaporates, it changes back to a liquid.
6. In a fractionating tower, petroleum is heated to about 85°C.
7. A monomer is a long chain of polymers.
8. Silk is an example of a natural polymer.
9. Polymerization involves the chemical bonding of monomers into polymers.
10. Plastics are examples of natural polymers.

CONCEPT REVIEW: SKILL BUILDING

Use the skills you have developed in the chapter to complete each activity.

1. **Making graphs** Figure 27–3 shows the yield in percent of products that are derived from petroleum. On a sheet of graph paper, plot the type of product on one axis and the percentage yield of that product on the other. What conclusions can you draw from your finished graph?

2. **Making predictions** Select five objects in your home that are made from naturally occurring substances such as wool or silver. For each object, predict whether a synthetic polymer may be developed to replace the naturally occurring substance. Describe the characteristics each synthetic polymer should have to make it more suitable than the naturally occurring substance.

3. **Applying technology** You are an engineer whose task is to design a car that is fuel efficient yet meets all of the current standards for safety and durability. What kinds of materials would you consider using? What properties must the materials used in the engine have? The materials used in safety belts? The materials used in seat cushions?

4. **Analyzing data** You are an oil prospector who has sent three scientists to explore three regions of the earth—Alphaland, Betaland, and Gammaland. You get the following reports.
Alphaland: No fossils in rocks at any depth. Warm climate for millions of years. Betaland: Fossils at great depths. Present climate warm. Gammaland: Fossils at relatively shallow depths. Present climate very cold.
You can choose only one location at which to sink a well. Based on your data, which location would you choose? Explain your answer.

CONCEPT REVIEW: ESSAY

Discuss each of the following in a brief paragraph.

1. Describe some of the uses of synthetic polymers in your life. Then describe what changes you would have to make in your life style if these polymers were not available.

2. Many people use and enjoy the products derived from petroleum. However, some of the chemical processes used to make these products, as well as the burning of petroleum fuels, add to the pollution of the air, the land, and the water in the United States. So people often must decide whether manufacturing a certain product is worth the damage done to the environment. In other words, people often must make a trade-off between products they want and the effects on the environment. What is your feeling on this issue?

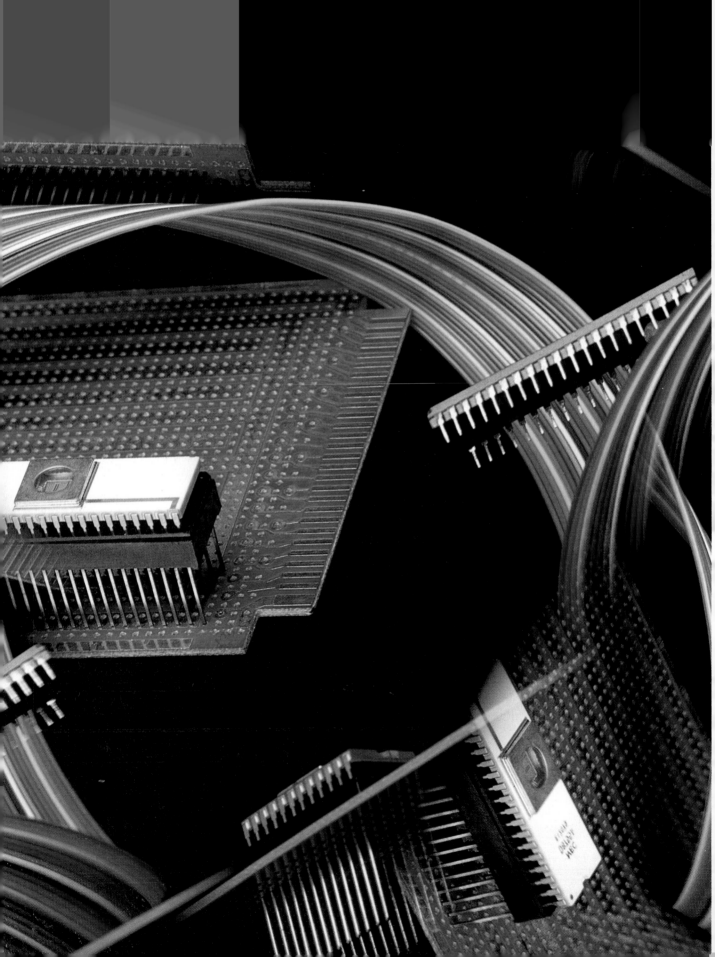

Electronics and Computers 28

CHAPTER SECTIONS

28–1 Electronic Devices

28–2 Transmitting Sound

28–3 Transmitting Pictures

28–4 Computers

CHAPTER OBJECTIVES

After completing this chapter, you will be able to

28–1 Define electronics.

28–1 Describe the structure and applications of vacuum tubes.

28–1 Relate semiconductors to the operation of transistors and integrated circuits.

28–2 Explain how a telephone and a radio work.

28–3 Describe the operation of a cathode-ray tube and its use in television.

28–4 Discuss the development and the components of a modern computer.

28–4 Use the binary system to represent numbers.

It was 1952, and not many people were familiar with computers. In fact, there were some who had never even heard the word! But on Election Day of that year, the inevitable happened. Millions of Americans came face to face with the computer age for the first time. For some it was a rather shocking encounter.

The presidential contest that year pitted Republican Dwight D. Eisenhower against Democrat Adlai E. Stevenson. Early in the evening, even before the voting polls had closed, newscaster Walter Cronkite announced to television viewers that an "electronic brain" was going to predict the outcome of the election.

The "electronic brain" was the huge UNIVAC I computer. For weeks before the election, computer scientists had been feeding district-by-district results of the presidential elections of 1944 and 1948 into UNIVAC's computer memory. They also had instructed the computer how to analyze the early 1952 voting returns by comparing them with the results of the last two elections.

What UNIVAC predicted, based on just 3 million votes, was a landslide victory for Eisenhower. A shocked and disbelieving nation sat by their television sets into the early hours of the morning, convinced that the "electronic brain" had made a giant mistake.

UNIVAC was not wrong, however. When all the votes were counted, the computer's prediction turned out to be remarkably close to the actual results. As Eisenhower became president, the computer age dawned for most Americans. In this chapter, you will learn about some of the devices that have brought the computer age to where it is now.

This photographer's view of computer technology shows some of the basic hardware—chips, multichip board, and computer cable.

28–1 Electronic Devices

Your world would be very different without electricity and the numerous devices that use electricity. Were you awakened this morning by the buzz of an alarm clock and the flash of numbers? Did you rely on a radio or a cassette player to get the day started with music? Did your breakfast include food that was warmed in a microwave oven? Can you get through the day without using the telephone?

Few people can answer these questions without realizing that electric devices make life easier and more enjoyable. The branch of technology that has developed electric devices is called **electronics.** Electronics is a branch of physics. **Electronics is the study of the release, behavior, and effects of electrons as it relates to use in helpful devices.**

Electronic technology can be traced to the nineteenth century, when electricity was used to power simple devices such as lamps, heaters, and welding arcs. In such devices, the kinetic energy of moving electrons was converted into heat and light energy. The flow of electrons, however, was not modified or regulated in any precise way. Today, scientists and engineers know that if electrons are carefully controlled, they can be made to carry messages, magnify weak signals, draw pictures, and even do arithmetic!

Figure 28–1 *The control panel in an airplane consists of electronic instruments that make flying easier, more accurate, and safer (left). Here are some electronic devices that you may be familiar with (right). What energy conversion is involved in electronic devices?*

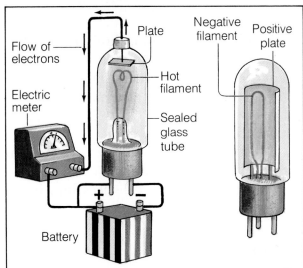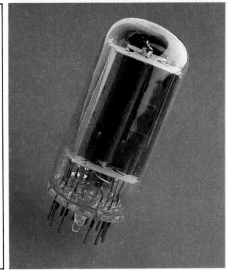

Figure 28–2 *A diode is the simplest type of vacuum tube. In a diode, electrons flow from the negatively charged filament to the positively charged plate, creating a one-way flow of electrons. Diodes are used as rectifiers in many electronic devices. Why?*

Vacuum Tubes

The ability to control electrons carefully began with the invention of the **vacuum tube.** The vacuum tube is a one-way valve, or gate, for a flow of electrons. Electrons are permitted to move in only one direction through the vacuum tube.

The simplest type of vacuum tube is called a **diode.** A diode consists of a filament, or wire, and a plate. The filament is negatively charged, and the plate is positively charged. Electrons flow from the negatively charged filament to the positively charged plate. Both the filament and the plate are contained in a sealed glass tube, from which almost all the air has been removed. How does this fact explain the name given to this tube?

Because vacuum tubes produce a one-way current, they have many applications in electronics. Two important applications of vacuum tubes are as rectifiers and amplifiers. Vacuum tubes also acted as switches in early electronic computers.

Rectifiers

A **rectifier** is a vacuum tube diode that converts alternating current (AC) to direct current (DC). The current supplied to your home by an electric power plant is alternating current. In alternating current, the electrons move back and forth, not just in one

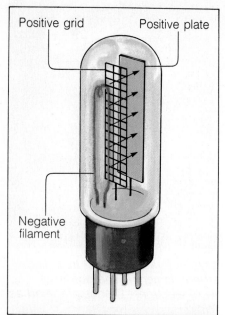

Figure 28-3 *A triode vacuum tube consists of a filament, a plate, and a grid. The addition of the grid allows the electron flow to be amplified, or strengthened (top). Triodes are used in microphones to amplify sound (bottom).*

direction. Certain household appliances cannot operate on alternating current. They need direct current. So these appliances have rectifiers built into their circuits. As the alternating current passes through the rectifier, it is changed into direct current.

Rectifiers are used in devices such as televisions, stereos, and computers. Converters that allow you to plug battery-operated devices into household electric outlets contain rectifiers.

Amplifiers

An **amplifier** is an electronic device that increases the strength of an electric signal. In an amplifier, a small input current is converted to a large output current. The large output current produces a stronger signal. The strengthening of a weak signal is called amplification. Amplification is perhaps the most important function of an electric device.

Amplifiers are **triode** vacuum tubes. A triode consists of a filament, a plate, and a wire screen, or grid. The addition of the grid allows the flow of electrons between the negatively charged filament and the positively charged plate to be better controlled. The invention of the triode was responsible for the rapid growth of the radio and television industry.

Amplifiers strengthen both sound and picture signals. The signals that carry sound and picture information are often very weak as a result of traveling long distances through the air. By the time an antenna picks up the signals, they are too weak to produce an accurate copy of the original signal. Radio and television amplifiers strengthen the incoming signals. Fully amplified signals can be millions or billions of times stronger than the signal picked up by the antenna!

Without amplifiers, devices such as hearing aids, public-address systems, tape recorders, and radar would not operate. Amplifiers also are essential to the operation of medical instruments used to diagnose certain injuries and diseases. Human heart waves and brain waves can be studied by doctors because the weak electric signals given off by these organs are amplified.

Semiconductors

Electronic technology took a giant step with the discovery of **semiconductors.** Semiconductors are materials that are able to conduct electric currents better than insulators but not as well as metals. Devices that use semiconductors are called **solid-state devices.**

Silicon and germanium, two metalloids, are the most commonly used semiconductors. These elements have crystal structures that cause them to act like diodes. In these two elements current passes easily in one direction but not in the other.

Solid-state devices have several advantages over vacuum tubes. Using crystals of semiconductors makes solid-state devices much smaller and lighter than vacuum tubes. A tiny piece of semiconductor material can be made into a very small crystal diode. Such a diode gives off less heat, uses far less power, is more dependable, and lasts longer.

To increase the conductivity of semiconductors, certain impurities must be added to them. Adding impurities to semiconductors to increase their conductivity is called **doping.**

There are two types of semiconductors. These types are based on the impurity used to dope the semiconductor. If the impurity contributes extra electrons to the semiconductor, the semiconductor is called an n-type, meaning negative-type. Silicon doped with arsenic is an n-type semiconductor. Semiconductors that have fewer electrons, or extra protons, are called p-type semiconductors. What do you think p-type means? Silicon doped with gallium is a p-type semiconductor.

Figure 28–4 *Radios that used vacuum tubes were large, heavy, and cumbersome. They also gave off a considerable amount of heat. Radios that use semiconductors can be made extremely small. In addition, they are more dependable, last longer, use less power, and give off less heat. What are devices that use semiconductors called?*

Figure 28–5 *Doping a semiconductor increases its conductivity. What impurity is used to make an n-type semiconductor? A p-type?*

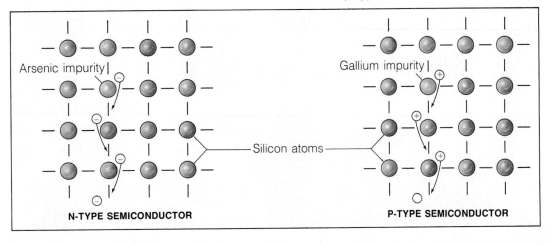

N-TYPE SEMICONDUCTOR   Arsenic impurity   Silicon atoms   Gallium impurity   **P-TYPE SEMICONDUCTOR**

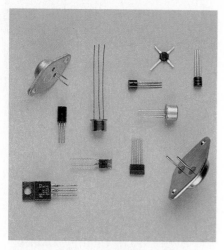

Figure 28–6 *Transistors come in a variety of shapes and sizes. What does a transistor do?*

Transistors

Semiconductors also are used to make solid-state devices called **transistors.** A transistor—a sandwich of three semiconductor crystals—is used to amplify an electric current or signal. It is the arrangement of the impurities in the semiconductors that enables them to act as amplifiers. A weak signal, corresponding to a weak current, enters the transistor and is amplified so that a strong signal is produced.

Transistors come in a variety of shapes and sizes. Perhaps you are familiar with some of them. Transistors are commonly used in radios, televisions, stereos, computers, and calculators. The small size, light weight, and durability of transistors has helped in the development of communication satellites.

Integrated Circuits

An **integrated circuit** combines many diodes and transistors on a thin slice of silicon crystal. This razor-thin piece of silicon is often called a **chip.** A single integrated circuit, or chip, may contain thousands of diodes and transistors in a variety of complex combinations.

To turn a silicon chip into an integrated circuit, it must be doped in some places with arsenic and in other places with gallium. Certain areas of the chip become diodes, while other areas become transistors. Connections between these diodes and transistors are then made by painting thin "wires" on the chip. Wires are attached to the integrated circuit so it can be connected to other devices.

Figure 28–7 *An integrated circuit, or chip, contains thousands of diodes and transistors in complex combinations on a thin slice of silicon crystal. Here, you see the size of a chip in comparison to the wafer from which it is made (left). This photograph of a computer chip, magnified 175 times by a scanning electron microscope, shows the integrated circuit paths. A human hair is wider than 150 of these paths (right).*

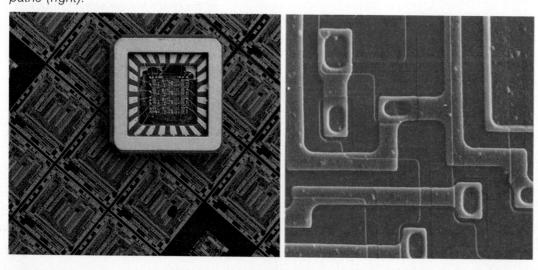

Integrated circuits are used as amplifiers and switches in a wide variety of devices. Computers and microcomputers, calculators, radios, watches, washing machines, refrigerators, and even robots use integrated circuits.

SECTION REVIEW

1. What is electronics?
2. What is a vacuum tube? How is a vacuum tube used as a rectifier? As an amplifier?
3. What is a semiconductor?
4. How are semiconductors used to make integrated circuits? What are some advantages of the use of integrated circuits?

Figure 28–8 *A computer scientist designs a new computer chip by first drawing a large version and then having the design miniaturized.*

28–2 Transmitting Sound

Section Objective

To describe how sound-transmitting devices work

The birth and growth of the communications industry has been due to advances in electronic technology. Since the first telegraph line in 1844, people have become accustomed to instant communication. Each improvement in the speed, clarity, and reliability of a communication device has been based on a discovery in the field of electronics.

Telephone Communication

The first telephone was invented in 1876 by Alexander Graham Bell. Although modern telephones hardly resemble Bell's, the principle on which all telephones work is the same. **A telephone sends and receives sound by means of electric currents.** A telephone has two main parts.

TRANSMITTER The transmitter is located behind the mouthpiece of a telephone. The transmitter converts sound waves into a pattern of electric waves. The electric waves travel over wires to a receiver.

Sound waves produced when a person speaks into a telephone cause vibrations in the transmitter. These vibrations vary according to the particular sound. The vibrations regulate the amount of electric current produced and sent out over telephone

Figure 28–9 *The first telephone was invented in 1876 by Alexander Graham Bell. Today, you push buttons or dial to make calls. But up until the early 1950s, telephone calls were placed by switchboard operators, whose familiar phrase was, "Number, please."*

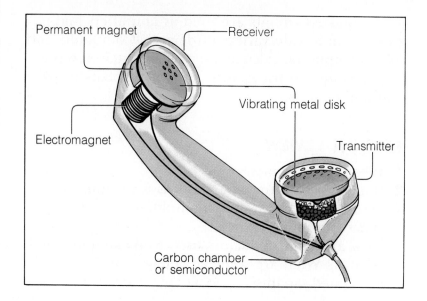

Figure 28-10 *A telephone, consisting of a transmitter and a receiver, sends and receives sounds by means of electric currents. Where are transistors used? For what purpose?*

Permanent magnet — Receiver
Electromagnet
Vibrating metal disk
Transmitter
Carbon chamber or semiconductor

wires. You can think of the electric current as "copying" the pattern of the sound waves.

RECEIVER The receiver, located in the earpiece, converts the pattern of electric waves sent out by a transmitter back into sound. The receiver uses an electromagnet to produce this conversion.

Electric current transmitted by another telephone activates the electromagnet. The electromagnet moves in such a way that it causes vibrations in a thin, round metal disk attached to it. The vibrations produce sound waves that are heard by the listener.

Alexander Graham Bell used carbon grains in the transmitter to convert sound to electricity. Today's telephones use a small semiconductor crystal. Transistors then amplify the electric signal. In modern telephone earpieces, semiconductor devices have replaced electromagnets.

Radio Communication

All devices that produce sound—such as radios, stereos, and tape recorders—are closely related to the telephone. They all involve the interconversion of sound and electric energy.

Radios work by changing sound vibrations into electromagnetic waves, or radio waves. The radio waves, which travel through the air at the speed of light, are converted back into sound vibrations when they reach a radio receiver.

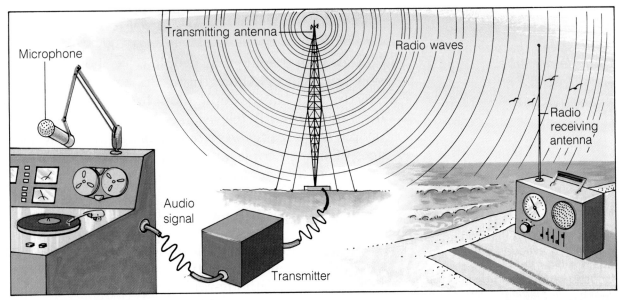

Figure 28–11 *Radios work by converting sound vibrations, usually produced at a broadcast station, into electromagnetic waves. The waves are amplified by a transmitter and then sent out into the air from a transmitting antenna. Picked up by a receiving antenna, the radio waves are converted back into sound waves by a receiver. What else does the receiver do with the radio waves?*

A radio program usually begins at a radio station. Here, a microphone picks up the sounds that are being broadcast. An electric current running through the microphone is disturbed by the sound vibrations in such a way that it creates its own vibrations that match the sound.

The electromagnetic waves that represent the sounds of a broadcast are now sent to a transmitter. The transmitter amplifies the waves and sends them to a transmitting antenna. The antenna sends the waves out into the air as radio waves. Why do you think many radio stations locate their antennas at high elevations or open areas or on top of towers?

Radio waves are converted back into sound waves by means of a radio receiver. A radio receiver picks up and amplifies the radio waves originally sent out from a radio station. When a radio receiver picks up sounds corresponding to a specific frequency, it is described as being tuned in. The main parts of a radio are the antenna, tuner, amplifier, and loudspeaker.

SECTION REVIEW

1. What are the two main parts of a telephone? What energy conversions are made in each part?
2. Describe the broadcast of a radio program.
3. How have solid-state devices affected telephones and radios?

28–3 Transmitting Pictures

Can you imagine that people once thought television was useless? About fifty years ago, that was exactly what many people thought about the demonstration of early television. Of course, what these people were seeing were blurry black-and-white images of other people waiting in the next room to have their turn to see television!

Cathode-ray Tubes

Figure 28–12 *A cathode-ray tube is a sealed evacuated tube in which a beam of electrons is focused on a screen coated with fluorescent material (bottom). As electrons strike the fluorescent material, visible light is given off and an image is formed (top).*

Television images are produced on the surface of a special type of vacuum tube called a **cathode-ray tube,** or **CRT.** Cathode-ray tubes are also responsible for images produced by computer displays, video games, and radar devices.

A cathode-ray tube is an electronic device that uses electrons to produce images on a screen. The electrons, moving as a beam, sweep across the screen and cause it to glow. The screen glows because it is coated with fluorescent material. Fluorescent material glows when struck by electrons.

The electrons in a CRT come from the negatively charged filament within the sealed glass vacuum tube. An electric current heats the metal filament and causes electrons to "boil" off it. The electrons are accelerated toward the screen and focused into a narrow beam. The moving electrons produce a magnetic field that can be used to control the direction of the beam. Electromagnets placed outside the CRT cause the beam to change its

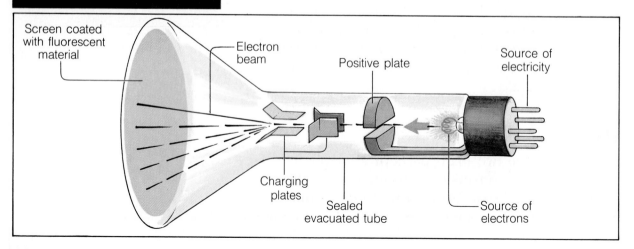

Screen coated with fluorescent material

Electron beam

Positive plate

Source of electricity

Charging plates

Sealed evacuated tube

Source of electrons

direction, making it move rapidly up and down and back and forth across the screen.

At each point where the beam of electrons strikes the fluorescent material of the CRT screen, visible light is given off. The brightness of the light is determined by the number of electrons that strike the screen. The more electrons, the brighter the light. The continuous, rapid movement of the beam horizontally and vertically across the screen many times per second produces a pattern of light, or a picture, on the screen. The electron beam in a CRT traces 525 lines as it zigzags up and down, creating a whole picture 30 times each second.

Television Transmission

A cathode-ray tube in a color television differs from a simple cathode-ray tube in two important ways. One, the screen of a color television is coated with three different materials placed close together in clusters of dots or in thin stripes at each point on the screen. Such material glows with a different color of light—red, blue, or green—when struck by

Figure 28–13 *The CRT in a color television contains three electron guns—one each for red, blue, and green signals. The screen of the CRT is coated with three different fluorescent materials, each of which glows with a different primary color of light when struck by a beam of electrons. What is the purpose of transistors in CRTs?*

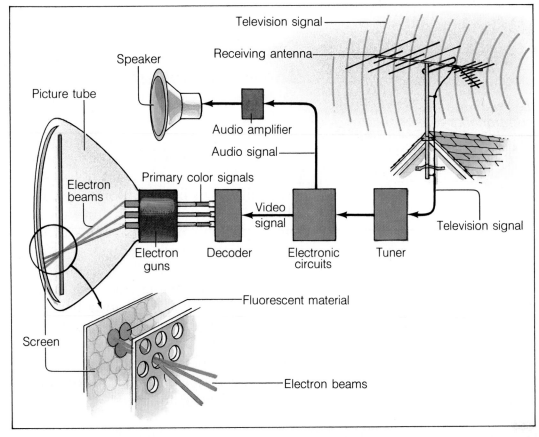

Telephone and Radio History

The invention of the telephone and the invention of the radio were two important advances in electronic technology. Using books and other reference materials in the library, find out about the invention of each. Be sure to include answers to the following questions?

1. Who invented the device?
2. When was it invented?
3. Were there any interesting or unusual circumstances surrounding the invention?
4. How was the invention modified through the years?

a beam of electrons. Various colors are produced by adjusting the strengths of the electron beams. For example, red is produced when electrons strike only the red material. Purple is produced when electrons strike red and blue material. When do you think white is produced?

The other difference is that a color television CRT contains three electron guns—one each for red, blue, and green signals. The information for controlling and directing the beams is coded within the color picture signal that is transmitted from a TV station.

All cathode-ray tubes, including those in televisions, use transistors. The transistors amplify the electric signals received by the CRT. These signals cannot be used unless they are amplified.

SECTION REVIEW

1. What is a cathode-ray tube?
2. Describe the operation of a cathode-ray tube.
3. How does a color television CRT differ from a simple CRT?
4. Photographs of a TV picture taken with an ordinary camera often show part of the screen filled. Explain why.

28–4 Computers

A **computer** is an electronic device that performs calculations and processes information. A modern electronic computer can do thousands of calculations per second. At equally incredible speed, it can file away billions of bits of information in its memory. Then it can rapidly search through all that information to pick out particular items. It can change numbers to letters to pictures to sounds—and then back to numbers again.

Using these abilities, modern computers are guiding spaceships, navigating boats, diagnosing diseases and prescribing treatment, forecasting weather, and searching for ore. Computers can make robots move, talk, and obey commands. Computers can play games and make music. They even can design new computers!

Computer Development

The starting point of modern computer development is considered to be 1890. In preparation for the United States census that year, Herman Hollerith devised an electromagnetic machine that could handle information punched into cards. The holes allowed small electric currents to pass and activate counters. Using this system, Hollerith completed the 1890 census in one-fourth the time it had taken to do the 1880 census! Hollerith's punch card became the symbol of the computer age.

The first American-built computer was developed in 1946 by the United States Army. The Electronic Numerical Integrator and Calculator, or ENIAC, consisted of thousands of vacuum tubes and occupied a warehouse. It cost millions of dollars to build and millions of dollars to maintain. It was constantly breaking down and had to be rebuilt each time a new type of calculation was done. ENIAC required great amounts of energy, generated huge amounts of heat, and was very expensive. By today's standards, ENIAC was slow. It could do only 100,000 calculations per second!

The first general purpose computer was introduced in 1951. It was called the Universal Automatic Computer, or UNIVAC. UNIVAC was certainly an improvement over ENIAC, but it was still large, expensive, and slow.

Increased demand for computers encouraged more advanced computer technology. Technical breakthroughs such as transistors and integrated circuits reduced the size and cost of computers. They also increased the efficiency, speed, and uses of

Sharpen Your Skills

Computing Speed

Shuffle a deck of playing cards. Have a friend time you as you sort the cards, first into the four suits, and then from the 2 through the ace in each suit. Determine how many "sorts" you made. Remember, each time you place a card somewhere, it is a sort. Calculate how many sorts you made per second.

A bank check-sorting machine can make 1800 sorts a minute. How long would it take this machine to do the same number of sorts you did? How much faster than you is this machine?

Figure 28–14 *The uses of computers are many and varied. Computer applications include the identification of worldwide ozone concentrations (left), the aerodynamic design of cars (center), and the determination of controls and seat positions in automobiles (right).*

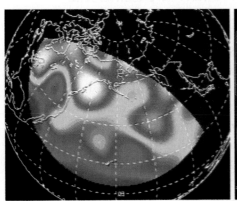
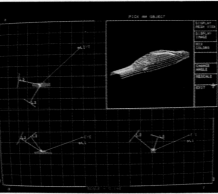
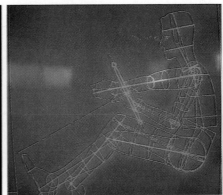

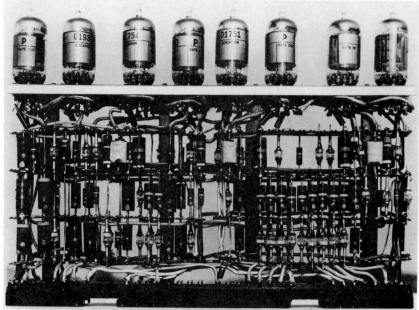

Figure 28–15 *Early computers used large vacuum tubes such as these, which were neither fast nor reliable (left). Tiny computer chips have replaced the larger transistor boards in modern computers. Here, you see the size of a chip as compared to the eye of a needle (right).*

computers. And equally important, they brought the computer within everyone's reach.

The future of computers lies in both the very small and the very large. Integrated circuits called **microprocessors** can hold the entire processing capability on one small chip. At the other extreme, groups of computers are being linked together to form supercomputers.

Computer Hardware

Computer **hardware** refers to the physical parts of a computer. **Computer hardware includes a central processing unit, main storage, input devices, and output devices.**

The brain of a computer is the **central processing unit,** or **CPU.** A CPU controls the operation of all the components of a computer. It executes the arithmetic and logic instructions that it receives in the form of a **computer program.** A computer program is a series of instructions that tells the computer how to perform a certain task. A computer program can be written in one of several different computer languages.

The main storage of a computer is often referred to as the **main memory.** The main memory contains data and operating instructions that are processed by the CPU. In the earliest computers, the main memory consisted of thousands of vacuum tubes. Modern computer memory is contained on

Figure 28–16 *Computer hardware includes a central processing unit, main memory, an input device, and an output device. What is the function of each?*

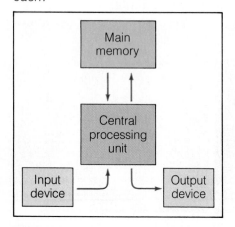

chips. The most advanced memory chip can store as much information as 1 million vacuum tubes can.

Data are fed to the central processing unit by an **input device.** One common input device is a keyboard. A keyboard looks very much like a typewriter. Using a keyboard, a person can communicate data and instructions directly to a computer. Other input devices include magnetic tape, optical scanners, and disk or diskette drives.

A **disk drive** reads information off a disk or diskette and enters it into the computer's memory or into the CPU. Information from a disk drive can be placed into a computer very quickly.

Information produced by the computer can be removed and stored on a disk. So a disk drive is also an **output device.** An output device receives data from the central processing unit. Output devices include printers, cathode-ray tubes, magnetic-tape drives, and voice synthesizers. Even robots are output devices!

Like a disk drive, a **modem** is an input and output device. A modem changes electronic signals

Sharpen Your Skills

Building ENIAC

Scientists worked 24 hours a day for 30 months to create ENIAC. Assuming an average month of 30 days, how many total hours did they work?

CAREER

Computer Artist

HELP WANTED: COMPUTER ARTIST to direct a series of animated educational videos. High school diploma, technical training, and a lively imagination required. Knowledge of computer programming helpful.

Just a few years ago, computer programmers were frustrated by the difficulties they faced when trying to make an image appear three-dimensional on a flat computer monitor. But today, even things that have never actually been seen, such as the details of subatomic particles, can be produced with three-dimensional clarity by a **computer artist.**

A computer artist creates scientific, technical, or artistic images through computer graphics. A computer artist may be required to write computer programs. Depending on the capabilities of the computer being used, the program can be written to allow simple two-dimensional outlines or realistic-looking three-dimensional images.

A computer artist combines creativity with practical knowledge of computers. Computer artists create special effects for movies, educational materials, advertisements, and other types of artwork. Most animated films and cartoons are drawn and colored by computer artists.

If you would like more information about becoming a computer artist, contact the National Computer Graphics Association, 2722 Merrilee Drive, Fairfax, VA 22031.

from a computer into sounds that can be carried over telephone lines. It also changes the sounds back into computer signals. A modem allows a computer to communicate with other computers, often thousands of kilometers away. As computers link in this way, they form a network in which information can be shared. A modem allows use of this network by accessing information from a central **data bank.** A data bank is a vast collection of information stored in a large computer.

The Binary System

Computer hardware would be useless without **software.** Software is the program or set of programs the computer follows. Software must be precise because a computer cannot think on its own. It can only follow instructions. For example, to add two numbers, a program must tell a computer to get one number from memory, hold it, get the other number from memory, combine the two numbers, and print the answer. After completing that instruction, the computer must be told what to do next.

A computer executes instructions by counting with just two numbers at a time. The numbers are 0 and 1. The system that uses just these two numbers is called the **binary system.** The operation of all computers is based on the binary system.

Computer circuits are composed of diodes. As you learned, diodes are gates that are either open or closed to electric current. If the gate is open, current is off. If the gate is closed, current is on. To a

Figure 28–17 *Computers are used to study body mechanics (left) and to design circuitry for future computers (right). What is the name for the program, or set of instructions, a computer follows?*

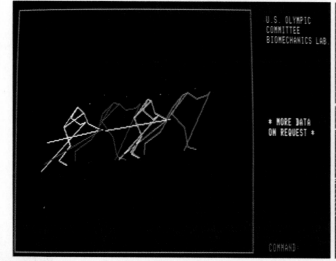
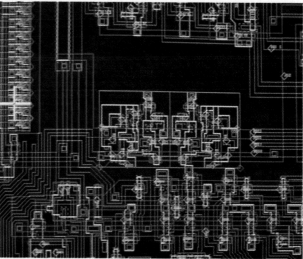

Byte representation	128	64	32	16	8	4	2	1	Numeral
0 0 0 1 0 0 0 1									17
0 1 1 0 1 0 1 0									106
0 0 1 1 0 0 1 1									51
1 1 0 1 1 1 0 0									220

Figure 28–18 *All computers execute instructions by using the binary system. The off/on positions of these light bulbs correspond to the off/on positions of electronic switches, or bits. What is the name for a string of 8 bits?*

computer, 0 is current off and 1 is current on. Each digit, then, acts as a tiny electronic switch, flipping on and off at unbelievable speed.

Each single electronic switch is called a **bit.** A string of bits—usually 8—is called a **byte.** Numbers, letters, and other symbols can be represented as a byte. For example, the letter A is 01000001. The letter K is 11010010. The number 9 is 00001001. See Figure 28–18. What do you think the code for the number 7 is? For the number 83? What is the value of the largest number that can be represented by one byte?

You do not need to be reminded of the importance of computers. You have only to look around you! The uses of computers are many, and their presence is almost universal. Any list of computer applications cannot really be completed today. For by the time today is over, another new application will have been devised.

SECTION REVIEW

1. What are the four hardware components of a computer system? What is the function of each?
2. What is a modem? How is it related to a data bank?
3. How is the binary system used by a computer?
4. Show how the following numbers would be represented by a byte: 175, 139, 3, 45, 17.

Sharpen Your Skills

Helpful Prefixes

Several terms related to electronic devices may be easier for you to understand if you know the meaning of their prefixes. Find out the meaning of each prefix that is underlined in the words below. Then write a sentence explaining how that prefix will help you learn the definition of the word.

binary system
diode
integrated circuit
microprocessor
semiconductor
triode
transistor

The First Calculator: The Abacus

Purpose

To determine how an abacus works as a counting machine

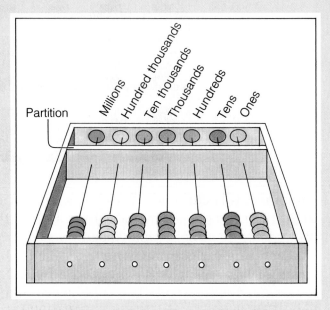

Partition — Millions, Hundred thousands, Ten thousands, Thousands, Hundreds, Tens, Ones

Procedure

1. The columns of beads on the abacus represent, from right to left, units of ones, tens, hundreds, thousands, ten thousands, hundred thousands, and millions.
2. The single bead in the upper section of each column, above the partition, equals five beads in the lower section of that column.
3. Always start from the lower section of the far right, or ones, column.
4. Count to three by sliding three beads up from the lower section of the ones column to the partition.
5. Continue counting to eight. Slide the fourth bead up to the partition. You should be out of beads in this section. Slide all four beads back down and slide the single bead from the upper section of this column down to the partition. Remember that the top bead equals five lower beads. Continue counting from six to eight by sliding the beads in the lower section of the ones column up to the partition. Before doing any further counting, check with your teacher to see that you are using the abacus correctly.
6. Continue counting to twelve. Slide the last bead in the ones column up to the partition. You should now have a total of nine. And you should be out of beads in the ones column. Slide all these beads back to their original zero position. Slide one bead in the lower section of the tens column up to the partition. This repre-

sents ten. Continue counting in the ones column until you reach twelve.

Observations

1. Count to each of these numbers on the abacus: 16, 287, 5016, 1,816,215.
2. How would you find 8 + 7 on the abacus? Start by counting to eight on the abacus. Then continue adding seven more beads. Find the following sums: 7 + 8, 3 + 4, 125 + 58.

Conclusions

1. On what number system is the operation of the abacus based?
2. How does this compare with the operation of a computer?
3. Could the numbers you counted in the Observations be represented on a computer? Which numbers could be represented with an 8-bit byte? Give the representation for these numbers.

CHAPTER REVIEW

SUMMARY

28–1 Electronic Devices

❏ Electronics is the study of the release, behavior, and effects of electrons as it relates to use in helpful devices.

❏ In a vacuum tube, electrons are permitted to move in only one direction.

❏ A rectifier is an electronic device that converts alternating current to direct current.

❏ An amplifier is an electronic device that increases the strength of an electric signal.

❏ Semiconductors are materials that are able to conduct electric currents better than insulators but not as well as metals.

❏ Adding impurities to semiconductors to increase their conductivity is called doping.

❏ An integrated circuit combines diodes and transistors on a thin slice of silicon crystal.

28–2 Transmitting Sound

❏ A telephone sends and receives sound by means of electric currents.

❏ A telephone has two main parts: a transmitter and a receiver.

❏ Radios work by changing sound vibrations into electromagnetic waves, or radio waves.

28–3 Transmitting Pictures

❏ A cathode-ray tube, or CRT, is an electronic device that uses electrons to produce images on a screen.

❏ The screen in a color television cathode-ray tube is coated with three different materials to produce the various colors.

❏ A cathode-ray tube in a color television contains three electron guns—one each for red, blue, and green signals.

28–4 Computers

❏ Early computers were large, expensive, slow, and subject to breakdown.

❏ Integrated circuits called microprocessors can hold the entire processing capability on one small chip.

❏ Computer hardware consists of a central processing unit, main storage, input devices, and output devices.

❏ A computer program is a series of instructions that tells the computer how to perform a certain task.

❏ The operation of all computers is based on the binary system.

VOCABULARY

Define each term in a complete sentence.

amplifier	data bank	modem
binary system	diode	output device
bit	disk drive	rectifier
byte	doping	semiconductor
cathode-ray tube	electronics	software
central processing unit	hardware	solid-state device
chip	input device	transistor
computer	integrated circuit	triode
computer program	main memory	vacuum tube
	microprocessor	

659

CONTENT REVIEW: MULTIPLE CHOICE

On a separate sheet of paper, write the letter of the answer that best completes each statement.

1. Diode vacuum tubes are used as
   a. transistors.　　b. rectifiers.　　c. amplifiers.　　d. triodes.
2. Which electronic device was important to the rapid growth of the radio and television industry?
   a. triode　　b. diode　　c. punch card　　d. disk drive
3. Which of the following is a semiconductor?
   a. copper　　b. plastic　　c. silicon　　d. oxygen
4. A sandwich of three semiconductor crystals used to amplify an electric signal is a (an)
   a. diode.　　b. transistor.　　c. integrated circuit.　　d. modem.
5. Radios work by changing sound vibrations into
   a. electromagnetic waves.　　b. gamma rays.　　c. electric current.　　d. bytes.
6. Which is *not* an advantage of the use of solid-state devices in telephones and radios?
   a. smaller size　　b. increased cost
   c. better amplification　　d. greater energy efficiency
7. Which of the following is *not* an application of a computer?
   a. store data　　b. perform complex calculations
   c. rectify alternating current　　d. design new computers
8. The physical parts of a computer are collectively referred to as computer
   a. software.　　b. peripherals.　　c. programs.　　d. hardware.
9. Which of the following is computer software?
   a. printer　　b. disk drive　　c. program　　d. memory
10. In the binary system, the number 86 would be represented as
    a. 01100110.　　b. 01010110.　　c. 10101001.　　d. 11010010.

CONTENT REVIEW: COMPLETION

On a separate sheet of paper, write the word or words that best complete each statement.

1. The branch of physics that deals with the behavior of electrons as it relates to use in helpful devices is called _____.
2. An electronic device used to increase the strength of an electric signal is called a (an) _____.
3. Two common semiconductors are _____ and _____.
4. Adding impurities to semiconductors to increase their conductivity is called _____.
5. Diodes and transistors combined on a thin slice of silicon is a (an) _____.
6. The two main parts of a telephone are the _____ and the _____.
7. An electronic device that uses electrons to produce images on a screen is called a (an) _____.
8. The brain of a computer is called the _____.
9. The device that allows computers to communicate with one another is a (an) _____.
10. The number system on which the operation of all computers is based is called the _____ system.

CONTENT REVIEW: TRUE OR FALSE

Determine whether each statement is true or false. Then on a separate sheet of paper, write "true" if it is true. If it is false, change the underlined word or words to make the statement true.

1. A device that converts alternating current to direct current is a <u>rectifier</u>.
2. The conductivity of <u>transistors</u> is between that of conductors and insulators.
3. A telephone sends and receives sound by means of <u>magnetic</u> current.
4. The beam of electrons in a <u>cathode-ray tube</u> produces a picture.
5. A color television CRT has <u>two</u> electron guns.
6. The first American-built computer was <u>UNIVAC</u>.
7. <u>Microprocessors</u> are integrated circuits that can hold the entire processing capability of a computer on one chip.
8. <u>Output</u> devices feed data to a computer.
9. A <u>data bank</u> is a vast collection of information stored in a large computer.
10. A string of bits, usually eight in number, is called a <u>byte</u>.

CONCEPT REVIEW: SKILL BUILDING

Use the skills you have developed in the chapter to complete each activity.

1. **Making diagrams** Draw a diagram that shows how the four main hardware components of a computer are related.
2. **Sequencing events** The sentences below describe some of the energy conversions required for a local telephone call. Arrange them in their proper order.

   Sound vibrates a metal plate.
   An electromagnet is energized.
   A vibrating magnet produces sound.
   Vibrating vocal cords produce sound.
   Mechanical energy is converted into an electric signal.
3. **Making calculations** The pictures on a television screen last for one-thirtieth of a second. How many pictures are flashed on a screen during a 30-minute program?
4. **Classifying computer devices** Many methods of putting data into a computer are similar to methods of getting data out of a computer. Identify each of the following as an input device, an output device, or both: typewriter keyboard, CRT, printer, optical scanner, magnetic tape, disk drive, punched cards, voice synthesizer.
5. **Applying definitions** Write the following numbers in binary form: 19, 57, 1, 95, 161, 129, 255.
6. **Applying concepts** A program is a list of instructions that tells a computer how to perform a task. Write a program that describes the steps involved in your task of waking up and arriving at school for your first class.

CONCEPT REVIEW: ESSAY

Discuss each of the following in a brief paragraph.

1. In what ways are semiconductor diodes and transistors better than their vacuum-tube ancestors?
2. Compare the functions of rectifiers and amplifiers. What type of vacuum tube is used for each?
3. Use the following terms in one or two sentences to describe an integrated circuit: diodes, silicon crystal, chip, transistors, doping.
4. Describe how a cathode-ray tube creates a picture.

Adventures in Science

STAN OVSHINSKY: PIONEERING A NEW TYPE OF GLASS

One day in the late 1960s, physicist Hellmut Fritzsche paid a visit to Stan Ovshinsky. Ovshinsky, a self-taught inventor, claimed to have developed a kind of glass that could conduct electricity. Even more startling than Ovshinsky's claim of invention was his suggestion that this new electronic glass could surpass transistors.

Fritzsche, like most physicists of the day, did not believe such a thing was possible. After all, glass is an insulator, not a conductor. And the idea of making computer chips or transistors out of it was ridiculous. "Just lead me into the laboratory," he told Ovshinsky. "Let me do the experiments and at the end of the day I'll explain this mystery to you." By the end of the day, however, Fritzsche had changed his tune. "I cannot explain it," he told Ovshinsky. "All I can say is that it is the most important thing I've ever seen."

A RADICAL NOTION

The operation of almost all modern electronic products is based on devices made from crystals of specific elements. The atoms in a crystal are arranged in an orderly fashion. This arrangement lets electricity flow freely through the crystal. In amorphous materials such as glass, the atoms are flung around randomly, or haphazardly. So it is difficult for an electric current to pass through amorphous materials.

But Ovshinsky believed that if he chose the right mixture of elements, he could melt them together into a glasslike material that would have the same kind of electronic properties as crystals. It was a radical notion, but as it turned out, a correct one. Yet it took Ovshinsky almost ten years to prove it.

AN AVID LEARNER

Stanford Ovshinsky grew up in Akron, Ohio. He spent his childhood experimenting with chemicals in the basement of his home and reading all the books he could get. But because the budding inventor did not like school, he never considered going to college. "I just wasn't interested," he says. "I was interested in what was going on out in the world." So after graduating from high school, Ovshinsky became a machinist.

Then, as now, what really interested Ovshinsky was how things actually work. This fascination included the human brain as well as machinery. Over the next ten years, Ovshinsky learned as much as he could about the brain. He was looking for links between the workings of the brain and the workings of machines similar to the ones he used in his shop. Human brain cells, he knew, have no orderly structure. Yet the cells are able to store and process information in much the same way that computers do. Ovshinsky reasoned that if brain cells could store and process information, so could amorphous materials such as glass.

ELECTRONIC GLASS

For nine years Ovshinsky and his wife, who has a Ph.D. in biochemistry, worked to create electronic switches out of a type of glass called chalcogenide. They sandwiched a thin layer of the glass between two pieces of metal. When a strong current was used, the glass allowed it to pass through. Ovshinsky's electronic glass had the ability to act as a semiconductor—an ability that up until then had been a property only of crystals.

The Ovshinskys continued to develop electronic devices using chalcogenide. One of their inventions is a device similar to the memory switches in computers. But their device continues to store its memories even after the power is shut off!

Today, products using Ovshinsky's invention bear the name ovonic devices. They include inexpensive and efficient solar cells.

Stan Ovshinsky at work with his wife, Iris.

Issues in Science

200 WEST AREA
DRY WASTE STORAGE
BURIAL GARDEN
TRANSURANIC
WASTE
· MINIMUM CLOTHING ·
1. ONE PAIR COVERALLS
2. CANVAS BOOTS
3. RUBBERS
4. HEAD COVERING
5. CANVAS GLOVES
NO ENTRY OR WASTE
DISPOSAL WITHOUT
PERMISSION OF
TFS & O MANAGEMENT
PHONE 3-2284 or 3-2396
R.M./E & OS PHONE 2-2731

NUCLEAR WASTE:

What can be done with DEADLY GARBAGE?

"Arbitrary, . . . uncaring, and unreasonable," protested the governor of Texas.

"I am worried about earthquakes and groundwater contamination," declared the governor of Washington.

"Nevada has already done its share," fumed that state's governor.

The topic that has aroused such argument and emotion—and made its way to the state capital—is garbage. But not ordinary garbage. This waste is nuclear waste—the deadliest garbage of all.

In 1984, after a two-year study, the federal government selected Texas, Washington, and Nevada as sites in which to bury 40,000 tons of nuclear waste—radioactive nuclear waste!

Radioactive trash is generated primarily by the nation's 95 nuclear power plants. Each year, nearly 2000 tons of this waste are produced. By the year 2020, there will be about 100,000 tons of radioactive waste in need of a burial site. Permanent disposal sites that present no health and safety hazards must be found for this deadly garbage.

If we cannot find a place on the earth to get rid of nuclear garbage, why not send it into space? Rockets loaded with nuclear wastes could be launched into orbit between the earth and Venus. Traveling at the right speeds, the rockets could stay in orbit for a million years or more without bumping into either planet.

Critics of this idea point to its cost and potential danger. An accident during rocket launch could harm thousands of people. These critics believe that we should not seek a solution in the stars but on the earth.

The Antarctic ice sheet is more than 2500 meters thick in some places. Could nuclear wastes be buried under this huge frozen blanket? No, according to some critics of this idea. Not enough is known about the behavior of ice sheets. And what is known is not comforting. For example, ice sheets move rapidly about every 10,000 years. Their movement might allow the wastes to get loose. In addition, nuclear wastes produce a tremendous amount of heat—enough heat, in fact, to melt the ice. Where the ice melted, nuclear radiation might leak out into the oceans and the air.

If not under the Antarctic ice sheet, then how about a nuclear cemetery under the ocean floor? Thick smooth rock layers have been building up there for millions of years. Nuclear wastes deposited in these rock layers probably would remain there almost forever.

But as with other proposals, there are problems with this idea. At present, the technology to do the job does not exist. And not enough is known about the various forces to which such rock is exposed.

With ice sheet cemeteries and underwater graveyards all but impossible, one idea still remains. That idea is to put nuclear wastes in "rooms" dug out of underground rock.

In order to determine the best place to bury nuclear wastes, scientists must know all they can about the rock. Here are the properties scientists have determined are best. The rock must be strong, heat resistant, and waterproof. The rock must be at least 6100 meters deep. And the ground where the rock exists must be very dry and free of earthquakes and other geologic problems. These rock properties seem to be characteristic of rock layers in Texas, Washington, and Nevada.

There are four kinds of rocks that scientists believe will be the best: basalt, granite, salt, and tuff. Each of these rocks, however, has certain properties that also make it unsuitable for burying radioactive wastes.

So far, scientists have been unable to find the perfect graveyard for nuclear wastes. But the search goes on. Unfortunately, in the meantime the wastes pile up, and people continue to be concerned about their land, water, and—most importantly—their health.

Nuclear wastes must be buried deep below the earth's surface. This diagram shows the parts of a proposed burial site. The relative depth is shown by a comparison with the Washington Monument.

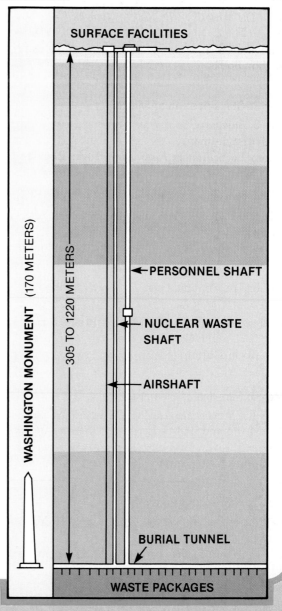

For Further Reading

If you have an interest in a specific area of Physical Science or simply want to know more about the topics you are studying, one of the following books may open the door to an exciting learning adventure.

Chapter 1: Exploring Physical Science

Lapp, R.E., and the editors of Time-Life Books. *Matter.* New York: Time.

Ruchlis, H. *Discovering Scientific Method.* New York: Harper and Row.

Chapter 2: Properties of Matter

Adler, I. *The Wonders of Physics: An Introduction to the Physical World.* New York: Golden Press.

Asimov, I. *A Short History of Chemistry.* Garden City, NY: Anchor Books.

Chapter 3: Classification of Matter

Asimov, I. *Building Blocks of the Universe.* New York: Abelard-Schuman.

Dickinson, E. *Colloids in Foods.* New York: Elsevier.

Chapter 4: Structure of Matter

Adler, I., and R. Adler. *Atoms and Molecules.* New York: John Day.

Frisch, O.J. *Working with Atoms.* New York: Basic Books.

Chapter 5: The Periodic Law

Kelma, P., and A.H. Stone. *Mendeleev: A Prophet of Chemical Elements.* Englewood Cliffs, NJ: Prentice-Hall.

Seaborg, G.T., and E.G. Valens. *Elements of the Universe.* New York: Dutton.

Chapter 6: Families of Elements

Smith, N.F. *The Inside Story of Metal.* New York: Messner.

Weeks, M.E., and H.M. Leicester, *Discovery of the Elements.* New York: Chemical Education Publishing Company.

Chapter 7: Atoms and Bonding

Asimov, I. *How Did We Find Out About Atoms?* New York: Walker.

Snell, C.T. *Chemistry Made Easy.* New York: Chemical Education Publishing Company.

Chapter 8: Chemical Reactions

Carona, P.B. *Chemistry and Cooking.* Englewood Cliffs, NJ: Prentice-Hall.

Woodburn, J.H. *Excursions into Chemistry.* Philadelphia: Lippincott.

Chapter 9: Solution Chemistry

Gilfond, H. *Water: A Scarce Resource.* New York: Watts.

Stone, A.H. *The Chemistry of a Lemon.* Englewood Cliffs, NJ: Prentice-Hall.

Chapter 10: Carbon Chemistry

Cross, W. *Coal.* Chicago: Children's Press.

Kraft, B. *Oil and Natural Gas.* New York: Watts.

Chapter 11: Nuclear Chemistry

Asimov, I. *How Did We Find Out About Nuclear Power?* New York: Walker.

Fermi, L. *The Story of Atomic Energy.* New York: Random House.

Chapter 12: Motion

Dalton, S. *Caught in Motion.* New York: Van Nostrand Reinhold.

Valens, E. *Motion.* New York: World.

Chapter 13: Forces

Ipsen, D.C. *Isaac Newton: Reluctant Genius.* Hillside, NJ: Enslow.

Milgrom, H. *First Experiments with Gravity.* New York: Dutton.

Chapter 14: Forces in Fluids

Adkins, J. *Moving Heavy Things.* Boston: Houghton Mifflin.

Grey, J. *The Facts of Flight.* Philadelphia: Franklin Institute Press.

Chapter 15: Work, Power, and Simple Machines

James, E. *The Simple Facts of Simple Machines.* New York: Lothrop.

Weitzman, D. *Windmills, Bridges and Old Machines: Discovering Our Industrial Past.* New York: Scribner's.

Chapter 16: Energy

Adler, I. *Energy.* New York: John Day.
Satchwell, J. *Energy at Work.* New York: Lothrop.

Chapter 17: Heat

Adler, I. *Hot and Cold: The Story of Temperature From Absolute Zero to the Heat of the Sun.* New York: John Day.
Cobb, V. *Heat.* New York: Watts.

Chapter 18: Uses of Heat

Kavaler, L. *A Matter of Degree: Heat, Life and Death.* New York: Harper.
Stone, A.H., and B. Siegel. *The Heat's On.* Englewood Cliffs, NJ: Prentice-Hall.

Chapter 19: Electric Charges and Currents

Asimov, I. *How Did We Find Out About Electricity?* New York: Walker.
Cooper, A. *Electricity.* Morristown, NJ: Silver Burdett.

Chapter 20: Magnetism

Arley, N. *Exploring Magnetism.* New York: Watts.
Vogt, G. *Electricity and Magnetism.* New York: Watts.

Chapter 21: Waves

Kentzer, M. *Waves.* Morristown, NJ: Silver Burdett.
Pierce, J. *Almost All About Waves.* Cambridge, MA: MIT Press.

Chapter 22: Sound

Kettlekamp, L. *The Magic of Sound.* New York: Morrow.
Stevens, S.S., and F. Warshorsky. *Sound and Hearing.* New York: Time-Life.

Chapter 23: Light

Adler, I. *The Story of Light.* New York: Harvey House.
Ubell, E. *The World of Color and Candle.* New York: Atheneum.

Chapter 24: Light and Its Uses

Maurer, A. *Lasers: Light Wave of the Future.* New York: Arco.
Muirden, J. *How to Use an Astronomical Telescope.* New York: Linden.

Chapter 25: Energy Resources

Cross, W. *Petroleum.* Chicago: Children's Press.
Knight, C. *Harnessing the Sun.* New York: Morrow.

Chapter 26: Energy and the Environment

Hoke, J. *Solar Energy.* New York: Watts.
Satchwell, J. *Future Sources.* New York: Watts.

Chapter 27: Chemical Technology

Cobb, V. *The Secret Life of Hardware: A Science Experiment Book.* New York: Lippincott.
Milne, L., and M. Milne. *Nature's Great Carbon Cycle.* New York: Atheneum.

Chapter 28: Electronics and Computers

Knight, D. *Robotics: Past, Present & Future.* New York: Morrow.
O'Brian, L. *Computers.* New York: Watts.

The metric system of measurement is used by scientists throughout the world. It is based on units of ten. Each unit is ten times larger or ten times smaller than the next unit. The most commonly used units of the metric system are given below. After you have finished reading about the metric system, try to put it to use. How tall are you in metrics? What is your mass? What is your normal body temperature in degrees Celsius?

COMMONLY USED METRIC UNITS

Length   The distance from one point to another

meter (m)

(a meter is slightly longer than a yard)

1 meter = 1000 millimeters (mm)

1 meter = 100 centimeters (cm)

1000 meters = 1 kilometer (km)

Volume   The amount of space an object takes up

liter (L)

(a liter is slightly larger than a quart)

1 liter = 1000 milliliters (mL)

Mass   The amount of matter in an object

gram (g)

(a gram has a mass equal to about one paper clip)

1000 grams = 1 kilogram (kg)

Temperature   The measure of hotness or coldness

degrees Celsius (°C)

0°C = freezing point of water

100°C = boiling point of water

METRIC—ENGLISH EQUIVALENTS

2.54 centimeters (cm) = 1 inch (in)
1 meter (m) = 39.37 inches (in)
1 kilometer (km) = 0.62 miles (mi)
1 liter (L) = 1.06 quarts (qt)
250 milliliters (mL) = 1 cup (c)
1 kilogram (kg) = 2.2 pounds (lb)
28.3 grams (g) = 1 ounce (oz)
C° = 5/9 × (F° − 32)

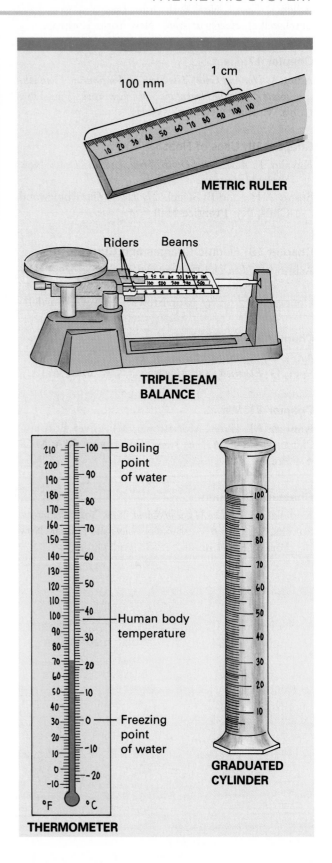

METRIC RULER

TRIPLE-BEAM BALANCE

THERMOMETER

GRADUATED CYLINDER

Appendix B

One of the first things a scientist learns is that working in the laboratory can be an exciting experience. But the laboratory can also be quite dangerous if proper safety rules are not followed at all times. To prepare yourself for a safe year in the laboratory, read over the following safety rules. Then read them a second time. Make sure you understand each rule. If you do not, ask your teacher to explain any rules you are unsure of.

Dress Code

1. Many materials in the laboratory can cause eye injury. To protect yourself from possible injury, wear safety goggles whenever you are working with chemicals, burners, or any substance that might get into your eyes. Never wear contact lenses in the laboratory.

2. Wear laboratory aprons or coats whenever you are working with chemicals or heated substances.

3. Tie back long hair to keep your hair away from any chemicals, burners and candles, or other laboratory equipment.

4. Remove or tie back any article of clothing or jewelry that can hang down and touch chemicals and flames before working in the laboratory.

General Safety Rules

5. Read all directions for an experiment several times. Follow the directions exactly as they are written. If you are in doubt about any part of the experiment, ask your teacher for assistance.

6. Never perform activities that are not authorized by your teacher. Obtain permission before "experimenting" on your own.

7. Never handle any equipment unless you have specific permission.

8. Take extreme care not to spill any material in the laboratory. If spills occur, ask your teacher immediately about the proper cleanup procedure. Never simply pour chemicals or other substances into the sink or trash container.

9. Never eat in the laboratory. Wash your hands before and after each experiment.

First Aid

10. Report all accidents, no matter how minor, to your teacher immediately.

11. Learn what to do in case of specific accidents such as getting acid in your eyes or on your skin. (Rinse acids on your body with lots of water.)

12. Become aware of the location of the first aid kit. But your teacher should administer any required first aid due to injury. Or your teacher may send you to the school nurse or call a physician.

13. Know where and how to report an accident or fire. Find out the location of the fire extinguisher, phone, and fire alarm. Keep a list of important phone numbers such as the fire department and school nurse near the phone. Report any fires to your teacher at once.

Heating and Fire Safety

14. Again, never use a heat source such as a candle or burner without wearing safety goggles.

15. Never heat a chemical, you are not instructed to heat. A chemical that is harmless when cool can be dangerous when heated.

16. Maintain a clean work area, and keep all materials away from flames.

17. Never reach across a flame.

18. Make sure you know how to light a Bunsen burner. (Your teacher will demonstrate the proper procedure for lighting a burner.) If the flame leaps out of a burner toward you, turn off the gas immediately. Do not touch the burner. It may be hot. And never leave a lighted burner unattended!

19. A test tube or bottle that is being heated should be pointed away from you and others. Chemicals can splash or boil out of a heated test tube.

20. Never heat a liquid in a closed container. The expanding gases produced may blow the container apart, injuring you or others.

21. Never pick up a container that has been heated without first holding the back of your hand near it. If you can feel the heat on the back of your hand, the container may be too hot to handle. Use a clamp or tongs when handling hot containers.

Using Chemicals Safely

22. Never mix chemicals for the "fun of it." You might produce a dangerous, possibly explosive substance.

23. Never touch, taste, or smell a chemical that you do not know for a fact is harmless. Many chemicals are poisonous. If you are instructed to note the fumes in an experiment, gently wave your

hand over the opening of a container and direct the fumes toward your nose. Do not inhale the fumes directly from the container.

24. Use only those chemicals needed in the activity. The lids should be kept on chemicals that are not being used. Notify your teacher whenever chemicals are spilled.

25. Dispose of all chemicals as instructed by your teacher. To avoid contamination, never return chemicals to their original containers.

26. Be extra careful when working with acids or bases. Pour such chemicals over the sink, not over your work bench.

27. When diluting an acid, pour the acid into water. Never pour water into the acid.

28. Thoroughly rinse with water any acids on your skin or clothing. Immediately notify your teacher of any acid spill.

Using Glassware Safely

29. Never force glass tubing into a rubber stopper. When inserting glass tubing into rubber stoppers or rubber tubing, use a lubricant and a turning motion. Your teacher will demonstrate the proper way to insert glass tubing.

30. Never heat glassware that is not thoroughly dry. Use a wire or asbestos screen to protect glassware from any flame.

31. Keep in mind that hot glassware will not appear hot. Never pick up glassware without first putting the back of your hand near it to see if it is hot.

32. If you are instructed to cut glass tubing, fire-polish the ends first to remove sharp edges.

33. Never use broken or chipped glassware. If glassware breaks, notify your teacher and dispose of the glassware in the proper trash container.

34. Never eat or drink from laboratory glassware. Thoroughly clean glassware before putting it away.

Using Sharp Instruments

35. Handle scalpels or razor blades with extreme care. Never cut material toward you; cut away from you.

36. Notify your teacher immediately if you are cut in the laboratory.

End-of-Experiment Rules

37. When an experiment is completed, clean up your work area and return all equipment to its proper place.

38. Wash your hands after every experiment.

39. Turn off all candles and burners before leaving the laboratory. Check that the gas line leading to the burner is off as well.

Appendix C

This mathematics refresher is designed to review those topics that may trouble you when you study physical science. You may wish to study this material before working on problems presented in the text. The material in this Appendix, although not presented in great detail, is sufficient to enable you to solve the chapter problems.

Working with Fractions

1. Addition and Subtraction: Same Denominators
To add or subtract fractions that have the same denominator, add or subtract the numerators, then write the sum or difference over the denominator. Express the answer in lowest terms. (See Examples 2 and 3.)

Examples

1. $\dfrac{1}{5} + \dfrac{2}{5} = \dfrac{1 + 2}{5} = \dfrac{3}{5}$

2. $\dfrac{5}{14} + \dfrac{1}{14} + \dfrac{1}{14} = \dfrac{5 + 1 + 1}{14} = \dfrac{7}{14} = \dfrac{1}{2}$

3. $\dfrac{11}{12} - \dfrac{5}{12} = \dfrac{11 - 5}{12} = \dfrac{6}{12} = \dfrac{1}{2}$

4. $\dfrac{4}{7} - \dfrac{2}{7} - \dfrac{1}{7} = \dfrac{4 - 2 - 1}{7} = \dfrac{1}{7}$

2. Addition and Subtraction: Different Denominators
To add or subtract fractions that do not have the same denominator, find the least common denominator. Express the fractions as equivalent fractions using the least common denominator. Then add or subtract the numerators. Write the sum or difference over the denominator. Express the answer in lowest terms. (See Example 2.)

Examples

1. $\dfrac{1}{2} + \dfrac{1}{3} = \dfrac{3}{6} + \dfrac{2}{6} = \dfrac{3 + 2}{6} = \dfrac{5}{6}$

2. $\dfrac{2}{5} + \dfrac{1}{10} = \dfrac{4}{10} + \dfrac{1}{10} = \dfrac{4 + 1}{10} = \dfrac{5}{10} = \dfrac{1}{2}$

3. $\dfrac{7}{8} - \dfrac{1}{4} = \dfrac{7}{8} - \dfrac{2}{8} = \dfrac{7 - 2}{8} = \dfrac{5}{8}$

4. $\dfrac{7}{8} - \dfrac{1}{3} = \dfrac{21}{24} - \dfrac{8}{24} = \dfrac{21 - 8}{24} = \dfrac{13}{24}$

3. Multiplication

To multiply two or more fractions, multiply the numerators to obtain the numerator of the product. Multiply the denominators to obtain the denominator of the product. Because it is easier to work with smaller numbers, whenever possible divide any numerator and denominator by their greatest common factor before multiplying. (See Examples 3 and 4.) Express the answer in lowest terms. (See Example 2.)

Examples

1. $\dfrac{7}{8} \times \dfrac{3}{5} = \dfrac{7 \times 3}{8 \times 5} = \dfrac{21}{40}$

2. $\dfrac{1}{2} \times \dfrac{1}{3} \times \dfrac{2}{5} = \dfrac{1 \times 1 \times 2}{2 \times 3 \times 5} = \dfrac{2}{30} = \dfrac{1}{15}$

3. $\dfrac{1\!\!\!/4}{5} \times \dfrac{3\!\!\!/16}{16} = \dfrac{1 \times 3}{1 \times 4} = \dfrac{3}{4}$

4. $\dfrac{1}{2} \times \dfrac{48}{16} \times \dfrac{1}{7} = \dfrac{1 \times 4 \times 1}{1 \times 3 \times 7} = \dfrac{4}{21}$

4. Division

To divide one fraction by another, invert the divisor and then multiply the two fractions. Express the answer in lowest terms.

Examples

1. $\dfrac{1}{2} \div \dfrac{1}{3} = \dfrac{1}{2} \times \dfrac{3}{1} = \dfrac{1 \times 3}{2 \times 1} = \dfrac{3}{2} = 1\dfrac{1}{2}$

2. $\dfrac{2}{5} \div \dfrac{8}{15} = \dfrac{2}{5} \times \dfrac{15}{8} = \dfrac{1 \times 3}{1 \times 4} = \dfrac{3}{4}$

3. $\dfrac{2}{3} \div \dfrac{4}{5} = \dfrac{2}{3} \times \dfrac{5}{4} = \dfrac{1 \times 5}{3 \times 2} = \dfrac{5}{6}$

4. $\dfrac{9}{16} \div \dfrac{3}{4} = \dfrac{9}{16} \times \dfrac{4}{3} = \dfrac{3 \times 1}{4 \times 1} = \dfrac{3}{4}$

Converting a Fraction to a Decimal

To convert a fraction to a decimal, divide the numerator by the denominator, carrying the answer to the required number of decimal places.

Examples

1. Convert $\dfrac{2}{5}$ to a decimal.

$$5\overline{)2.0} \quad \begin{array}{c} .4 \\ \underline{2\,0} \end{array} \quad = \quad .4$$

2. Convert $\frac{2}{7}$ to a two-place decimal.

$$\begin{array}{r} .285 \\ 7\overline{\smash{\big)}\ 2.000} \\ \underline{1\ 4} \qquad = \quad .29 \\ 60 \\ \underline{56} \\ 40 \\ \underline{35} \\ 5 \end{array}$$

3. Convert $\frac{45}{85}$ to a three-place decimal.

$$\begin{array}{r} .529 \\ 85\overline{\smash{\big)}\ 45.000} \\ \underline{425} \qquad = \quad .529 \\ 250 \\ 170 \\ 800 \\ 765 \\ 35 \end{array}$$

Converting a Fraction to a Percent

To convert a fraction to a percent, divide the numerator by the denominator and multiply the result by 100 percent.

Examples

1. Convert $\frac{18}{25}$ to a percent.

$$\begin{array}{r} .72 \\ 25\overline{\smash{\big)}\ 18.00} \\ \underline{17\ 5} \qquad .72 \times 100\% = 72\% \\ 50 \\ 50 \end{array}$$

2. Convert $\frac{7}{50}$ to a percent.

$$\begin{array}{r} .14 \\ 50\overline{\smash{\big)}\ 7.00} \\ \underline{5\ 0} \qquad = \quad .14 \times 100\% = 14\% \\ 2\ 00 \\ 2\ 00 \end{array}$$

3. Convert $\frac{7}{4}$ to a percent.

$$\begin{array}{r} 1.75 \\ 4\overline{\smash{\big)}\ 7.00} \\ \underline{4} \qquad 1.75 \times 100\% = 175\% \\ 3\ 0 \\ \underline{2\ 8} \\ 20 \\ 20 \end{array}$$

Converting a Percent to a Decimal

To convert a percent to a decimal, write the number without the percent sign and move the decimal point two places to the left.

Examples

1. Convert 84% to a decimal.
84% = .84

2. Convert 0.6% to a decimal.
0.6% = .006

3. Convert 160% to a decimal.
160% = 1.60, or 1.6

4. Convert 27.5% to a decimal.
27.5% = .275

Working with Ratios and Proportions

A ratio compares two numbers. A ratio is often written as a fraction in which the number being compared is the numerator and the number to which it is compared is the denominator. The fraction is then expressed in lowest terms. A ratio also may be written with a colon.

Examples

1. Express the ratio of 12 to 4.
$$12 \text{ to } 4 = \frac{12}{4} = \frac{3}{1}, \text{ or } 3:1$$

2. Express the ratio of 4 to 12.
$$4 \text{ to } 12 = \frac{4}{12} = \frac{1}{3}, \text{ or } 1:3$$

3. Express the ratio 25 cm to 75 cm.
$$25 \text{ cm to } 75 \text{ cm} = \frac{25}{75} = \frac{1}{3}, \text{ or } 1:3$$

Proportions

A proportion is a mathematical sentence that states that two ratios are equivalent. To write a proportion, place an equal sign between the two equivalent ratios. In this case, the equal sign stands for "is the same as." You can use a colon instead of a fraction.

Examples

1. Write as a proportion: 6 compared to 9 is the same as 8 compared to 12.
$$\frac{6}{9} = \frac{8}{12}, \text{ or } 6:9 = 8:12$$

2. Write as a proportion: 56 is to 14 as 76 is to 19.
$$\frac{56}{14} = \frac{76}{19}, \text{ or } 56:14 = 76:19$$

To write a proportion in which the value of one number is unknown, use X to represent the unknown number.

Examples

1. Some number compares to 45 as 8 compares to 10.
$\frac{X}{45} = \frac{8}{10}$, or X : 45 = 8 : 10

2. Some number compares to 30 as 9 compares to 54.
$\frac{X}{30} = \frac{9}{54}$, or X : 30 = 9 : 54

To find the value of the unknown number in a proportion, cross multiply, then divide both sides of the equal sign by the number that precedes X. Check your answer by substituting the value you found for X in the original proportion.

Examples

1. $\frac{X}{45} \diagdown \frac{8}{10}$

$10 \times X = 8 \times 45$

$10X = 360$

$\frac{10X}{10} = \frac{360}{10}$

$X = 36$

2. $\frac{X}{30} \diagdown \frac{9}{54}$

$54 \times X = 9 \times 30$

$54X = 270$

$\frac{54X}{54} = \frac{270}{54}$

$X = 5$

Working with Equations

An equation is a mathematical sentence that contains a variable and an equal sign. An equation expresses a relationship between two or more quantities. A formula is a special kind of equation. A formula shows relationships between quantities that are always true. A formula is a mathematical rule. In physical science, you will be dealing with formulas. In Appendix D, you will find a list of the formulas used in this textbook.

To solve a formula, follow these three steps:
Step 1 Write the formula.
Step 2 Substitute given numbers and units.
Step 3 Solve for the unknown variable.

Examples

1. Using the formula for the area of a circle, $A = \pi r^2$, calculate the area of a circle whose radius is 2 cm:

Step 1 Write the formula. $A = \pi r^2$

Step 2 Substitute given numbers and units.

$A = \frac{22}{7} \times (2 \text{ cm})^2$

Step 3 Solve for the unknown variable.

$A = \frac{22}{7} \times 4 \text{ cm}^2 = \frac{88 \text{ cm}^2}{7} = 12.5 \text{ cm}^2$

2. Using the formula for density, $D = \frac{m}{v}$, find the mass of a sample of aluminum whose volume is 5 cm^3 and whose density is 2.7 g/cm^3:

Step 1 Write the formula. $D = \frac{m}{v}$

Step 2 Substitute given numbers and units.

$2.7 \text{ g/cm}^3 = \frac{m}{5 \text{ cm}^3}$

Step 3 Solve for the unknown variable.

$m = 2.7 \text{ g/cm}^3 \times 5 \text{ cm}^3$

$m = 13.5 \text{ g}$

1. Density (Chapter 1)

$$\text{density} = \frac{\text{mass}}{\text{volume}} \qquad D = \frac{m}{v}$$

2. Volume of a Regular Solid (Chapter 1)

volume = height × length × width

$v = h \times l \times w$

3. Speed (Chapter 12)

$$\text{speed} = \frac{\text{distance}}{\text{time}}$$

4. Acceleration (Chapter 12)

$$\text{acceleration} = \frac{\text{final velocity} - \text{original velocity}}{\text{time}}$$

5. Momentum (Chapter 12)

momentum = mass × velocity

6. Force (Chapter 13)

force = mass × acceleration

7. Weight (Chapter 13)

weight = mass × acceleration due to gravity

$w = m \times g$

8. Pressure (Chapter 14)

$$\text{pressure} = \frac{\text{force}}{\text{area}}$$

9. Work (Chapter 15)

work = force × distance

$W = F \times d$

10. Power (Chapter 15)

$$\text{power} = \frac{\text{work}}{\text{time}}$$

$$P = \frac{W}{t} \quad \text{or} \quad P = \frac{F \times d}{t}$$

11. Work Input (Chapter 15)

work input = effort force × effort distance

$W_I = F_E \times d_E$

12. Work Output (Chapter 15)

work output = resistance force × resistance distance

$W_O = F_R \times d_R$

13. Mechanical Advantage (Chapter 15)

$$\text{mechanical advantage} = \frac{\text{resistance force}}{\text{effort force}}$$

$$MA = \frac{F_R}{F_E}$$

14. Efficiency (Chapter 15)

$$\text{efficiency} = \frac{\text{work output}}{\text{work input}} \times 100$$

$$\text{Efficiency} = \frac{W_O}{W_I} \times 100$$

15. Mechanical Advantage of a Lever (Chapter 15)

$$\text{mechanical advantage} = \frac{\text{effort arm length}}{\text{resistance arm length}}$$

16. Kinetic Energy (Chapter 16)

$$\text{kinetic energy} = \frac{\text{mass} \times \text{velocity}^2}{2}$$

$$\text{K.E.} = \frac{m \times v^2}{2}$$

17. Gravitational Potential Energy (Chapter 16)

gravitational potential energy = weight × height

18. Einstein's mass–energy relationship (Chapter 16)

energy = mass × speed of light^2

$E = m \times c^2$

19. Heat Gained or Lost (Chapter 17)

$$\text{heat gained or lost} = \text{mass} \times \text{change in temperature} \times \text{specific heat}$$

Heat gained or lost = $m \times \Delta T \times \text{s.h.}$

20. Ohm's Law (Chapter 19)

$$\text{current} = \frac{\text{voltage}}{\text{resistance}}$$

$$I = \frac{V}{R}$$

$$\text{amperes} = \frac{\text{volts}}{\text{ohms}}$$

21. Electric Power (Chapter 19)

electric power = voltage × current

$P = V \times I$

watts = volts × amps

22. Electric Energy (Chapter 19)

electric energy = power × time

$E = P \times t$

23. Wave Speed (Chapter 21)

speed = frequency × wavelength

24. Law of Reflection (Chapter 21)

angle of incidence = angle of reflection

NAME	SYMBOL	ATOMIC NUMBER	ATOMIC MASS†	NAME	SYMBOL	ATOMIC NUMBER	ATOMIC MASS†
Actinium	Ac	89	(227)	Neon	Ne	10	20.2
Aluminum	Al	13	27.0	Neptunium	Np	93	(237)
Americium	Am	95	(243)	Nickel	Ni	28	58.7
Antimony	Sb	51	121.8	Niobium	Nb	41	92.9
Argon	Ar	18	39.9	Nitrogen	N	7	14.01
Arsenic	As	33	74.9	Nobelium	No	102	(255)
Astatine	At	85	(210)	Osmium	Os	76	190.2
Barium	Ba	56	137.3	Oxygen	O	8	16.00
Berkelium	Bk	97	(247)	Palladium	Pd	46	106.4
Beryllium	Be	4	9.01	Phosphorus	P	15	31.0
Bismuth	Bi	83	209.0	Platinum	Pt	78	195.1
Boron	B	5	10.8	Plutonium	Pu	94	(244)
Bromine	Br	35	79.9	Polonium	Po	84	(210)
Cadmium	Cd	48	112.4	Potassium	K	19	39.1
Calcium	Ca	20	40.1	Praseodymium	Pr	59	140.9
Californium	Cf	98	(251)	Promethium	Pm	61	(145)
Carbon	C	6	12.01	Protactinium	Pa	91	(231)
Cerium	Ce	58	140.1	Radium	Ra	88	(226)
Cesium	Cs	55	132.9	Radon	Rn	86	(222)
Chlorine	Cl	17	35.5	Rhenium	Re	75	186.2
Chromium	Cr	24	52.0	Rhodium	Rh	45	102.9
Cobalt	Co	27	58.9	Rubidium	Rb	37	85.5
Copper	Cu	29	63.5	Ruthenium	Ru	44	101.1
Curium	Cm	96	(247)	Samarium	Sm	62	150.4
Dysprosium	Dy	66	162.5	Scandium	Sc	21	45.0
Einsteinium	Es	99	(254)	Selenium	Se	34	79.0
Erbium	Er	68	167.3	Silicon	Si	14	28.1
Europium	Eu	63	152.0	Silver	Ag	47	107.9
Fermium	Fm	100	(257)	Sodium	Na	11	23.0
Fluorine	F	9	19.0	Strontium	Sr	38	87.6
Francium	Fr	87	(223)	Sulfur	S	16	32.1
Gadolinium	Gd	64	157.2	Tantalum	Ta	73	180.9
Gallium	Ga	31	69.7	Technetium	Tc	43	(97)
Germanium	Ge	32	72.6	Tellurium	Te	52	127.6
Gold	Au	79	197.0	Terbium	Tb	65	158.9
Hafnium	Hf	72	178.5	Thallium	Tl	81	204.4
Helium	He	2	4.00	Thorium	Th	90	232.0
Holmium	Ho	67	164.9	Thulium	Tm	69	168.9
Hydrogen	H	1	1.008	Tin	Sn	50	118.7
Indium	In	49	114.8	Titanium	Ti	22	47.9
Iodine	I	53	126.9	Tungsten	W	74	183.9
Iridium	Ir	77	192.2	Unnilennium	Une	109	(266?)
Iron	Fe	26	55.8	Unnilhexium	Unh	106	(263)
Krypton	Kr	36	83.8	Unniloctium	Uno	108	(265)
Lanthanum	La	57	138.9	Unnilpentium	Unp	105	(262)
Lawrencium	Lr	103	(256)	Unnilquadium	Unq	104	(261)
Lead	Pb	82	207.2	Unnilseptium	Uns	107	(262)
Lithium	Li	3	6.94	Uranium	U	92	238.0
Lutetium	Lu	71	175.0	Vanadium	V	23	50.9
Magnesium	Mg	12	24.3	Xenon	Xe	54	131.3
Manganese	Mn	25	54.9	Ytterbium	Yb	70	173.0
Mendelevium	Md	101	(258)	Yttrium	Y	39	88.9
Mercury	Hg	80	200.6	Zinc	Zn	30	65.4
Molybdenum	Mo	42	95.9	Zirconium	Zr	40	91.2
Neodymium	Nd	60	144.2				

†Numbers in parentheses give the mass number of the most stable isotope.

Glossary

absolute zero: temperature at which all molecular motion ceases; 0°K, −273°C

acceleration (ak-sehl-uh-RAY-shuhn): rate of change in velocity

acid: compound with a pH below 7 that tastes sour, turns blue litmus paper red, reacts with metals to produce hydrogen gas, and ionizes in water to produce hydrogen ions; proton donor

acid rain: droplets of weak sulfuric acid and nitric acid that form in the atmosphere and mix with rainwater

acoustics: the science of sound

actinoid series: second row of rare-earth elements in the periodic table, which with the exception of three elements are radioactive and synthetic

activation energy: energy needed to form a short-lived, high-energy, extremely unstable molecule whose atoms are rearranged to form products in a chemical reaction

active solar heating: heating system that uses a solar collector to store heat from the sun and an arrangement of hot water heater and pipes to circulate heat throughout a building

alcohol: substituted hydrocarbon in which one or more hydrogen atoms have been replaced by an –OH group, or hydroxyl group

alkali metal: element in Group IA

alkaline earth metal: element in Group IIA

alkane: straight-chain or branched-chain saturated hydrocarbon in which all the bonds between carbon atoms are single covalent bonds

alkene: unsaturated hydrocarbon in which at least one pair of carbon atoms is joined by a double covalent bond

alkyne: unsaturated hydrocarbon in which at least one pair of carbon atoms is joined by a triple covalent bond

alloy: solution of two metals or a metal and a nonmetal that has the properties of a metal

alpha decay: release of an alpha particle, or helium nucleus, from the nucleus of a radioactive atom

alternating current (AC): electrons moving back and forth through a wire, changing direction over and over again

amino acid: organic acid that contains carbon, hydrogen, oxygen, nitrogen, and sometimes sulfur and phosphorus; monomer from which proteins are made

amorphous (uh-MOR-fuhs) **solid:** solid that loses its shape under certain conditions

ampere: unit used to measure electric current

amplifier: electronic device that increases the strength of an electric signal

amplitude: (AM-plih-tyood): maximum distance the molecules of a medium are displaced from their rest position

angle of incidence (i): angle formed by the incident ray and a line perpendicular to the barrier (normal)

angle of reflection (r): angle formed by a line perpendicular to the barrier (normal) and the reflected ray

anthracite (AN-thruh-sight): hard, brittle coal formed when bituminous coal undergoes pressure

antinode: point at which constructive interference of waves causes maximum energy displacement

anvil: second bone in the middle ear, transmits vibrations from the hammer to the stirrup

aqueous (A-kwee-uhs) **solution:** solution in which the solvent is water

Archimedes' principle: principle that states that the buoyant force on an object is equal to the weight of the fluid displaced by the object

aromatic hydrocarbon: ring of 6 carbon atoms joined by alternating single and double covalent bonds; has a strong, often pleasant odor

atom: smallest particle of an element that has the properties of that element

atomic mass: average of the masses of all the existing isotopes of an element

atomic mass unit (amu): unit used to measure the masses of subatomic particles; a proton has a mass of 1 amu

atomic number: number of protons in the nucleus of an atom

average speed: measure of speed obtained by dividing the total distance by the total time

balanced force: force that is opposite and equal to another force

base: compound with a pH above 7 that tastes bitter, is slippery to the touch, turns red litmus paper blue, and ionizes in water to produce hydroxide ions; proton acceptor

battery: series of dry cells connected to one another

Bernoulli's principle: principle that states that the pressure in a moving stream of fluid is less than the pressure in the surrounding fluid

beta decay: release of a beta particle, or negatively charged electron, from the nucleus of a radioactive atom

bimetallic strip: strip consisting of two different metals that expand at different rates and cause the strip to bend; switch in a thermostat

binary system: number system that uses only the numbers 0 and 1, on which computer operation is based

binding energy: energy associated with the strong force

biomass: plants, animal wastes, and all other forms of matter that come from living things, which can be burned to generate heat

bit: single electronic switch in a computer

bituminous (bigh-TOO-muh-nuhs) **coal:** soft coal formed when lignite undergoes pressure

boiling: process in which particles inside a liquid as well as those on the surface change to a gas

boiling point: temperature at which a substance changes from the liquid phase to the gas phase

boiling point elevation: increase in the boiling point of a pure liquid solvent caused by the addition of solute

Boyle's Law: law that states that the volume of a fixed amount of gas varies inversely with the pressure of the gas

Brownian motion: constant movement of particles in a colloid

brush: contact through which electric current is supplied to the commutator in an electric motor

bubble chamber: instrument used to detect radioactivity using a superheated liquid

buoyancy (BOI-uhn-see): force of a fluid that pushes an object up

byte: a string of bits, usually 8 bits

calorie: unit used to measure heat

calorimeter (kal-uh-RIHM-uh-tuhr): instrument used to measure the heat given off in chemical reactions

carbohydrate: organic molecule of carbon, hydrogen, and oxygen in which there are two atoms of hydrogen for every atom of oxygen

carboxyl group: –COOH, group that characterizes all organic acids

carburetor (KAHR-buh-rayt-uhr): part of an internal-combustion engine in which gasoline is turned into vapor and mixed with air in the intake stroke

catalyst (KAT-uhl-ihst): substance that increases the rate of a reaction but is not itself changed by the reaction

cathode-ray tube (CRT): electronic device that uses electrons to produce images on a screen

Celsius (SEHL-see-uhs): metric temperature scale on which water freezes at 0° and boils at 100°

centimeter (cm): one-hundredth of a meter

central heating system: system that generates heat for an entire building or group of buildings from one central location

central processing unit (CPU): brain of a computer, which controls and processes information, controls the operation of all the components, and executes the arithmetic and logic instructions it receives

centripetal (sehn-TRIHP-uh-tuhl) **acceleration:** acceleration that is directed toward the center of a circular path

Charles's Law: law that states that the volume of a fixed amount of gas varies directly with the temperature of the gas

chemical bonding: combining of atoms of elements to form new substances

chemical change: process by which a substance becomes a new and different substance

chemical energy: energy that bonds atoms or ions together

chemical equation: expression in which symbols and formulas are used to represent a chemical reaction

chemical formula: combination of chemical symbols usually used to represent a compound

chemical property: property that describes how a substance changes into a new substance

chemical reaction: process in which the physical and chemical properties of the original substance change as a new substance with different physical and chemical properties is formed

chemical symbol: shorthand way of representing an element

chemistry: study of what substances are made of and how they change and combine

chip: razor-thin piece of silicon

circuit breaker: switch that flips open when the current flow becomes too high, thus breaking the circuit and stopping the flow

cloud chamber: instrument containing evaporated alcohol; used to detect radioactivity

cochlea (KAHK-lee-uh): snail-shell-shaped, liquid-filled structure in the inner ear, contains nerve fibers and special cells that convert movements of the liquid into electric impulses transmitted to the brain

coefficient (koh-uh-FIHSH-uhnt): number placed in front of a symbol or formula in a chemical equation that indicates how many atoms or molecules of the substance are involved in the reaction

coherent light: light that is in phase

collision theory: theory that says that reacting molecules must collide with sufficient energy if they are to form products

colloid (KAHL-oid): homogenous mixture that is not a true solution

combustion: process in which hydrocarbons in fossil fuels are combined with oxygen at high temperatures and heat and light are released; the burning of a fuel

commutator: special reversing switch in an electric motor that runs on DC that switches the direction of the current so that the magnetic poles of the electromagnet reverse and the electromagnet spins

complementary color: one of two colors that combine to form white light

compound: two or more elements chemically combined

compound machine: combination of two or more simple machines

compression (kuhm-PREHSH-uhn): space in a medium in which the molecules are crowded together

compression stroke: process in an internal-combustion engine in which the gasoline-air mixture is compressed in a cylinder and ignited by a spark from a spark plug

compressor: part of a cooling system where the pressure of the refrigerant vapor is increased

computer: electronic device that performs calculations and processes information

computer program: series of instructions that tells a computer how to perform a certain task

concave lens: lens that is thicker at the edges and thinner in the center so that it diverges light rays

concave mirror: mirror with a surface that curves inward

concentrated solution: solution in which a lot of solute is dissolved in a solvent

concentration: measure of the amount of a substance in a given unit of volume; amount of solute dissolved in a certain amount of solvent

condensation (kahn-duhn-SAY-shuhn): change of a gas to a liquid

condenser coil: part of a cooling system that cools the refrigerant vapor and changes it back into a liquid

conduction (kuhn-DUHK-shuhn): heat transfer through a substance or from one substance to another by the direct contact of molecules; method of charging objects with static electricity that involves the direct contact of objects

conductor: material that permits electric charges to move easily

cone: nerve cell in the retina of the eye that is sensitive to a primary color

conservation: wise and careful use of natural resources

constant speed: speed that does not change

constructive interference: process in which waves combine in such a way that the crests of one wave meet the crests of the other

control rod: rod usually made of cadmium that controls the speed of a nuclear reaction

control setup: part of an experiment that does not contain the variable

convection (kuhn-VEHK-shuhn): heat transfer in liquids and gases as molecules move in currents

conversion factor: fraction that always equals one, which is used for dimensional analysis

convex lens: lens that is thicker in the center than at the edges so that it converges light rays

convex mirror: mirror with a surface that curves outward

cooling system: system that removes heat from a building, room, or other space through evaporation

cooling tower: part of a factory or power plant in which water containing waste heat is cooled as it flows through pipes

core: central part of a nuclear reactor, where nuclear fission takes place

corrosion: gradual wearing away of a metal due to a chemical reaction in which the metal element is changed into a metallic compound

covalent bonding: chemical bonding in which electrons are shared rather than transferred

crest: high point of a wave; maximum displacement upward of a particle of the medium

crystal (KRIHS-tuhl): solid in which the particles are arranged in a regular, repeating pattern

crystal lattice: huge numbers of ions grouped together in a regular, repeating pattern

crystalline solid: solid made up of crystals

cubic centimeter (cm³ or cc): metric unit used to measure the volume of solids; equal to a milliliter

cycloalkane: saturated hydrocarbon ring

cylinder: tube in an external-combustion engine in which a piston moves back and forth; part of an internal-combustion engine in which a piston moves and compresses the gasoline-air mixture to one-seventh of its original volume

data: recorded observations and measurements

data bank: vast collection of information stored in a large computer

decay series: series of steps by which a radioactive nucleus decays into a nonradioactive nucleus

deceleration (dee-sehl-uh-RAY-shuhn): decrease in velocity

decibel: unit in which the intensity of sound is measured

decomposition reaction: chemical reaction in which a complex substance breaks down into two or more simpler substances

denatured alcohol: ethanol to which a poisonous compound such as methanol has been added

density: mass per unit volume of a substance

destructive interference: process in which waves combine in such a way that the crests of one wave meet the troughs of the other

diatomic element: two atoms covalently bonded

diesel engine: internal-combustion engine in which only air is taken in during the intake stroke

diffraction (dih-FRAK-shuhn): bending of waves around the edge of a barrier

diffuse (dih-FYOOS) **reflection:** reflected light that is scattered in many different directions due to an irregular surface; produces a "fuzzy image"

dilute solution: solution in which there is a little solute dissolved in a solvent

dimensional analysis: converting one unit to another

diode: simplest type of vacuum tube consisting of a filament and a plate

direct current (DC): electrons continuously moving in the same direction through a wire

disk drive: input/output device that reads information off a disk or diskette and enters it into or receives it from a computer's memory, or CPU

dissociation: separation of ions from a compound during solution

distillation: process that involves heating a liquid until it vaporizes and then allowing the vapor to cool until it condenses back into a liquid

doping: adding impurities to semiconductors to increase their conductivity

Doppler effect: change in the frequency and pitch of a sound that occurs because of the movement of the sound source or the listener

double-replacement reaction: chemical reaction in which different atoms in two different compounds replace each other

drag: opposition to thrust caused by fluid friction

dry cell: electrochemical cell that consists of a positive electrode, a negative electrode, and a pastelike electrolyte

ductile: able to be drawn into a thin wire

ear canal: located between outer ear and eardrum, conducts sound waves into the ear

eardrum: tightly stretched membrane located at the end of the ear canal that vibrates when struck by sound waves

effervescence (ehf-er-VEHS-ehns): escape of a gas from a liquid solution

efficiency: comparison of work output to work input

effort arm: distance from the effort force to the fulcrum

effort distance (d_E): distance through which a machine moves, or distance through which the effort force is applied to a machine

effort force (F_E): force that is applied to a machine

electric charge: positive or negative condition of a particle due to unequal numbers of protons and electrons in the atom

electric current: flow of electrons through a wire

electric discharge: loss of static electricity as electric charges move off an object

electric field: region surrounding a charged particle in which an electric force affecting other charged particles is noticeable.

electricity: energy associated with electrons that have moved from one place to another

electric motor: motor that converts electric energy into mechanical energy

electrochemical cell: cell in which chemical energy produced by a chemical reaction is changed into electric energy

electrode: metal plate in a wet cell

electrolysis: process of decomposing water into hydrogen and oxygen by passing an electric current through water

electrolyte: conducting liquid in a wet cell

electromagnet: powerful temporary magnet made by wrapping a coil of wire around a soft iron core and passing an electric current through the wire

electromagnetic energy: energy produced by moving electric charges

electromagnetic force: force of attraction or repulsion between particles in an atom

electromagnetic induction: process by which a current is produced by the motion of a conductor in a magnetic field

electromagnetic spectrum: arrangement of electromagnetic waves in order of their wavelengths, and thus their frequency

electromagnetic wave: wave that is both electric and magnetic in nature; light wave

electromagnetism: relationship between electricity and magnetism

electron: subatomic particle with a negative charge

electron affinity: tendency of an atom to attract electrons

electron cloud: space in which electrons are likely to be found

electron-dot diagram: representation of the electron-sharing that takes place in covalent bonding

electronics: study of the release, behavior, and effects of electrons as it relates to use in helpful devices

electroscope: instrument, consisting of a metal rod with two thin metal leaves at one end, used to detect radioactivity; instrument that can detect an electric charge

element: simplest type of pure substance

endothermic (ehn-duh-THER-mihk) **reaction:** chemical reaction in which energy is absorbed

energy: ability to do work

energy conversion: change in the form of energy

energy level: most likely location in an electron cloud in which an electron can be found

ester: compound that results from the chemical combination of an alcohol and an organic acid

esterification: reaction that produces an ester

evaporation (ih-vap-uh-RAY-shuhn): vaporization that takes place at the surface of a liquid

exhaust stroke: process in an internal-combustion engine in which gases are expelled from the cylinder through the exhaust valve

exhaust valve: part of an internal-combustion engine through which gases are expelled from the cylinder

exothermic (ehks-uh-THER-mihk) **reaction:** chemical reaction in which energy is released

experimental setup: part of an experiment that contains the variable

external-combustion engine: engine in which fuel is burned outside the engine; a steam engine

family: column of elements in the periodic table; group

farsightedness: condition in which a person has difficulty seeing nearby objects

fat: large complex ester formed from the reaction between the alcohol glycerol and fatty acids that is a solid at room temperature

fermentation (fer-muhn-TAY-shuhn): process in which yeast converts the sugar in a grain into ethanol and carbon dioxide

fiberglass: common insulating material consisting of long thin strands of glass packed together

fiber optics: field that deals with the transfer of light through long thin flexible fibers of glass or plastic called optical fibers

first law of motion: Newton's law that states that an object at rest will remain at rest and an object in motion will remain in motion at constant velocity unless an unbalanced force acts upon it

flammability (flam-uh-BIHL-uh-tee): ability to burn

fluid friction: friction produced when an object moves through a fluid

fluorescent (floo-REHS-uhnt): type of light produced by the electron bombardment of gas molecules contained at low pressure

focal length: distance between the center of the mirror or lens and the focal point

focal point: point in front of a mirror where the reflected rays meet

force: push or pull that gives energy to an object, causing it to start moving, stop moving, or change its motion

force of attraction: force that pulls objects together

force of repulsion: force that pushes objects apart

fossil fuel: fuel formed over hundreds of millions of years by heat and great pressure on plant and animal remains

fraction: petroleum part with its own boiling point

fractionating tower: place where fractional distillation of petroleum takes place

frame of reference: object or point from which movement is determined

freezer unit: part of a cooling system in which the liquid refrigerant absorbs heat and evaporates

freezing: change of a liquid to a solid

freezing point: temperature at which a substance changes from the liquid phase to the solid phase

freezing point depression: lowering of the freezing point of a liquid solvent by dissolving a solute in it

Freon (FREE-ahn): common refrigerant used in cooling systems

frequency (FREE-kwuhn-see): number of complete waves, or complete cycles, per unit time

friction (FRIHK-shuhn): force that opposes the motion of an object; method of charging an object with static electricity

fulcrum (FUL-kruhm): fixed point at which a lever pivots

fundamental tone: tone with the lowest possible frequency and pitch; occurs when a string vibrates as a whole

fuse: device containing a thin metal strip that melts and breaks the flow of electricity if the current becomes too high

galvanometer: instrument used to detect small currents

gamma decay: release of gamma rays, or electromagnetic waves of very high frequency and energy, from the nucleus of an atom

gamma ray: highest frequency electromagnetic wave

gas: matter with no definite shape or volume

gasohol: mixture of gasoline and alcohol

Geiger counter: instrument designed to detect and measure radioactivity by producing an electric current in the presence of a radioactive substance

generator: device that converts mechanical energy into electric energy

geothermal energy: heat energy deep within the earth's crust

geyser: fountain of steam and boiling water that bursts forth from the earth through a crack or weak spot in the earth's crust

gram (g): one-thousandth of a kilogram

gravitational (grav-ih-TAY-shuhn-uhl) **potential energy (G.P.E.):** energy that is dependent on height above the earth's surface

gravity: force of attraction between all objects in the universe

grounding: providing a path for the discharge of static electricity to reach the earth

group: column of elements in the periodic table; family

half-life: amount of time it takes for half the atoms in a given sample of a radioactive element to decay

halogen (HAL-uh-juhn): element in Group VIIA

halogen derivative: substituted hydrocarbon that contains halogens

hammer: first bone in the middle ear, picks up vibrations from the eardrum

hardware: physical parts of a computer

hard water: water that contains large amounts of dissolved metal ions

heat conductor: substance that conducts heat more effectively than other substances

heat energy: internal motion of particles of matter

heat engine: machine that changes heat energy into mechanical energy in order to do work

heat of fusion: amount of heat needed to change a substance from the solid phase to the liquid phase

heat of vaporization: amount of heat needed to change a substance from the liquid phase to the gas phase

heat pump system: heating system that takes heat from the outside air and brings it inside

heat transfer: movement of heat from a warmer object to a colder one

hertz (Hz): unit used to measure wave frequency; one wave per second

heterogeneous (heht-uhr-uh-JEEN-ee-uhs) **matter:** matter that has parts with different properties

heterogeneous mixture: mixture that does not appear to be the same throughout

hologram: image produced by holography

holography: technology that uses laser light to produce a three-dimensional image of an object or scene

homogeneous (hoh-muh-JEEN-ee-uhs) **matter:** matter that has identical properties throughout

homogeneous mixture: mixture that appears to be the same throughout

horsepower (hp): 745.56 watts; originally, the power necessary for a strong horse to move a 750-newton object one meter in one second

hot water system: heating system in which hot water is pumped through pipes to a convector that heats the room through convection currents

hydrocarbon: organic compound that contains only hydrogen and carbon

hydroelectric: using water to produce electricity

hydrogen ion: proton produced by an acid dissolved in water

hydronium ion (H_3O^+): hydrated hydrogen ion

hydroxide ion: ion produced when a base is dissolved in water

hydroxyl group: –OH, group that characterizes all organic alcohols

hypothesis (high-PAHTH-uh-sihs): proposed solution to a scientific problem

illuminated (ih-LOO-muh-nayt-uhd): able to be seen only by reflected light

incandescent (ihn-kuhn-DEH-suhnt): type of light produced from heat

incident wave: wave coming in toward a barrier

inclined plane: slanted surface used to raise an object

index of refraction: measure of the amount by which a material refracts light

indicator: compound that shows a definite color change when mixed with an acid or a base

induction: method of charging an object with static electricity that involves a rearrangement of electric charges

inert: not readily combining with other elements to form compounds

inertia (ihn-ER-shuh): tendency of objects to remain in motion or stay at rest unless acted upon by an unbalanced force

infrared ray: electromagnetic wave with a frequency slightly lower than visible red light

inner ear: part of the ear that contains the liquid-filled cochlea; here sound vibrations are converted into electric impulses that travel through a nerve to the brain

input device: device used for feeding data into the central processing unit of a computer; keyboard, magnetic tape, optical scanner, disk or diskette drive

insoluble: unable to be dissolved in water

insulation: prevention of heat loss by reducing the transfer of heat that occurs by conduction and convection

insulator: material that does not allow electrons to flow freely; substance that does not conduct heat easily

intake stroke: process in an internal-combustion engine in which the gasoline is vaporized, mixed with air, and transferred from the carburetor through the intake valve to a cylinder

intake valve: part of an internal-combustion engine through which the gasoline-air mixture is transferred from the carburetor to a cylinder

integrated circuit: circuit that combines many diodes and transistors on a thin slice of silicon crystal

intensity: the amount of energy in a wave; determines loudness of a sound

interference: process in which two or more waves arriving at the same point at the same time combine to produce a single new wave

internal-combustion engine: engine in which the burning of fuel takes place inside the engine; a gasoline engine

internal energy: energy contained in a substance

invisible spectrum: waves with frequencies less than 430 trillion hertz or greater than 760 trillion hertz that are thus invisible to the human eye

ion: charged particle formed when an atom gains or loses electrons

ionic bonding: chemical bonding that involves a transfer of electrons

ionization (igh-uhn-ih-ZAY-shuhn): process of removing an electron and forming ions; formation of ions from solute molecules by the action of a solvent

ionization energy: energy needed for ionization

iris: colored area surrounding the pupil of the eye that controls the amount of light that enters the pupil

isomer: organic compound that has the same molecular formula as another organic compound but a different structure

isotope (IGH-suh-tohp): atom of an element that has the same number of protons as another atom of the same element but a different number of neutrons

joule (J): one newton-meter; unit in which energy is measured

Kelvin scale: metric temperature scale on which 0° represents absolute zero, the boiling point of water is 373°, and the freezing point of water is 273°

kilogram (kg): basic unit of mass in the metric system

kilometer (km): 1000 meters

kilowatt (kW): 1000 watts

kilowatt-hour: 1000 watts of power used for one hour of time; measure of electric energy

kinetic (kih-NEHT-ihk) **energy:** energy that a moving object has due to its motion; energy of motion

kinetics: study of reaction rates

land reclamation: process of restoring land

lanthanoid series: first row of rare-earth elements in the periodic table; soft, malleable metals that have a high luster and conductivity

laser: device that concentrates light into a narrow intense beam

law: scientific theory that has been tested many times and is generally accepted as true

law of conservation (kahn-ser-VAY-shuhn) **of energy:** law that states that energy can be neither created nor destroyed by ordinary means

law of conservation of mass: law that states that matter can be neither created nor destroyed in a chemical reaction

law of conservation of momentum: law that states that the total momentum of any group of objects remains the same unless outside forces act on the objects

law of reflection: law that states that the angle of incidence is equal to the angle of reflection

law of universal gravitation: Newton's law that states that all objects in the universe attract each other by the force of gravity

lens: any transparent material that refracts light

lever: a bar that is free to pivot, or move about, a fixed point when an effort force is applied

lift: upward force

lightning: discharge of static electricity

lightning rod: pointed metal rod placed above the roof of a building as protection from lightning

lignite (LIHG-night): soft woody type of coal formed when peat undergoes pressure

lipid (LIHP-ihd): any of the class of organic compounds consisting of fats and oils

liquid: matter with no definite shape but with a definite volume

liter (L): basic unit of volume in the metric system

longitudinal (lahn-juh-TYOOD-uhn-uhl) **wave:** wave consisting of a series of compressions and rarefactions in which the motion of the medium is parallel to the direction of the wave

lubricant: substance that changes sliding friction to fluid friction

luminous (LOO-muh-nuhs): giving off its own light

luster: shininess

machine: device that makes work easier by changing the size or direction of the applied force

magnetic domain: region in which the magnetic fields of atoms are grouped together

magnetic field: region in which magnetic forces act

magnetic induction: process by which a material is made into a magnet

magnetic lines of force: lines that define the magnetic field of an object

magnetic variation: error in a compass caused by the difference in location of the earth's magnetic and geographic poles

magnetism: force of attraction or repulsion due to an arrangement of electrons

magnetosphere: region of the earth's magnetic field

main memory: main storage of a computer that contains data and operating instructions

malleable: able to be hammered into a thin sheet

mass: amount of matter in an object

mass number: sum of the protons and the neutrons in the nucleus of an atom

matter: anything that has mass and volume

mechanical advantage (MA): number of times a machine multiplies the effort force

mechanical energy: energy associated with motion

medium: any substance or region through which a wave is transmitted

melting: change of a solid to a liquid

melting point: temperature at which a substance changes from the solid phase to the liquid phase

meniscus (mih-NIHS-kuhs): point at the bottom of the curve of the liquid in a graduated cylinder

metal: element that is a good conductor of heat and electricity, is shiny, has a high melting point, is ductile and malleable, and forms positive ions

metallic bond: bond formed by the atoms of metals, in which the outer electrons of the atoms form a common electron cloud

metalloid (MEHT-uhl-oid): element that has properties of both metals and nonmetals

meter (m): basic unit of length in the metric system

metric system: standard system of measurement used by all scientists

microprocessor: integrated circuit that can hold the entire processing capability of a computer on one small chip

microwave: radio wave with a frequency between 1 billion hertz and 1 trillion hertz

middle ear: part of the ear that contains the three smallest bones in the body whose function it is to transmit sound vibrations from the eardrum to the inner ear

milligram (mg): one-thousandth of a gram

milliliter (mL): one-thousandth of a liter

millimeter (mm): one-thousandth of a meter

mirror: any smooth surface that reflects light and forms images

miscible (MIHS-uh-buhl): able to be dissolved in another liquid

mixture: matter that consists of two or more substances mixed together but not chemically combined

modem: input and output device that changes electronic signals from a computer into sounds that can be carried over telephone lines and vice versa

moderator: material that slows down neutrons in a nuclear reaction

modulation (mahj-uh-LAY-shuhn): variation in either amplitude or frequency of a wave

molecule (MAHL-uh-kyool): combination of atoms formed by a covalent bond

momentum: mass of an object multiplied by its velocity

monomer (MAHN-uh-mer): smaller molecule that joins with other smaller molecules to form a polymer

motion: change in position relative to a frame of reference

natural frequency: the characteristic frequency of vibration of a particular medium

natural magnet: naturally occurring substance that has magnetic properties

nearsightedness: condition in which a person has difficulty seeing objects at a distance

neon: type of light produced when electrons pass through glass tubes filled with neon gas; bright red light

network solid: covalently bonded substance that does not have a low melting point

neutralization (noo-truhl-uh-ZAY-shuhn): reaction of an acid with a base to produce a salt and water

neutron: subatomic particle with no electric charge

newton-meter (N-m): unit of work; joule

noble gas: element in Group VIIIA

node: point at which destructive interference of waves results in no energy displacement

nonelectrolyte: substance that forms an aqueous solution that does not conduct an electric current

nonmetal: element that is a poor conductor of heat and electricity, has a dull surface, low melting point, is brittle, breaks easily, and forms negative ions

nonrenewable resource: natural resource that cannot be replaced by nature

normal: line perpendicular to the barrier

north magnetic pole: end of the magnet that points toward the north

nuclear chain reaction: continuous series of fission reactions

nuclear energy: energy released by the splitting of the nucleus of an atom; energy locked within the nucleus by the strong force

nuclear fission (FIHSH-uhn): splitting of an atomic nucleus into two smaller nuclei of approximately equal mass, during which nuclear energy is released

nuclear fusion: joining of two atomic nuclei of smaller masses to form a single nucleus of larger mass

nuclear radiation: particles and energy released by radioactive decay

nuclear waste: radioactive substance associated with the use of radioactive materials or the production of nuclear power

nucleus (NOO-klee-uhs; plural: nuclei, NOO-klee-igh): small dense positively charged center of an atom

ohm: unit of resistance

Ohm's Law: law that states that the current in a wire is equal to the voltage divided by the resistance

oil: large complex ester formed from the reaction between the alcohol glycerol and fatty acids that is liquid at room temperature

opaque (oh-PAYK): unable to transmit light

optical axis: straight line drawn through the center of a mirror or lens

optical fiber: long thin flexible fiber of glass or plastic

orbital motion: motion that results from the combination of the object's forward inertia and the downward pull of gravity on an object

organic acid: substituted hydrocarbon that contains the –COOH group, or carboxyl group

organic chemistry: study of carbon compounds

organic compound: compound that contains carbon

outer ear: part of the ear that funnels sounds into the ear canal

output device: device that receives data from the central processing unit of a computer, such as a printer, cathode-ray tube, magnetic tape drive, or voice synthesizer

overtone: sounds of higher frequencies produced when sections of a string vibrate

oxidation number: number of electrons an atom gains, loses, or shares when it forms chemical bonds

parallel circuit: electric circuit in which the different parts of the circuit are on separate branches

particle accelerator: instrument in which artificial transmutation takes place

passive solar heating: heating system in which a building is heated directly by the rays of the sun

peat: soft type of coal made of decayed plant fibers

period: horizontal row of elements in the periodic table

periodic: repeating according to the same pattern

periodic law: law that states that the physical and chemical properties of the elements are periodic functions of their atomic numbers

permanent magnet: magnet made of a material that is difficult to magnetize but stays magnetized

petroleum: crude oil

phase: state in which matter can exist: solid, liquid, gas, or plasma

phase change: physical change of matter from one phase to another

phosphor: substance that absorbs ultraviolet photons and glows, producing visible light

photoelectric effect: production of electrons by photons of light

photon (FOH-tahn): tiny packet of energy

photovoltaic cell: device that converts sunlight directly into electricity

physical change: change in which physical properties of a substance are altered but the substance remains the same kind of matter

physical property: property of a substance that can be observed without changing the identity of the substance

physics: study of forms of energy and the laws of motion

piston: metal plate in a combustion engine that moves back and forth in a cylinder and passes mechanical energy to a connecting rod, which does work

pitch: how high or low a sound is

plane mirror: mirror with a perfectly flat surface

plasma: high-energy phase of matter

polarity (poh-LAR-uh-tee): property of a molecule with oppositely charged ends

polarized light: light whose waves vibrate along a single plane

pole: end of a magnet

pollution: release of substances into the environment that changes the environment for the worse

polyatomic ion: group of covalently bonded atoms that acts like a single atom when combining with other atoms

polymer (PAHL-ih-mer): giant molecule made up of smaller molecules joined together; many molecular units strung together in a chain

polymerization (puh-lihm-er-ih-ZAY-shuhn): process of chemically bonding monomers to form polymers

potential (poh-TEHN-shuhl) **energy:** energy stored in an object due to its position

power: rate at which work is done, or the amount of work done per unit time

power stroke: process in an internal-combustion engine in which the explosion of hot gases forces the piston back down and energy is transferred from the piston to the wheels of the car

precipitate (prih-SIHP-uh-tayt): insoluble substance that crystallizes out of a solution

precipitation: process by which a precipitate forms

pressure: "push" that fluids exert on an object; force that acts over a certain area

primary coil: coil of insulated wire wrapped around an iron core in a transformer that creates a magnetic field when alternating current passes through it

primary color: one of three colors that can be mixed to produce iight of any color; red, blue, or green

primary pigment: yellow, cyan, or magenta

prism (PRIHZ-uhm): piece of glass that forms a spectrum when white light is passed through it

product: substance that is produced by a chemical reaction

projectile: any object thrown in the air that moves forward due to its inertia and accelerates downward due to gravity

projectile motion: curved path of a projectile

property: characteristic of a substance

protein: organic compound made up of amino acids

proton: subatomic particle with a positive charge

pulley: chain, belt, or rope wrapped around a wheel

pupil: opening in the eye through which light enters

pure substance: substance made of only one kind of material having definite properties

quality: property of a sound that is determined by the blending of its fundamental tone with its overtones

quark (kwahrk): particle that makes up all other known particles in the nucleus of an atom

radar: radio detecting and ranging; short-wavelength microwaves used in locating objects, calculating distances to objects, and monitoring speed

radiant electric system: heating system in which electricity passes through wires or cables that resist the flow of current and give off heat through radiation

radiant hot water system: heating system in which hot water runs through a continuous coil of pipe in the floor of a room, and heats the room through radiation

radiation (ray-dee-AY-shuhn): energy given off when certain substances decay; heat transfer through space

radioactive: giving off radiation

radioactive decay: spontaneous breakdown of an unstable atomic nucleus

radioactivity: release of energy and matter that results from changes in the nucleus of an atom

radioisotope: artificially produced radioactive isotope of a common element

radio wave: electromagnetic wave with a frequency between 10,000 hertz and 1 trillion hertz

rarefaction (rair-uh-FAK-shuhn): space in a medium in which there are fewer molecules

reactant (ree-AK-tuhnt): substance that enters into a chemical reaction

reaction rate: measure of how quickly reactants turn into products

real image: image formed by a mirror or lens that is the result of the actual converging of light rays

rectifier: vacuum tube diode that converts alternating current to direct current

recycling: form of conservation in which discarded materials that can be used again are sent to factories where they are reclaimed

reflected wave: wave that bounces back from a barrier

reflection (rih-FLEHK-shuhn): bouncing back of a wave after it strikes a barrier that does not absorb the wave's energy

refraction (rih-FRAK-shuhn): bending of waves due to a change in speed

refrigerant: liquid that is evaporated in a cooling system

regular reflection: reflected light in which the rays are reflected parallel to each other with very little scattering; produces a clearly defined image

resistance: opposition to the flow of electricity

resistance arm: distance from the resistance force to the fulcrum

resistance distance (d_R): distance through which the resistance force is applied, or distance through which the object moves

resistance force (F_R): force applied by a machine

resonance: ability of an object to vibrate when it absorbs energy of its own natural frequency

retina: part of the eye on which light converges to form an image

reverberation: combination of reflected sound waves

rod: nerve cell in the retina of the eye that is sensitive to light and dark

rolling friction: friction produced when an object rolls over a surface

safety system: system in a nuclear power plant, consisting of a cooling system and a concrete casing around the reactor, that helps prevent nuclear accidents

saturated hydrocarbon: hydrocarbon in which all the bonds between carbon atoms are single covalent bonds

saturated solution: solution that contains all the solute it can possibly hold at a given temperature

scientific method: systematic approach to problem solving

screw: inclined plane wrapped around a cylinder to form a spiral

secondary coil: coil of insulated wire wrapped around an iron core in a transformer in which a current flows

second law of motion: Newton's law that states that force equals mass times acceleration

semiconductor: material that is able to conduct electric currents better than insulators but not as well as metals

series circuit: electric circuit in which all the parts of the circuit are connected one after another

single-replacement reaction: chemical reaction in which an uncombined element replaces an element that is part of a compound

sliding friction: friction produced when two solid objects slide over each other

slope: slant of a line connecting two points that indicates the change in the Y axis as compared to the change in the X axis

software: programs a computer follows

soft water: water that does not contain metal ions

solar collector: device that collects the sun's energy

solar energy: energy given off by the sun

solar heating system: heating system that uses the energy of the sun to produce heat

solid: matter with a definite shape and a definite volume

solid-state device: device that uses semiconductors

solubility: maximum amount of solute that can be dissolved in a definite amount of solvent at a specific temperature

soluble: able to be dissolved

solute (SAHL-yoot): substance that is dissolved in a solution

solution (suh-LOO-shuhn): homogeneous mixture in which one substance is dissolved in another substance

solvent (SAHL-vuhnt): substance that does the dissolving in a solution

sonar: "*s*ound *n*avigation *a*nd *r*anging" system that uses high-frequency ultrasonic waves

south magnetic pole: end of a magnet that points toward the south

spark plug: part of an internal-combustion engine that produces an electric spark that ignites the fuel

specific gravity: comparison, or ratio, of the mass of a substance to the mass of an equal volume of water

specific heat: ability of a substance to absorb heat energy

speed: distance traveled by a moving object per unit of time

standing wave: wave that results when constructive interference and destructive interference produce stationary nodes and antinodes

starch: carbohydrate made of a long chain of sugar molecules hooked together

static electricity: buildup of electric charge on an object

steam heating system: heating system in which steam is forced through pipes from a boiler to a convector, which heats the room through convection currents

step-down transformer: transformer that decreases the voltage in alternating current

step-up transformer: transformer that increases the voltage in alternating current

stirrup: one of the three bones in the middle ear

storage tank: part of a cooling system that holds the refrigerant

strip mining: process in which entire hills are cut apart by large earth-moving machines to obtain coal

strong force: force that binds protons and neutrons in the nucleus

structural formula: formula that shows the kind, number, and arrangement of atoms in a molecule

subatomic particle: proton, neutron, or electron

sublimation (suhb-lih-MAY-shuhn): change from the solid phase of matter directly into the gas phase

subscript: small number placed to the lower right of a chemical symbol that gives the number of atoms of the element in the compound

substituted hydrocarbon: hydrocarbon formed when one or more hydrogen atoms in a hydrocarbon chain or ring is replaced by a different atom or group of atoms

sugar: carbohydrate

supersaturated solution: solution that is made to hold more solute at a given temperature than is normal

suspension: heterogeneous mixture in which the solute particles are larger than atoms, ions, or molecules

synthesis (SIHN-thuh-sihs) **reaction:** chemical reaction in which two or more simple substances combine to form a new, more complex substance

synthetic element: element produced by artificial transmutation; transuranium element

temperature: measure of the motion of molecules

temperature inversion: condition that occurs when cool air and pollutants near the earth's surface are trapped under a layer of warm air

temporary magnet: magnet made of a material that is easily magnetized but quickly loses its magnetism

terminal velocity: velocity reached when the pull of gravity equals the air resistance and the falling object no longer accelerates

theory: most logical explanation of events that occur in nature

thermal expansion: expansion of a substance due to heat

thermal pollution: damage to the environment by waste heat that causes an unnatural rise in temperature of air or in bodies of water such as lakes and streams

thermocouple: device that changes heat energy into electric energy

thermometer: instrument used for the measurement of temperature

thermostat (THER-muh-stat): device that helps control temperature in an indoor area or in an appliance

third law of motion: Newton's law that states that for every action there is an equal and opposite reaction

thrust: forward force

tidal power: power produced by the rise and fall of tides

timbre: quality of a sound

tincture (TIHNK-chuhr): solution in which alcohol is the solvent

toxic: poisonous

tracer: radioactive element whose pathway through the steps of a chemical reaction can be followed

transformer: device that increases or decreases the voltage of alternating current

transistor: sandwich of three semiconductor crystals used to amplify an electric current or signal

transition metal: element that has properties similar to other transition metals and to other metals but whose properties do not fit in with those of any other family.

translucent (tranz-LOO-suhnt): able to transmit light but no detail of that light

transmutation: process by which the nucleus of an atom changes so that a new element is formed

transparent: able to transmit light readily

transuranium element: element produced by artificial transmutation; synthetic element

transverse wave: wave in which the motion of the medium is at right angles to the direction of the wave

triode: vacuum tube that consists of a filament, a plate, and a wire screen, or grid

trough: low point of a wave; maximum displacement downward of a particle of the medium

turbine: paddle wheel in an external-combustion engine that rotates, producing mechanical energy

ultrasonic (uhl-truh-SAHN-ihk): sounds with frequencies higher than 20,000 hertz

ultraviolet ray: electromagnetic wave with a frequency just higher than visible violet light

unbalanced force: force that is not opposite and equal to another force and causes motion or a change in motion

unsaturated hydrocarbon: hydrocarbon in which one or more of the bonds between carbon atoms is a double covalent or triple covalent bond

unsaturated solution: solution that contains less solute than it can possibly hold at a given temperature

vacuum tube: one-way valve, or gate, for a flow of electrons

valence electron: electron in the outermost energy level of an atom

vaporization (vay-puhr-ih-ZAY-shuhn): change of a liquid to a gas

variable: factor that is being tested in an experiment

velocity: speed in a given direction

virtual image: image formed by a mirror or lens in which the rays of light do not actually converge

viscosity (vihs-KAHS-uh-tee): resistance of a liquid to flow

visible spectrum: portion of the electromagnetic spectrum to which human eyes are sensitive; light waves with frequencies between 430 trillion hertz and 760 trillion hertz

volt: unit of voltage

voltage: measure of the energy available to move electrons

voltaic cell: wet cell

volume: amount of space an object takes up

warm air system: heating system in which heated air is forced through ducts to vents and moves throughout the room by convection currents

watt (W): one joule per second; unit of electric power; volts times amps

wave: disturbance that transfers energy through matter or space

wavelength: distance between two consecutive crests or troughs of a wave

weak force: force that is responsible for radioactive decay

wedge: inclined plane that moves

weight: response of mass to the pull of gravity

wet cell: electrochemical cell that consists of a positive electrode, a negative electrode, and a liquid electrolyte; voltaic cell

wheel and axle: lever that rotates in a circle, made of two wheels of different sizes

work: product of a force applied to an object and the distance through which the force is applied; force times distance

work input (W_I): work done on a machine

work output (W_O): work done by a machine

X-ray: electromagnetic wave with a frequency just above ultraviolet

Index

Absolute zero, 401
Acceleration, 295–298
  centripetal, 298
  force, mass, and, 315–316
  graphing, 296
  negative, 295
Acetic acid, 222, 246
Acetylene, 242
Acid rain, 615, 616
Acids, 221–223, 225–227
  properties, 221–222
  in solution, 225–227
  uses, 221
Acoustics, 525
Actinoid series, 147
Activation energy, 194–195, 199
Active metals, 135–138
  alkali, 135–137
  alkaline earth, 137–138
Active solar energy, 591, 592
Active solar heating, 421–422
Air, buoyant force of, 336
Air pollution, 613–615
Air pressure, 331
  boiling point and, 49–50
Air resistance, gravity and, 319
Alcohols, 245–246
  as solvent, 207
Alkali, 136
Alkali metals, 135–137
Alkaline earth metals, 137–138
Alkanes, 239–240
Alkenes, 241–242
Alkynes, 242
Alloys, 68–69, 133, 142, 143, 147,
  210
Alnico, 471
Alpha decay, 263
Alpha particle, 263, 272
  symbol for, 266
Alternating current (AC), 455,
  643–644
Aluminum, 140, 446
Amino acids, 251, 632
Ammonia, 142, 424
Amorphous solids, 42
Ampere, 451
Amplifiers, 643, 644
Amplitude, 517
  of waves, 501–502
Amplitude modulation (AM), 541
Angle of incidence, i, 505
Angle of reflection, r, 505
Anthracite, 588–589
Antimony, 142
Antinode, 507
Aperture, 571

Aqueous solutions, 207
  conductivity, 208–209
Archimedes' principle, 334, 335
Argon, 145, 146, 162
Aromatic hydrocarbons, 243–244
Arsenic, 142, 646
Artificial transmutation, 265
Asphalt, 629
Astatine, 143
Atomic bomb, 597
Atomic mass, 121
Atomic mass unit, 98
Atomic models, 90–96
  Bohr's, 95
  Dalton's, 91–92
  Greek, 90–91
  Rutherford's, 93–95
  Thomson's, 93
  wave, 96
Atomic theory, 536
  Dalton's, 92
Atoms, 92, 442–443
  bonding capacity, 184
  combining capacity, 174–175
  elements and, 70
  forces within, 103–105
  origin of term, 91
  subatomic particles, 96–103
Auroras, 467, 472
Average speed, 292–293

Balance, 36
Balanced chemical equation, 186
Balanced forces, 310–311
  motion and, 315
Barium, 137
Barium-141, 597
Bases, 136, 223–225
  properties, 224
  in solution, 225–227
Battery, 454
Bauxite, 140
Becquerel, Henri, 258–259, 272
Bell, Alexander Graham, 647, 648
Benzene, 217, 244
Bernoulli's principle, 339–341
Beryllium, 137
Beta decay, 264
Beta particles, 264, 273
  symbols for, 66
Bimetallic strip, 409
Binary system, 656–657
Binding energy, 260, 268
Biomass, 600, 602–603
Bismuth, 142
Bit, 657

Bituminous coal, 588
Bohr, Niels, 95
Boiling, 49
Boiling point, 49, 406
Boiling point elevation, 219
Bonding
  of carbon atoms, 235–236
  chemical, 160–163
  covalent, 167–171
  ionic, 163–167
  metallic, 172
  predicting types, 173–175
Bonding capacity, 184
Boron, 140
Boron family, 140
Boyle's Law, 45, 46
Brass, 133
Bromine, 143, 169, 247
Bromthymol blue, 226
Brownian motion, 221
Brushes, 479
Bubble chamber, 272, 273–274
Buoyancy, 333–336
Byte, 657

Cadmium rods, 598
Calcium, 137
Caloric theory, 396
Calorie, 402
Calorimeter, 404
Cameras, 570–571
Cancer, radiation treatment, 275
Carbohydrates, 249–250
Carbon, 141, 159, 170
  bonding of, 235–236
  electron arrangement, 237
  in organic compounds, 234, 235
  oxidation number, 175
  See also Organic compounds.
Carbon-12, 261
Carbon-14, 261, 264
  half-life, 267
Carbon-14 dating, 267
Carbon family, 141
Carboxyl group, 246
Carburetor, 426
Catalysts, reaction rates and, 197–
  199
Cathode-ray tube, 650–651
Cellulose, 632
Celsius scale, 19, 401
Celsius thermometer, 21, 25
Centimeter, 15
  cubic, 18
Central heating systems, 418–422

Central processing unit (CPU), 654
Centripetal acceleration, 298
Cesium, 135
Charles's Law, 45–46
Chemical bonding, 160–163, 184
Chemical changes, 54–55
Chemical energy, 373, 381
Chemical equations, 76–77, 185–188
  balancing, 186–188
Chemical formulas, 74–76, 170
Chemical properties, 54–55
  metals, 133
  nonmetals, 134
Chemical reactions, 55, 181–199
  capacity to react, 184–185
  characteristics, 182–184
  chemical equations, 185–189
  defined, 183
  energy of, 192–196
  rates, 196–199
  types, 189–192
Chemical symbols, 70–72
  of elements in periodic table, 121
Chemistry, 14
Chip, 646
Chlorine, 143, 247
  covalent bonding in, 168–169
  oxidation number, 175
Circuit breaker, 461
Circular motion, 297–298
Cloud chamber, 272, 273
Coal, 588–589
  pollution and, 614–615
  scrubber system for burning, 620
  strip mining, 611
Cobalt, 471
Coefficients, 77, 186
Coherent light, 573
Collision theory, 196–199
Colloids, 218, 219–220
Color, 550–552
  light and, 540, 549–550
  of objects, 550–551
  primary and complementary light, 551
  primary and complementary pigments, 552
Combustible material, 602–603
Combustion, 142–143, 193, 588
  in heat engines, 425–427
Commutator, 478
Compass, 472–473
Complementary colors, 551
Compound machines, 365
Compounds, 63, 72–77, 160
  defined, 73
  ionic, 166–167
  molecules and, 73–74
  properties, 73
Compression, 500

Compression stroke, 427
Compressor, 424, 425
Computer program, 654
Computers, 652–657
  binary system, 656–657
  development, 653–654
  hardware, 654–656
Concave lens, 567–568
Concave mirror, 563–565
Concentrated solution, 212
Concentration
  reaction rates and, 197
  of solutions, 212–214
Conclusion, stating, 13
Condensation, 47, 50, 405
Condenser coils, 424, 425
Conduction, 397–398
  charging by, 446
Conductivity, 172, 208–209
Conductors, 446
  metalloids as, 135
  metals as, 132
Conservation, 619–620
Conservation of energy, law of, 382–383
Conservation of mass, law of, 186
Conservation of momentum, law of, 299
Constant speed, 292
Constructive interference, 506, 507, 524
Control rods, 597–599
Control setup, 11
Convection, 397–399
Conversion factor, 19
Convex lens, 567–568, 571
Convex mirror, 565–566
Cooling systems, 424–425
Cooling tower, 429
Copper, 139, 446
  oxidation number, 155
Core, in nuclear reactor, 597–598
Corrosion, 133, 189
  acids and, 222
Covalent bonding, 167–171, 173–174, 184
  in carbon compounds, 236
Covalent compounds, ionization of, 209
Crude oil, 589
Crystal lattice, 166
Crystals, 41
  measuring mass of, 23
Cubic centimeter, 18, 23
Curie, Marie, 259, 275
Curie, Pierre, 259
Cycloalkanes, 243
Cylinder, 426

Dalton, John, 91
Data, 11
  recording and analyzing, 11–13
Data bank, 656

Data table, 12
Dead spot, 524
Decay series, 262
Deceleration, 295
Decibel, 518
Decomposition reaction, 189, 190
Decomposition, of water, 603
Democritus, 90, 91
Denatured alcohol, 246
Density, 38–40
  buoyancy and, 335, 336
  defined, 18
  measuring of, 18–19, 39–40
  of a medium, 497–498
Destructive interference, 506–507, 524–525
Diatomic elements, 143–144, 169
Diesel engine, 427
Diffraction, 506
Diffuse reflection, 547
Dilute solution, 212
Dimensional analysis, 19–21
Diode, 643, 656
Direct current (DC), 455, 643–644
Disk drive, 655
Dissociation, 208
Distance, defined, 290
Doping, 645
Doppler effect, 520
Double-replacement reaction, 189, 191–192, 227
Drag, 341
Dry cell, 453–454
Dry ice, 51
Ductility, 122, 132, 135, 172

Ear, 528–529
Earth, as magnet, 471–473
Effervescence, 212
Efficiency, of machines, 356
Effort arm, 362
Effort distance, 354
Effort force, 354
Einstein, Albert, 383
Elasticity of a medium, 498
Electric charge, 442–445
  electric fields, 444–445
  force and, 443–444
  subatomic particles and, 443
Electric circuit, 456–458
  parallel, 457–458
  parts, 456–457
  series, 457
Electric current, 451
  direction, 455
  producing, 453–455
Electric discharge, 448
Electric energy, 73, 381, 459–460
Electric field, 444–445
Electric motor, 478–479
Electric power, 458–461
  calculating, 458–459

electric energy, 459–460
electric safety, 460–461
Electricity, 440–461
  defined, 445
  electric charge, 442–445
  electric circuit, 456–458
  electric power, 458–461
  from electrolysis, 603
  flow, 451–455
  magnetism and, 476–483
  from nuclear power plants, 599
  solar energy and, 592–593
  static, 445–450
  voltage, 450
Electrochemical cell, 453, 454
Electrodes, 454
Electrolysis, 603
Electrolytes, 208, 454
Electromagnetic energy, 373–374
Electromagnetic force, 104
Electromagnetic induction, 480
Electromagnetic spectrum, 539–543
  invisible, 540–543
  visible, 540
Electromagnetic waves, 537–538, 539
Electromagnetism, 476–479
Electromagnets, 477–479
  in telephone, 648
Electron affinity, 165, 167
Electron cloud, 101, 161
Electron-dot diagram, 168
Electron pressure, 453, 454
Electronic devices, 642–647
Electronics, 642
Electrons, 95, 100–103, 161
  chemical bonding and, 162–163
  chemical reactions and, 184
  covalent bonding and, 167–169
  discovery, 93
  electron charge, 443, 444
  energy levels and, 161–162
  ionic bonding and, 163–165
  light and, 536–537
  magnetism and, 474
  in metallic bonding, 172
  oxidation number, 174–175
  wave mechanics and, 96
  See also Electricity.
Electroscope, 272, 447–448
Elements, 63, 69–72
  atoms and, 70
  chemical formulas, 75
  chemical symbols, 70–72
  diatomic, 169
  periodic properties, 123–125
  radioactive, 259–261
  transmutation, 262–267
Emulsification, 224
Endothermic reactions, 192, 194
Energy, 371–383
  in chemical reactions, 183, 192–195

conservation, 382–383
conversions, 377–382
forms, 373–374
kinetic, 375–376
in nuclear fission, 269
in nuclear fusion, 271–272
phases of matter and, 47
potential, 375, 376–377
waves and, 496–497
  See also Energy sources.
Energy conversions, 378–382
Energy levels, 95, 101, 161–162
Energy sources, 587–603
  alternative, 600–603
  fossil fuels, 588–591
  nuclear energy, 596–599
  solar energy, 591–595
Engines, 381–382
ENIAC, 653
Environment, balance in, 610
  See also Pollution.
Enzymes, 199
Esterification, 247
Esters, 245, 247
Ethane, 239
Ethanol, 245–246, 601
Ethene, 241
Ethyl alcohol, 601
Ethylene glycol, 246
Ethyne, 242
Evaporation, 49
  cooling systems and, 424
Exhaust stroke, 427
Exhaust valve, 427
Exothermic reactions, 14, 192, 193–194
Experimental setup, 10
Experiments, performing, 9–11
External-combustion engine, 381–382, 426
Eye, 552–553

Facts, 7
Families, of elements, 116–117
Faraday, Michael, 479–480
Farsightedness, 553, 569–570
Fats and oils, 249, 250
Fatty acids, 250
Fermi, Enrico, 268
Fiber optics, 575
Fiberglass, 423
Filament, 452, 561, 643, 644
Fixed pulley, 363, 364
Flammability, 54
Flash tube, 573
Fluid friction, 308–309
Fluid pressure, 330–332
Fluids, forces in, 329–341
  Bernoulli's principle, 339–341
  buoyancy, 333–336
  fluid pressure, 330–332
  hydraulics, 336–339
Fluorescence, 258

Fluorescent light, 560, 561
Fluorine, 143, 163, 164, 169, 247
Focal length, 564
Focal point, 564
Force of attraction, 443
Force of repulsion, 443
Forces, 305–323
  balanced and unbalanced, 310–312
  electric charge and, 443–444
  in fluids, 329–341
  gravity, 318–322
  motion and, 313–318
  nature, 306–309
  weight and mass, 322–323
Fossil fuels, 588–591
  coal, 588–589
  natural gas, 590
  oil, 589–590
  pollution and, 610, 614–615, 617
  shortages, 590–591
Fractional distillation, 628
Fractionating tower, 628–629
Fractions, of petroleum, 628
Frame of reference, movement and, 288–289
Franklin, Benjamin, 449–450
Free fall, 318–320
Freezer unit, 424, 425
Freezing, 47, 48, 405
Freezing point, 48–49, 406
Freezing point depression, 218
Freon, 248, 424, 425
Frequency, 501, 502
  of electromagnetic waves, 539
  natural, 523
  of sound, 517, 519–521
Frequency modulation (FM), 541
Friction, 307–309
  charging an object by, 446
Fuels, 239
  See also Fossil fuels.
Fulcrum, 361
Fundamental tone, 521, 522
Fuses, 461

Galileo, 318
Gallium, 140, 645, 646
Galvanometer, 479
Gamma decay, 264
Gamma rays, 264, 536, 539, 543
Gas
  characteristics, 43–46
  as solute, 212
  thermal expansion in, 408
Gas Laws, 46
Gasohol, 600, 601
Gasoline, 589
Gasoline engine, 426
Geiger, Hans, 273
Geiger counter, 272, 273
Generators, 480–482

Geothermal energy, 600, 601–602
Germanium, 141, 645
Geysers, 602
Gilbert, William, 471
Glass, 42
Glucose, 241, 249–250
Glycerin, 246
Glycerol, 246, 250
Gold, 139
Graduated cylinder, 21, 23–24
Gram, 18, 35
Granite, 63
Gravitational potential energy,
    376, 377
Gravity, 36–38, 104, 105, 318–
    322
  weight and, 37
Grease, 217
Greek atomic model, 90–91
Greeks, 468
Greenhouse effect, 417, 614
Grounding, 450
Groups of elements, 116–117

Half-life, 266–268, 612
Halogen derivatives, 245, 247–
    248
Halogens, 143–144, 247
Hard water, 217
Hardware, 654–656
Heat, 395–411
  as form of energy, 396–399
  internal energy and, 410–411
  measuring, 402–404
  phase changes and, 404–407
  pollution and, 428–429
  temperature and, 400–401
  thermal expansion, 408–410
  uses, 417–428
Heat conductors, 398
Heat energy, 373
  calculating, 403
  phases of matter and, 47, 51–
    53
Heat engines, 381–382, 425–427
Heat of fusion, 405
Heat pump system, 420–421
Heat transfer, 397–399
Heat of vaporization, 405
Heating curve, 406
Heating systems, 418–422
Height, gravitational potential
    energy and, 376, 377
Helium, 145, 146, 162
Henry, Joseph, 480
Hertz (Hz), 502
Hertz, Heinrich, 502
Heterogeneous matter, 63–64
Heterogeneous mixture, 67
High-level wastes, 612
Hollerith, Herman, 653
Hologram, 574
Holography, 574

Homogeneous matter, 63, 69
Homogeneous mixture, 67
Horsepower (hp), 352
Hot spots, 602
Hot water heating system, 418–
    419
Hydraulics, 336–339
Hydrocarbons, 238–248, 588
  alkanes, 239–240
  alkenes, 241–242
  alkynes, 242
  aromatic, 243–244
  cycloalkanes, 243
  naming, 240–241
  substituted, 244–248
Hydrochloric acid, 222
Hydroelectric power, 593
Hydrogen, 159
  acids and, 222
  covalent bonding in, 168
Hydrogen ion, 222
Hydrogen power, 600, 603
Hydronium ion, concentration in
    solutions, 225
Hydroxide ion, 224
Hydroxyl groups, 245
Hypothesis, 9

Ice, 409
Illuminated objects, 560
Incandescent light, 560–561
Incident wave, 505
Inclined plane, 357–359, 360
Index of refraction, 548
Indicators, 222, 226
Indirect evidence, 90
Indium, 140
Induction, charging by, 447
Inert gases, 145–146
Inertia, 35, 313–315
Infrared rays, 399, 536, 539, 542
Input device, 655
Insoluble substances, 215
Insulation, 423–424
Insulators, 398, 446–447
Intake stroke, 426
Intake valve, 426
Integrated circuit, 646–647
Intensity, 517–519
Interference, 506–507, 524–525,
    545
Internal-combustion engine, 382,
    426–427
Internal energy, 411
Invisible spectrum, 540–543
Iodine, 143, 169, 247
Ionic bonding, 163–167, 173, 184
Ionic compounds, 208
  arrangement of ions, 166–167
Ionic solutes, 217
Ionization, 165, 209
Ionization energy, 165, 167
Ions, 135, 163–165

arrangement in ionic
    compounds, 166–167
  conductivity and, 208
  polyatomic, 171
Iron, 471
  oxidation number, 175
Isomers, 237–238
Isotopes, 99
  radioactive, 260–261, 265, 267,
    274–275

Jet fuels, 589
Joule (J), 349, 372
Joule, James Prescott, 396–397,
    410
Joule per second (J/sec), 351

Kelvin scale, 401
Kerosene, 589
Keyboard, 655
Kilogram, 18, 22, 35
Kilometer, 17
Kilowatt (kW), 351, 459
Kilowatt-hours, 460
Kinetic energy, 375, 410
  conversion to potential energy,
    378–380
  temperature and, 400
Kinetics, 196
Krypton, 145, 146
Krypton-92, 597

Laboratory, science safety in, 25–
    27
Land pollution, 611–613
Land reclamation, 611
Lanthanoid series, 147
Laser, 374, 573–574
Law, 7
Law of conservation of energy,
    382–383
Law of conservation of mass, 186
Law of conservation of
    momentum, 299
Law of reflection, 505
Law of universal gravitation, 321–
    322
Laws of motion, 313–318
Lead, 141
Length, measuring, 15–16, 21–22
Lenses, 566–570
  concave, 568
  convex, 567–568
  defined, 66
  vision and, 569–570
Levers, 361–362
  classes, 361–362
  mechanical advantage, 362
Lift, 341
Light, 374, 536–553, 559–575
  color, 550–552

electromagnetic spectrum, 539–543

how you see, 552–553

nature, 536–538

optical instruments, 570–572

photoelectric effect, 544–545

reflection, 546–547, 562–566

refraction, 548–549, 566–570

sources, 560–562

speed, 515, 535, 537

technology and, 573–575

Light energy, 381, 536–537

Light-years, 559

Lightning, 448–450, 515–516

Lignin, 632

Lignite, 588

Limestone, 589

Lipids, 250

Liquid

change to gas, 49–50

change to solid, 48–49

characteristics, 42–43

measuring mass, 23

measuring volume, 18

pressure and, 331, 332

superheated, 273

thermal expansion in, 409

Liquid solutions, 210

Liter, 17, 18, 23

Lithium, 135

Litmus paper, 222, 224, 226

Lodestone, 468

Longitudinal waves, 498, 500

Loudness, 517–519

Low-level wastes, 612

Lubricants, 309

Luminous objects, 560

Luster, 132

Mach 1, 513

Machines, 353–365

compound, 365

defined, 353

efficiency, 356

effort force, 354

friction, role of, 356–357

mechanical advantage, 355–356

resistance force, 355

simple, 357–365

Magnesium, 137

oxidation number, 174

Magnetic domain, 474–476

Magnetic field, 469–470

of earth, 471–472

Magnetic induction, 470–471

Magnetic lines of force, 470

Magnetic poles, 468–469

of earth, 471, 472

Magnetic variation, 473

Magnetism, 467–483

defined, 408

earth as magnet, 471–473

electromagnetic induction, 479–483

electromagnetism, 476–479

explanation of, 474–476

properties of magnets, 468–471

Magnetite, 468

Magnetosphere, 472

Magnets

earth as, 471–473

properties, 468–471

Main memory, 654

Malleability, 122, 132, 135, 172

Mass, 322–323

constancy, 37

defined, 35

force, acceleration and, 315–316

gravity and, 36, 321

kinetic energy and, 376

law of conservation of, 186

measuring, 18, 22–23, 35–36

Mass number, 100

Matter

chemical properties and changes, 53–55

classification, 62–64

phase changes, 47–53

phases, 40–46

properties, 34–40

Measurement, 15–25

See also Scientific measurement.

Mechanical advantage, 355–356

Mechanical energy, 373, 381

Medicine, radioactivity in, 275

Medium, waves through, 497–498

Melting, 47, 48, 405

Melting point, 48, 49, 405

covalently bonded solids, 170

halogens, 143

ionic solids, 166

metals, 132, 172

nonmetals, 122

organic compounds, 236

transition metals, 139

Mendeleev, Dmitri, 112–115

Meniscus curve, 4

Mercury (element), 446

Mercury vapor, 561, 562

Metallic bonds, 172, 173

Metalloids, 122, 134–135, 140, 142

in periodic table, 123

Metals, 121–122, 173, 446

alkali, 135–137

alkaline earth, 137–138

alloys, 133

chemical properties, 133

corrosion, 189

metalloids, 134–135

periodic properties, 124

in periodic table, 123

physical properties, 132

properties, 122

transition, 139

as transmitters of sound, 515

Meter, 5

Meterstick, 22

Methane, 5, 239, 590

Methanoic acid, 246

Methanol, 245

Methyl butylacetate, 233

Methyl chloride, 247

Methyl orange, 226

Metric ruler, 21

Metric system, 15–19

Microprocessors, 654

Microscopes, 572

Microwaves, 536, 541

Milligram, 18

Milliliter, 17, 18, 23

Millimeter, 17

Mirrors, 562–566

concave, 563–565

convex, 565–566

plane, 562–563

Miscible liquids, 210

Mixture, 63

defined, 64

properties, 65–66

types, 66–69

Models, 90

atomic, 90–96

Modem, 655–656

Moderator, 597–598

Modulation, 541

Molecules

chemical equations, 76–77

chemical formulas, 74–76

chemical reactions and, 185

compounds and, 73–74

formation, 169–171

heat and, 397–398, 400, 402, 408–409

polar and nonpolar, 216–217

Momentum, 298–299

law of conservation of, 299

Monomer, 250, 630, 632, 633

Moseley, Henry, 115

Motion, 287–299

acceleration, 295–298

defined, 290

frames of reference, 288–289

heat and, 397

momentum, 298–299

Newton's laws of, 313–318

orbital, 321

projectile, 320

speed, 291–293

velocity, 293–294

Motor vehicles, air pollution and, 615, 620–621

Movable pulley, 363, 364

Music, 526–527

Musical instruments, 526–527

n-type semiconductor, 645

Natural frequency, 523

Natural gas, 239, 590

Natural magnet, 470
Nearsightedness, 553, 569
Negative acceleration, 295
Neon, 145, 146, 162
Neon light, 560, 562
Network solids, 170
Neutralization, 227
Neutrons, 98, 443
  composition, 264
  isotopes and, 99
  radioactivity and, 260–261
  symbol, 266
Newton (N), 37, 315
Newton, Isaac, 305, 307
  laws of motion, 313–318
  law of universal gravitation, 321–322
Newton-meter (N-m), 349
Newton-meter per second
    (N-m/sec), 351
Nickel, 139, 471
Nitric acid, 222
Nitrogen, 142, 159, 169
Nitrogen family, 142
Nitrogen oxides, pollution and, 615
Noble gases, 145–146
Node, 507
Noise, 527–528
Noise pollution, 527–528
Nonelectrolytes, 209
Nonmetals, 122, 142, 173
  chemical properties, 134
  halogens, 143–144
  on periodic table, 123
  physical properties, 133–134
Nonpolar molecules, 217
Nonpolar solutes, 217
Nonpolar solvents, 217
Nonrenewable resources, 590–591
Normal, 505
North magnetic pole, 469
North pole, 472–473
Nuclear bullet, 268, 269
Nuclear chain reaction, 269, 597
Nuclear energy, 373, 374, 596–599
  nuclear fission, 596–597
  nuclear fusion, 599
  nuclear power plants, 597–598
Nuclear fission, 268–269, 596–597
  in nuclear reactor, 597–599
Nuclear fusion, 270–272, 374, 383, 574, 599
Nuclear power, water pollution and, 617–618
Nuclear power plants, 597–599
Nuclear radiation, 262
Nuclear reactions
  equations for, 265–266
  rail guns and, 257
Nuclear reactors, 597–599
Nuclear wastes, 612

Nucleus, 94–95, 97–98, 161, 374
  radioactivity and, 260
Nutrients, 249–251
  carbohydrates, 249–250
  fats and oils, 250
  proteins, 250–251

Oersted, Hans Christian, 476–477
Ohm, 452
Ohm's law, 452–453
Oil, 217, 589–590, 627, 628
  See also Petroleum.
Oil shale, 590
Oil spills, 617, 621
Oils, fats and, 249, 250
Opaque substance, 550–551
Optical axis, 563, 564
Optical fibers, 575
Optical instruments, 570–572
Orbital motion, 321
Organic acids, 245, 246–247
Organic chemistry, 235, 237
  naming of compounds, 240–241
Organic compounds, 141, 233–236
  carbohydrates, 249–250
  fats and oils, 250
  hydrocarbons, 239–248
  isomers, 237–238
  properties, 236
  proteins, 250–251
  structural formulas, 237
Output device, 655
Overtones, 522
Oxidation number, 139, 174–175
Oxygen, 142–143, 159, 169
Oxygen family, 142–143

p-type semiconductor, 645
Parallel circuit, 457–458
Particle accelerator, 265
Particle theory of light, 545
Passive solar energy, 591–592
Passive solar heating, 421, 422
Peat, 588
Pendulum, 380
Periodic law, 115
Periodic properties, 113
Periodic table
  development, 112–115
  modern, 115–120
  periodic properties of elements, 123–125
  predicting bond type and, 173–174
  using, 120–122
Periods, of elements, 117, 120, 124
Permanent magnets, 471
Petrochemical products, 630–635

Petroleum, 239, 589–590, 628–635
  fuels from, 628–629
  petrochemical products, 630–635
  pollution and, 17
pH, 225–226
  determining, 226
pH paper, 226
pH scale, 225–226
Phase-change diagram, 406
Phases of matter, 36–40
  changes in, 47–53, 404–407
Phenol, 246
Phenolphthalein, 222, 224, 226
Phosphors, 561
Phosphorus, 142
Phosphorus-32, 274–275
Photoelectric effect, 544–545
Photons, 537, 538
  in lasers, 573
  photoelectric effect and, 544–545
Photosynthesis, 142
Photovoltaic cell, 592
Physical changes, 47–48
Physical properties, 40
  acids, 221–222
  bases, 224
  metals, 132
  nonmetals, 133–134
  organic compounds, 236
Physical science, branches, 14
Physics, 14
Pictures, transmitting, 650–652
Pigments, 131, 552
Piston, 426
Pitch, 519–521
Pitchblende, 259
Plane mirror, 562–563
Plasma (phase of matter), 46, 270
Plastics, 632
Platinum, 139
Plum pudding model, 93
Polar molecule, 216–217
Polar solutes, 216–217
Polar solvents, 216–217
Polarity of water molecule, 216
Polarized light, 538
Poles, magnetic, 468–469
Pollution, 600, 609–621
  air, 613–615
  land, 611–613
  nature, 610
  noise, 527–528
  reducing, 619–621
  thermal, 428–429
  water, 218, 616–619
Pollution chain, 616
Polonium, 142, 143
  discovery, 259
Polyatomic ions, 171
Polymer chemistry, 630
Polymerization, 632

Polymers, 250, 630–635
  natural, 632
  synthetic, 632–635
Potassium, 135
Potential difference, 450
Potential energy, 375–377
  conversion to kinetic energy, 378–380
Powder, measuring mass, 23
Power, 350–352
  defined, 350, 458
  horsepower, 352
  measuring, 351
Power stroke, 427
Precipitate, 227
Precipitation, 227
Pressure
  defined, 330
  fluid, 331–332
  solubility and, 211, 212
Primary coil, 482
Primary colors, 551
Primary pigments, 552
Prism, 549
Product, defined, 183
Projectile, 320
Projectile motion, 320
Propane, 239
Propene, 241
Properties of matter, 34–40
Proteins, 249, 250–251, 632
Proton acceptors, bases as, 224
Proton donors, acids as, 222
Protons, 97–98, 371
  electric charge, 443, 444
  radioactivity and, 260–261
Pulley, 363–364
Pulley system, 364
Pure substance, 69, 72, 73

Quality of sound, 517, 521–522
Quark, 103

Radar, 41
Radiant electric system, 419–420
Radiant hot water system, 419
Radiation
  in cancer treatment, 275
  discovery, 259
  heat transfer through, 397–399
Radio communication, 648–649
Radio waves, 374, 536, 537, 539–541, 648–649
Radioactive decay, 262–264, 268
Radioactive elements, 147, 259–267
  transmutation, 262–267
  See also Radioactivity.
Radioactive isotopes, 265, 267
Radioactive wastes, 612
  water pollution and, 618
Radioactivity, 259–275, 609

atomic structure and, 260–261
defined, 259
detecting and measuring, 272–274
nuclear fission, 268–269
nuclear fusion, 270–272
transmutation of elements, 262–267
uses, 274–275
Radioisotopes, 274–275
Radium, 137
  discovery, 259
Radon, 145, 146
Rainbow, 549
Rare-earth elements, 147
Rarefaction, 500
Reactant, defined, 183
Reaction rates, 196–199
Real image, 564
Receiver, telephone, 648
Rectangular solid, 24
Rectifiers, 643–644
Recycling, 620
Refining, 629
Reflected wave, 505
Reflecting telescope, 572
Reflection, 504–505, 546–547
  mirrors and, 562–566
Refracting telescope, 571
Refraction, 505–506, 548–549
  lenses and, 566–570
Refrigerant, 424
Refrigerator system, 425
Regular reflection, 546
Regular solid, volume, 24
Relativity, theory, 383
Resistance, 452
Resistance arm, 362
Resistance distance, 355
Resistance force, 355
Resonance, 523–524
Respiration, 142
Reverberation, 525
Rhythm, 526
Rocket, launching, 294
Rolling friction, 308
Rubber, 632
Rubidium, 135
Ruby laser, 573
Rumford, Count, 396, 410
Rusting, 133, 189
Rutherford, Ernest, 93–95

Safety
  electric, 460–461
  laboratory, 25–27
Salts, 144
  formation, 226–227
Sandstone, 589
Saturated fat, 250
Saturated hydrocarbons, 239
Saturated solution, 213–214
Science, nature, 6, 7

Scientific measurement, 15–21
  density, 18–19
  dimensional analysis, 19–21
  length, 16–17, 21–22
  mass, 18, 22–23
  temperature, 19, 25
  volume, 17–18, 23–25
Scientific method, 7–14
Scientific theory, 7
Scientists, role, 6, 7
Screw, 360
Scrubber system, for burning coal, 620
Sea of electrons, 172
Secondary coil, 482
Selenium, 142, 143
Semiconductors, 645
Series circuit, 457
Shale, 589
Silicon, 141, 645
Silicon chip, 646
Silver, 446
Simple machines, 357–365
Single-replacement reaction, 189, 190–191
Sliding friction, 308
Slope, 292
Sodium, 35, 163, 164
  oxidation number, 174
Sodium vapor lamps, 562
Soft coal, 588
Soft water, 217–218
Software, 656
Solar cells, 544, 592–593
Solar collector, 421–422, 592
Solar energy, 591–595
  direct, 591–593
  indirect, 593–595
Solar heating system, 421–422
Solid-state devices, 645
Solid wastes, 612
Solids
  change to gas, 50–51
  change to liquid, 48
  characteristics, 41–42
  measuring mass, 22
  measuring volume, 18, 24
  solubility, 211
  solutions of, 210
  thermal expansion in, 408
Solubility, 211–212
Soluble compounds, 211
Solute, 207
Solutions, 63, 67–69
  acids and bases in, 225–227
  concentration of, 212–214
  defined, 67, 206
  process of, 209
  properties, 68, 207–209
  rate, 210–211
  special properties, 218–219
  types, 210
  water, universal solvent, 215–218

Solvent, defined, 207
Sonar, 521
Sonic boom, 513
Sound, 513–529
    combining, 524–525
    how you hear, 528–529
    music, 526–527
    noise, 527–528
    properties, 517–522
    resonance, 523–524
    speed of, 515–516
    transmitting, 515, 647–649
    wave model of, 514
Sound navigation and ranging, 521
South magnetic pole, 469
South pole, 472, 473
Space Shuttle, 316–317, 321
Spark plug, 427
Specific gravity, 40
Specific heat, 403
Speed, 291–293
Stable nucleus, 260
Stainless steel, 133
Stalactites, 205
Stalagmites, 205
Standing wave, 507
Starches, 249, 250
Static electricity, 445–450
    electroscope, 447–448
    lightning, 448–450
    methods of charging, 446–447
Steam engine, 351, 352, 426
Steam heating system, 419
Steel, 133
Step-down transformer, 483
Step-up transformer, 483
Storage tank, in cooling system, 424
Strip mining, 611, 612, 617
Strong force, 104–105, 596
Strontium, 137
Structural formulas, 237
Subatomic particles, 96–103
    electric charge, 443
Sublimation, 47, 50–51
Subscripts, 75
Substituted hydrocarbons, 244–248
    alcohols, 245–246
    esters, 47
    halogen derivatives, 247–248
    organic acids, 246–247
Sugars, 249–250
Sulfur, 142, 143
    pollution and, 615
Sulfuric acid, 222
Sun
    fusion in, 599
    temperature, 395
Supercomputers, 654
Superconductors, 488
Superheated liquid, 273
Supersaturated solution, 213, 214
Surface area, reaction rates and, 197

Suspensions, 218–219
Synthesis reaction, 189
Synthetic elements, 265

Tar sands, 590, 591
Technology
    light and, 573–575
    pollution reduction and, 620–621
Telephone communication, 647–648
Telescopes, 559, 571–572
Television, 650–652
Tellurium, 142, 143
Temperature
    heat and, 400–401, 402
    heat energy, phase change and, 405–407
    measuring, 19, 25, 401
    nuclear fusion and, 270–271
    reaction rates and, 197, 198
    solubility and, 211–214
Temperature inversion, 14
Temporary magnets, 471
Terminal velocity, 320
Tetrachloroethane, 248
Thallium, 140
Theory, 7
Thermal expansion, 408–410
    applications, 409–410
Thermal pollution, 428–429, 618
Thermocouple, 454–455
Thermometer, 401
Thermonuclear reaction, 270
Thermostat, 409–410
Thompson, Benjamin, 396
Thomson, J.J., 93
Thrust, 341
Thunder, 449, 515–518
Tidal power, 593–594
Timbre, 521, 522
Tin, 141
Tincture, 207
Toxic chemicals, 612
Tracer, 274
Transformer, 482–483
Transistor, 141, 648
Transition metals, 31, 139
Translucent substance, 550
Transmitter, telephone, 647–648
Transmutation of elements, 262–267
Transparent substance, 550, 551
Transuranium elements, 265
Transverse waves, 498–499
Triode, 644
Triple-beam balance, 21, 22
Tungsten, 561
Turbine, 426

Ultrasonic sounds, 519
Ultraviolet light, 561

Ultraviolet rays, 417, 536, 539, 542–543
Unbalanced forces, 311–312
    motion and, 315, 316
UNIVAC I, 641, 653
Universal gravitation, law of, 321–322
Universal solvent, 215
Unsaturated hydrocarbons, 239
Unsaturated solution, 213, 214
Unstable nucleus, 260, 262
Uranium, 47, 258–259
Uranium-235, 268, 596–599
Uranium-238, 263, 266, 267
Urea, 234

Vacuum cleaner, 332
Vacuum tubes, 643–644
Valence, 113
Valence electrons, 162
    chemical reactions and, 184
Valence number of elements, 124
Vaporization, 49, 405
Variable, 10
Velocity, 293–294
    gravity and, 319–320
    kinetic energy and, 375–376
Virtual image, 563, 565, 568
Viscosity, 43
Visible spectrum, 540
Vision, lenses and, 569–570
Voltage, 450
Voltaic cell, 454
Volts, 450
Volume, 18
    measuring, 17–18, 23–25, 38

Water, 74
    boiling point, 49
    conductivity, 208
    density, 19
    expansion when cooling, 409
    molecular structure, 216
    polarity, 216–217
    quality, 217–218
    as solvent, 207, 215–218
Water pollution, 616–619
    fossil fuels and, 617
    nuclear power and, 617–618
    other sources, 618–619
Water power, 593–594
Water vapor, 50
Warm air heating system, 420
Watt (W), 351, 458
Watt, James, 351, 352
Wave mechanics, 96
Wave theory of light, 544
Wavelength, 501, 502
Waves, 495–507
    characteristics, 501–502
    electromagnetic, 537–539

interactions, 504–507
nature, 496–498
sound, 514, 524
speed, 503
types, 498–500
See also Sound.
Weak force, 104, 105
Wedge, 359–360
Weight, 36–38, 322, 323
gravitational potential energy
and, 376–377

gravity and, 37
measuring, 37
Wet cell, 455
Wheel and axle, 364–365
Wind power, 595
Wire electric, 452
Wöhler, Friedrich, 234
Wood, as fuel, 588
Work, 348–350
defined, 348
heat, motion, and, 410–411

measuring, 349
Work input, 354
Work output, 355

X-rays, 258–259, 374, 536, 537,
539, 543
Xenon, 145, 146

Zinc, 139

358 top left: Alan Goldsmith/The Stock Market; top right: Mike Yamashita/Woodfin Camp; bottom: Ken Karp; 359 center: Ken Karp; right: Ken Karp; 360 Palmer/Kane/The Stock Market; 362 Walter Frenck/Odyssey Productions; 363 Philip Jon Bailey/The Picture Cube; 364 top: Gabe Palmer/The Stock Market; bottom left: Hugh Rogers/Monkmeyer Press; bottom right: Dr. E.R. Degginger; 370 Nasa; 372 top: Hale Observatories; bottom left: Arjen Ueraik/The Stock Market; bottom right: P. Degginger/H. Armstrong Roberts; 373 top: Jean Paul Nacivet/Leo deWys; bottom: Malcom S. Kirk/Peter Arnold; 374 left: Tom Martin/The Stock Market; right: John Blaustein/Woodfin Camp; 375 David Madison/Duomo; 376 top: Wally McNamee/Duomo; bottom: Paul J. Sutton/Duomo; bottom: Paul J. Sutton/Duomo; 377 left: Dan Helms/Duomo; right: J. Alex Langley/DPI; 378 top: Knotts Berry Farms; bottom: Thomas Braise/The Stock Market; 379 Bruce Curtis/Peter Arnold; 380 top: Russ Kinne/Photo Researchers; bottom: John Scheiber/The Stock Market; 383 top; Leo deWys; bottom: The Granger Collection; 388 Randa Bishop/DPI; 389 Don Siddle/Liaison; 390–391 Dan McCoy/Rainbow; 391 Karen Kasmauski/Wheeler Pictures; 392 Dr. Ray Clark & Mervyn Goff/Science Photo Library/Photo Researchers; 394 C. Allan Morgan/Peter Arnold; 398 Phil Degginger; 400 Jack C. Whitt/DPI; 401 Werner Wolff/Balck Star; 402 left: Mark A. Mittelman/Taurus Photos; center: Clyde H. Smith/Peter Arnold; 405 top: Jack McConnell/DPI; bottom: Stan Osolinski/The Stock Market; 406 Dan McCoy/Rainbow; 408 left: Richard Choy/Peter Arnold; right: Dr. E.R. Degginger; 409 Peter Arnold; 410 Ken Karp; 411 David Burnett/Woodfin Camp; 416 Jet Propulsion Lab; 418 Gabe Palmer/The Stock Market; 422 top left: Paolo Koch/Photo Researchers; top right: Arthur Tress/Photo Researchers; bottom: J. Alex Langley/DPI; 423 top: Jerry L. Holt/Photo Researchers; bottom: NASA/Phot Researchers; 424 C. Bonington/Daily Telegraph Magazine/Woodfin Camp; 426 Marilyn Leger/DPI; 428 Davidson/Magnum/Corning Glass Works; 429 top: Bill Pierce/Woodfin Camp; bottom: Ottmar Bierwagen/Black Star; 434 Robert Severi; 435 top: Collier/Condit/Stock Boston; bottom: Atlantic Research Corp., Alexandria, Virginia; 436 Guy Billout/Discover maga-

zine; 437 Roy H. Blanchard/DPI; 438 David Barnes/The Stock Market; top: Steve Elmore/The Stock Market; bottom: Harry Grossman/DPI; 442 Michael Phillip Manheim; 447 Ken Karp; 448 top: Russ Kinne/Photo Researchers; bottom: Randa Bishop/DPI; 449 David Pollack/The Stock Market; 450 top: Culver Pictures; bottom: I. Kennedy/International Stock Photo; 455 Paul Shambroom/Photo Researchers; 457 John V.A. Neal/International Stock Photo; 458 top: Thomas Braise/The Stock Market; bottom: Ken Karp; 466 Ned Haines/Photo Researchers; 468 left: Ken Karp; right: Richard Megna/Fundamental Photographs; 469 all: Richard Megna/Fundamental Photographs; 470 all: Richard Megna/Fundamental Photographs; 472 The University of Iowa; 475 Jon Riley/Medichrome Div./The Stock Shop; 477 Ken Karp; 478 Dick Durrance/Woodfin Camp; 481 top: Terrence Moore/Woodfin Camp; center: Steve Firebaugh/The Stock Market; bottom: Richard Megna/Fundamental Photographs; 483 Peter Vadnai/The Stock Market; 488 Joe McNally/Discover magazine 6/84, Time Inc.; 489 Joe McNally/Discover magazine 6/84, Time Inc.; 490 Ed Cooper/H. Armstrong Roberts; 491 Philip Jon Bailey/Stock Boston; 492 Chuck O'Rear/West Light/Woodfin Camp; 494 Duomo; 496 left: M. Dohrn/Science Photo Library/Photo Researchers, right: Stuart Cohen/Stock Boston; 497 C. West/The Stock Market; 499 Hank Morgan/Photo Researchers; 504 O. Andrews/Leo deWys; 505 Fundamental Photographs; 506 Ken Karp; 512 both: U.S. Air Force Photo; 514 left: Richard Steedman/The Stock Market; right: NASA; 515 Lowell Georgia/Photo Researchers; 517 left: Jim Anderson/Woodfin Camp; right: Tim Davis/Photo Researchers; 519 top: Michael Melford/Wheeler Pictures; bottom: Stephen Green-Armytage/The Stock Market; 521 both: Fundamental Photographs; 522 Ken Karp; 524 AP Wide World Photos; 525 Jules Zalon/DPI; 526 top: Robert Frenck; bottom left: Margaret McCarthy/Peter Arnold; bottom right: Micky Palmer/DPI; 534 National Optical Astronomy Observatories; 536 Lee L. Waldman/The Stock Market; 540 Akuma Takegami/International Stock Photo; 542 left: Dr. R.P. Clark & M. Goff/Photo Researchers; center: Terry Dominco/Earth Images; right: Biophoto Assoc./Photo Researchers; 543 Howard Sochurek/Woodfin Camp; 544 NASA;

545 Ken Karp; 546 Charles E. Dorris/Photo Unique; 547 Erwin & Peggy Bauer/Bruce Coleman; 549 top: Cesar Paredes/The Stock Market; bottom: Sil Strung/The Stock Market; 550 both: Ken Karp; 551 both: Ken Karp; 553 Lennart Nilsson/Behold Man; 558 NASA/Science Source/Photo Researchers; 560 left: Ned Haines/Photo Researchers; right: Sharon Beals/Photo Researchers; 561 left: Runk/Schoenberger/Grant Heilman; center: Chris Collins/The Stock Market; right: P.A. Hinchliffe/Bruce Coleman; 562 top: Joel Gordon; center: John Maher/The Stock Market; bottom: Dan McCoy/Rainbow; 563 Ron Watts/Black Star; 564 top: Richard Megna/Fundamental Photographs; bottom: M.J. Pettypool/Uniphoto Picture Agency; 565 Michael Heron/Woodfin Camp; 566 Fundamental Photographs; 568 top: A.G.E. Foto Stock/Peter Arnold; center: John Scheiber/The Stock Market; bottom: Fundamental Photographs; 570 all: Tom Stack; 571 Yerkes Observatory; 572 Hale Observatories; 573 Alexander Tsiaras/Science Source/Photo Researchers; 574 top: Nancy Safford/Woodfin Camp; bottom: Ken Karp; 575 William James Warren/West Light; 580 Hologram-Dan Schweitzer-Paradox-1985–6/Photography Ronald R. Erickson 1986; 581 University of Alabama in Huntsville; 582 David Burnett/Contact; 583 Martin Levick/Black Star; 584 Jerry Liebmann/Leo deWys; 588 Soames Summerhays/Photo Researchers; 589 Vince Streano/The Stock Market; 590 The Stone Flower Studio/DPI; 591 Dick Durrance/Woodfin Camp; 592 left: D. Kirkland/Sygma; right: Tom McHugh/Photo Researchers; 594 top left: Jeffrey E. Blackman/The Stock Market; bottom: Alexas Urba/The Stock Market; 595 Thomas Braise/The Stock Market; 598 top: U.S. Department of Energy; bottom: Jerry Mason/Photo Researchers; 599 Russ Kinne/Photo Researchers; 600 left: Sandia National Laboratories; right: University of Rochester; 601 top: Edward Sonner/DPI; bottom: Barry Griffiths/Photo Researchers; 602 all: Paul Chesley/Photographers Aspen; 604 Ken Karp; 610 left: Art Sokoloff/DPI; right: Keith Gunnar/Bruce Coleman; 611 left: Bob Hahn/Taurus Photos; right: Cary Wolinsky/Stock Boston; 612 top left: Chris Collins/The Stock Market; top right: Mike Yamashita/Woodfin Camp; bottom: James Mason/Black

Star; 613 Chris Jones/The Stock Market; 614 J. Barry O'Rourke/The Stock Market; 615 top: Hans Paul/Woodfin Camp; bottom: Roger J. Cheng; 616 left: Roger J. Cheng; right: Roger J. Cheng/Atmospheric Science Research Center; 617 Larry Lefever/Grant Heilman; 618 top: Roger J. Cheng/Atmospheric Science Research Center; bottom: Tom Stack; 620 Chris Jones/The Stock Market; 621 top: Chris Reeberg/DPI; bottom: Walley McNamee/Woodfin Camp; 626 American Petroleum Institute; 628 left: J. Alex Langley/DPI; right: North Wind Picture Archives; 629 Dr. E. R. Degginger; 631 top clockwise: Jim Merithew/Picture Group; Michael Furman/The Stock Market; Ken Karp; Seth H. Goltzer/The Stock Market; bottom clockwise: Vince Streano/The Stock Market; © Joel Gordon; Ken Karp; © Joel Gordon; © Ted Horowitz/The Stock Market; 632 left: William E. Ferguson; right: Hal Yaeger/DPI; 633 top left: Life Science Library/Giant Molecules/Photograph by John Zimmerman © 1986 Time, Inc., Time-Life Books, Inc. Publisher; top right: Life Science Library/Giant Molecules/Photograph by Donald Miller © 1986 Time, Inc., Time-Life Books, Inc. Publisher; bottom top: Dan McCoy/Rainbow; bottom bottom: Dan McCoy/Rainbow; 634 top: Palmer/Kane/The Stock Market; bottom: Life Science Library/Photography by Bruce Roberts © Time-Life Books, Inc.; 635 left: E.I. duPont de Nemours; right: E.I. duPont de Nemours; 636 Ken Karp; 640 Joel Gordon; 642 left: Chris Sorensen; right: Ken Karp; 643 Ken Karp; 644 Roy Morsch/The Stock Market; 645 Ken Karp; 646 top: Ken Karp; bottom left: Joel Gordon; bottom right: Alfred Pasieka/Taurus Photos; 647 top: Chuck O'Rear/Woodfin Camp; bottom: Culver Pictures; 650 Ken Karp; 653 left: NASA/Science Source/Photo Researchers; center: Hank Morgan/Photo Researchers; right: George Hailing/Photo Researchers; 654 left: IBM; right: Joel Gordon; 655 Ken Karp; 656 left: Dan McCoy/Rainbow; right: C. Mula & Haramaty/Phototake; 662 Henry Groskinsky/Discover magazine 11/84, Time Inc.; 663 Henry Groskinsky/Discover magazine 11/84, Time Inc.; 664 Glenn Cruickshank/West Stock.

PERIODIC TABLE

1 —New designation
IA —Original designation

Key

	6	— Atomic number
	C	— Element's symbol
	Carbon	— Element's name
	12.011	— Atomic mass

Transition Metals

1	2	3	4	5	6	7	8	9
IA	**IIA**	**IIIB**	**IVB**	**VB**	**VIB**	**VIIB**	← VIIIB →	

1
| 1 |
| **H** |
| Hydrogen |
| 1.00794 |

2
3	4
Li	**Be**
Lithium	Beryllium
6.941	9.0122

3
11	12
Na	**Mg**
Sodium	Magnesium
22.990	24.305

4
19	20	21	22	23	24	25	26	27
K	**Ca**	**Sc**	**Ti**	**V**	**Cr**	**Mn**	**Fe**	**Co**
Potassium	Calcium	Scandium	Titanium	Vanadium	Chromium	Manganese	Iron	Cobalt
39.098	40.08	44.956	47.88	50.94	51.996	54.938	55.847	58.9332

5
37	38	39	40	41	42	43	44	45
Rb	**Sr**	**Y**	**Zr**	**Nb**	**Mo**	**Tc**	**Ru**	**Rh**
Rubidium	Strontium	Yttrium	Zirconium	Niobium	Molybdenum	Technetium	Ruthenium	Rhodium
85.468	87.62	88.9059	91.224	92.91	95.94	(98)	101.07	102.906

6
55	56	57 to 71	72	73	74	75	76	77
Cs	**Ba**		**Hf**	**Ta**	**W**	**Re**	**Os**	**Ir**
Cesium	Barium		Hafnium	Tantalum	Tungsten	Rhenium	Osmium	Iridium
132.91	137.33		178.49	180.95	183.85	186.207	190.2	192.22

7
87	88	89 to 103	104	105	106	107	108	109
Fr	**Ra**		**Unq**	**Unp**	**Unh**	**Uns**	**Uno**	**Une**
Francium	Radium		Unnilquadium	Unnilpentium	Unnilhexium	Unnilseptium	Unniloctium	Unnilennium
(223)	226.025		(261)	(262)	(263)	(262)	(265)	(266)

The new group designations are those assigned by IUPAC in 1984.

Rare-Earth Elements

Lanthanoid Series

57	58	59	60	61	62
La	**Ce**	**Pr**	**Nd**	**Pm**	**Sm**
Lanthanum	Cerium	Praseodymium	Neodymium	Promethium	Samarium
138.906	140.12	140.908	144.24	(145)	150.36

Actinoid Series

89	90	91	92	93	94
Ac	**Th**	**Pa**	**U**	**Np**	**Pu**
Actinium	Thorium	Protactinium	Uranium	Neptunium	Plutonium
227.028	232.038	231.036	238.029	237.048	(244)

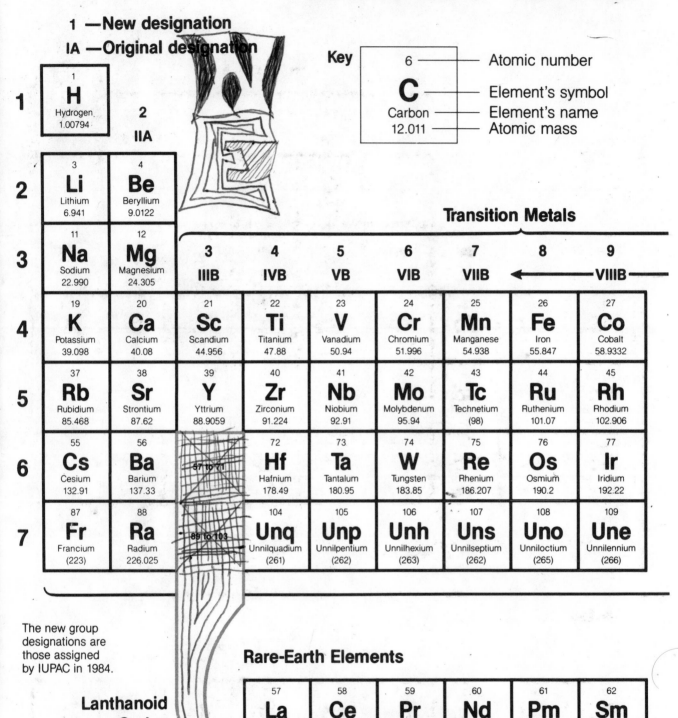